Teacher's Resource

Food for Today

Fourth Edition

Helen Kowtaluk
Home Economics Writer and Consultant

Alice Orphanos Kopan
Educational Consultant, C.H.E.
Former Supervisor of Home Economics,
  Chicago Public Schools

Glencoe
A Division of Macmillan Publishing Company
Mission Hills, California

Send all inquiries to:
Glencoe Publishing Company
15319 Chatsworth Street
P.O. Box 9509
Mission Hills, California 91345-9509

Printed in the United States of America

ISBN 0-02-676130-0 (Teacher's Resource Book — Softbound)
ISBN 0-02-676150-5 (Teacher's Resource Binder — Loose-leaf)

1 2 3 4 5 6 7 8 9 10   93 92 91 90 89

Contributors

Patricia D. Godfrey, R.D.
Nutrition and Food Associates
Plymouth, Minnesota

Brenda Barrington Mendiola
Home Economics Teacher
Irion County Schools
Mertzon, Texas

Connie R. Sasse
Former Editor, *Tips and Topics*
Texas Tech University
Lubbock, Texas

Food Science Section

Developed by:
Ellen Carlos, D.Ed. • Karen Lacy
Co-developers, Food Science Curriculum
Fairfax County Public Schools
Fairfax County, Virginia

Reviewed by:
Shirley P. Reagan, Ph.D.
Professor of Home Economics
Louisiana Tech University
Ruston, Louisiana

Contents

Overview

Teaching with *Food for Today*

Welcome to the Fourth Edition of *Food for Today*. Like its predecessors, this revised edition is a trend-setter. It combines the strengths of previous editions with improvements like these:

- Even better teaching support, including the all-new Teacher's Wraparound Edition.
- More color than ever before.
- Updated information, including the latest nutrition findings, consumer and lifestyle trends, and new technology.
- Additional emphasis on special aspects such as food science, management, and higher-level thinking skills.

However, the primary goal of *Food for Today* remains unchanged. Now more than ever, it is a flexible, comprehensive program for teaching and learning.

- **Flexible.** *Food for Today* is designed for flexibility in teaching. You can use the text for full-year, one-semester, or shorter courses; beginning or advanced level; single or sequential courses. It can be used equally well in schools with traditional or modular class scheduling. The chapters are arranged in a logical order, but can be used in any sequence to fit your course outline. Cross-references and capsule summaries of relevant information in other chapters help insure integrated learning. And the teaching materials provide you with a wealth of options from which to choose.
- **Comprehensive.** *Food for Today* is a complete foods and nutrition textbook. Its scope and depth will help your students go beyond superficial learning. The text emphasizes the fundamental areas of nutrition, consumer skills, and food preparation. It also broadens students' understanding of the impact food has on their lives — the diet-health link, cultural heritage and diversity, and career opportunities in foods and nutrition.
- **Teaching.** *Food for Today* maximizes teaching effectiveness. The supplements not only put hundreds of discussion and activity ideas at your fingertips, but also provide ready-to-use worksheets, handouts, tests, color transparencies, and more. The easy-to-use teaching materials will save you hours of preparation while helping you reach out to *all* your students.
- **Learning.** *Food for Today* focuses on learning. It is designed to spark and sustain interest, motivate students, and make the study of food and nutrition come alive. The text's clear and readable style, logical organization, visual appeal, and special learning features help build success.

To accomplish these goals, the Fourth Edition of *Food for Today* makes use of a completely integrated program of components. They include:

- **Student Text.** The core of the program is this 640-page handbook for learning about foods and nutrition.
- **Teacher's Wraparound Edition.** This all-new component provides complete lesson plans, teaching suggestions, cross-references, supplemental information, and more — conveniently "wrapped" around every page of the student text.
- **Student Workbook.** The student activity sheets in this softbound book are designed to maximize learning.
- **Teacher's Resource Book.** Turn to this component for reference materials and time-saving reproducible masters.
- **Color Transparency Package.** Ready-to-use color transparencies can enliven your presentations and enhance learning.
- **Test Construction Software.** Computer technology gives you the capability to create your own personalized tests.

On the following pages, you will find more information about each of these components as well as suggestions for using them effectively. We hope that both you and your students enjoy discovering what *Food for Today* has to offer.

We welcome comments from teachers and students on this and other Glencoe Home Economics publications. Address your letters to:

Director of Home Economics
Glencoe Publishing Company
809 West Detweiller Drive
Peoria, Illinois 61615

Getting Acquainted with the Student Text

At the heart of the *Food for Today* program is the student textbook. This proven learning tool will help your students become resourceful and well-informed about their food choices and lifestyle. It is a logically organized resource of information, visual reinforcement, and special features that make learning a positive experience.

HOW IS THE TEXT ORGANIZED?

The *Food for Today* text is divided into seven units, or Parts. Each Part deals with a major concept.

Part One: Food and People examines the personal, social, and cultural aspects of food.

Part Two: Nutrition for Good Health introduces scientific principles of nutrition and the relationship between eating habits and good health. Students are encouraged to develop a personalized nutrition program.

Part Three: Consumer Decisions applies management and decision-making skills to the purchase and storage of food and equipment.

Part Four: Food Skills focuses on the basic knowledge needed for food preparation — tools, techniques, meal management, table setting and service.

Part Five: Food Preparation gives guidelines for selecting, storing, and preparing each type of food. Microwave techniques are included.

Part Six: Creative Cuisine introduces the cultural food traditions of the United States and other countries and encourages students to go beyond the basics of good cooking.

Part Seven: Exploring Careers highlights career opportunities in foods and nutrition and teaches job skills applicable to any employment.

Each unit (Part) consists of a logical sequence of chapters — 39 in all, each dealing with a specific topic. Together the units and chapters provide well-balanced coverage of food and nutrition concepts.

The completeness of the *Food for Today* text gives it the flexibility to meet your individual needs. Choose how many and which chapters to use depending on the length and level of your course.

WHAT ARE THE LEARNING FEATURES OF EACH CHAPTER?

Each chapter of the text includes a number of carefully designed features to enhance student interest and learning.

Chapter Opening Page

The first page of each chapter is designed to motivate students, orient them to the chapter content, and set the stage for learning. This page includes:

- **A full-color illustration** portraying the theme of the chapter.
- **Student objectives** listed under the heading "To help you to." These clearly stated objectives establish specific goals for students before the chapter is read. They can also be used in planning course objectives and documenting student learning.
- **"Look for These Terms,"** a list of important, but perhaps unfamiliar, terms that appear in the chapter. The terms are listed in order of use. (This list coordinates with other vocabulary development features throughout the text and teaching materials.)
- **Motivational opening paragraphs** that spark students' interest and lead them into the chapter content.

Writing Style and Organization

Individual chapters, like the book as a whole, follow a logical order of presentation. The body of each chapter is clearly organized into major topics and subtopics through the use of distinctive color headings.

The text of *Food for Today* is carefully written at a comfortable reading level for high school students. Topics are clearly explained, often with concrete examples. The writing style is factual, but never dry or dull.

As a teacher, you want a textbook that strikes the right balance of information — neither skimpy and simplistic nor clouded with irrelevant detail. *Food for Today* is such a textbook. Students are given enough information for complete understanding, yet the text is clear and concise. Special care has been taken to ensure that key ideas are easy to find and understand. These features are just part of what makes *Food for Today* such an informative, interesting, and highly readable text.

Presentation of Vocabulary Terms

Vocabulary development, which begins on the chapter opening page with "Look for These Terms," is carried through in the body of the chapter. When first used in the chapter, each vocabulary term is printed in **boldface type** for easy reference. A clear definition is given, as well as examples or further explanation when needed. Phonetic pronunciation guides are included for terms that may be difficult to pronounce.

Visual Elements

Food for Today is packed with hundreds of color photographs and drawings. The illustrations and fresh, contemporary design provide visual and personal appeal to make the book come alive for students. Yet the illustration program does more than add interest — it enriches and supports the text material. In short, these are *illustrations that teach.*

- **Photographs** show teens and others in realistic situations, as well as appealing foods. The photos serve to instruct, to reinforce text learning, to heighten students' awareness, and to improve their observation skills.
- **Captions** are more than just informative. Many ask questions to help students review facts, apply text concepts, and develop higher-level thinking skills.
- **Drawings** make learning concrete by clearly showing equipment and step-by-step procedures.
- **Charts** are designed for clarity. They summarize and highlight key points, extend the text, help students organize information and make comparisons.

Recipes

Chapters in Part Five, "Food Preparation," include easy-to-follow recipes which illustrate preparation principles. These recipes have been chosen for student appeal, nutrition, and suitability for foods labs.

Each recipe includes a color photograph of the finished product. Both metric and customary ingredient measurements are provided. Directions are clearly given in a series of numbered steps with key words highlighted. Whenever appropriate, directions for microwave preparation are included.

To reinforce students' nutrition awareness, a nutritional analysis is given for each recipe. The analysis includes the calorie count per serving and the amount (in grams) of protein, carbohydrate, fat, cholesterol, and sodium. Look for this analysis at the bottom of each recipe.

Feature Pages

The *Food for Today* text includes over 35 high-interest feature articles, each one or two pages in length. These features extend the text content with timely topics and provide students with new perspectives. There are four categories of features:

- **Healthy Living** provides an in-depth look at special topics related to health, wellness, and fitness. Examples include teen athletes, low-cholesterol products, and the controversies of nutrition claims in advertising.
- **Technology** examines the impact of past, present, and future developments in areas such as consumer products, computers, and the food processing industry.
- **Food Science** explores the "why" behind facts of food preparation and nutrition. Students will discover how calories are measured, why freezer burn occurs (and how to prevent it), and the molecular changes that occur in a frying egg.
- **Window on the World** helps students develop a global view of food habits and concerns. They will learn about unusual foods from around the world, explore issues of the global food supply, and trace the roots of some familiar dishes.

Each feature concludes with two questions under the heading "Thinking It Through." These stimulating questions are designed to encourage class discussion and challenge students' thinking skills. (The questions are supported by teaching guidelines in the Teacher's Wraparound Edition.)

Chapter Review Page

Each chapter ends with a full-page section titled "Let's Review." This comprehensive review section can be used to check how well students have mastered chapter content and to help them prepare for the chapter test. There are four components of "Let's Review":

- **Key Ideas** is a short summary of major chapter concepts.
- **Chapter Checkup** provides objective questions based on information presented in the chapter. (Answers are provided in the Teacher's Wraparound Edition.)
- **Explore and Report** consists of activities that can be used in the classroom or with the help of the school library. They are designed to help students reinforce, apply, and extend chapter learning. In addition, they provide practice in the basic skills of reading, writing, math, and science. For easy reference, the activities appear in a consistent sequence according to skill area and are labeled with the symbols shown on the next page.

Key to "Let's Review" Symbols

Explore and Report:

Reading

Writing

Math

Science

What Would YOU Do?:

Higher-Level
Thinking Skills

- **What Would YOU Do?** presents several open-ended, "real life" scenarios related to the chapter content. These exercises are designed to provide practice in such skills as problem-solving, decision-making, critical thinking, creativity, communication, and interpersonal relations. Because of the nature of these exercises, there are no firm right or wrong answers. Students' responses will depend on their own knowledge, past experiences, and perceptions.

WHAT'S IN THE BACK OF THE BOOK?

The reference materials in the back of the *Food for Today* text can serve as valuable resources. They include:

- **Glossary.** The Glossary defines all of the chapter vocabulary terms, as well as additional terms used in the text. Pronunciation guides are included for difficult terms. Students can use the glossary to quickly review their understanding of new terms.
- **Appendix Section.** Five appendices provide useful supplementary information for the text. They include RDA and U.S. RDA charts; a listing of nutrients in foods; the procedure for calculating the percentage of calories from protein, carbohydrate, and fat; and a guide to the metric system.
- **Index.** A complete alphabetical index provides easy reference to the subject matter.

Using the Teacher's Resource Book

The *Food for Today* Teacher's Resource Book (TRB) is a sourcebook of reference materials for your own use and reproducible masters for classroom use. It is available in two forms:

- The softbound Teacher's Resource Book has perforated pages. You may wish to detach sheets for duplicating, then store them in file folders or a notebook for later reuse.
- The Teacher's Resource Binder contains the same material as the softbound version, but conveniently arranged in a tabbed loose-leaf binder.

The binder version of the TRB includes a set of ready-to-use color transparencies with suggestions for use. (See the description on page 14.) If you are using the softbound version of the TRB, you may purchase the color transparency package separately.

Following is a description of the sections of the Teacher's Resource Book with suggestions for using them effectively.

OVERVIEW

The Overview — the section you are reading now — describes each component of the *Food for Today* program. In addition, the Overview section includes:

- **Special Applications of the *Food for Today* Program.** Beginning on page 15, the Overview explains how the elements of the program work together to help you accomplish specific goals: reinforcing basic academic skills, higher-level thinking skills, and life management skills; introducing food science concepts; helping students work successfully in the foods lab; and meeting individual student needs.
- **Teaching Techniques:** Turn to pages 19-23 for suggestions of classroom techniques — from brainstorming to videos — that can add variety and creativity to your lessons.

REFERENCES

This section of the Teacher's Resource Book provides a complete reference list for each unit of the textbook. The books listed here may be useful as classroom references or for student research projects. In addition, the reference list includes materials to enhance learning and enrich your classroom presentation: pamphlets and other educational materials, software, and audiovisual programs (filmstrips, audio cassettes, films, and videotapes). The source is given for each.

PLANNING CHARTS

This section of the TRB conveniently groups together several planning aids.

- **Scope and Sequence Chart.** This chart shows how major themes are woven throughout the text. The chart is useful for planning and sequencing courses and for emphasizing particular course themes.
- **Suggested Course Outlines.** This chart suggests some ways courses might be structured using *Food for Today*. It shows how many class periods might be spent on each chapter of the text for a one-semester (18-week) and year (36-week) course. The suggested outlines can easily be adapted to fit your own needs.
- **Worksheets for Lesson Planning.** This chart is a more detailed planning tool. For each chapter of *Food for Today*, the chart lists main topics and their page numbers, student objectives, and related TRB reproducible materials. Space is left for you to personalize the chart with your own notes — perhaps the dates you plan to cover the material, special points of emphasis, or an evaluation of the lesson's effectiveness.
- **Monthly Planner.** This blank monthly calendar can be reproduced and filled in with dates and notes. You may find it helpful for developing your lesson plans, seeing the scope of your plans at a glance, and monitoring progress.

TRANSPARENCY MASTERS

Over 60 black-line masters are provided which can be used to make your own transparencies for the overhead projector. Their visuals and key words can help you introduce topics, summarize main points, stimulate discussion, and review concepts.

The transparency masters have been designed with simple, clear illustrations and large type for easy visibility. Although ideal for making transparencies, these masters can also be duplicated as student handouts. Many can be converted to oral or written quizzes by simply blocking out the print.

The transparency masters are identified in the upper outside corner by number (TM-1, TM-2, etc.) and by the related chapter of the text. They are arranged according to chapter sequence. However, many of the transparency masters would be appropriate for use in other chapters as well. At the front of the section, a topical index is provided to help you quickly find any transparency masters that relate to a given subject.

HANDOUT MASTERS

Over 50 reproducible handout masters are provided in this section of the TRB. Most fall into one of the following categories:

- **Supplemental information.** Some handouts expand on chapter topics for in-depth learning. They can be read and discussed by the whole class or given to selected students for enrichment, extension, or extra background information.
- **Reprint or summary of material from the textbook.** These handouts provide important information and charts in a reproducible format. Encourage your students to add their own notes, underlining, etc., to these handouts (rather than marking in their textbooks). Students can use them as study aids and keep them for reference after completion of the course. These handouts are especially useful if each student does not have his or her own textbook.
- **Skill-builder handouts.** Step-by-step, illustrated directions are given for many food preparation procedures. Students can take these handouts into the lab and follow the steps as they practice their skills.
- **Evaluation of products prepared in the foods lab.** "Standards Scorecards" and "Problem Solvers" are ideal follow-ups to foods lab activities. They can be used either for teacher evaluation or student self-evaluation. With "Standards Scorecards," the student's product can be rated against standards for appearance, taste, texture, and other characteristics. "Problem Solvers" help students pinpoint possible causes of product shortcomings so that the problem can be avoided next time.

Like the transparency masters, the handout masters are identified by number (HO-1, HO-2, etc.) and by chapter, and are arranged in chapter sequence. A topical index is provided at the beginning of the section to help you locate handouts on any particular topic.

RECIPE WORKSHEETS

This section of the TRB includes over 50 tested recipes. They were chosen with foods lab requirements in mind — preparation time, skill level, and cost.

At the beginning of the section you will find a sequential list of all the recipes. This is followed by an index according to the type of product (appetizers, beverages, and so on).

On pages 221-222 is a reproducible foods lab safety and sanitation handout. It explains basic safety and sanitation procedures for the school foods lab and includes a student/parent signature form. The handout and signature form may be given to students at the beginning of the school year or at any point prior to hands-on food preparation.

Next, you will find a special student handout, "Foods Lab Work Plan" (page 223-224). This form can be given to students before each foods lab experience. Each lab group should fill in the spaces to show how tasks will be divided among group members and what sequence will be followed. Using this form will help students develop teamwork, time management skills, and good work habits.

The rest of this section of the TRB consists of the actual recipe worksheets. They are identified in the upper outside corner by number (R-1, R-2, etc.) and by the suggested text chapter. Each worksheet has two main parts — the recipe itself (with related material) on the first page, and questions for the student to answer on the second page.

The first page of the recipe worksheet is designed for step-by-step use in the foods lab. At the top of the page, an equipment list is provided. Students can check off equipment as they gather it before preparing the recipe. They can also check off the items on the ingredients list as they are gathered. Ingredient amounts are given in both metric and customary units.

Directions are given in the form of a step-by-step list with key words highlighted. Again, blanks are provided so students can check off each step as it is completed. Microwave directions are included when appropriate.

A box (usually near the bottom of the first page) provides information on the recipe's yield and nutritional value. Nutrition information includes not only calories, protein, carbohydrate, fat, cholesterol, and sodium, but also the percentage of U.S. RDA for five vitamins, calcium, and iron.

Many of the recipe worksheets also include "Kitchen Management Tips." These provide helpful information and reminders related to safety, sanitation, conservation, and efficient work methods.

The second page of each recipe worksheet is titled "Thinking About . . ." It is divided into two sections. The "Questions" section asks students to read and analyze the recipe. The questions deal with topics such as nutrition, safety and sanitation, ingredient content, and preparation methods. (Answers are provided in the TRB Answer Key section.) For greatest effectiveness, you may wish to have students complete the "Questions" section before going into the foods lab (although it can also be used afterward if desired). "Evaluation" asks students to evaluate the lab experience and their finished product. Together, these two parts of "Thinking About . . ." encourage the habit of analyzing any recipe before use and evaluating it afterwards.

FOOD SCIENCE MATERIAL

If you wish to help your students explore food science concepts in greater depth, turn to this section of the TRB. It includes reproducible experiment sheets and complete teacher guidelines. Flexibility is encouraged — you may want to use this section in whole or in part, either integrated with your course lesson plans or as a separate unit.

The experiments in this section use food and equipment normally found in a high school foods laboratory. They range from simple ones, such as making butter, to more complex ones that involve making several variations of a recipe for comparison. Further explanation of the food science experiments begins on page 347.

Perhaps food science intrigues you, but you are unsure about introducing scientific experiments into your foods and nutrition course. You may be interested in the special article "Why Food Science?" which begins on page 345. It explains some of the benefits of food science experiments in relation to life management skills, reading and writing skills, consumerism, and other areas.

TESTING PROGRAM AND ANSWER KEYS

The final three sections of the Teacher's Resource Book include the Testing Program, TRB Answer Key, and Student Workbook Answer Key. The testing program provides a complete set of chapter and unit (Part) tests in reproducible format. Matching, true-false, multiple choice, and completion items are included. The answer key sections include answers to recipe worksheet questions, chapter and unit tests, and Student Workbook activities.

Using Other Program Components

TEACHER'S WRAPAROUND EDITION

The Teacher's Wraparound Edition is one of the most exciting features of the new *Food for Today* program. It provides maximum teaching support in a convenient, easy-to-use format.

"Wraparound" Annotations

The Teacher's Wraparound Edition allows you to follow along page-by-page with the student text. Replicas of the student text pages are slightly reduced to allow more room for teaching material, which fills the side and bottom margins of your page.

The teaching material is arranged in a consistent, easy-to-use pattern. Each set of facing pages is self-contained. As you cover each page of the student text in class, the corresponding references and teaching suggestions are right in the margins where you need them.

The wraparound annotations fall into four basic categories: lesson plans, "Focus" boxes, supplementary information, and special teaching helps.

Lesson Plans

The "core" of the Teacher's Wraparound Edition is the lesson plan material found in the side margins. This material provides you with complete suggestions for:

- *Introducing* **each Part (unit) and each chapter.** Special "perspective" sections on unit opening pages help students see the purpose of what they are about to study and its relation to other text topics. Chapter lesson plans begin with motivators and discussion of chapter goals.
- *Teaching* **the content of the chapter.** "Content Development" sections help you take students step-by-step through the main ideas covered in the text. A wide variety of "Student Experiences" are provided to help you reinforce and extend student learning — including activities suitable for reteaching and enrichment. Specific suggestions are given for effectively using the feature pages in the text.
- *Completing* **the study of each chapter and unit.** Each chapter lesson plan concludes with suggestions for review, application, skill building, and evaluation.

"Focus" Boxes

Color-coded "Focus" boxes supplement the core lesson plan material. Use them to focus in on whatever special areas *you* want to emphasize throughout the course:

- Management
- Nutrition
- Food Science
- Safety and Sanitation
- Thinking Skills
- Vocabulary Skills
- Recipe Skills

The "Focus" boxes are found in the side margins, below the basic lesson plan. They are flexible tools that can be used as desired for emphasis, review, reinforcement, extension, and skill application.

Supplementary Information

At the bottom of most pages, you'll find mini-articles that tell you "More About" the topics that are covered in the student text.

Special Teaching Helps

To help make the Teacher's Wraparound Edition easy to use, the marginal notes include features such as:

- A "Quick Scan" of each unit, found on the unit opening pages. It includes unit theme and chapter overviews to help you see the scope of the unit at a glance.
- An outline at the beginning of each chapter, showing major headings and page numbers.
- A resources list at the beginning of each chapter.
- "See Also" boxes providing cross-references to other parts of the program.
- Answers to chapter review questions.

Teacher's Manual

The Teacher's Wraparound Edition also includes a 32-page Teacher's Manual at the front of the book. Refer to the Teacher's Manual (pages T-11 through T-15) for a more detailed explanation of the Teacher's Wraparound Edition and suggestions for using it effectively.

STUDENT WORKBOOK

The *Food for Today* Student Workbook provides a variety of well-planned, ready-to-use activity sheets for each chapter. They are designed to help students master the text content and vocabulary, extend their learning, apply basic academic skills, and strengthen higher-level thinking skills.

The activity sheets in the Student Workbook can be integrated into your lesson plan at points suggested in the Teacher's Wraparound Edition or wherever you choose. They are ideal for:

- In-class work.
- Out-of-class assignments.
- Pre- and post-testing.
- Independent study or extra credit assignments.

Directions for the activity sheets are easy to follow with a minimum of teacher guidance. The 8½" × 11" sheets are perforated so that they can be easily detached and turned in for checking. (You may want to ask students to keep their completed assignments in a folder or notebook.) Answers to Student Workbook activity sheets are found in the Teacher's Resource Book.

Please note that the *Food for Today* Student Workbook is designed as a consumable workbook for use by one student. Reproduction of activity sheets for classroom use is a violation of copyright.

COLOR TRANSPARENCY PACKAGE

This package provides 36 ready-to-use transparencies in full color, including photographs, diagrams, and graphic charts. Included in the package are specific teaching suggestions to help you make the most effective use of each transparency. You will find them a valuable tool for introducing topics, reinforcing concepts, sparking discussion, and developing higher-level thinking skills.

As explained earlier, the color transparencies and teaching suggestions are included in the binder version of the TRB. The package is also available for purchase separately.

TEST CONSTRUCTION SOFTWARE

This computer program helps you vary and personalize tests quickly and easily. It can also be used to create quizzes, homework assignments, and study sheets.

Hundreds of objective test items are stored in the program, arranged by chapter and unit. You may choose the test items you want to use, ask the computer to select items randomly, or add questions of your own. You can arrange items in any order and scramble them to create multiple versions of the same test. Answer keys can be printed out to accompany each test. The software is "user friendly" and comes with a complete set of operating instructions.

Special Applications of the *Food for Today* Program

The previous pages have described individual components of the *Food for Today* program. But it should be apparent that these components are not meant to be used individually. They provide a coordinated team of teaching and learning tools, each enhancing the use of the others.

One of the ways in which the components are linked together is by subject matter. That is, each component is coordinated to the chapters of the student text, providing a complete package of learning materials for each chapter. But there are other links between text and supplements that may not be as obvious. For example, you may be interested in finding out what features in each component can help you reinforce basic skills or emphasize food science concepts. These links can be thought of as special applications within the *Food for Today* program.

The following pages are a guide to these special applications, listing all relevant features of the *Food for Today* program. For more information about each of the features described, refer to pages 7 through 14 and to the Teacher's Wraparound Edition.

REINFORCING BASIC SKILLS

The "back to basics" movement in education is as relevant to foods and nutrition courses as to any other subject matter. Teaching basic skills need not detract from teaching subject matter. Instead, all classes can reinforce and enhance skills to which students have already been exposed. By helping students to transfer these skills more effectively, a teacher can promote self-confidence and success as well as knowledge.

Before implementing basic skills techniques in the classroom, current skill levels of students should be assessed. Guidance counselors, standardized test scores, and student records aid in this process.

Reading and Writing Skills

The *Food for Today* program has many features useful in reinforcing reading and writing skills.

- The student text is carefully written and organized to aid comprehension.
- The student text includes a number of coordinated features for vocabulary development: "Look for These Terms" on the chapter opening pages; boldface, defined vocabulary terms within the chapter; pronunciation guides; and a complete Glossary at the back of the text.

- Chapter opening pages in the Teacher's Wraparound Edition give suggestions for introducing vocabulary goals.
- "Focus on Vocabulary Skills" boxes in the Teacher's Wraparound Edition give suggestions for helping students develop word analysis skills.
- Vocabulary development continues in the Student Workbook with a variety of puzzles and word games that focus on key terms.
- Each chapter review page includes "Explore and Report" activities specifically chosen to reinforce reading and writing skills.
- Many of the "Student Experiences" found in the Teacher's Wraparound Edition also reinforce reading and writing skills. Look for activities that involve library research, reports, creative writing, literary excerpts, etc.
- Many of the activity sheets in the Student Workbook require students to apply reading and writing skills. (For example, one activity sheet asks students to read and respond to "advice column" letters).
- Handout masters provided in the TRB can be used to give students additional practice in reading.

Math Skills

Foods and nutrition courses are naturally suited to the application of basic math skills. Analyzing nutrient and calorie needs, comparing unit prices, measuring ingredients, increasing or decreasing recipes — these and other topics provide ample opportunity to practice computation skills. *Food for Today* makes the most of these opportunities.

- Every chapter review page includes an "Explore and Report" activity specially chosen to reinforce math skills.
- Math-related activities are also found in the "Student Experiences" sections of the Teacher's Wraparound Edition.
- Charts found throughout the text and in the appendix section give students practice in analyzing numerical data. Information in the charts can be used as a springboard for math activities — for example, comparing the nutrient content of various menus.
- Both metric and customary measurements are used throughout the text. The metric system is explained in Chapter 15 and in Appendix F.

- Recipe worksheets in the Teacher's Resource Book include follow-up questions that often call for computational skills. For example, students may be asked to calculate the percentage of a food's calories that come from fat. (The procedure is explained in text Appendix E.)
- The Student Workbook provides practice in math skills in the context of food preparation, nutrition, and money management.

Science Skills

Science has only recently been added to the "basic skills" category with reading, writing, and math. With a little thought, it becomes obvious that basic science skills are transferable to other areas. This is especially true of foods and nutrition courses. *Food for Today* can help you enhance science concepts and skills in a number of ways.

- Chapter 3 of the text focuses on nutrition as a science and introduces students to the scientific method.
- Where appropriate, science concepts are integrated into the discussion of nutrition and food preparation throughout the text.
- "Technology" features scattered throughout the text illustrate the practical applications of science and provide a look at what's on the horizon.
- Chapter 38, "Careers in Food and Nutrition," includes an expanded discussion of the growing food technology field.
- Every chapter review page includes an "Explore and Report" activity that reinforces science skills.
- Science-related activities can also be found in the "Student Experiences" section of the Teacher's Wraparound Edition and in the Student Workbook.

In addition, the *Food for Today* program includes a number of special features for those teachers who wish to emphasize the food science aspects of the course. These are explained under "Teaching Food Science Concepts" on page **17**.

REINFORCING HIGHER-LEVEL THINKING SKILLS

Higher-level thinking skills can be defined as those which allow students to go beyond simple recall of facts and ideas. Educators have been criticized in recent years for failing to teach students how to reason, make realistic and careful judgements, and develop creative solutions to problems.

An important theme of the *Food for Today* program is to help students develop their skills in these areas. Knowledge of nutrition and foods must be applied to be useful. Yet the factors that affect food choices are numerous and complex. Without practice in higher-level thinking skills, much of the value of a foods and nutrition course would be lost.

What are some of the features of the *Food for Today* program that reinforce higher-level thinking skills?

- When appropriate, questions are integrated into the context of text chapters to encourage thought and discussion. (For example, on text page 86: "How many people do you know who substitute a candy bar and soft drink for a nutritious lunch? What might be the long-term effects of this habit?")
- Many of the photo captions also include questions for thought and discussion. Thus the illustrations can be used as teaching tools to reinforce, extend, and apply student learning.
- Every chapter review page includes "What Would YOU Do?" These open-ended hypothetical situations help students develop skills in problem solving, decision making, critical thinking, creativity, and other areas.
- Feature pages in the text conclude with "Thinking It Through," questions that help students see the relationship between facts, consider implications, and develop and support opinions.
- "Thinking It Through" is carried through on the corresponding pages of the Teacher's Wraparound Edition, where suggestions for leading a discussion are provided.
- "Focus on Thinking Skills" boxes appear in the Teacher's Wraparound Edition. These suggest ways to use the text material as a springboard for developing creativity, critical thinking, reasoning, and problem solving abilities.
- The "Content Development" and "Student Experiences" sections of the Teacher's Wraparound Edition include many discussion questions that can stimulate thinking abilities.
- Recipe worksheets in the TRB include questions to help students think about their lab experiences.
- The Student Workbook also provides opportunities for students to practice and improve thinking skills.
- The Color Transparency Package includes specific suggestions for leading thought-provoking discussion.

REINFORCING MANAGEMENT SKILLS

One of the most important philosophies of home economics education is to help students develop the management skills that will help them achieve success in all aspects of their lives. Foods and nutrition courses provide almost limitless opportunities to introduce or reinforce various management skills.

In *Food for Today*, the concept of management is woven throughout the text. Here are some examples:

- Chapter 1, "Your Food Choices," introduces the concepts of resources and management. Steps for successful management are outlined and the importance of sound decision-making is emphasized.

- Part Two, "Nutrition for Good Health," helps students see how management skills can be used to achieve the goal of a balanced, healthful diet.

- Part Three is built around the theme reflected in its title, "Consumer Decisions." Students are shown the techniques and benefits of planning, kitchen organization, money management, and related consumer skills.

- Chapter 15, "Meal Management," focuses on the steps that help streamline food preparation, such as making a work plan and schedule, working efficiently, and avoiding waste.

- The food preparation chapters in Part Five include further tips for good kitchen management, such as conserving nutrients.

- Part Seven, "Exploring Careers," emphasizes management-related concepts such as planning and carrying out a job search and using time management skills to balance work and personal life.

The creators of the *Food for Today* program recognize, however, that weaving management themes throughout the text is not always enough. In order for students to truly recognize these management-related concepts and see their interconnectedness, some teacher guidance and reinforcement is needed.

For this reason, the Teacher's Wraparound Edition includes "Focus on Management" boxes. They provide suggestions for reinforcing and extending students' management skills through review, discussion, and activities. Use these to highlight and emphasize the management-related content found throughout the text.

TEACHING FOOD SCIENCE CONCEPTS

Foods and nutrition courses have always included science-related content. Nutrition is a science in itself with links to biology, chemistry, and the medical sciences; food preparation involves principles of chemistry and physics.

Today many foods and nutrition courses are placing more emphasis on the scientific aspects of foods and nutrition. This can be done for any of several purposes. In some cases, the goal is to develop a food science course comparable to other sciences in the curriculum. In other cases, the goal may be to reinforce general science skills, to give students a foundation for more advanced courses in food science and technology, or to make students aware of related career opportunities.

The Fourth Edition of *Food for Today* includes several new or expanded features that can help you introduce or emphasize food science concepts.

- "Food Science" feature pages in the student text expand on chapter content by explaining the scientific principles behind the facts.

- "Focus on Food Science" boxes in the Teacher's Wraparound Edition suggest ways for you to develop food science concepts through further explanation, discussion, activities, and simple experiments.

- The Teacher's Resource Book provides a special section of food science materials including student experiment sheets and teacher guidelines.

These elements of the *Food for Today* program are designed for maximum flexibility. You have the option of integrating any of these special features into your daily lesson plans to whatever extent you wish. Or you may draw upon them to create lessons or units of study devoted specifically to food science concepts. If you do not choose to use any of these features, the *Food for Today* program remains a complete, traditional foods and nutrition course. For more information, refer to the food science section beginning on page 343 of this Teacher's Resource Book.

FOOD FOR TODAY AND YOUR FOODS LAB

Foods and nutrition courses involve not only classroom study but hands-on learning. The *Food for Today* program is designed to help students achieve success in both the classroom and the foods lab.

- The text content gives students a solid foundation of knowledge — from kitchen organization to basic tools and techniques to the procedures for preparing various foods.
- Safety and sanitation principles are thoroughly explained in Chapter 13 and reinforced in subsequent chapters.
- "Focus on Safety and Sanitation" boxes in the Teacher's Wraparound Edition help you emphasize important points.
- The text not only provides at least one recipe in each food preparation chapter, but clearly explains many other step-by-step procedures for basic food preparation. Drawings illustrate many skills, such as how to cut up a chicken.
- The recipes in the student text and the Teacher's Resource Book have been selected and tested for use in the foods lab. In the TRB, reproducible recipe worksheets include ingredients and equipment lists, kitchen management tips, and follow-up questions.
- "Focus on Recipe Skills" boxes in the Teacher's Wraparound Edition help you make the most of the text recipes and related TRB material.
- Microwave directions are given for all recipes (when appropriate), and an entire chapter of the text is devoted to microwave techniques.
- The "Student Experiences" sections of the Teacher's Wraparound Edition provide many suggested foods lab experiences.
- The Teacher's Resource Book includes a reproducible work plan that can be used each time students work in the foods lab.
- Handouts in the Teacher's Resource Book include illustrated how-to explanations, scorecards to help students evaluate their products, and "problem solvers" to help students achieve success.

ADAPTING THE COURSE TO FAST AND SLOW LEARNERS

Within any classroom, students have a wide range of intelligence, maturity, interests, and abilities. The practice of mainstreaming mentally and physically handicapped students broadens that spectrum. It tests the ingenuity and resourcefulness of the teacher to provide the best possible learning experience for each student.

A number of approaches are possible. Some teachers rely on individualized instruction so students can work at their own pace. Others feel the benefits of group participation are too important to sacrifice and choose a more traditional classroom experience for students. Many teachers combine some individualized instruction with group learning. Each of these approaches has its advantages and drawbacks. Determine the one best suited to your students and teaching style.

The activities suggested in the student text and Teacher's Wraparound Edition of *Food for Today* are useful in planning flexible assignments because they require different levels of skill. If you set up a pattern of varying activities within the class, no one need be overtly labeled as "slow" or "smart."

Slower students need activities that concentrate on the basic chapter information. You may wish to give extra emphasis to the "Content Development" sections of the Teacher's Wraparound Edition as you work with these students. This will help them distinguish the main points of each text section, as well as help you assess comprehension. Also look for student experiences labeled "Reteaching" in the Teacher's Wraparound Edition. Many of the other student experiences listed could also be successful learning experiences for slower students.

More challenging and subjective activities are appropriate for bright students. You may wish to choose from the student experiences labeled "Enrichment" or adapt others to fit the abilities of the student. A student-teacher conference early in the course can set up a plan of independent projects, the completion dates, and how the results will be graded. Give students a voice in these decisions. Remember, too, that it is as important to compliment fast learners for academic achievement as it is to encourage slow learners to reach their highest potential. The feelings of personal satisfaction are the same.

Physically and mentally handicapped students mainstreamed into the regular classroom have special needs. It is important to find out how to best meet these needs by conferring with the resource or special education teacher early in the course. The law governing mainstreaming requires that an individual plan of instruction (IEP) be devised for each student. Taking part in this planning will give you an opportunity to learn more about the student's strengths and limitations. You can also find out what resources (professional personnel, aides, equipment, etc.) will be available to you to make the student's experience successful. Your attitude will be important in determining whether or not the handicapped student is accepted by classmates. Mainstreaming can provide positive experiences for both the handicapped student and the rest of the class.

Teaching Techniques

"How can I bring a fact or concept to life?" is a troublesome yet challenging question confronting the educator. No matter how important the message, it likely won't be internalized unless its presentation stimulates student interest.

You are competing for your students' attention. Their minds may be absorbed with many thoughts besides the study of food and nutrition. Furthermore, they have been conditioned to the communications power and showmanship of television — and often expect a similar performance in the classroom.

More than ever before, you are faced with the task of selecting techniques that make daily lessons exciting and worthwhile. Along with watching and listening, your students need to become actively involved in the learning process.

Enthusiasm is contagious. Communicate ideas enthusiastically by choosing and adapting a variety of teaching techniques to activate interest and learning in the minds of your students. No one tool is superior to another. Only you can decide which approach best meets the needs of your students.

The following outline is designed to assist you in pinpointing some of the "whys" for using each teaching technique.

BRAINSTORMING

- Induces a quantity of spontaneous ideas.
- Provides a climate of free expression without making value judgements.
- Generates creative solutions to specific problems.
- Alters pace of learning and adds variety to experiences.
- Gives insight to the importance of alternatives in reaching decisions.

BULLETIN BOARDS

- Attract attention and stimulate participation.
- Offer planning opportunities for committees.
- Introduce and coordinate new ideas on a specific topic.
- Induce new concepts in a variety of ways.
- Permit flexibility in the use of visuals.
- Encourage originality in conveying ideas.

BUZZ SESSIONS, COMMITTEES

- Allow personalized interaction in smaller groups.
- Develop leadership and management skills by having leaders set limits and guidelines.
- Permit free and open discussion on different aspects of a problem.
- Utilize the techniques of problem solving.
- Help to involve introvertive students in greater participation.
- Foster the sharing of responsibilities and cooperative effort.
- Save valuable class time by pooling ideas quickly.

CASE STUDIES

- Encourage objectivity in solving problems.
- Add insight to human relationships.
- Permit situations to be either open-ended or with final outcomes.
- Sharpen students' skills in critical thinking.
- Provide a common basis for in-depth discussion.

CHALKBOARD

- Permits easy placement and removal of timely information.
- Focuses on major points and assignments quickly.
- Saves money when cost is compared to frequency of use.
- Comes in a variety of sizes and colors and can be stationary or portable.

CHARTS, MAPS, GLOBES

- Assist in seeing relationships of land, water, and climate to cultures and products.
- Serve as a frame of reference to places, people, and time.
- Help to clarify points or grasp sequence of steps in a process.

CHECKLISTS, QUESTIONNAIRES

- Serve as quick indicators in obtaining an overview of attitudes or learnings.
- Obtain information needed for a particular situation without jeopardizing the confidentiality of students and/or their families.
- Induce student self-awareness and self-evaluation in a skill performance or attitude.
- Give impetus for making adjustments in curriculum planning.

COMPUTER

- Allows students to work independently at their own pace.
- Gives immediate feedback to student responses.
- Develops eye-hand coordination.
- Can be used with gifted students to extend subject matter covered in the classroom.
- Encourages students to see a relationship between technology, home, and the workplace.
- Can be used for a variety of tasks including instructing, training, and evaluating students.
- When connected to a classroom television monitor, can allow the entire class to participate by viewing the results of each student's entry into the computer.
- Benefits students with physical handicaps, those who are academically disadvantaged, and those with limited English proficiency by reinforcing subject matter presented in the classroom.
- Involves the senses of sight, sound, and touch.

DEBATES

- Cover both sides of a question by discussing pros and cons.
- Set the climate for audience involvement in the discussion.
- Encourage the search for new evidence.
- Bring values to surface.

DEMONSTRATIONS

- Set up standards for work skills.
- Increase the interest in learning a specific skill or method.
- Require and reveal systematic organization from planning through execution.
- Allow full view of performance by total class.
- Reinforce learnings through practice and observation.
- Appeal to all senses in making the learning process more lasting.
- Replace and/or supplement a laboratory experience at low cost.

EXHIBITS, DISPLAYS, MOBILES, MODELS, PROJECTS

- Extend learning to the levels of application and synthesis.
- Stimulate interest and aid in summarizing main ideas.
- Combine individual and group effort in completion of a project.
- Develop sensitivity to aesthetic appeals in conveying central themes.
- Extend an illusion of authenticity through three-dimensional expressions.
- Publicize departmental programs creatively.
- Permit use of a wide variety of materials.
- Encourage self-expression and creativity, which enhance self-concept.

EXPERIMENTS

- Allow step-by-step, practical application of skills through learning-by-doing.
- Help to clarify relationships through the application of principles.
- Give students experience in planning, scheduling, and carrying out activities.
- Encourage self-direction toward new learnings and independent action in applying the scientific method.

FELT AND FLANNEL BOARDS, POSTERS

- Illustrate graphically the sequential progression of an idea or event.
- Simplify and clarify processes in an eye-catching manner.

FIELD TRIPS

- Give first-hand experiences that cannot be had in the classroom.
- Develop skills in observation.
- Aid in seeing relationships of school learnings to realities of the outside world.
- Tend to be remembered in later years more than other educational experiences.

FLASH CARDS

- Help in developing "drill" activities.
- Aid in vocabulary building and knowledge of word meanings.
- Elicit free and open responses to symbols, words, and pictures.
- Can be easily stored and reused by individuals or groups.

GAMES

- Provide an opportunity to see familiar material in a new way.
- Combine reality and make-believe without being "gimmicky."
- Encourage participation of slow and fast learners.
- Remove inhibitions for some participants.

HOMEWORK, INDEPENDENT STUDY

- Reinforce and supplement classroom learnings.
- Help to identify and plan for individual student differences.
- Teach responsibility and development of positive study habits.
- Encourage exploration and discovery, which may lead to self-actualization through self-direction.

INTERVIEWS, SURVEYS

- Give first-hand oral testimony on how people think and feel about a particular situation.
- Sharpen experiences in public relations and concise questioning.
- Serve as a prelude to planning topics to be covered in a unit or lesson.

LECTURES

- Impart large amounts of information within a designated period of time.
- Give background data needed for gaining insight into learning experiences.
- Reach total group at one time.

NEWSPAPERS, MAGAZINES

- Update and highlight current information and trends.
- Extend and expand on textual materials used in the classroom.
- Offer opportunities for developing skills in discriminatory reading.
- Stimulate discussion and evaluation of often highly motivating information.

NOTEBOOKS, SCRAPBOOKS

- Induce self-expression and creativity.
- Help in retaining important information for future reference.

PANEL DISCUSSIONS

- Enrich experiences through the use of panels comprising students and/or guest speakers.
- Permit interaction between panelists and the audience.
- Contribute to new and differing insights and points of view.

PICTURES, CARTOONS

- Get ideas across succinctly.
- Add humor and zest to the learning process.
- Activate discussion or convey information pertinent to the subject.

PROGRAMMED LEARNING, INDIVIDUALIZED INSTRUCTION

- Allow students to work independently at their own rate of speed.
- Help students get immediate feedback to their responses and therefore aid them in reinforcing learnings.
- Allow review or "catching up" for a variety of reasons.
- Expand options to meet individual interests, abilities, and needs.
- Activate responsible behavior, self-discipline, and self-evaluation.

PROJECTORS — OPAQUE, OVERHEAD

- Offer the use of a wide range of materials to hold students' attention.
- Introduce, supplement, or reinforce ideas.
- Simplify concepts and enlarge illustrations.
- Avoid the need to reproduce items repeatedly.
- Enable students to copy information readily.

QUESTION BOX

- Gives opportunity for questions to be posed that might not otherwise arise in class discussions.
- Obtains information that may be useful to the teacher in making curriculum decisions.

QUESTIONS

- Aid in identifying learning gaps.
- Offer an opportunity to find out how thoroughly the students understand learnings by checking their learning processes of memory, translation, interpretation, application, analysis, synthesis, or evaluation.
- Use the five w's — who, what, when, where, why — so that in-depth analysis can be made.

REPORTS

- Utilize diverse resource materials and supplement basic textbooks.
- Develop basic research skills of finding and compiling data.
- Open new avenues of exploration for further inquiry.
- Inform others of extensive information in a short time.

RESOURCE SPEAKERS

- Contribute expertise in a specialized area.
- Increase student motivation by bringing the outside world into the classroom.
- Offer a quick way to obtain updated and accurate information.

SLIDES, FILMS, FILMSTRIPS

- Unify attention of students by focusing on a common experience.
- Give an "armchair" field trip by viewing scenes in the classroom.
- Provide sequential and closeup views of processes.
- Help to establish standards for the appearance of a product.
- Provide permanent records of experiences or occasions.

TEAM TEACHING

- Maximizes talent of personnel.
- Upgrades curriculum.
- Aids in reaching larger numbers of students.

TEXTBOOKS

- Organize and unify various units of study.
- Identify important old and new learnings.
- Serve as a convenient reference for basic information.
- Allow follow-up reading experiences beyond the classroom.
- Can be used in large and small groups.
- Offer features such as glossaries, illustrations, and bibliographies that assist students in understanding content.
- Help in achieving established course objectives.

TELEVISION, RADIO, VIDEOTAPES

- Extend learning beyond the classroom.
- Offer opportunities for enrichment through professionally produced programs.
- Accentuate the use of the senses and increase mental and visual imagery.
- Reach large audiences.
- Observe and evaluate performances.

VIDEO RECORDING EQUIPMENT

- Allows students to see their competency at skills and tasks.
- Offers the advantages of field trips without students ever leaving the classroom.
- Gives students opportunities for self-evaluation.
- Preserves demonstrations, lectures, and other events for future use.
- Effective in showing sequence, before and after steps, and how-to demonstrations.
- Provides a permanent record of events for future observation.
- Allows self-evaluation of teaching effectiveness.

References

Selected References

On the following pages is a list of references for each unit of *Food for Today*. Each list is subdivided according to the type of material: books; pamphlets and other educational materials; software; and audiovisuals (filmstrips, audio cassettes, films, and videotapes).

Current addresses of book publishers can usually be obtained from bookstores and libraries. Addresses for sources of other material are provided below each listing. Further information and/or catalogs are available from these sources.

Two additional sources of food and nutrition information are the U.S. Government Printing Office and the Food and Nutrition Service of the USDA. You may write to either office for a catalog of pamphlets and booklets.

U.S. Government Printing Office
Superintendent of Documents
Washington, DC 20402

Editorial and Printing Service Branch
Office of Governmental Affairs and
  Public Information
Food and Nutrition Service/USDA
3101 Park Center Drive
Alexandria, VA 22302

PART ONE: FOOD AND PEOPLE

Books

Brown, Lester
State of the World
W.W. Norton, published yearly

Chalmers, Irena
The Great American Food Almanac
Harper & Row, 1986

Goldsmith, Edward, and Nicholas Hillyard, eds.
The Earth Report
Price Stern Sloan, 1988

Levenstein, Harvey
Revolution at the Table
Oxford University Press, 1988

Lowenberg, Miriam, et al.
Food and People
Macmillan Publishing, 1979

Myers, Norman, ed.
GAIA — An Atlas of Planet Management
Doubleday, 1984

Tannahill, Reay
Food in History
Stein and Day, 1974

Winter, Ruth
A Consumer's Dictionary of Food Additives
Crown, 1984

Pamphlets and Other Educational Materials

- *Chemical Cuisine*
  Poster lists food additives and rates them according to how well they've been tested.
    Center for Science in the Public Interest
    1501 16th St., N.W.
    Washington, DC 20036

Software

- *Nutri-bytes*
  (Apple, IBM PC)
  Tests students on their knowledge of food additives. Also teaches grocery shopping skills and nutrition information.
    Center for Science in the Public Interest
    1501 16th St., N.W.
    Washington, DC 20036

- *Chemicals in Foods*
  (Apple II series)
  Tests students' ability to identify common foods by the additives they commonly contain.
    MECC
    2520 Broadway Dr.
    St. Paul, MN 55113

Audiovisual

- *Exploding Nutrition Myths*
  (filmstrips, cassettes, guide)
    Bergwall Productions
    839 Stewart Ave.
    P.O. Box 238
    Garden City, NY 11530

- *Food: A Cross-Cultural Study*
  (filmstrip on videotape, guide)
  Explores the ways people around the world satisfy their need for food and shows ceremonies associated with eating.
    Educational Design
    47 W. 13th St.
    New York, NY 10011

- *Cultural Influences on Food Choices*
  (filmstrip, cassette, duplicating masters, guide)
- *Food Additives: Helps or Hazards?*
  (filmstrip, cassette, duplicating masters, wall chart, guide)
  > Glencoe Publishing
  > 15319 Chatsworth St.
  > P.O. Box 9509
  > Mission Hills, CA 91345-9509

- *That's Inedible*
  (filmstrips, cassettes)
  Helps students sort out misinformation and half-truths about foods.
- *What's in the Food? What You Should Know About Food Additives*
  (filmstrips, cassettes, teacher's guide)
  > The Learning Seed
  > 330 Telser Rd.
  > Lake Zurich, IL 60047

PART TWO: NUTRITION FOR GOOD HEALTH

Books

Adams, Catherine F.
Nutritive Value of Foods
  (Home and Garden Bulletin #72)
U.S. Government Printing Office, 1981

Berland, Theodore
The Dieter's Almanac
Ballantine Books, 1984

Better Homes and Gardens editors
The Dieter's Cookbook
Meredith, 1982

Carper, Jean
Jean Carper's Total Nutrition Guide
Bantam Books, 1987

Charley, Helen
Food Science
Macmillan, 1982

Cooper, Kenneth
Aerobic Program for Total Well-Being: Exercise, Diet and Emotional Balance
Bantam, Books, 1983

Fleck, Henrietta
Introduction to Nutrition
Macmillan, 1981

Gooch, Sandy
If You Love Me, Don't Feed Me Junk
Reston, 1983

Guthrie, Helen
Introductory Nutrition
C.V. Mosby, 1986

Ikeda, Joanne
Winning Weight Loss for Teens
Bull Publishing, 1987

Kirschmann, John, and Lavon Dunne
Nutrition Almanac
McGraw-Hill, 1985

Kowtaluk, Helen
Discovering Nutrition
Glencoe, 1986

Krause, Marie V., and Kathleen Mahan
Food, Nutrition and Diet Therapy
W.B. Saunders, 1984

Lappe, Francis
Diet for a Small Planet
Ballantine Books, 1984

Lappe, Francis, and Joseph Collins
World Hunger: Twelve Myths
Grove Press, 1986

Nutrition 88/89 (an anthology of journal articles about nutrition)
Dushkin Publishing Group

Robertson, Laurel; Carol Flinders; and Brian Ruppenthal
The New Laurel's Kitchen
Ten Speed Press, 1986

Saltman, Paul; Joel Gurin; and Ira Mothner
The California Nutrition Book
Little, Brown, 1987

Time-Life editors
The Body in Motion
(Fitness, Health, and Nutrition Series)
Time-Life Books, 1988

Time-Life editors
Wholesome Diet
(Library of Health)
Time-Life Books, 1981

Whitney, Eleanor N., and Eva M. Hamilton
Understanding Nutrition
West Publishing, 1987

Worthington-Roberts, Bonnie
Contemporary Developments in Nutrition
C.V. Mosby, 1981

Yetiv, Jack A.
Popular Nutritional Practices:
   A Scientific Appraisal
Popular Medicine Press, 1986

Pamphlets and Other Educational Materials

- *Fast Food Eating Guide* (poster)
- *The Lifesaver Fat and Calorie Guide* (poster)
- *New American Eating Guide* (poster)
- *Nutrition Scorecard* (poster)
- *Sugar Scoreboard* (poster)
   Center for Science in the Public Interest
   1501 16th St., N.W.
   Washington, DC 20036

- *Digestive System Model*
   This full-color plastic anatomical model depicts the human digestive system in three dimensions. Includes guide.
   Hubbard Scientific
   1946 Raymond Dr.
   P.O. Box 104
   Northbrook, IL 60065-9976

- *Basic 4*
   This game teaches the four basic food groups, the nutrients in each, and recommended daily amounts of foods required for a balanced diet.
- *Nutriquest*
   "Trivia" game that promotes nutrition concepts.
- *Nutrition and Exercise*
   A board game designed to teach good diet habits and the importance of physical exercise.
   Nasco
   901 Janesville Ave.
   Fort Atkinson, WI 53538

Software

- *Nutri-Calc*
   (IBM PC/XT/AT)
   Analyzes nutrition and exercise.
   Camde Corporation
   4435 S. Rural Rd.
   Suite 331
   Tempe, AZ 85282

- *Nutrition Wizard*
   (IBM PC)
   Offers a comprehensive nutrition and weight-change program.
   Center for Science in the Public Interest
   1501 16th St., N.W.
   Washington, DC 20036

- *Apple Pie*
   (Apple, IBM PC)
   This seven-program series includes: *You are What You Eat!; Sweet Tooth; Salty Dog; Food for Thought; Jumping Jack Flash!; Munchies;* and *Grease.*
- *Nutrient Analysis System 2*
   (Apple II series, IBM PC)
   Personalized analysis of food intake variables and recommendations for dietary changes.
   DDA Software
   P.O. Box 26
   Hamburg, NJ 07419

- *The Food Processor II*
   (IBM, Apple II series, Macintosh-512K)
   Program creates user-specified diet.
   ESHA Research
   P.O. Box 13028
   Salem, OR 97309

- *Nutri-Venture*
   (Apple II series, TRS-80)
   Three game programs designed to reinforce nutrition concepts.
   Kellogg's Nutri-Venture
   P.O. Box 5159
   Kalamazoo, MI 49003-5159

- *Calorie Awareness Training*
   (Apple II)
- *Cholesterol Countdown*
   (Apple II)
   Students learn about cholesterol and test their knowledge.
- *Fast Food Microguide*
   (Apple II)
   Students can evaluate the nutritional value of fast-food meals.
- *Menucalc*
   (Apple II)
   User enters caloric and nutritional variables and computer shows a variety of menus that meet the criteria.
- *Nutrient Data Bank*
   (Apple II)
- *Nutrition Pursuit*
   (Apple II)
   Players race to the finishing line by correctly answering nutrition questions.
- *Fast Food Micro-Guide*
   (Apple II)
   Evaluates the nutritional content of leading fast-food restaurant meals.

- *Snackmaster or Snackmonster*
  (Apple II, TRS-80, IBM PC)
  Students select the food with lowest calorie content from 3 choices. The student with the lowest total score wins.
- *What Did You Eat Yesterday*
  (Apple, IBM PC, TRS-80)
  Students can use the 900-food database to analyze their nutrient and calorie intake.
    The Learning Seed
    330 Telser Rd.
    Lake Zurich, IL 60047

- *Food Facts*
  (Apple II series)
  Five programs: *Cereals, Chemicals in Foods, Fast Foods, Food Graphs,* and *Vitamins.*
- *Food Intake Analysis*
  (Apple II series)
  Analyzes food intake in terms of calories consumed and the nutritional value.
- *Lean*
  (Apple II series)
  This diet-assessment program calculates student's ideal weight; determines the ideal balance of protein, carbohydrate, and fat; and assesses the nutritional content of the foods eaten for the past one to three days.
    MECC
    2520 Broadway Dr.
    St. Paul, MN 55113

- *Food for Thought*
  (Apple II, TRS-80, IBM)
  Tests student's nutrition "IQ."
    Nasco
    901 Janesville Ave.
    Fort Atkinson, WI 53538

- *Nutrition: The Game Format*
  (Apple II)
- *Nutrient Analysis*
  (Apple II)
- *Foods: The Digestive System*
  (Apple II)
    Orange Juice Software
    338 S. Arch Ave.
    New Richmond, WI 54017

- *Vitamins and Minerals*
  (Apple)
    Queue, Inc.
    562 Boston Ave.
    Bridgeport, CT 06610

- *Food for Thought: A Nutrition Game and Data Base*
  (Apple II series)
  Interactive game sends students to the video "supermarket" to select foods containing certain nutrients.
    Sunburst Communications
    39 Washington Ave.
    Pleasantville, NY 10570-9971

Audiovisuals

- *Controlling Cholesterol*
  (videotape)
- *Diet: The Cancer Connection*
  (videotape)
- *A Matter of Fat*
  (videotape)
  Explores the seesaw relationship between dieting and regaining weight lost, and the "set point" theory.
- *Junk Food and Nutrition*
  (videotape)
- *Sweetness and Health*
  (videotape)
  Looks at the effects of sugar used in moderation and at the nature and safety of various sugar substitutes.
- *The Nutritional Advocate*
  (videotape)
  Explores the crucial relationship between diet and health.
- *Women and Weight Loss*
  (videotape)
  Examines the on-again/off-again problem of dieting.
    Films for the Humanities and Sciences
    P.O. Box 2053
    Princeton, NJ 08543

- *Diets And Weight Control*
  (filmstrip on videotape, guide)
    Franklin Clay Films
    P.O. Box CDE-2036
    Costa Mesa, CA 92638-1036

- *Eating Disorders*
  (filmstrip and cassette or transfer video, study sheets, wall chart, guide)
  Covers how eating disorders develop, how to recognize them, and what can be done.
- *Food for Fitness*
  (filmstrip, cassette, duplicating masters, wall chart, guide)
  Helps students see the connection between the "fuel" you take in and your body's performance.

- *Nutrition on the Run*
  (filmstrip and cassette or transfer videotape, duplicating masters, wall chart, guide)
  Students learn how to make "fast food" part of a nutritious, balanced diet.
- *Vegetarian Cooking Made Easy*
  (filmstrip, cassette, duplicating masters, guide)
- *Vegetarian Culture and Cuisine*
  (filmstrip, cassette, duplicating masters, guide)
- *Watch Your Weight*
  (filmstrip, cassette, duplicating masters, wall chart, guide)
  Students learn how to determine and maintain their proper weight.
  Glencoe Publishing
  15319 Chatsworth St.
  P.O. Box 9509
  Mission Hills, CA 91345-9509

- *Fast Food*
  (filmstrip, cassette, guide)
- *The Fats of Life*
  (filmstrips on videotape or filmstrips with cassettes, guide)
  Explains the difference between saturated and unsaturated fats and explains the cholesterol problem.
- *Food and Cancer Prevention*
  (filmstrip on videotape or filmstrips with cassettes)
- *Snackology: How to Have Your Snacks and Eat Them Too*
  (videotape)
  Helps students choose those snacks that are lower in fat and calorie content.
- *Snacks: The Food You Hate to Love*
  (filmstrips, cassettes)
  Gives tips for escaping tempting situations snack-free.
- *Vitamin Basics*
  (filmstrips, cassettes, worksheets, guide)
  Presents the history of vitamins — from their discovery as essential nutrients to the vitamin crazes of today.
  The Learning Seed
  330 Telser Rd.
  Lake Zurich, IL 60047

- *The New Nutrition: What It Means to Teenagers*
  (filmstrip on videotape or filmstrip with cassette, guide)
  Shows teens that the food decisions they make now can affect them their whole lifetime.

- *Nutrition and Exercise*
  (videotape, guide)
  Focuses on nutrients and the importance of each to maintaining good health. Also discusses the food groups.
- *Nutrition for Teenagers Only*
  (filmstrip on videotape or filmstrips with cassettes, guide)
  Covers special nutritional needs of teenagers, making food decisions, and improving eating habits.
- *Nutrition on the Run: Snacks and Fast Foods*
  (filmstrip on videotape or filmstrips with cassettes, activity booklets, guide)
- *Smoking: A Research Update*
  (filmstrip on videotape or filmstrips with cassettes, guide)
  Answers questions students raise about smoking.
- *Your Health: It's Your Responsibility*
  (filmstrip on videotape or filmstrips with cassettes, guide)
  Presents wellness concept.
  Sunburst Communications
  101 Castleton St.
  Pleasantville, NY 10570-9971

PART THREE: CONSUMER DECISIONS

Books

Consumer Reports Books
Guide to Kitchen Equipment
Consumers Union, 1986

Goldbeck, Nikki, and David Goldbeck
Goldbeck's Guide to Good Food
North American Library, 1987

Jacobson, Michael
Fast-Food Guide
Center for Science in the Public Interest, 1986

Kimbrell, Grady, and Susan Kern
The Savvy Consumer
Glencoe, 1984

Kitchen Tools: Cooking with a Twist and a Flair!
Index, 1985

Kratzer, Brice, et al.
Nutrition: Where Have All These Labels Been?
Dallas Sandt, 1987

Maedke, Wilmer O.; Ross E. Lowe; and Charles A. Malouf
Consumer Education
Glencoe, 1984

Pickett, Mary S.
Household Equipment
Macmillan, 1984

Pamphlets and Other Educational Materials

- *Kitchen Tools and Gadgets*
  Card game acquaints students with kitchen gadgets and their uses.
  Nasco
  901 Janesville Ave.
  Ft. Atkinson, WI 53538

Software

- *Know it All!*
  (Apple)
  Uses games like hangman and tic-tac-toe to teach food safety and storage principles and kitchen equipment and appliance information.
  DDA Software
  P.O. Box 26
  Hamburg, NJ 07419

- *The Grocery Games*
  (Apple)
  Focuses on grocery shopping skills.
- *Understanding Food Labels*
  (Apple, IBM PC)
  The Learning Seed
  330 Telser Rd.
  Lake Zurich, IL 60047

- *Buyer Beware*
  (Apple)
  Provides information and practice to help students develop consumer skills.
- *Food Labels*
  (Apple)
  Students take a simulated trip through a grocery store learning to use food label information.
  MCE, Inc.
  Suite 250
  157 S. Kalamazoo Mall
  Kalamazoo, MI 49007

- *The Daily Menu Analyzer*
  (Apple II)
  Students learn about labeling and menu analysis, plus the food groups and essential nutrients.
  Orange Juice Software
  338 S. Arch Ave.
  New Richmond, WI 54017

Audiovisual

- *What's in a Label*
  (filmstrips, cassettes, guide)
  Career Aids
  20417 Nordhoff St., Dept. EC
  Chatsworth, CA 91311

- *Choosing and Using Small Appliances*
  (filmstrip, cassette, duplicating masters, wall chart, guide)
- *Look and Cook: A Complete Introduction to Food and Nutrition*
  (filmstrips, cassettes, transparencies, duplicating masters, wall charts, guides)
  Includes information on buying foods, on making wise food decisions, and on kitchen equipment.
- *Spending Your Food Dollars*
  (filmstrip, cassette, duplicating masters, guide)
  Shows students how to choose produce, read labels for ingredients and nutrients, figure unit costs, and evaluate additives.
- *Supermarket Shopping: A Guide to Grocery Store Services*
  (filmstrip, cassette, duplicating masters, wall chart, guide)
  Glencoe Publishing
  15319 Chatsworth St.
  P.O. Box 9509
  Mission Hills, CA 91345-9509

- *Advanced Grocery Shopping*
  (filmstrips, cassettes, book)
- *Food Safety*
  (filmstrips, cassettes, poster, guide)
  Includes information on storing foods safely.
- *Kitchenware: A Quality Guide*
  (videotape)
- *Nutri-Max*
  (filmstrips, cassettes, cookbook, guide)
  Suggests ways to stretch your food dollar to get the most nutrition for the least money.
- *Super Marketing: The Art of Buying Fresh Food*
  (filmstrips, cassettes, book, reproducible pages, guide)
- *Winning the Grocery Game: Language and the Supermarket*
  (filmstrip, cassettes, consumer kit, guide)
  The Learning Seed
  330 Telser Rd.
  Lake Zurich, IL 60047

- *Kitchen Survival Kit*
  (filmstrip, cassette, wall chart, brochures)
  Designed to increase student safety awareness at home, especially in the kitchen.
    Nasco
    901 Janesville Ave.
    Fort Atkinson, WI 53538

- *Small Kitchen Equipment*
  (filmstrips, cassettes, recipes, guide)
  Six programs present information on small kitchen appliances, cookware, baking equipment, cutlery, microwaves, gadgets.
    RMI Corp.
    341 Broadway
    Cambridge, MA 02139

PART FOUR: FOOD SKILLS

Books

Bean, John, and Marina Bean
How to Repair Food
Ten Speed Press, 1987

Church, Beverly R., and Bethany E. Bultman
Joys of Entertaining
Abbeville Press, 1987

Cone, Marcia, and Thelma Snyder
Mastering Microwave Cooking
Simon and Schuster, 1986

Cox, Beverly, and Joan Whitman
Cooking Techniques: How to Do Anything a Recipe Tells You to Do
Little, Brown

Ginders, James
Napkin Folding: 44 Ways to Turn a Square of Linen into a Work of Art
Harmony Books, 1987

Harris, Barbara
Let's Cook Microwave
Microwave Cooking Services, 1987

Jester, Pat
Microwave Cookbook: The Complete Guide
HP Books, 1988

Kinder, Faye, and Nancy Green
Meal Management
Macmillan, 1983

Methven, Barbara
Basic Microwaving
Cy DeCosse, 1987

Post, Elizabeth L.
The New Emily Post's Etiquette
Funk & Wagnalls, 1984

Pamphlets and Other Educational Materials

- *Activities for Foods Classes*
  Duplicating masters.
- *Activities for Table Setting Fun*
  Duplicating masters.
- *Calorie and Nutrition Meal Planning*
  Board game designed to teach meal planning skills.
- *Tic-Tac-Toe*
  Game in which players answer questions about meal planning, table setting, and using food groups.
    Nasco
    901 Janesville Ave.
    Fort Atkinson, WI 53538

Software

- *Menu Planning on a Budget*
  (Apple)
    C.W. Publications
    P.O. Box 744
    Sterling, IL 61081

- *Food Poisoning, Sanitation, and Preservation*
  (Apple II)
- *The Microwave Oven*
  (Apple II)
    Orange Juice Software
    338 S. Arch Ave.
    New Richmond, WI 54017

Audiovisuals

- *The Language of Cooking*
  (filmstrips, cassettes, guide)
  Introduces students to food preparation techniques.
- *Microwave Cooking*
  (filmstrips, cassettes, guide)
    Bergwall Productions
    839 Stewart Ave.
    P.O. Box 238
    Garden City, NY 11530

- *Microwaving the Microwhiz Way*
  (videotape, student activity sheets, guide)
    Career Aids
    20417 Nordhoff St., Dept. EC
    Chatsworth, CA 91311

- *Microwave Cooking and Safety*
  (videotape, guide)
    Franklin Clay Films
    P.O. Box CDE-2036
    Costa Mesa, CA 92638-1036

- *Food and Kitchen Safety*
  (filmstrip and cassette or transfer video, duplicating masters, wall chart, guide)
- *Measure Up*
  (filmstrip, cassette, duplicating masters, wall chart, guide)
  Teaches basic measuring skills using both metric and conventional systems.
- *Nutrition Makes a Difference*
  (filmstrip, cassette, duplicating masters, guide)
  Students learn to plan meals using the Five Food Groups as guidelines.
- *Organizing Meals on Your Own*
  (filmstrip, cassette, duplicating masters, guide)
  Shows students how to plan, prepare, and serve meals efficiently, attractively, and economically.
- *The Meal Planning Series*
  (filmstrips, cassettes, duplicating masters, transparencies, wall chart, guide)
  Includes four programs: *Principles of Meal Planning, Meal Management, Meal Planning in Action, Meal Planning for the Future.*
- *Micro-cooking*
  (filmstrip, cassette, duplicating masters, wall chart, guide)
  Demonstrates how microwave ovens work, save energy, and improve nutrition.
  Glencoe Publishing
  15319 Chatsworth St.
  P.O. Box 9509
  Mission Hills, CA 91345-9509

- *Microwave Tips, Tricks and Techniques*
  (videotape by Reynolds Metals Co., free on loan)
  Karol Media
  22 Riverview Dr.
  Wayne, NJ 07470

- *Beautiful Food*
  (filmstrips, cassettes, guide)
  Covers meal planning and serving.
  The Learning Seed
  330 Telser Rd.
  Lake Zurich, IL 60047

- *Marvels of Microwave*
  (filmstrip, cassette, poster, duplicating masters, guide)
  Nasco
  901 Janesville Ave.
  Fort Atkinson, WI 53538

PART FIVE: FOOD PREPARATION

Books

American Heart Association Cookbook
Ballantine Books, 1984

Beard, James
Beard on Bread
Ballantine Books, 1981

Beard, James
The James Beard Cookbook
Dell Publishing, 1987

Beard, James
James Beard's Theory and Practice of Good Cooking
Alfred A. Knopf, 1984

Bennion, Marion
Introductory Foods
Macmillan, 1985

Berolzheimer, Ruth, ed.
Culinary Arts Institute Encyclopedic Cookbook
Putnam Publishing Group, 1986

Cunningham, Marion
The Fannie Farmer Cookbook
Alfred A. Knopf, 1984

Freeland-Graves, Jeanne H., and Gladys Peckham
Foundations of Food Preparation
Macmillan, 1987

Grosser, Arthur E.
The Cookbook Decoder, or Culinary Alchemy Explained
Warner Books, 1981

Hagler, Louise
Tofu Cookery
The Book Publishing Co., 1982

Handbook of Food Preparation
American Home Economics Association, 1980

Hertzberg, Ruth, et al.
Putting Food By
Stephen Greene Press, 1984

Ingoe, Robert S.
Dictionary of Food Ingredients
Van Nostrand Reinhold, 1983

Kowtaluk, Helen
Discovering Food
Glencoe, 1982

Lindsay, Anne
The American Cancer Society Cookbook
Hearst Books, 1988

McGee, Harold
On Food and Cooking: The Science and Lore of the Kitchen
Charles Scribner's Sons, 1984

Moosewood Collective
New Recipes from the Moosewood Restaurant
Ten Speed Press, 1987

Nicholas, Herbert L.
Cooking with Understanding
North Castle Books, 1971

Rombauer, Irma S., and Marion R. Becker
Joy of Cooking
Macmillan, 1988

Scott, David, and Paddy Byrne
Seasonal Salads
Garden Way Publishing, 1987

Stearns, Jane, and Michael Stearns
Real American Food
Alfred A. Knopf, 1986

Sunset editors
Easy Basics for Good Cooking
Lane Publishing, 1983

Underwood, Greer
The Enlightened Gourmet
The Globe Pequot Press, 1987

Vegetarian Times editors
Vegetarian Times Cookbook
Macmillan, 1984

Pamphlets and Other Educational Materials

- *Beef Butcher Block Game*
  Players match photographs of retail meat cuts to their names.
- *Food Preservation*
  Puzzles are designed to spark student interest in food preservation techniques.
- *Food Replicas*
  Plastic foods that can be used in demonstrations.
  Nasco
  901 Janesville Ave.
  Fort Atkinson, WI 53538

- *Seafood Resource for Educators*
  Offers nutritional information, seafood lesson plans, cooking instructions, and recipes.
  National Fisheries Education and
      Research Foundation
  2000 M Street, NW, Suite 580
  Washington, DC 20036

- *Fresh Fruits and Vegetables:
  The Natural Choice Poster*
      United Fresh Fruit and
          Vegetable Association
      Dept. S
      727 N. Washington St.
      Alexandria, VA 22314

Software

- *Identifying and Preparing Meats*
  (Apple)
- *Recipe Measurements Drill*
  (Apple II, TRS-80)
      Cotton Computer Service
      Rt. 1, Box 34
      Bristow, OK 74010

- *Something's Cooking: Know It All!*
  (Apple II)
  Students learn about buying, storing, and preparing meat, fish, beans, eggs, fruits, vegetables, breads, and cereals.
      DDA Software
      P.O. Box 26
      Hamburg, NJ 07419

- *The Principles of Egg Cookery*
  (Apple II)
  Written as an adventure story told to a person from outer space.
      Orange Juice Software
      336 S. Arch Ave.
      New Richmond, WI 54017

Audiovisuals

- *Baking Basics: Quick Breads*
  (filmstrip on videotape or filmstrip and cassette, duplicating masters, wall chart, guide)
      Glencoe Publishing
      15319 Chatsworth St.
      P.O. Box 9509
      Mission Hills, CA 91345-9509

- *Freezing Food: The Cold Facts*
  (film, guide, resource booklet, wall chart, free courtesy of Reynolds Metals Co.)
      Karol Media
      22 Riverview Dr.
      Wayne, NJ 07470

- *The Way to Cook Series*
  (videotapes, booklets)
  In six videos, Julia Child demonstrates how to cook poultry, soups, salads, bread, meat, fish, eggs, vegetables, and desserts.
      Alfred A. Knopf
      201 E. 50th St.
      New York, NY 10022

- *Buying Meat*
  (filmstrip on videotape or filmstrips with cassettes, booklet)

- *Pasta Presto*
  (videotape, guide)
  Shows how to make pasta and sauces from scratch.
  > The Learning Seed
  > 330 Telser Rd.
  > Lake Zurich, IL 60047

- *So Easy to Preserve*
  (videotape series)
  Cassettes cover these topics: food preservation, canning fruits and tomatoes, canning vegetables, pickling, jams and jellies, freezing foods, drying foods, food safety and storage.
  > Management Operations
  > Cooperative Extension Service
  > The University of Georgia
  > Athens, Georgia 30602

- *Desserts and Snacks*
  (videotape, recipe booklet)
  Low-calorie desserts and snacks are prepared.
- *Hearty and Healthy Breakfasts*
  (videotape, recipe booklet)
  Demonstrates how to prepare cholesterol-free, fiber-rich recipes.
- *Light and Lively Fish and Chicken*
  (videotape, recipe booklet)
  Demonstrates how to prepare fish and chicken recipes.
- *Pasta, Soup, and Salad*
  (videotape, recipe booklet)
  Demonstrates how to prepare low-calorie, low-fat pasta dishes.
  > National Health Video
  > 12021 Wilshire Blvd., Suite 550
  > Los Angeles, CA 90025

- *Food Preparation*
  (filmstrip on videotape or filmstrip with cassette, guide)
  This series includes information on cooking meats, seafood, poultry, and vegetables, and on preparing and using fruits and vegetables.
  > Vocational Media Associates
  > Box 1050
  > Mount Kisco, NY 10549

PART SIX: CREATIVE CUISINE

Books

Bauer, Linda
The American Sampler Cookbook
McClanahan Publishing, 1986

Booth, Letha, and Joan P. Dutton
The Williamsburg Cookbook
Holt, Rinehart and Winston, 1976

Child, Julia
Mastering the Art of French Cooking
   (two volumes)
Alfred A. Knopf, 1983

Claiborne, Craig
The New York Times Food Encyclopedia
New York Times Books, 1985

Costner, Susan
Gifts of Food
Crown, 1984

Encyclopedia of International Cooking
Knapp Press, 1983

Epstein, Becky Sue, and Hilary Dole Klein
Substituting Ingredients: A Cooking Reference Book
   East Woods Press, 1986

Gisslen, Wayne
Professional Cooking
John Wiley & Sons, 1983

Killeen, Jacqueline, et al.
The Whole World Cookbook
Charles Scribner's Sons, 1979

Lang, Jenifer Harvey
Larousse Gastronomique
Crown Publishers, 1988

Lust, John
The Herb Book
Bantam Books, 1974

Mothershead, Alice B.
Dining Customs Around the World
Garrett Park Press, 1982

Rosengarten, F.
The Book of Spices
Jove, 1973

Sunset editors
The Barbecue Cook Book
Lane Publishing, 1986

Sunset editors
Easy Basics for International Cooking
Lane Publishing, 1984

Warner, Margaret B., and Ruth A. Haywood
What's Cooking? Favorite Recipes from Around the World
Little, Brown, 1981

Wilde, Mary Poulos
The Best of Ethnic Home Cooking
J.P. Tarcher, 1987

Pamphlets and Other Educational Materials

- *Activities for Food Garnishing*
  Duplicating masters.
    Nasco
    901 Janesville Ave.
    Fort Atkinson, WI 53538

- *Cooking Around the World*
  Duplicating masters provide crossword, scrambled word, and word search puzzles plus fill-in, matching, and multiple-choice questions to familiarize students with foods of many countries.
    J. Weston Walch
    P.O. Box 658
    Portland, ME 04104-0658

Software

- *Cultural Foods: Know It All!*
  (Apple)
  Students become acquainted with foods of the Orient, Europe, and regions of the United States.
    DDA Software
    P.O. Box 26
    Hamburg, NJ 07419

Audiovisuals

- *Food: A Cross-cultural Study*
  (filmstrips on videotapes or filmstrips with cassettes, guides)
  Explores foods, cooking, and customs around the world.
    Educational Design, Inc.
    47 W. 13th St.
    New York, NY 10011

- *The Cultures and Cuisines Series:*
  Black American Culture and Cuisine
  Chinese-American Culture and Cuisine
  Chinese Cooking Made Easy
  French Cooking Made Easy
  French Culture and Cuisine
  German-American Culture and Cuisine
  German Cooking Made Easy
  Italian-American Cooking Made Easy
  Italian-American Culture and Cuisine
  Mexican-American Culture and Cuisine
  Mexican Cooking Made Easy
  Native American Cooking Made Easy
  Native American Culture and Cuisine
  Soul Food Cooking Made Easy
  (filmstrips, cassettes, duplicating masters, guide)
    Glencoe Publishing Co.
    15319 Chatsworth St.
    P.O. Box 9509
    Mission Hills, CA 91345-9509

PART SEVEN: EXPLORING CAREERS

Books

Bolles, Richard N.
What Color Is Your Parachute?
Ten Speed Press, 1989

Como, Jay
Surviving on the Job
Glencoe, 1989

Cornelius, Ethelwyn G.
Food Service Careers
Glencoe, 1984

Farr, Michael J., et al.
The Work Book: Getting the Job You Want
Glencoe, 1987

Karlin, Muriel S.
Solving Your Career Mystery
Rosen Group, 1982

Kelly, Joan M., and Ruth Volz-Patton
Career Skills
Glencoe, 1984

Kimbrell, Grady, and Ben S. Vineyard
Entering the World of Work
Glencoe, 1989

Ray, Mary F., and Evelyn J. Lewis
Exploring Professional Cooking
Glencoe, 1987

The Student Guide to Federal Financial Aid Programs
(updated annually)
Federal Student Aid Programs
P.O. Box 84
Washington, DC 20044

U.S. Department of Labor
Dictionary of Occupational Titles
U.S. Government Printing Office, 1977
  (4th Edition Supplement, 1986)

Pamphlets and Other Educational Materials

- *Employability Inventory*
  Self-assessment cards let students practice dealing with hypothetical situations and problems.
    Education Associates, Inc.
    8 Crab Orchard Rd.
    P.O. Box Y
    Frankfort, KY 40602

- *Job Survival Skills*
  Skillsbook and guide. Teaches decision-making techniques, attitudes, and skills needed to deal with typical job situations and problems.

- *Me and Jobs*
  Skillsbook and guide. Includes aptitudes and problems checklists, sample application, and interviews.
    Educational Design, Inc.
    47 W. 13th St.
    New York, NY 10011

- *Jobs for the 90's: 100 Photos of People at Their Work*
  Boxed set of photo cards.
    J. Weston Walch
    P.O. Box 658
    Portland, ME 04104-0658

Software

- *How to Get and Hold a Job*
  (Apple II, TRS-80, IBM)
- *Survival Skills — Interviewing*
  (Apple II, TRS-80, IBM)
    Aquarius People Materials
    P.O. Box 128
    Indian Rocks Beach, FL 33535

- *Computerized Career Assessment and Planning*
  (Apple, TRS-80, IBM)
    Cambridge Career Products
    1 Players Club Dr., Dept. CC2
    Charleston, WV 25311

- *Career Scan IV*
  (Apple II, TRS-80, IBM, Commodore)
  Locates occupations with attributes similar to those the user chooses.
    Career Aids
    20417 Nordhoff St., Dept. CV 5
    Chatsworth, CA 91311

- *The Employability Inventory*
  (Apple, TRS-80, IBM)
  Includes finding job openings, developing resumés, following up job leads, completing job applications, interviewing, and job communications skills.
- *Job Applications: Answering the Employer's Questions*
  (Apple, TRS-80, IBM)
- *The Resume: Presenting Yourself in Writing*
  (Apple, TRS-80, IBM)
- *Successful Interviewing: Selling Yourself*
  (Apple, TRS-80, IBM)
    Education Associates, Inc.
    8 Crab Orchard Rd., P.O. Box Y
    Frankfort, KY 40602

- *Choices and Goals: An Individualized Career Exploration Computer Program*
  (Apple II series)
    Glencoe Publishing
    15319 Chatsworth St.
    P.O. Box 9509
    Mission Hills, CA 91345-9509

- *Emerging Occupations Interest Inventory*
  (Apple, IBM PC)
  Matches student interests with the characteristics of about 100 occupations.
- *Filling Out Job Applications*
  (Apple, IBM PC)
- *Job Attitudes: Assessment and Improvement*
  (Apple, IBM PC)
- *Jobs in Today's World*
  (Apple, IBM PC)
  Helps non-college-bound students match interests with jobs.
- *Resumes Made Easy*
  (Apple, IBM PC)
- *Successful Job Interviewing*
  (Apple, IBM PC)
- *There's a Career for You in Home Economics*
  (Apple, IBM PC)
  Matches student interests with home economics careers.
- *Job Success Series*
  (Apple)
  Includes four programs: *Your Personal Habits, Your Work Habits, First Days on the Job,* and *Looking Good.*
    MCE, Inc.
    157 S. Kalamazoo Mall, Suite 250
    Kalamazoo, MI 49007

- *Career Directions*
  (Apple II)
  Helps students identify personal likes, dislikes, and abilities and match them with suitable career options.
    Systems Design Associates
    723 Kanawha Blvd. East
    Charleston, WV 25301

Audiovisuals

- *Careers in Food and Nutrition*
  (filmstrips, cassettes, guide)
  A four-part series describing a wide variety of career choices in the food industry.
    Educational Activities
    1937 Grand Ave.
    Baldwin, NY 11510

- *Positive Attitudes 1: Getting a Job*
  (transfer videotape or filmstrip and cassette)
- *Positive Attitudes 2: Keeping a Job*
  (transfer videotape or filmstrip and cassette)
- *Up Close and in Person*
  (transfer videotape or filmstrip and cassette)
  Demonstrates skills needed to handle interview situations.
- *Writing Your Way Up the Job Ladder*
  (transfer videotape or filmstrip and cassette)
  Covers writing letters of application, resumés, and interview follow-up letters.
- *Your Appearance 1: The Interview*
  (transfer videotape or filmstrips and cassettes)
  Education Associates, Inc.
  8 Crab Orchard Rd.
  P.O. Box Y
  Frankfort, KY 40602

- *Career/Education/Life Options*
  (filmstrips on videotape or filmstrips and cassettes, duplicating masters, guide)
  Explores critical career choices young people must make.
- *Communicating on the Job*
  (filmstrips on videotape or filmstrips and cassettes, guide)
- *First Jobs*
  (filmstrips on videotape or filmstrips and cassettes, guide)
  Shows students how to get and keep a job.
- *Job Attitudes and Habits*
  (filmstrips on videotape or filmstrips and cassettes, guide)
- *Job Interview Skills*
  (filmstrips on videotape or filmstrips and cassettes, guide)
  Educational Design, Inc.
  47 W. 13th St.
  New York, NY 10011

- *Careers in Food Science*
  (slides, printed commentary, guide)

- *The Job Hunt: Getting Started and Surviving the Interview*
  (filmstrip, cassette, guide)
  Fairchild Books and Visuals
  7 East 12th St.
  New York, NY 10003

- *Careers Related to Home Economics*
  (filmstrip, cassette, guide)
- *Your Job Interview*
  (filmstrip, cassette, guide)
  Franklin Clay Films
  P.O. Box EA-1413
  Costa Mesa, CA 92628-1413

- *Home Economics Career Series*
  (filmstrips, cassettes, reproducible worksheets, guides)
  Series includes these programs: *Careers That Help with Relationships, Careers Helping Children, Careers in Management and Consumer Relations, Careers in Food and Nutrition, Careers in Clothing and Textiles*, and *Careers in Housing*.
  Glencoe Publishing
  15319 Chatsworth St.
  P.O. Box 9509
  Mission Hills, CA 91345-9509

- *Preparing for the Jobs of the 1990's: What You Should Know*
  (filmstrip on videotape or filmstrip with cassette)
- *Working for a Living: Job Skills for the Real World*
  (filmstrip on videotape or filmstrip with cassette)
  Guidance Associates
  Communications
  Box 3000
  Mount Kisco, NY 10549

- *Resumes that Get Interviews; Interviews that Get Jobs*
  (videotape, guide)
- *You and Your Job Interview*
  (filmstrip, cassettes, guide)
  Vocational Media Associates
  Box 1050
  Mount Kisco, NY 10549

Planning Charts

MONTHLY PLANNER

Month: _____

Monday ___	Tuesday ___	Wednesday ___	Thursday ___	Friday ___
Monday ___	Tuesday ___	Wednesday ___	Thursday ___	Friday ___
Monday ___	Tuesday ___	Wednesday ___	Thursday ___	Friday ___
Monday ___	Tuesday ___	Wednesday ___	Thursday ___	Friday ___
Monday ___	Tuesday ___	Wednesday ___	Thursday ___	Friday ___

ORGANIZING SUBJECT MATTER

Diversity is a unique characteristic of schools in the United States. This diversity allows and encourages flexibility in curricular decisions to meet local needs. In such a milieu, a myriad of factors must be considered before planning for the use of available resources.

The responsibility for overall course planning varies from school to school. Some teachers — especially in large districts — are expected to teach from predetermined outlines. Other teachers may need to write their own course outlines or may be free to adapt existing outlines to their own needs.

Factors that you need to review in planning unit and lesson plans include the following:

- Traditional, modular, or other type of scheduling.
- Philosophy and objectives of the school.
- Length of course and school term.
- Amount of class time daily and total per week.
- Laboratory and lecture facilities and equipment.
- Department budget.
- Class size.
- Abilities, interests, and needs of students.
- Articulation of scope and sequence of courses.
- Resources available in the school and community.

Selecting a Starting Point

After considering these many variables, your next concern as an educator is to ask yourself: "What do I want to emphasize in this course? How do I reach these objectives?"

To help you plan units and lessons, the creators of *Food for Today* have:

- Developed content around concepts and used these as chapter headings. This arrangement allows for flexibility in organizing units and lessons to meet your particular school needs. You can coordinate content from several chapters or from several main topics within a given chapter. The main topics within each chapter are identified by red, uppercase headings.

- Identified organizing themes that can be used as starting points for emphasis throughout the study of food and nutrition and meal management. These themes, and the chapters which give emphasis to them, are found in the Scope and Sequence chart on pages 42-49.

Planning Units and Lessons

Once you have selected your teaching approach or organizing theme for the course, you need to choose relevant content for units and lessons and plan how much time to spend on each. To help you do this, several additional planning aids are provided on the following pages.

- The Suggested Course Outlines on pages 50-51 show three examples of course planning. These outlines can help you see how much time might be allotted to each chapter of the text, depending on course length and emphasis. You may want to use these as a starting point, adapting one or more to fit your individual needs.

- The Worksheets for Lesson Planning on pages 52-64 identify the main topics in each chapter, list student objectives, and recommend which TRB reproducibles to use with each chapter. In addition, space is provided for you to check off and make notes on ideas that will fit your course goals and theme. You may want to duplicate these worksheets and retain the originals for future use.

- The Monthly Planner on page 40 is a reproducible chart to help you translate your course plans into action and monitor day-to-day progress.

If your course goals include an emphasis on food science concepts, pages 350-356 will also help you in planning. A chart is provided there which shows what food science material is provided in the student text, Teacher's Wraparound Edition, and Teacher's Resource Book for each chapter.

SCOPE AND SEQUENCE CHART

This chart shows how major themes are woven throughout *Food for Today*. You will find it useful for:

- Planning your course.
- Sequencing courses.
- Emphasizing particular course themes.
- Correlating *Food for Today* to your curriculum.

	Chapter 1 Your Food Choices
NUTRITION & HEALTH	■ Nutrients in food needed for health
CONSUMER INFORMATION	■ Advertising influences food choices
MANAGEMENT	■ Importance of food choices ■ Identifying resources ■ Managing resources ■ Improving management skills
SAFETY & SANITATION	
FOOD SCIENCE	
FOOD PREPARATION	
SOCIAL & CULTURAL ASPECTS	■ Food affects psychological health ■ Social and cultural influences on food choices ■ Origins of popular foods
TRENDS & TECHNOLOGY	■ Current food trends ■ Computer-assisted food choices

Chapter 2 Food Facts and Fallacies	Chapter 3 The Science of Nutrition	Chapter 4 The Nutrients You Need	Chapter 5 Food and Your Well-Being
■ Food fad dangers ■ Food and nutrition myths ■ Fortified and enriched foods	■ Nutrition defined ■ Role of nutrients ■ Nutrient teamwork ■ RDA and U.S. RDA ■ How nutrition affects health ■ Causes of malnutrition	■ Types of nutrients ■ Nutrient functions ■ Symptoms of deficiency and overuse ■ Relationship between diet and health ■ Protein complementarity	■ Wellness ■ How body uses food ■ Digestion ■ Dietary Guidelines ■ Sleep ■ Exercise ■ Smoking, alcohol, and other drugs
■ Avoiding food fraud ■ Organic and natural foods ■ Food additives ■ Sugar and fat substitutes ■ Antibiotics in meat ■ Pros and cons of food irradiation	■ Nutrient supplements are usually unnecessary and may be harmful	■ Food sources of nutrients ■ Evaluating advertising and nutrition claims ■ Using nutrition and food label information to lower fat and cholesterol intake	■ Choosing an exercise program
	■ Knowledge of nutrition affects food choices	■ Changing eating patterns	■ Developing a wellness plan ■ Stress management ■ Sleep management ■ Avoid harmful health habits
■ FDA controls additives ■ Food contamination ■ Food recall procedures	■ Overdoses of nutrients may be harmful		
■ Functions of food additives	■ Scientific method	■ Properties of saturated and unsaturated fats ■ Explanation of hydrogenation ■ Chemical nature of nutrients	■ Caloric measurement of energy in foods ■ Food as fuel ■ Chemistry of digestion ■ Basal metabolism
■ Emotional appeals of food quacks		■ American eating patterns	■ Lifestyle and emotions affect health ■ Taking personal responsibility for one's health ■ America's eating habits ■ Sedentary lifestyles
■ Food fraud and scientific discoveries ■ Irradiated foods	■ Nutrition research		■ Wellness

	Chapter 6 Plan Your Daily Food Choices	Chapter 7 Controlling Your Weight	Chapter 8 Special Food Needs
NUTRITION & HEALTH	■ Daily Food Guide ■ Nutrient density ■ U.S. RDA ■ Vegetarian diet	■ Determining ideal weight ■ Health risks of improper weight ■ Energy balance ■ Losing weight ■ Gaining weight ■ Eating disorders — anorexia nervosa and bulimia	■ Nutrition needs change ■ Pregnancy ■ Infants ■ Children ■ Adolescents ■ Teen athletes ■ Adults ■ Older adults ■ Nutrition and medical problems
CONSUMER INFORMATION	■ Eating out ■ Choosing food wisely	■ Dieting and eating out ■ Evaluating diets and diet plans	■ Food assistance programs
MANAGEMENT	■ Evaluating eating habits ■ Planning meals and snacks	■ Steps for losing or gaining weight ■ Changing eating habits ■ Maintaining ideal weight	■ Eating alone ■ Planning nutritious meals to meet individual needs ■ Managing food intake for athletic performance ■ Balancing food intake with body's needs
SAFETY & SANITATION	■ Food safety for packed lunches		■ Food safety for infants and children ■ Kitchen safety considerations for elderly
FOOD SCIENCE			
FOOD PREPARATION	■ Packing a lunch		■ Making baby foods
SOCIAL & CULTURAL ASPECTS	■ Lifestyle and diet ■ Meal patterns	■ Cultural interpretation of "ideal" weight ■ Lifestyle and weight problems ■ Diet clubs and support groups ■ Eating disorders	■ Teen pregnancy ■ Encouraging good eating habits in children
TRENDS & TECHNOLOGY	■ Trends in eating patterns ■ Vegetarianism		■ Eating trends of teens

Chapter 9 Your Kitchen	Chapter 10 Kitchen Equipment & Appliances	Chapter 11 Buying Food	Chapter 12 Storing Food
■ Diet food labels		■ Nutrition labeling	■ Proper storage preserves nutrients
■ Basic kitchen plans ■ Decorating and remodeling kitchens ■ Kitchens for handicapped	■ Buying cookware, tools and appliances ■ Sources of information ■ EnergyGuide labels ■ Performance and safety seals ■ Warranties ■ Buying used appliances ■ Care of appliances	■ Food processing ■ Convenience foods ■ Food prices ■ Types of food stores ■ Using food labels, open dating, UPC, unit pricing ■ Comparison shopping ■ Consumer responsibilities	■ Storage guidelines and times
■ Kitchen arrangement and organization ■ Work centers ■ Analyzing work flow ■ Evaluating kitchens ■ Storage	■ Determining equipment and appliance needs ■ Budgeting ■ Organizing warranties and product information	■ Selecting a store ■ Planning food purchases ■ Using coupons/refunds ■ Complaint procedures	■ Choosing appropriate storage techniques ■ Keeping inventories ■ Rotating stock
■ Electrical wiring ■ Planning for sanitation and safety ■ Safety considerations for the handicapped	■ Appliance safety ■ Copper cookware precautions	■ Inspecting food items before purchase	■ Storage hazards ■ Food spoilage ■ Thawed foods
	■ Methods of heat and energy transfer in cooking	■ Processed foods	■ Cellular and molecular changes in frozen food ■ Causes of food spoilage and rancidity
	■ Use of portable appliances ■ Use of major appliances		■ Packaging and labeling food for storage ■ Thawing foods
■ Kitchens as multipurpose rooms		■ Factors affecting food prices ■ Family changes alter shopping patterns	
■ Kitchen planning centers	■ Appliance trends ■ New appliance features ■ How microwave and convection ovens work	■ Food processing ■ Packaging trends ■ Computerized grocery check-out	

	Chapter 13 Safety and Sanitation	Chapter 14 Food Preparation Tools	Chapter 15 Food Preparation Techniques
NUTRITION & HEALTH	■ First aid procedures ■ Food poisoning symptoms ■ Personal hygiene ■ Kitchen sanitation		■ Cooking methods that help retain nutrients ■ Methods that reduce fat intake
CONSUMER INFORMATION		■ Selecting food preparation tools ■ Selecting cleaning equipment	■ Symbols & abbreviations ■ Metric system ■ Equivalents
MANAGEMENT	■ Planning a safe environment ■ Emergency procedures ■ Preventing accidents ■ Preventing food-borne illness	■ Assessing tool needs	■ Evaluating recipes ■ Substitutions ■ Increasing/decreasing yield
SAFETY & SANITATION	■ Safety hazards in the kitchen: falls, cuts, fires, burns, choking, shock, poisons ■ Food-borne illnesses	■ Equipment for safety and sanitation	■ Cooking safety
FOOD SCIENCE	■ Microorganisms and toxins in contaminated foods		■ Metrics in food science ■ Changes in food caused by cooking
FOOD PREPARATION	■ Safety and sanitation in food preparation ■ Outdoor meals ■ Parties	■ Food preparation tools	■ Using recipes ■ Measuring techniques ■ Food preparation techniques ■ Basic cooking methods
SOCIAL & CULTURAL ASPECTS	■ Children — safety considerations ■ Elderly — safety considerations	■ Kitchen tools from the past	
TRENDS & TECHNOLOGY			■ Metrics in food preparation

Chapter 16 Microwave Cooking	Chapter 17 Meal Management	Chapter 18 Serving and Eating Food	Chapters 19-33 Preparing Foods
■ Nutrient retention	■ Planning for nutrition	■ Nutritious table decorations	■ Nutritional value of specific foods ■ Protein alternates ■ Dairy substitutes ■ Nutritious food substitutions ■ Satisfying a sweet tooth with nutritious foods
■ Pros & cons of microwave cooking ■ Principles of microwave cooking ■ Microwave containers and materials	■ Saving energy and resources	■ Buying and caring for tableware	■ Buying guidelines for specific foods ■ Convenience forms ■ Food processing and marketing ■ Case against soft drinks
■ Time & energy savings ■ Planning microwave meals ■ Adapting conventional recipes	■ Management principles ■ Meal planning ■ Resources ■ Work simplification & efficiency ■ Computer analysis of food and food costs ■ Conserving water, energy, food, money, and time ■ Using leftovers ■ Recycling materials	■ Dishwashing tips ■ Table settings ■ Planning parties	■ Storage guidelines for specific foods ■ Serving suggestions ■ Modifying recipes to add nutritional value
■ Microwave safety	■ Cleanup ■ Food safety	■ Food safety at buffets ■ Washing dishes	■ Food safety controls — purchased foods ■ Precautions for using sprouts
			■ Composition of foods ■ Effects of cooking on different foods ■ Extracting gelatin from meats ■ Gluten formation ■ How leavening agents work ■ Factors that affect baking process ■ Food processing
■ Microwave techniques ■ Microwave snacks	■ Efficient preparation ■ Prepreparation ■ Recipes on computers	■ Creating nutritious table decorations	■ Food preparation techniques for fruits, vegetables, salads, dairy foods, meat, poultry, fish and shellfish, eggs, grain products, breads, desserts, soups and sauces, beverages
	■ World food crisis ■ Causes of famine ■ Working to reduce food shortages	■ Types of service ■ Table manners ■ Entertaining ■ Atmosphere affects eating enjoyment	■ Fruits and vegetables from around the world ■ International pasta dishes ■ International soups
■ Microwave cooking	■ Computers in the kitchen		■ Microwave cooking techniques ■ New varieties of fruits & vegetables ■ Dairy product substitutes ■ Fish farming ■ Mass production of baked goods ■ Soft drinks

	Chapter 34 Preserving Food at Home	Chapter 35 Foods of the World	Chapter 36 American Regional Foods
NUTRITION & HEALTH	■ Retaining nutrients in preserved foods	■ Food supply in developing countries ■ Effects of national prosperity on diet and health ■ Relationship between diet and life expectancy	
CONSUMER INFORMATION	■ Costs of home preservation	■ Foreign menu terms	■ Regional convenience foods
MANAGEMENT	■ Evaluating home preservation ■ Organizing preservation ■ Storing preserved foods	■ Affluence affects food choices	
SAFETY & SANITATION	■ Food safety in home preservation ■ Sanitation methods		
FOOD SCIENCE	■ Destroying micro-organisms and enzymes through food processing ■ Chemistry of gels ■ Molecular changes that occur in making jelly		
FOOD PREPARATION	■ Freezing ■ Canning ■ Pickling ■ Jams & jellies ■ Drying ■ Using home-preserved foods	■ Types of food ■ Methods of preparation ■ Use of spices in other countries	■ Types of food ■ Methods of preparation
SOCIAL & CULTURAL ASPECTS		■ Impact of culture, climate, and geography on diet & cuisine ■ European food customs ■ Near and Middle East ■ Africa ■ Asia ■ Latin America	■ Foods of American Indians ■ Impact of other cultures on American cuisine ■ Regional food history and customs
TRENDS & TECHNOLOGY			

Chapter 37 Creative Cooking	Chapter 38 Careers in Food and Nutrition	Chapter 39 How to Get and Keep a Job
	■ Careers in nutrition ■ Good health as a job requirement	
■ Convenience foods ■ Gourmet foods on a budget	■ Educational requirements ■ Sources of career information	■ Job information ■ Employment agencies

■ Adapting recipes
■ Serving food
■ Step-saving cooking ideas
■ Money-saving cooking ideas
	■ Choosing a career
	■ Career ladders
	■ Food service management
	■ Careers in business and
	  government
	■ Entrepreneurship
		■ Gaining work experience
		■ Preparing résumés and
		  applications
		■ Time management

■ Outdoor cooking safety	■ Careers in sanitation	
■ Effects of cooking on herbs and spices	■ Careers in food science	
■ Making mixes ■ Casseroles ■ Seasonings ■ Garnishes ■ Outdoor cooking	■ Preparing food for spaceflights ■ Careers in food preparation	■ Student-run catering company

■ Food as gifts
■ Food preparation as creative
  outlet
	■ Communication skills
	■ Customer service careers
	■ Social skills contribute to
	  business success
		■ Job interviews
		■ Getting along on the job
		■ Balancing work and personal
		  life
		■ Leaving the job

	■ Careers in food technology ■ Space food technology	■ HERO programs

SUGGESTED COURSE OUTLINES

The chart on these pages suggests some ways classes might be structured using the *Food for Today* text. Included are plans for an 18-week course covering all chapters; an 18-week course in which some chapters are skipped or summarized so that others can be treated in more depth; and a 36-week course. These outlines can easily be adapted to meet your particular needs. Space is left for you to plan your own outline if desired.

Chapter	Suggested Number of Days			
	18 weeks (Option 1)	18 weeks (Option 2)	36 weeks	Your Course
1. Your Food Choices	2	2	3	
2. Food Facts and Fallacies	2	2	4	
3. The Science of Nutrition	1	1	2	
4. The Nutrients You Need	3	5	6	
5. Food and Your Well-Being	4	5	7	
6. Plan Your Daily Food Choices	2	5	6	
7. Controlling Your Weight	2	5	7	
8. Special Food Needs	2	5	5	
9. Your Kitchen	2	4	4	
10. Kitchen Equipment and Appliances	4	5	7	
11. Buying Food	3	5	5	
12. Storing Food	2	*	4	
13. Safety and Sanitation	3	3	4	
14. Food Preparation Tools	3	4	5	
15. Food Preparation Techniques	3	4	5	
16. Microwave Cooking	2	*	5	
17. Meal Management	2	5	5	
18. Serving and Eating Food	2	*	5	

*These chapters can be summarized.

Chapter	Suggested Number of Days			
	18 weeks (Option 1)	18 weeks (Option 2)	36 weeks	Your Course
19. Fruits	3	3	5	
20. Vegetables	3	3	5	
21. Salads and Salad Dressings	3	*	5	
22. Dairy Foods	3	3	6	
23. Meat	3	2	5	
24. Poultry	2	1	4	
25. Fish and Shellfish	2	1	4	
26. Eggs	2	1	4	
27. Grain Products	3	3	5	
28. The Basics of Baking	1	*	3	
29. Quick and Yeast Breads	3	3	5	
30. Cookies, Cakes, and Frostings	1	*	3	
31. Pies and Pastries	2	*	4	
32. Stocks, Soups, and Sauces	1	*	3	
33. Beverages	1	*	3	
34. Preserving Food At Home	2	*	5	
35. Foods of the World	2	3	5	
36. American Regional Foods	3	3	5	
37. Creative Cooking	2	*	3	
38. Careers in Foods and Nutrition	2	2	4	
39. How to Get and Keep a Job	2	2	5	
TOTAL	90 days	90 days	180 days	

*These chapters can be summarized.

WORKSHEETS FOR LESSON PLANNING

These worksheets outline the contents found in the student textbook of *Food for Today*, including the main topics covered in each chapter and their page numbers. They also list the student objectives that are identified in the beginning of each textbook chapter. Last, they list the related transparency masters, handout masters, recipe worksheets, and tests that can be found in this Teacher's Resource Book, as well as color transparencies.

By having this tabular overview, you can determine the sections that best serve your specific purposes

within your time frame and for your audience. You can also check (✔) those student objectives which you may want to emphasize in class.

The left column has been left blank for you to add dates and notes. You may wish to use this space to list other *Food for Today* program materials that fit your needs, such as food science experiments, Student Workbook activities, and teaching ideas from the Teacher's Wraparound Edition.

Weeks/Dates/Notes	Units/Chapters/ Main Topics	To help you to . . .	TRB Materials
	Part One: Food and People 1: Your Food Choices (pp. 2-15) • Food in Your Life (p. 3) • What Does Food Provide? (pp. 3-5) • What Influences Your Food Choices? (pp. 5-13) • Using Management to Make Food Choices (p. 14)	___ Identify needs met by food. ___ Describe the influences on food choices. ___ Explain the reasons for differences in food customs among various cultures. ___ Use management skills to make food choices.	Advertising Appeals to Basic Needs (TM-1) Management Skills (TM-2) Chapter Test The "Food for Today" Program (CT-1, CT-2) Food Choices (CT-3)
	2: Food Facts and Fallacies (pp. 16-27) • The Truth behind Food Fads (pp. 17-20) • What Are Additives? (pp. 20-23) • What Are Contaminants? (pp. 25-26) • Food Recall Procedures (p. 26)	___ Appraise the truth behind food fads. ___ Recognize how food quacks operate. ___ Understand why food additives are used. ___ Know how food additives and contaminants are controlled.	Bioconcentration in the Food Web (TM-3) Commonly Used Additives and What They Do (HO-1) Chapter Test Part Test
	Part Two: Nutrition for Good Health 3: The Science of Nutrition (pp. 30-36) • What's So Important About Nutrients? (pp. 31-35) • How Does Nutrition Affect Your Health? (p. 35)	___ Learn why you need nutrients. ___ Understand how a knowledge of nutrition can help you. ___ Recognize the links between science, food, and your health.	Nutrition Highlights (TM-4) Malnutrition in the World (TM-5) Chapter Test

TM: transparency master   HO: handout master   R: recipe worksheet   CT: color transparency

Weeks/Dates/Notes	Units/Chapters/ Main Topics	To help you to . . .	TRB Materials
	4: The Nutrients You Need (pp. 37-54) • The Nutrients (pp. 38-53)	___ Understand how nutrients work in the human body. ___ Identify the best food sources of each nutrient. ___ Recognize the effects of using too little or too much of a nutrient.	Nutrient Power (TM-6) Steps to Prevent Osteoporosis (TM-7) Know Your Nutrients (HO-2) Chapter Test Complete Proteins from Plants (CT-4) Rating Your Favorites (CT-5)
	5: Food and Your Well-Being (pp. 55-74) • What is Wellness? (p. 56) • The Miracle of the Human Body (pp. 56-65) • A Wellness Plan (pp. 66-73)	___ Understand the importance of well-ness in your own life. ___ Analyze what happens to food in the human body. ___ Recognize the steps you can take to develop a personal wellness plan.	Coping with Stress (TM-8) Your Personal Wellness Plan (HO-3) Chapter Test How Food is Digested (CT-6) How Cells Receive Nutrients (CT-7) Exercise (CT-8)
	6: Plan Your Daily Food Choices (pp. 75-90) • Food and Your Life-style (p. 76) • The Daily Food Guide (pp. 76-82) • How Well Do You Eat? (pp. 82-83) • Daily Meals (pp. 85-88) • Eating Out (pp. 88-89)	___ Recognize how life-styles influence meal patterns. ___ Apply nutrition information to your food choices. ___ Evaluate your daily food choices.	Daily Food Guide (TM-9) Diet Analysis Worksheet (HO-4) Vegetarian Meals (HO-5) How To Compute the Percentage of Calories from Nutrients (HO-6) Chapter Test Milk-Cheese Group (CT-9) Fruit-Vegetable Group (CT-10) Meat-Poultry-Fish-Beans Group (CT-11) Bread-Cereal Group (CT-12)
	7: Controlling Your Weight (pp. 91-105) • What Is Your Best Weight? (pp. 92-94) • If You Are Over-weight (pp. 94-103) • If You Are Under-weight (pp. 103-104) • Maintaining Your Ideal Weight (p. 104)	___ Understand why it is important to maintain the right weight. ___ Identify the reasons people have weight problems. ___ Achieve and maintain your ideal weight. ___ Recognize fraudulent diet practices.	Balance — the Key to Weight Control (TM-10) Textures Tell the Story (TM-11) Calorie Builders (TM-12) Hints for Controlling Weight (HO-7) Chapter Test

TM: transparency master   HO: handout master   R: recipe worksheet   CT: color transparency

Weeks/Dates/Notes	Units/Chapters/ Main Topics	To help you to . . .	TRB Materials
	8: Special Food Needs (pp. 106-123) • Food Needs and the Life Cycle (pp. 107-119) • Food for Medical Problems (pp. 120-122)	____ Identify food needs for different stages of the life cycle. ____ Understand how health problems can affect food needs. ____ Choose appropriate foods for special needs.	Daily Food Guide for Pregnant Women (TM-13) Calorie Summary for the Life Cycle (TM-14) Chapter Test Part Test
	Part Three: Consumer Decisions 9: Your Kitchen (pp. 126-139) • Kitchen Concepts (p. 127) • Kitchen Organization (pp. 127-132) • How to Evaluate a Kitchen (p. 132) • Updating a Kitchen (pp. 132-137)	____ Identify kitchen work centers and storage areas. ____ Evaluate basic types of kitchens. ____ Understand electrical safety in the kitchen. ____ Make the best use of your kitchen to meet your needs.	Kitchen Centers, Work Triangle, and Traffic Patterns (TM-15) Five Basic Kitchen Plans (TM-16) Use Electricity Safely (HO-8) Chapter Test
	10: Kitchen Equipment and Appliances (pp. 140-160) • Equipping a Kitchen (p. 141) • Buying Cookware (pp. 141-143) • Buying Food Preparation Tools (p. 144) • Buying Appliances (pp. 144-148) • Small Electric Appliances (pp. 148-150) • Major Appliances (pp. 150-157) • Buying Used Appliances (pp. 157-158)	____ Recognize quality features in cookware and food preparation tools. ____ Analyze warranties and credit terms. ____ Recognize which appliances are the most energy-efficient. ____ Decide which appliances and equipment are suitable for your needs. ____ Use and care for appliances and equipment properly.	Evaluating Kitchen Appliances (TM-17) If an Appliance Doesn't Work (TM-18) Buying Cookware (HO-9) Chapter Test Buying Major Appliances (CT-13) How a Microwave Oven Works (CT-14)

TM: transparency master   HO: handout master   R: recipe worksheet   CT: color transparency

Weeks/Dates/Notes	Units/Chapters/ Main Topics	To help you to . . .	TRB Materials
	11: Buying Food (pp. 161-177) • Be a Better Buyer (p. 162) • How Food Gets to You (pp. 162-166) • Using Food Labels (pp. 166-170) • Save Money When You Shop (pp. 171-175) • Your Responsibilities (p. 175) • When You Have Complaints (p. 175)	___ Explain the relationship between food supply and food prices. ___ Use the information on food labels. ___ Make careful decisions when you shop. ___ Know your responsibilities and rights as a shopper.	Nutrition Label (TM-19) When You Have A Complaint (HO-10) Chapter Test Anatomy of a Label (CT-15)
	12: Storing Food (pp. 178-189) • Storage Strategy (p. 179) • What Makes Food Spoil? (pp. 179-180) • Kinds of Food Storage (pp. 180-187) • Storage Tips (p. 188)	___ Understand why food must be properly stored. ___ Recognize the different kinds of food storage. ___ Choose correct storage procedures.	Purpose of Proper Storage (TM-20) What Makes Food Spoil? (TM-21) Food Storage Times (HO-11) Home from the Supermarket (HO-12) Chapter Test Part Test
	Part Four: Food Skills 13: Safety and Sanitation (pp. 192-208) • Proceed with Caution (p. 193) • Safety in the Kitchen (pp. 193-202) • Sanitation in the Kitchen (pp. 203-207)	___ Detect safety hazards in a kitchen. ___ Use safety practices to prevent accidents in kitchens. ___ Recognize the causes of food-borne illness. ___ Know how to prevent food-borne illness.	Common Kitchen Accidents (TM-22) Stop Food-Borne Illness (TM-23) Accidents — Prevention and First Aid (HO-13) Dealing with Household Chemicals (HO-14) How Would You Make This Kitchen Safe? (HO-15) Checklist for Food Service Sanitation (HO-16) Chapter Test Temperature Guide for Food Safety (CT-16)

TM: transparency master   HO: handout master   R: recipe worksheet   CT: color transparency

Weeks/Dates/Notes	Units/Chapters/ Main Topics	To help you to . . .	TRB Materials
	14: Food Preparation Tools (pp. 209-222) • Useful Utensils (p. 210) • Measuring Equipment (pp. 210-211) • Slicing and Cutting Tools (pp. 211-212) • Mixing Tools (p. 213) • Baking Tools (p. 214) • Cooking Tools (p. 216) • Kitchen Aids (pp. 217-218) • Cookware (pp. 218-221) • Cleaning Equipment (p. 221)	____ Identify a variety of food preparation tools. ____ Understand how to properly use utensils and equipment. ____ Recognize quality characteristics in kitchen tools.	How to Sharpen a Knife (TM-24) More Kitchen Tools (TM-25) Chapter Test
	15: Food Preparation Techniques (pp. 223-239) • Preparation Passwords (p. 224) • Using a Recipe (pp. 224-230) • Measuring Techniques (pp. 230-233) • Basic Cooking Methods (pp. 234-238)	____ Evaluate and use recipes successfully. ____ Use basic cooking tools and techniques correctly. ____ Choose the proper cooking method.	Recipe Basics (TM-26) Cooking in Liquid and Moist Heat (TM-27) Cooking in Fat (TM-28) How to Stir-Fry (TM-29) Cooking with Dry Heat (TM-30) Recipe Helpers (HO-17) Understanding Metrics (HO-18) Chapter Test Food Preparation Techniques (CT-17)
	16: Microwave Cooking (pp. 240-252) • Pros and Cons of the Microwave (p. 241) • How Microwave Ovens Work (pp. 241-242) • Containers for Microwave Cooking (pp. 242-244) • Microwave Techniques (pp. 245-250) • Adapting Conventional Recipes (p. 251)	____ Evaluate the benefits and limitations of microwave cooking. ____ Use the proper procedures when cooking with a microwave oven. ____ Select proper microwave cookware. ____ Adapt standard recipes for microwave cooking.	Cooking a Meal in a Microwave Oven (TM-31) Microwave Safety Tips (TM-32) Jogger's Snack Pak (R-1) Nachos — Pronto! (R-2) Snack-A-Pizza (R-3) Chapter Test

TM: transparency master   HO: handout master   R: recipe worksheet   CT: color transparency

Weeks/Dates/Notes	Units/Chapters/ Main Topics	To help you to . . .	TRB Materials
	17: Meal Management (pp. 253-266) • What is Meal Management? (p. 254) • Meal Planning (pp. 254-256) • Efficient Meal Preparation (pp. 257-259) • Conservation in the Kitchen (pp. 262-265)	___ Use basic manage- ment principles while working in the kitchen. ___ Conserve natural resources when preparing food. ___ Save time and energy in the kitchen. ___ Organize and simplify meal preparation.	Planning a Meal (TM-33) How to Time a Meal (TM-34) Conservation in the Kitchen (TM-35) How To Read Electric and Gas Meters (HO-19) Chapter Test Meal Management (CT-18) Steps in Meal Preparation (CT-19)
	18: Serving and Eating Food (pp. 267-281) • Tableware (pp. 268-270) • Table Linens (pp. 270-271) • Atmosphere (pp. 273) • Serving Food (pp. 273-276) • Table Manners (pp. 277-279) • Planning Parties (pp. 279-280)	___ Recognize quality tableware. ___ Set an attractive table for mealtime. ___ Know how to serve food properly. ___ Use good manners while eating. ___ Plan and organize a party.	Buying and Caring for Dinnerware (TM-36) Buying and Caring for Glassware (TM-37) Buying and Caring for Flatware (TM-38) How to Set a Table (HO-20) Nutritious Table Decorations (HO-21) Reception Table (HO-22) Chapter Test Part Test
	Part Five: Food Preparation 19: Fruits (pp. 284-296) • Fruit Facts (p. 285) • Buying and Storing Fruits (pp. 285-292) • Serving Fruits (p. 292) • Cooking Fruits (pp. 293-295) • Microwave Cooking (p. 295)	___ Buy and store fruits properly. ___ Decide how to serve fruits in a variety of ways. ___ Understand how cooking affects fruits. ___ Choose the correct cooking methods for fruits.	Buying Fresh Fruit (TM-39) Buying Guidelines for Fresh Fruit (HO-23) Storing Fresh Fruit (HO-24) Lemony Poached Pears (R-4) Sauteed Apple Rings (R-5) Chapter Test Fresh Fruit (CT-20)

TM: transparency master   HO: handout master   R: recipe worksheet   CT: color transparency

Weeks/Dates/Notes	Units/Chapters/ Main Topics	To help you to . . .	TRB Materials
	20: Vegetables (pp. 297-315) • The Versatile Vegetable (pp. 298-302) • Buying and Storing Vegetables (pp. 302-305) • Serving Fresh Vegetables Raw (p. 306) • Cooking Vegetables (pp. 306-312) • Microwave Cooking (pp. 312-313) • Using Leftover Vegetables (p. 314)	___ Buy and store vegetables properly. ___ Decide how to serve vegetables in a variety of ways. ___ Understand how cooking affects the nutrients, flavor, and appearance of vegetables. ___ Select the correct methods for cooking vegetables.	Buying Fresh Vegetables (TM-40) Cooking Vegetables in Liquid (TM-41) Buying and Cooking Legumes (HO-25) Standards Scorecard: Vegetables Cooked in Liquid (HO-26) Broccoli-Onion Casserole (R-6) Sauteed Collard Greens (R-7) Tofuburgers (R-8) Vegetarian Pizza (R-9) Chapter Test Plant Parts (CT-21) Vegetable I.D. (CT-22) Using Fresh Vegetables (CT-23)
	21: Salads and Salad Dressings (pp. 316-329) • Salad Facts (p. 317) • Buying Salad Greens (pp. 317-318) • Types of Salads (pp. 318-322) • Salad Dressings (pp. 322-323) • Making a Salad (pp. 324-325) • Creating a Salad Bar (p. 326)	___ Buy and store salad greens correctly. ___ Identify different kinds of salads. ___ Recognize different kinds of salad dressings. ___ Prepare and serve a variety of salads with appropriate salad dressings. ___ Set up a salad bar with nutritious and flavorful foods.	How to Core a Head of Lettuce (TM-42) How Do Seeds Sprout? (HO-27) At-Home Salad Bar (R-10) Dilled Cottage Cheese Dressing (R-11) Green Goddess Dressing (R-12) Chicken and Rice Salad (R-13) Avocado Dressing (R-14) Fresh Spinach Salad (R-15) Gelatin Squares (R-16) Taco Salad Toss (R-17) Chapter Test How to Unmold a Gelatin Salad (CT-24)
	22: Dairy Foods (pp. 330-345) • Dairy Food Data (pp. 331-338) • Storing Dairy Foods (pp. 338-339) • Preparing Dairy Foods (pp. 341-343) • Microwave Cooking (p. 343) • Using Convenience Forms (p. 343)	___ Make wise decisions when buying and using dairy foods. ___ Store dairy foods correctly to conserve their nutrients and flavor. ___ Choose the correct procedures for cooking milk and cheese. ___ Serve cheese and milk products in a variety of ways.	Storing Milk and Cream (TM-43) Storing Cheese (TM-44) Crepes (R-18) Cheese Filling for Crepes (R-19) Hearty Chowder with Toast (R-20) Chapter Test

TM: transparency master   HO: handout master   R: recipe worksheet   CT: color transparency

Weeks/Dates/Notes	Units/Chapters/Main Topics	To help you to . . .	TRB Materials
	23: Meat (pp. 346-368) • Meat Facts (p. 347) • Buying Meat (pp. 348-356) • Storing Meat (p. 356) • Cooking Meat (pp. 357-363) • Microwave Cooking (pp. 363-364)	___ Identify the different kinds, cuts, and forms of meat. ___ Make economical, nutritious choices when you shop for meat. ___ Store meat properly. ___ Choose the correct cooking methods for meat. ___ Use the microwave oven for cooking meat.	Bones — the Clue to Tenderness (TM-45) A Meat Label Tells the Story (TM-46) How to Use Tofu (HO-28) Standards Scorecard: Roast Meat (HO-29) Standards Scorecard: Meat Cooked with Moist Heat or Liquid (HO-30) Coney Islands (R-21) Creole Spaghetti (R-22) Sweet and Sour Pork (R-23) Surprise Burgers (R-24) Chapter Test
	24: Poultry (pp. 369-381) • Poultry Facts (p. 370) • Buying Poultry (pp. 370-372) • Storing Poultry (pp. 373-374) • Cooking Poultry (pp. 374-378) • Microwave Cooking (p. 379)	___ Identify different types of poultry. ___ Shop for poultry wisely. ___ Store poultry correctly. ___ Use proper cooking methods for poultry. ___ Use the microwave oven for cooking poultry.	Buying and Storing Poultry (TM-47) How to Cut Up a Chicken (HO-31) How to Carve a Turkey (HO-32) Standards Scorecard: Roast Poultry (HO-33) Oriental Chicken (R-25) Chapter Test
	25: Fish and Shellfish (pp. 382-393) • Fish Facts (p. 383) • Buying Fish and Shellfish (pp. 383-386) • Storing Fish and Shellfish (p. 386) • Cooking Fish and Shellfish (pp. 388-391) • Microwave Cooking (p. 391)	___ Identify the different kinds of fish and shellfish. ___ Buy fish and shellfish wisely. ___ Store fish and shellfish correctly. ___ Select the proper methods for cooking fish and shellfish. ___ Use the microwave oven for cooking fish and shellfish.	Buying Fresh Fish (TM-48) Standards Scorecard: Fish Cooked in Dry Heat (HO-34) Crispy Catfish (R-26) Italian Tuna Burgers (R-27) Tuna-Cheese Casserole (R-28) Chapter Test Fish and Shellfish (CT-25)

TM: transparency master   HO: handout master   R: recipe worksheet   CT: color transparency

Weeks/Dates/Notes	Units/Chapters/ Main Topics	To help you to . . .	TRB Materials
	26: Eggs (pp. 394-407) • The Egg Role (p. 395) • Buying Eggs (p. 395) • Storing Eggs (pp. 395-397) • Cooking Eggs (pp. 398-402) • Beating Egg Whites (pp. 403-405) • Microwave Cooking (p. 406)	____ Buy eggs wisely. ____ Store eggs correctly. ____ Use correct methods for cooking eggs. ____ Use proper techniques for beating egg whites. ____ Cook eggs properly in the microwave oven.	Buying Eggs (TM-49) Storing Eggs (TM-50) Cheese Omelet (R-29) Egg Foo Yung (R-30) Huevos Rancheros (R-31) Pumpkin Custard (R-32) Chapter Test Eggs as Ingredients (CT-26)
	27: Grain Products (pp. 408-421) • Grain Facts (p. 409) • The Kernel of Grain (p. 409) • Kinds of Grain Products (pp. 409-415) • Storing Grain Products (p. 416) • Cooking Grain Products (pp. 416-418) • Microwave Cooking (pp. 418-420)	____ Identify different kinds of grain products. ____ Use a variety of grain products in daily meals. ____ Buy and store grain products correctly. ____ Use correct cooking methods for grain products.	The Grain Kernel (TM-51) Common Pasta Shapes (HO-35) Broccoli and Cheese Spaghetti (R-33) Pizza with Rice Crust (R-34) Tabbouleh (R-35) Chapter Test Pasta Toppers (CT-27)
	28: The Basics of Baking (pp. 422-435) • Ingredients for Baking (pp. 423-431) • The Baking Process (pp. 431-434) • Microwave Baking (p. 434)	____ Recognize the roles ingredients play in baking. ____ Use proper methods for baking different products. ____ Select proper pans and prepare them correctly. ____ Compare conventional and microwave baking.	Leavening Agents (TM-52) Six Essential Steps in Baking (TM-53) Chapter Test

TM: transparency master   HO: handout master   R: recipe worksheet   CT: color transparency

Weeks/Dates/Notes	Units/Chapters/ Main Topics	To help you to . . .	TRB Materials

	29: Quick and Yeast
	Breads (pp. 436-451)
	• Bread Basics
	  (p. 437)
	• Making Quick
	  Breads
	  (pp. 438-440)
	• Storing Quick
	  Breads
	  (p. 441)
	• Making Yeast
	  Breads
	  (pp. 441-449)
	• Storing Yeast
	  Breads
	  (p. 449)
	• Microwave Baking
	  (p. 449)
		___ Use the correct tech-
		niques for preparing
		quick breads and
		yeast breads.
		___ Use the microwave
		oven for preparing
		breads.
			How To Shape Yeast
			  Rolls (HO-36)
			Standards Scorecard:
			  Biscuits (HO-37)
			Problem Solvers: Biscuits
			  (HO-38)
			Standards Scorecard:
			  Muffins and Quick
			  Breads (HO-39)
			Problem Solvers: Muffins
			  and Quick Breads
			  (HO-40)
			Standards Scorecard:
			  Yeast Breads and Rolls
			  (HO-41)
			Problem Solvers: Yeast
			  Breads and Rolls
			  (HO-42)
			Oatmeal Muffins (R-36)
			Spoon Bread (R-37)
			Tortillas (R-38)
			White Bread (R-39)
			Whole Wheat Bread (R-40)
			Chapter Test
			Quick Breads (CT-28)
			Yeast Breads (CT-29)

	30: Cookies, Cakes, and
	Frostings
	(pp. 452-464)
	• Sweet Treats
	  (p. 453)
	• Kinds of Cookies
	  (pp. 453-455)
	• Storing Cookies
	  (p. 456)
	• Kinds of Cakes
	  (pp. 458-460)
	• Frostings (p. 460)
	• Storing Cakes
	  (pp. 460-461)
	• Microwave Baking
	  (p. 462)
		___ Identify different
		kinds of cookies,
		cakes, and frostings.
		___ Use correct methods
		for preparing cookies,
		cakes, and frostings.
		___ Store cookies and
		cakes properly.
		___ Use the microwave
		oven for baking
		cookies and cakes.
			How To Mix Shortened
			  Cakes (TM-54)
			Standards Scorecard:
			  Cookies (HO-43)
			Problem Solvers:
			  Cookies (HO-44)
			Standards Scorecard:
			  Shortened Cakes (HO-45)
			Standards Scorecard:
			  Unshortened Cakes
			  (HO-46)
			Problem Solvers:
			  Shortened Cakes (HO-47)
			Problem Solvers:
			  Unshortened Cakes
			  (HO-48)
			Brownies (R-41)
			Double-Chocolate
			  Frosting (R-42)
			Carrot Cookies (R-43)
			Scandinavian Spice
			  Cookies (R-44)
			Swedish Spritz (R-45)
			Twinkle Cookies (R-46)
			Banana Bundt Cake (R-47)
			Pineapple Upside Down
			  Cake (R-48)
			Chapter Test
			Six Basic Cookies (CT-30)

TM: transparency master   HO: handout master   R: recipe worksheet   CT: color transparency

Weeks/Dates/Notes	Units/Chapters/ Main Topics	To help you to . . .	TRB Materials
	31: Pies and Pastries (pp. 465-476) • Tasty Pastry (p. 466) • Pies (pp. 466-472) • Tarts (p. 473) • Cream Puffs (pp. 473-474) • Storing Pies and Pastry (p. 474) • Microwave Baking of Pies (p. 475)	___ Identify different kinds of pastries. ___ Use correct tech- niques for making piecrust and cream puffs. ___ Use a microwave oven for baking pastry.	How To Make a Pie (HO-49) Standards Scorecard: Pies and Tarts (HO-50) Problem Solvers: Pies and Tarts (HO-51) Apple Pie (R-49) Chapter Test Tops for Pies (CT-31)
	32: Stocks, Soups, and Sauces (pp. 477-489) • Invest in Stock (p. 478) • Making Stock (pp. 478-481) • Making Soups (pp. 481-482) • Making Sauces (pp. 484-487) • Microwave Cooking (p. 487)	___ Identify different stocks and soups. ___ Use correct methods in preparing and stor- ing stocks and soups. ___ Recognize different kinds of sauces. ___ Use correct methods in preparing sauces. ___ Use the microwave oven for preparing soups and sauces.	How To Thicken with . . . (TM-55) Standards Scorecard: Thickened Foods (HO-52) Pea Soup with Ham (R-50) Hot Taco Dip (R-51) Chapter Test Thickened Foods (CT-32)
	33: Beverages (pp. 490-499) • Thirst Quenchers (p. 491) • Cocoa and Choco- late (p. 491) • Coffee (pp. 492-493) • Tea (pp. 494-497) • Punch (p. 497) • Microwave Cooking (p. 497)	___ Identify different kinds of beverages. ___ Be aware of nutrients and cost when buy- ing beverages. ___ Store beverages correctly. ___ Use correct procedures in preparing and serving beverages.	Fruit Juices and Beverages (TM-56) Standards Scorecard: Beverages (HO-53) Nectar Tempter (R-52) Peanut Banana Cooler (R-53) Chapter Test
	34: Preserving Food at Home (pp. 500-513) • Why Preserve Food at Home? (p. 501) • First Steps to Pre- serving (pp. 501-502) • Freezing Fruits and Vegetables (pp. 502-503) • Canning Fruits and Vegetables (pp. 503-510) • Storing Home- Canned Food (p. 510) • Using Home-Canned Food (p. 510) • Drying (pp. 510-511)	___ Decide whether you would like to preserve food at home. ___ Follow correct procedure in freezing, canning, and drying fresh foods. ___ Use correct methods for making jams and jellies.	The pH Guide to Canning (TM-57) How To Freeze Fresh Fruit (HO-54) Freezing Vegetables (R-54) Chapter Test Part Test Preserving Foods at Home (CT-33)

TM: transparency master   HO: handout master   R: recipe worksheet   CT: color transparency

Weeks/Dates/Notes	Units/Chapters/ Main Topics	To help you to . . .	TRB Materials
	Part Six: Creative Cuisine 35: Foods of the World (pp. 516-531) • Around the World (p. 516) • Europe (pp. 517-524) • The Near and Middle East (p. 525) • Africa (p. 526) • Asia (pp. 527-529) • Latin America (pp. 529-530)	___ Understand how food relates to the history, geography, and climate of a region. ___ Identify the food customs of other countries. ___ Recognize and prepare some typical foods served in different parts of the world.	Foods of the World — Eastern Hemisphere (TM-58) Foods of the World — Latin America (TM-59) Chapter Test International Foods (CT-34)
	36: American Regional Foods (pp. 532-542) • A Nation of Food Customs (p. 533) • Foods of the Native American Indians (p. 533) • Food Traditions of the Immigrants (pp. 534-535) • The Northeast (pp. 535-536) • The Midwest (p. 536) • The South (pp. 537-538) • The Southwest (pp. 538-539) • The Pacific Coast and the Northwest (pp. 539-540) • Hawaii (p. 540) • Regional Foods Today (p. 541)	___ Identify the food customs in different regions of the United States. ___ Understand how regional food customs developed and how they influenced American cooking. ___ Compare the typical foods characteristic of regional cooking. ___ Analyze why regional foods change from time to time.	Regional Foods — Northeast, South, and Midwest (TM-60) Regional Foods — Southwest, Pacific Coast and Northwest, Hawaii (TM-61) Chapter Test American Regional Foods (CT-35)

TM: transparency master   HO: handout master   R: recipe worksheet   CT: color transparency

Weeks/Dates/Notes	Units/Chapters/ Main Topics	To help you to . . .	TRB Materials
	37: Creative Cooking (pp. 543-553) • Food Finesse (p. 544) • Adapting Recipes (p. 544) • Convenience Foods (p. 545) • Make Your Own Mixes (p. 545) • Seasonings (pp. 547-548) • Finishing Touches (pp. 548-549) • Serve with a Flair (p. 550) • Food as Gifts (p. 550) • Cooking on an Outdoor Grill (pp. 551-552)	____ Cook creatively on a budget. ____ Enhance food flavors with herbs and spices. ____ Select, prepare, and package foods to give as gifts. ____ Choose equipment and food for outdoor cooking.	Finishing Touches (TM-62) More Finishing Touches (TM-63) How To Use an Outdoor Grill (HO-55) Creative Casseroles (R-55) Master Baking Mix (R-56) Master Mix Biscuits (R-57) Master Mix Carrot Bread (R-58) Master Mix Banana Bread (R-59) Chapter Test Part Test
	Part Seven: Exploring Careers 38: Careers in Food and Nutrition (pp. 556-568) • A Career for You (p. 556) • How to Choose a Career (pp. 558-559) • Career Opportunities (pp. 560-567)	____ Identify and explore career opportunities in food and nutrition. ____ Recognize the kinds of entry-level jobs available in food and nutrition. ____ Use information on careers in the food and nutrition industry in your own search for a career.	How To Choose a Career (TM-64) Are You an Entrepreneur? (TM-65) Chapter Test Food Careers (CT-36)
	39: How to Get and Keep a Job (pp. 569-580) • Where to Look for a Job (p. 570) • Experience Preferred (pp. 570-571) • Getting the Job (pp. 572-576) • How to Keep the Job (pp. 578-579) • Leaving the Job (p. 579)	____ Recognize sources you can use to help find a job. ____ Fill out an application form. ____ Interview for a job. ____ Identify and practice behavior that can increase your worth as an employee.	How Do You Spend Your Day? (TM-66) A Plan for Managing Your Time (TM-67) Application for Employment (HO-56) Chapter Test Part Test

TM: transparency master   HO: handout master   R: recipe worksheet   CT: color transparency

Transparency Masters

TABLE OF CONTENTS

Transparency Masters (TM)

No.	Title	Page

TOPICAL INDEX

Transparency Masters (TM)

Food Science and Technology

TM-3   Bioconcentration in the Food Web
TM-4   Nutrition Highlights
TM-5   Malnutrition in the World
TM-6   Nutrient Power
TM-19 Nutrition Label
TM-21 What Makes Food Spoil?
TM-23 Stop Food-Borne Illness
TM-27 Cooking in Liquid and Moist Heat
TM-28 Cooking in Fat
TM-30 Cooking with Dry Heat
TM-45 Bones — The Clue to Tenderness
TM-51 The Grain Kernel
TM-52 Leavening Agents
TM-57 The pH Guide to Canning

Human Body

TM-3   Bioconcentration in the Food Web
TM-7   Steps to Prevent Osteoporosis
TM-8   Coping with Stress
TM-10 Balance — The Key to Weight Control
TM-14 Calorie Summary for the Life Cycle

International Foods

TM-29 How to Stir-Fry
TM-58 Foods of the World —
     Eastern Hemisphere
TM-59 Foods of the World — Latin America

Kitchens

TM-15 Kitchen Centers, Work Triangle, and
     Traffic Pattern
TM-16 Five Basic Kitchen Plans
TM-17 Evaluating Kitchen Appliances
TM-18 If an Appliance Doesn't Work . . .
TM-22 Common Kitchen Accidents
TM-25 More Kitchen Tools
TM-35 Conservation in the Kitchen

Lifestyles

TM-8   Coping with Stress
TM-14 Calorie Summary for the Life Cycle
TM-60 Regional Foods — Northeast,
     South, Midwest
TM-61 Regional Foods — Southwest,
     Pacific Coast and Northwest, Hawaii
TM-64 How to Choose a Career

Life Cycle

TM-10 Balance — The Key to Weight Control
TM-13 Daily Food Guide for
     Pregnant Women
TM-14 Calorie Summary for the Life Cycle

Management

TM-2   Management Skills
TM-8   Coping with Stress
TM-9   Daily Food Guide
TM-14 Calorie Summary for the Life Cycle
TM-15 Kitchen Centers, Work Triangle, and
     Traffic Pattern
TM-33 Planning a Meal
TM-34 How to Time a Meal
TM-35 Conservation in the Kitchen
TM-66 How Do You Spend Your Day?
TM-67 A Plan for Managing Your Time

Maps

TM-58 Foods of the World —
     Eastern Hemisphere
TM-59 Foods of the World — Latin America
TM-60 Regional Foods — Northeast,
     South, Midwest
TM-61 Regional Foods — Southwest,
     Pacific Coast and Northwest, Hawaii

Meal Planning

TM-6   Nutrient Power
TM-7   Steps to Prevent Osteoporosis
TM-9   Daily Food Guide
TM-10 Balance — The Key to Weight Control
TM-11 Textures Tell the Story
TM-12 Calorie Builders
TM-13 Daily Food Guide for
     Pregnant Women
TM-14 Calorie Summary for the Life Cycle
TM-19 Nutrition Label
TM-31 Cooking a Meal in a Microwave Oven
TM-33 Planning a Meal
TM-34 How to Time a Meal
TM-35 Conservation in the Kitchen

Microwaving

TM-31 Cooking a Meal in a Microwave Oven
TM-32 Microwave Safety Tips

Advertising Appeals to Basic Needs

Management Skills

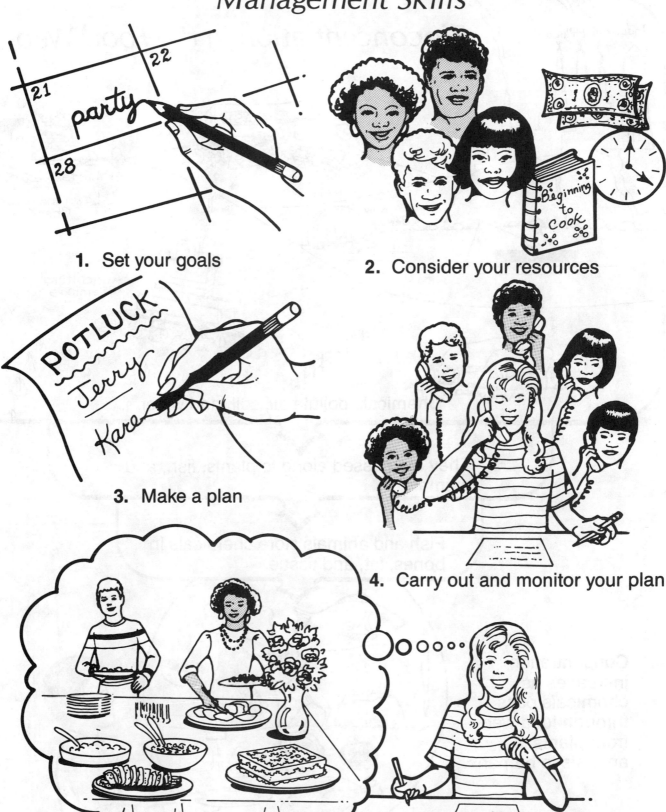

1. Set your goals

2. Consider your resources

3. Make a plan

4. Carry out and monitor your plan

5. Evaluate the results

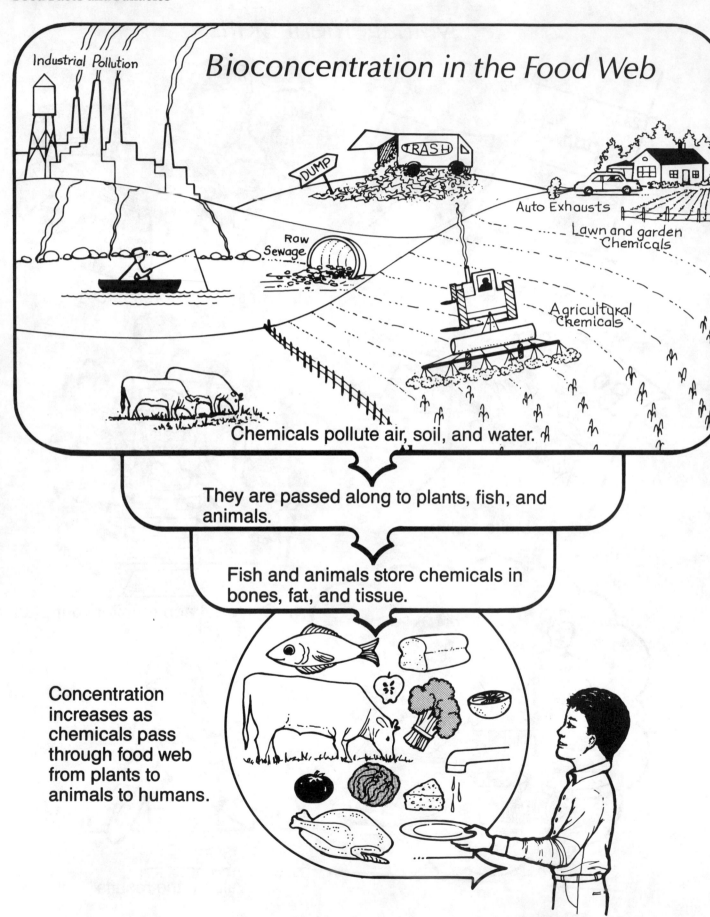

Bioconcentration in the Food Web

Industrial Pollution

TRASH

DUMP

Auto Exhausts

Lawn and garden Chemicals

Raw Sewage

Agricultural Chemicals

Chemicals pollute air, soil, and water.

They are passed along to plants, fish, and animals.

Fish and animals store chemicals in bones, fat, and tissue.

Concentration increases as chemicals pass through food web from plants to animals to humans.

Nutrition Highlights

1. Nutrients work as teams.

NUTRITION HIGHLIGHTS

4 important facts to remember . . .

2. The body needs specific amounts of each nutrient.

3. Needs for nutrients differ, depending on the life cycle.

4. Science is still researching nutrition.

Malnutrition in the World

1988 Estimate
World Population
5,100,000,000

12%

600,000,000
suffer from malnutrition

Estimated World Population by 2028: 10,200,000,000

Nutrient Power

Carbohydrates
Supply energy.

Proteins
Build and repair cells.

Fats
Supply twice as much energy as carbohydrates and proteins.

Vitamins
Used for many processes. Help speed chemical reactions in the body.

Minerals
Used for many body processes. Become part of the body.

Steps to Prevent Osteoporosis

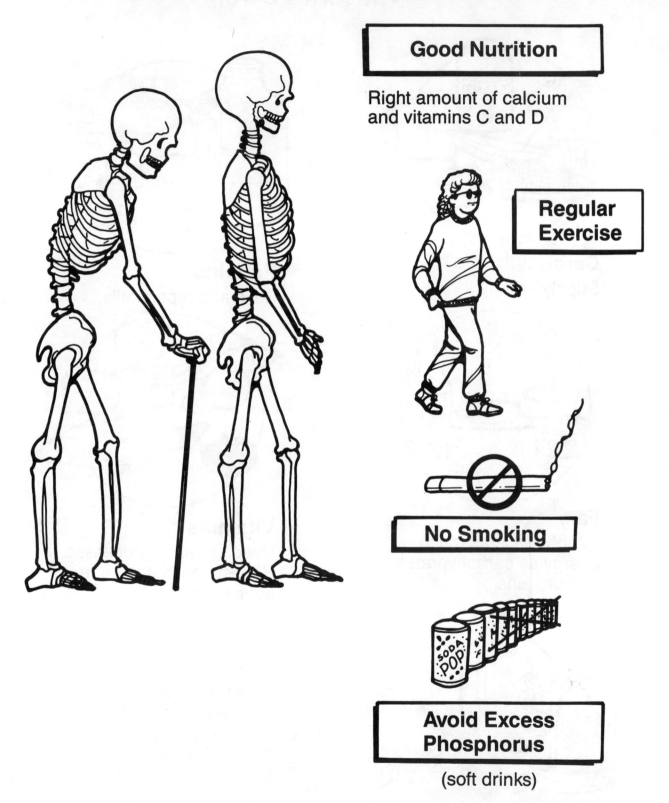

Good Nutrition

Right amount of calcium
and vitamins C and D

Regular Exercise

No Smoking

Avoid Excess Phosphorus

(soft drinks)

Coping with Stress

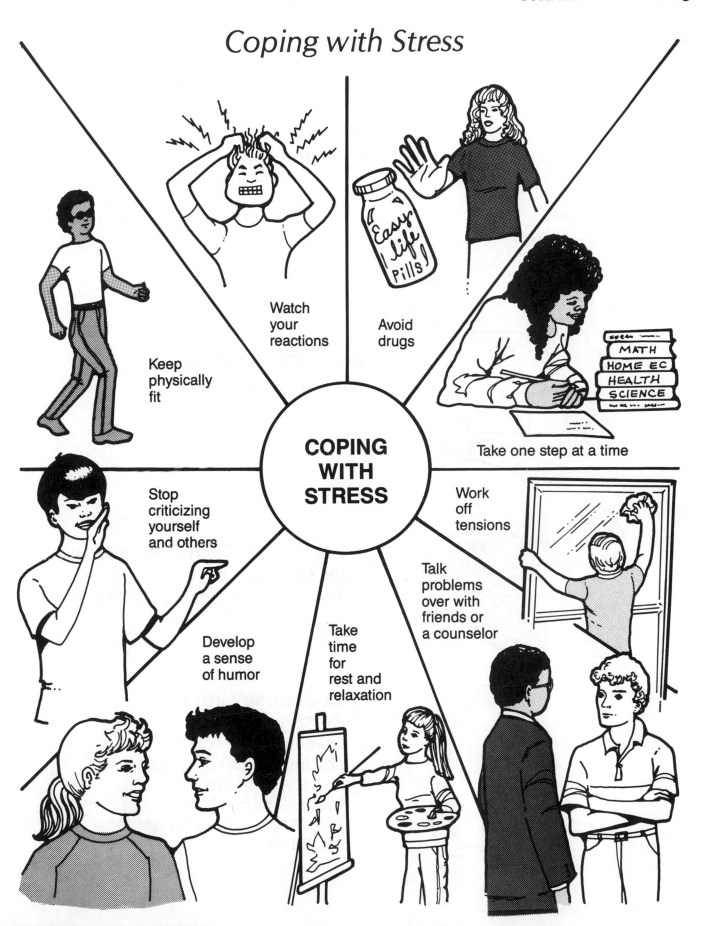

Watch your reactions

Avoid drugs

Keep physically fit

Take one step at a time

COPING WITH STRESS

Stop criticizing yourself and others

Work off tensions

Talk problems over with friends or a counselor

Develop a sense of humor

Take time for rest and relaxation

Daily Food Guide

Fruit-Vegetable Group
Daily Servings:
   1 serving citrus fruit or other source
   of vitamin C
   1 serving dark green or deep yellow
   vegetable
   2 other fruits and vegetables

Bread-Cereal Group
Daily Servings: 4

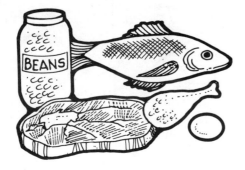

Meat-Poultry-Fish-Beans Group
Daily Servings: 2
   (Pregnant and nursing women: 3)

Milk-Cheese Group
Daily Servings:
   Children under 9: 2-3
   Children 9-12: 3 or more
   Teens: 4 or more
   Adults: 2 or more
   Pregnant and nursing women:
   4 or more

Balance — The Key to Weight Control

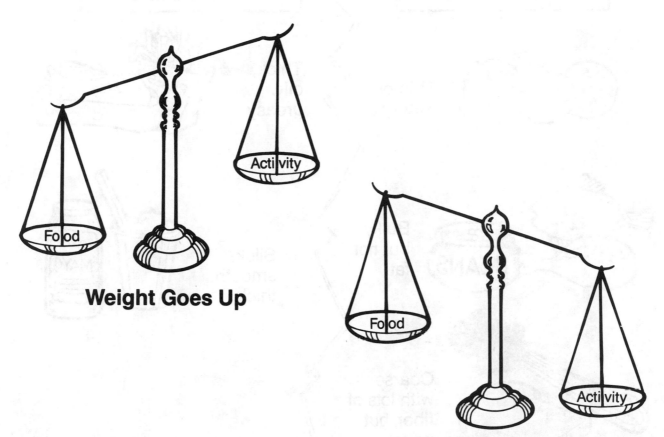

Weight Goes Up

Weight Goes Down

Weight Stays the Same

Textures Tell the Story

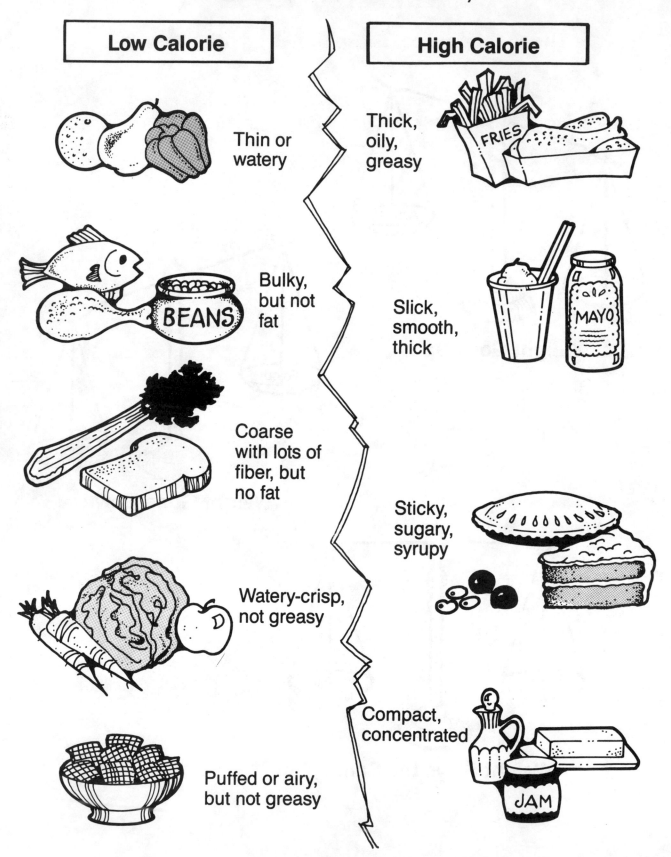

Low Calorie	High Calorie

Thin or watery

Thick, oily, greasy

Bulky, but not fat

Slick, smooth, thick

Coarse with lots of fiber, but no fat

Sticky, sugary, syrupy

Watery-crisp, not greasy

Compact, concentrated

Puffed or airy, but not greasy

Calorie Builders

These foods can ADD calories to other foods!

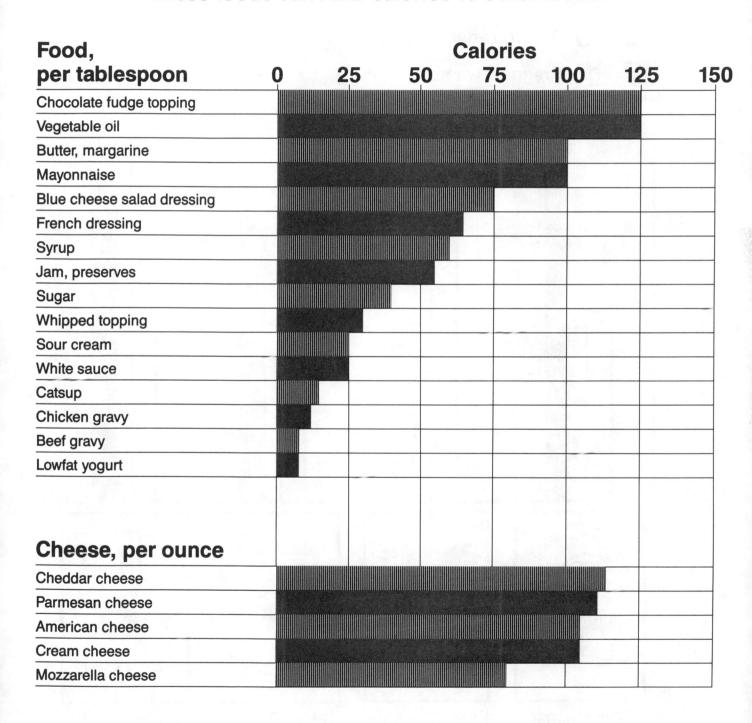

Food, per tablespoon	Calories 0	25	50	75	100	125	150
Chocolate fudge topping							
Vegetable oil							
Butter, margarine							
Mayonnaise							
Blue cheese salad dressing							
French dressing							
Syrup							
Jam, preserves							
Sugar							
Whipped topping							
Sour cream							
White sauce							
Catsup							
Chicken gravy							
Beef gravy							
Lowfat yogurt							

Cheese, per ounce

Cheddar cheese							
Parmesan cheese							
American cheese							
Cream cheese							
Mozzarella cheese							

Daily Food Guide for Pregnant Women

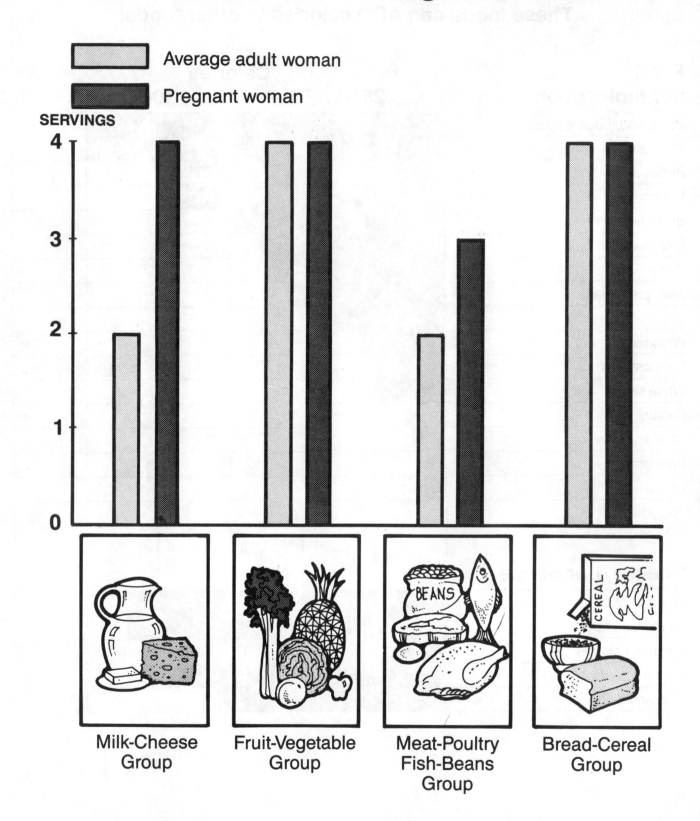

☐ Average adult woman

■ Pregnant woman

Milk-Cheese Group

Fruit-Vegetable Group

Meat-Poultry Fish-Beans Group

Bread-Cereal Group

Calorie Summary for the Life Cycle

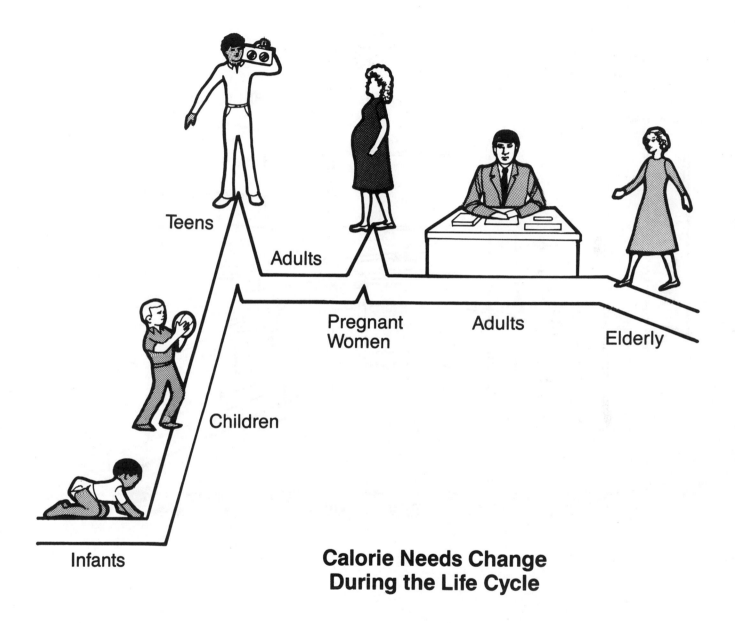

**Calorie Needs Change
During the Life Cycle**

Kitchen Centers, Work Triangle, and Traffic Pattern

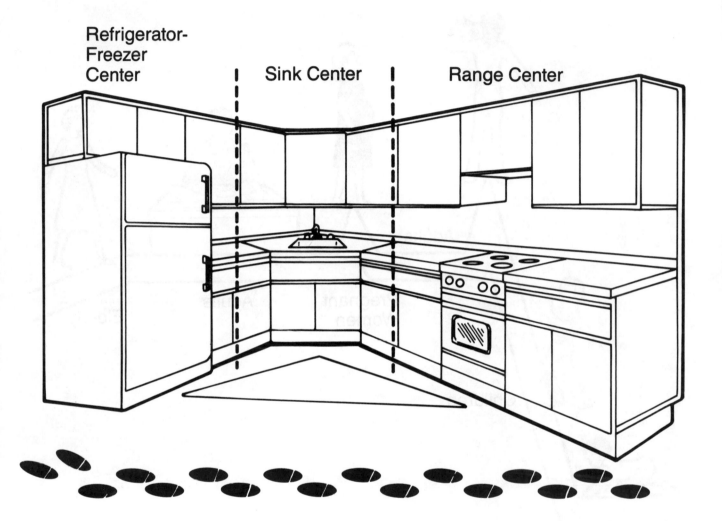

Refrigerator-Freezer Center

Sink Center

Range Center

FOOD FOR TODAY TEACHER'S RESOURCE BOOK
Protected by Copyright

Five Basic Kitchen Plans

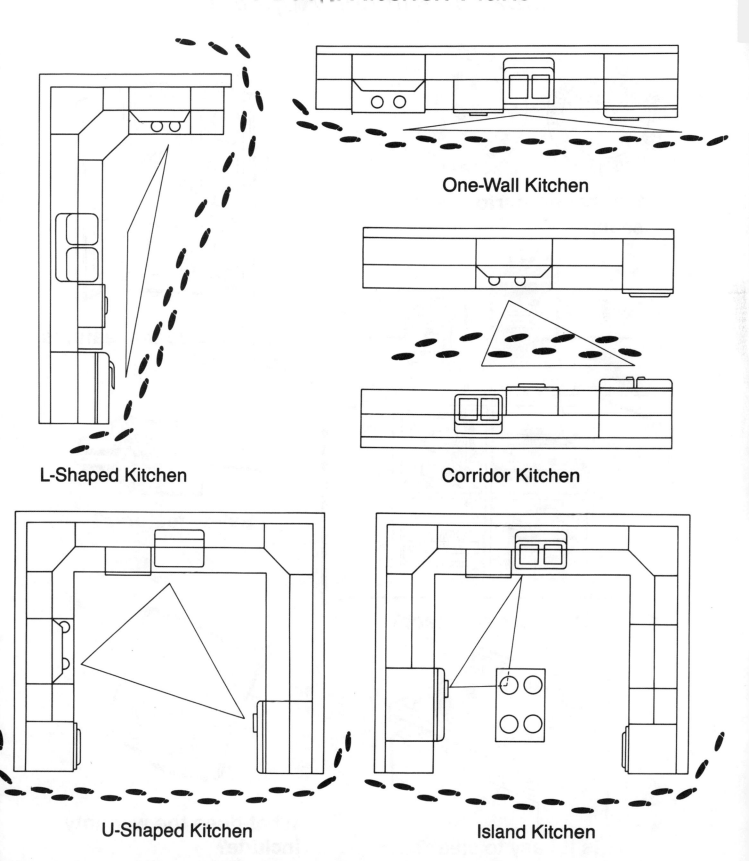

One-Wall Kitchen

L-Shaped Kitchen

Corridor Kitchen

U-Shaped Kitchen

Island Kitchen

Evaluating Kitchen Appliances

Safety and performance seals?

Does it have the features you want?

Do you have space?

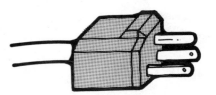

Safety features?

Is it easy to clean?

What does the warranty include?

If an Appliance Doesn't Work...

1. Read the owner's manual.

4. If it **still** doesn't work . . . Call store or service center.

2. Are the controls set properly?

3. If electric . . .
   - Is it plugged in?
   - Is the fuse blown?

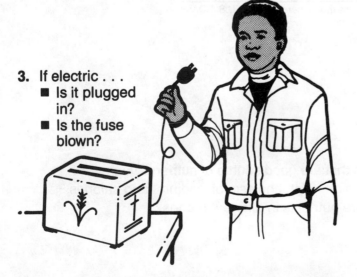

5. If the problem continues . . .
   - Talk to the store clerk or manager.
   - Write the manufacturer.
   - Contact the Better Business Bureau, state attorney general, or consumer action group.

Nutrition Label

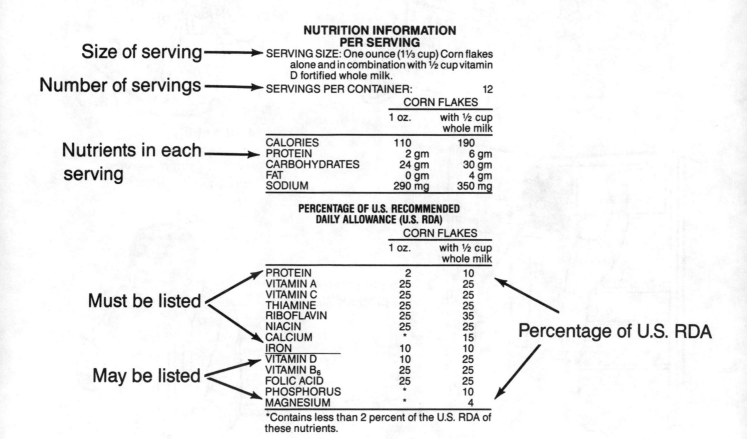

Size of serving

Number of servings

Nutrients in each serving

Must be listed

May be listed

Percentage of U.S. RDA

NUTRITION INFORMATION PER SERVING

SERVING SIZE: One ounce (1⅓ cup) Corn flakes alone and in combination with ½ cup vitamin D fortified whole milk.

SERVINGS PER CONTAINER: 12

	CORN FLAKES	
	1 oz.	with ½ cup whole milk
CALORIES	110	190
PROTEIN	2 gm	6 gm
CARBOHYDRATES	24 gm	30 gm
FAT	0 gm	4 gm
SODIUM	290 mg	350 mg

PERCENTAGE OF U.S. RECOMMENDED DAILY ALLOWANCE (U.S. RDA)

	CORN FLAKES	
	1 oz.	with ½ cup whole milk
PROTEIN	2	10
VITAMIN A	25	25
VITAMIN C	25	25
THIAMINE	25	25
RIBOFLAVIN	25	35
NIACIN	25	25
CALCIUM	*	15
IRON	10	10
VITAMIN D	10	25
VITAMIN B₆	25	25
FOLIC ACID	25	25
PHOSPHORUS	*	10
MAGNESIUM	*	4

*Contains less than 2 percent of the U.S. RDA of these nutrients.

Advantages

- Helps you select foods that are good source of nutrients you need.
- Helps you avoid foods high in fat, cholesterol, sodium, and calories.
- Enables you to compare nutrients in different brands.

How to Sharpen a Knife

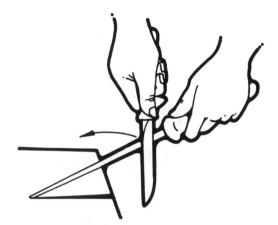

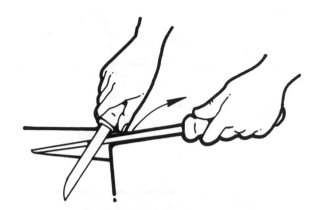

1. Hold the sharpening steel and knife as shown. Keeping the blade flat, move the knife down and across the steel. At the end of the stroke, the tip of the knife will be on the point of the steel.

2. Repeat Step 1 with the knife blade turned away from you and stroking from the point of the steel toward the handle.

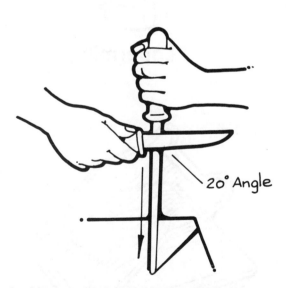

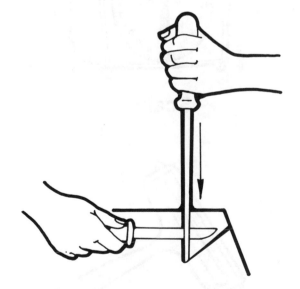

20° Angle

3. Next, hold the steel upright as shown. Holding the knife blade at a 20-degree angle to the steel, stroke down and back (handle to tip, as before).

4. Repeat Step 3 with the other side of the knife and steel. Alternate Steps 3 and 4 two or three more times.

More Kitchen Tools

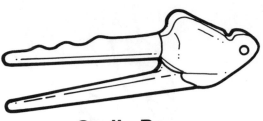

Garlic Press

Meat Tenderizing Mallet

Scale

Peppermill

Cheese Slicer

Egg Slicer

FOOD FOR TODAY TEACHER'S RESOURCE BOOK
Protcon Hm Copyright

Recipe Basics

A recipe should include . . .

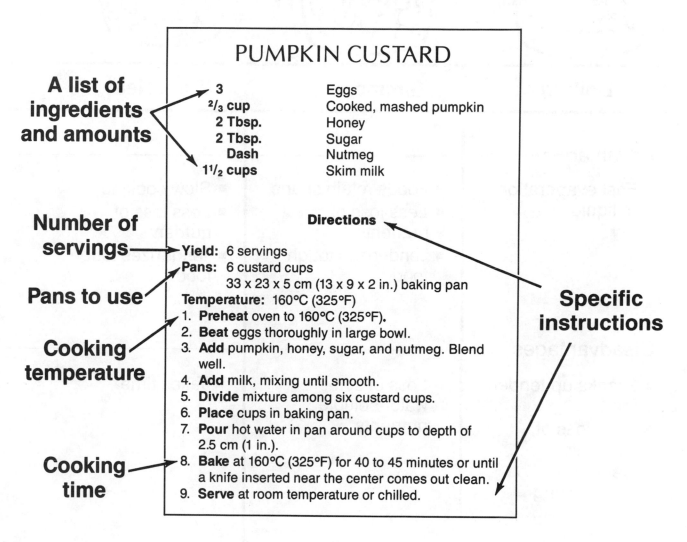

A list of ingredients and amounts

PUMPKIN CUSTARD

3	Eggs
2/3 cup	Cooked, mashed pumpkin
2 Tbsp.	Honey
2 Tbsp.	Sugar
Dash	Nutmeg
1 1/2 cups	Skim milk

Directions

Number of servings — **Yield:** 6 servings

Pans to use — **Pans:** 6 custard cups
33 x 23 x 5 cm (13 x 9 x 2 in.) baking pan

Cooking temperature — **Temperature:** 160°C (325°F)

1. **Preheat** oven to 160°C (325°F).
2. **Beat** eggs thoroughly in large bowl.
3. **Add** pumpkin, honey, sugar, and nutmeg. Blend well.
4. **Add** milk, mixing until smooth.
5. **Divide** mixture among six custard cups.
6. **Place** cups in baking pan.
7. **Pour** hot water in pan around cups to depth of 2.5 cm (1 in.).

Cooking time — 8. **Bake** at 160°C (325°F) for 40 to 45 minutes or until a knife inserted near the center comes out clean.
9. **Serve** at room temperature or chilled.

Specific instructions

Cooking in Liquid and Moist Heat

Boiling	Simmering	Moist Heat
Advantages		
■ Fast evaporation of liquid	■ Foods retain shape ■ Less loss of nutrients ■ Tenderizes tough food	■ Slow cooking ■ Less loss of nutrients ■ Tenderizes tough food
Disadvantages		
■ Breaks up tender food ■ High loss of nutrients ■ Danger of overcooking	■ Loss of some water-soluble nutrients	■ Takes time
Uses		
■ Bring liquid to boiling temperature ■ Reduce sauces, soup, stock	■ Gentle cooking in liquid ■ Vegetables ■ For tough cuts of meat	■ For tough cuts of meat ■ Steam vegetables

Cooking in Fat

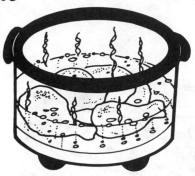

Pan Broiling, Frying, Sautéing	Deep-Fat Frying
Advantages	
▪ Can control amount of fat used ▪ Adds flavor and crispness to food ▪ Browns food	▪ Adds flavor and crispness to food ▪ Browns food
Disadvantages	
▪ Adds fat and calories to food ▪ Fat can overheat and smoke or catch fire	▪ Adds fat and calories to food ▪ Requires controlled temperatures to prevent over- and under-cooking ▪ Hot fat can spatter or bubble over the sides of the pan
Uses	
▪ Brown meat ▪ Cook tender foods	▪ Vegetables ▪ Tender foods like chicken or fish ▪ Mixtures, like fritters or doughnuts

How to Stir-Fry

1. Assemble ingredients.
   - Cut each type of food into small, uniform pieces.
   - Line up the food in the order it will be cooked.

2. Heat the wok over high heat.
   - When a drop of water sizzles on the wok, add the cooking oil.

3. Tilt the wok to coat it evenly with oil.

4. Add the ingredients to the wok as the recipe directs.
   - With a curved spatula or chopsticks, toss the ingredients until they are coated with oil.
   - Work quickly.
   - Stir the mixture constantly.
   - Do not overcook. Vegetables should be tender-crisp.

Cooking with Dry Heat

Baking and Roasting

Broiling

Advantages ———————————

- Controlled temperature
- Browns and flavors food

- Fat drips away from food
- Browns and adds crispness to food

Disadvantages ———————————

- Limited to tender foods

- Easy to under- or over-cook food
- Limited to tender cuts
- No temperature controls
- Drippings can catch fire

Uses ———————————

- Baking
- Tender cuts of meat, poultry, fish

- Tender cuts of meat, poultry, fish
- Browning toppings

Cooking a Meal in a Microwave Oven

Sequence for Timing a Meal

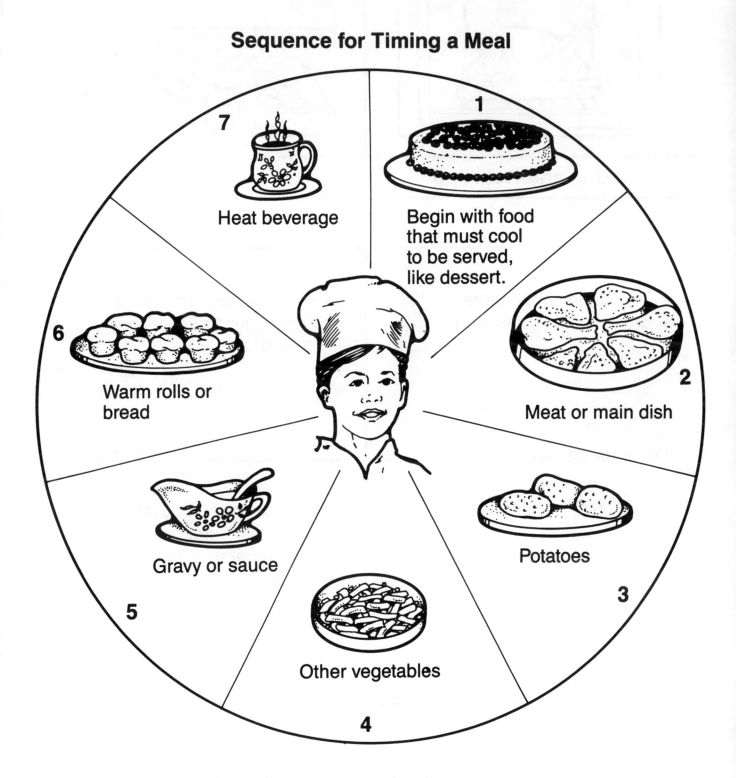

7 Heat beverage

1 Begin with food that must cool to be served, like dessert.

2 Meat or main dish

3 Potatoes

4 Other vegetables

5 Gravy or sauce

6 Warm rolls or bread

How to Time a Meal

1. Decide on the time the meal is to be served.

Menu
Baked Chicken
pieces - 60 min.
Green Bean Casserole
- 20 min.

2. Write out the menu. Include the cooking time for each food.

3. Make up a timetable for the meal.

FOOD	Preparation Time	Cooking Time	Total Time	Begin Preparation
Chicken	20 min.	60 min.	80 min.	4:40 p.m.
Green Beans	10 min.	20 min.	30 min.	5:30 p.m.

4. Make up a work schedule.
   - List work in the order in which it is to be done.
   - Begin with the foods that take the longest.
   - Set the table first, if possible.

WORK SCHEDULE
3:30 Set table
4:00 Assemble Ingredients
4:40 Prepare Chicken: put in oven.
5:30 Prepare Green Bean Casserole

Conservation in the Kitchen

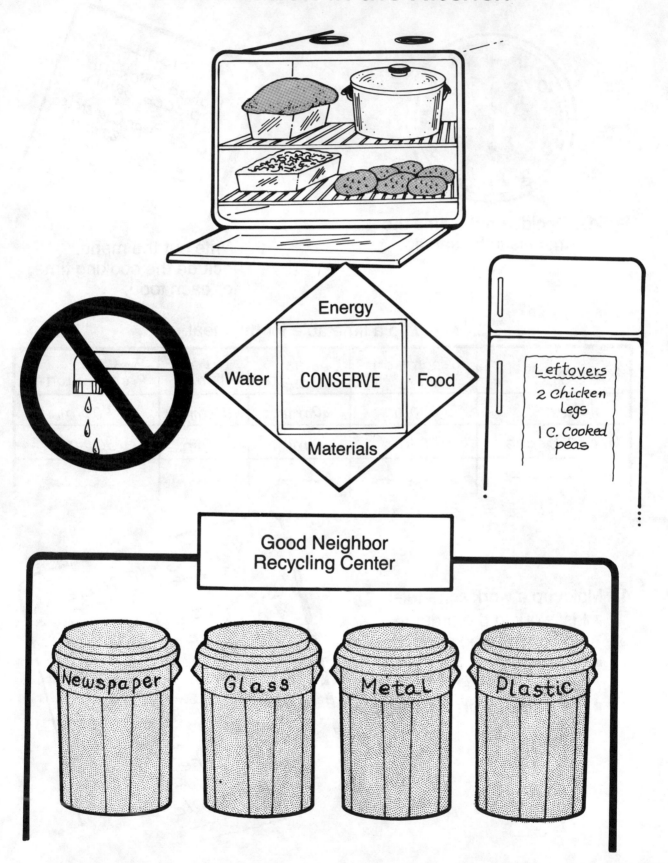

Energy

Water   CONSERVE   Food

Materials

Leftovers
2 chicken
legs
1 C. cooked
peas

Good Neighbor
Recycling Center

Newspaper   Glass   Metal   Plastic

Buying and Caring for Dinnerware

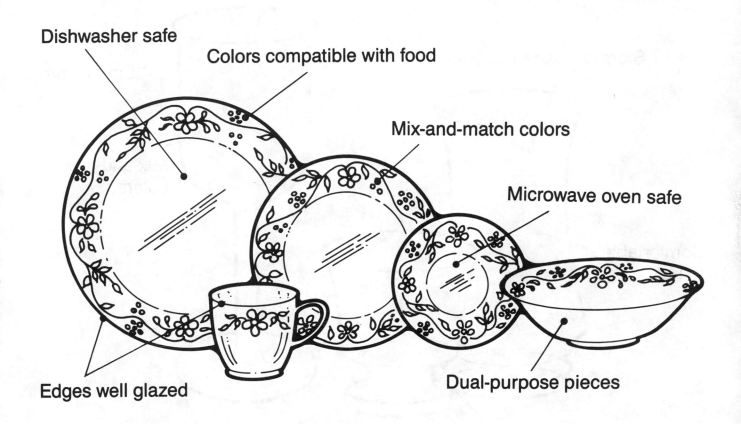

Dishwasher safe

Colors compatible with food

Mix-and-match colors

Microwave oven safe

Edges well glazed

Dual-purpose pieces

Care Guidelines

- Rinse dishes as soon as possible after use. Hardened food is difficult to remove.
- Avoid using scouring powder or pads, or steel wool. They can scratch the glaze.
- Stack pieces carefully to avoid chipping.

Buying and Caring for Glassware

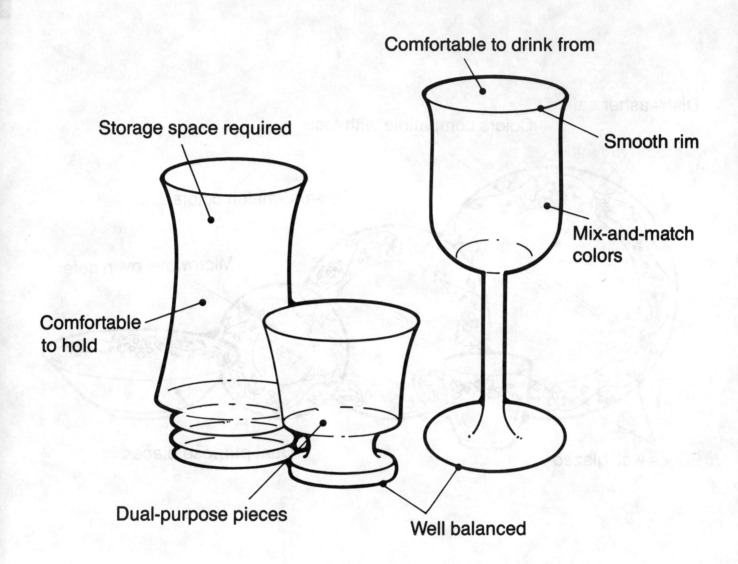

Comfortable to drink from

Smooth rim

Mix-and-match colors

Storage space required

Comfortable to hold

Dual-purpose pieces

Well balanced

Care Guidelines

- Handle carefully to avoid chipping and breaking.
- Don't put cold glassware into hot water. Sudden changes in temperature may cause it to crack.

Buying and Caring for Flatware

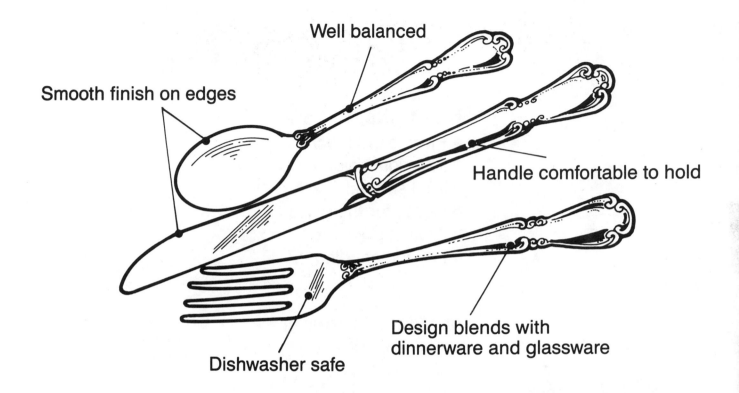

Well balanced

Smooth finish on edges

Handle comfortable to hold

Dishwasher safe

Design blends with
dinnerware and glassware

Care Guidelines

- Rinse as soon as possible after use. Hardened food is difficult to remove, especially from fork tines.
- Store in divided drawers to prevent scratches.

Buying Fresh Fruit

Buy fruits that are . . .

- Firm to the touch
- The right color
- Well shaped
- Heavy for their size
- Aromatic
- In good condition

Avoid fruits that are . . .

- Too soft
- Too hard
- Green or underripe
- Damaged
- Bruised
- Decayed
- Mildewed
- Discolored

Buying Fresh Vegetables

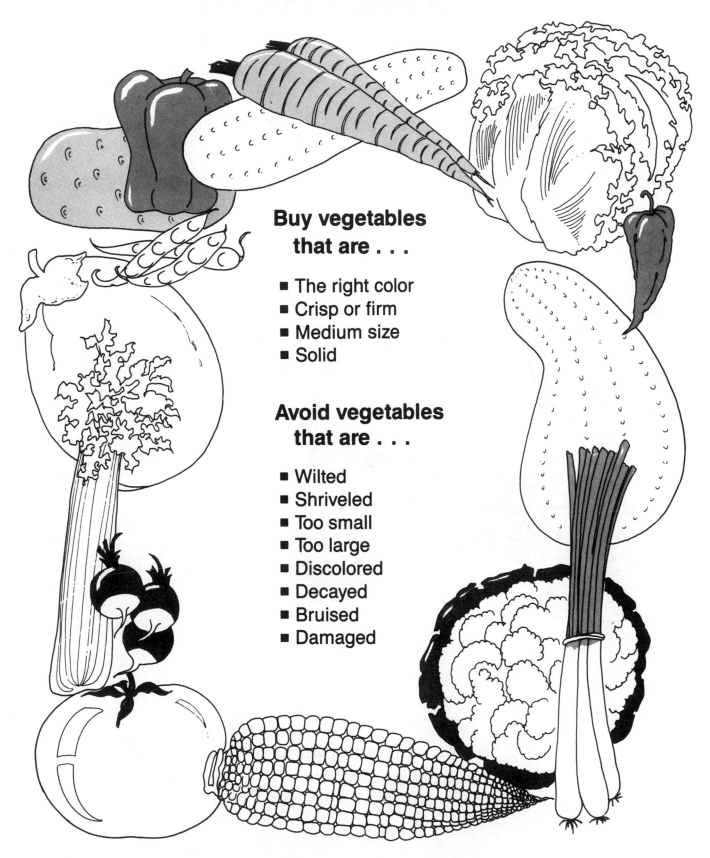

Buy vegetables that are . . .

- The right color
- Crisp or firm
- Medium size
- Solid

Avoid vegetables that are . . .

- Wilted
- Shriveled
- Too small
- Too large
- Discolored
- Decayed
- Bruised
- Damaged

Cooking Vegetables in Liquid

1. Bring a small amount of water to a boil.

2. Add fresh or frozen vegetables.

3. Cover the pan.

4. Simmer the vegetables.

5. Cook only until fork-tender.

Signs of Overcooking
- Vegetables discolor.
- Vegetables get soft and mushy.

How to Core a Head of Lettuce

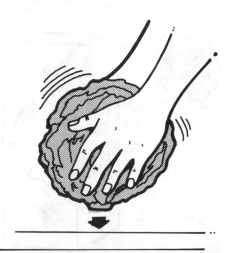

1. Hit the core (bottom of the head) against a flat surface.

2. Remove the core by twisting it. Do not cut it out.

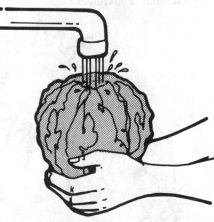

3. Run cold water into the core hole until it flows out between the leaves.

4. Turn the head over and let the water drain out.

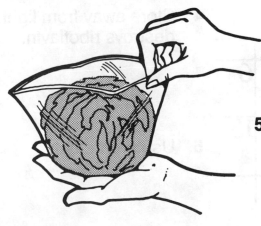

5. Store in a plastic bag or covered container.

Storing Milk and Cream

1. Store in the original container. Don't pour into another one for storage.

2. Keep the container tightly closed. Milk and cream can absorb odors.

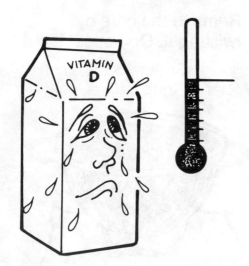

3. Don't let the container sit out at room temperature.

4. Store away from light. Light destroys riboflavin.

5. Use promptly.

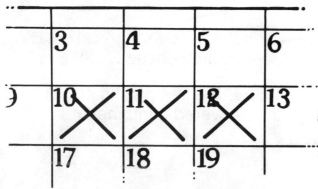

Storing Cheese

Fresh Cheese
- Refrigerate in the original container.
- Use within a few days.

Natural Cheese
- Refrigerate in the original wrapper or in plastic or foil.
- If the cheese has a strong odor, store in an airtight container.

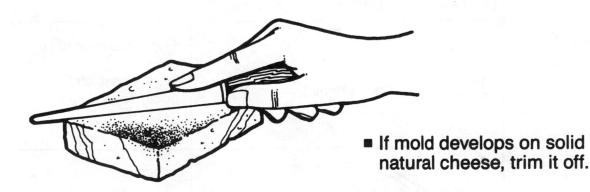

- If mold develops on solid natural cheese, trim it off.

Bones — The Clue to Tenderness

Cut	Bone	Tenderness/Cooking Method
Shoulder Arm cuts	Arm Bone	Not tender. Use moist heat; liquid.
Shoulder Blade Cuts (Cross Sections of Blade Bone)	Blade Bone (near neck) Blade Bone (center cuts) Blade Bone (near rib)	Only meat around bone near rib is tender. Use moist heat; liquid.
Rib Cuts	Back Bone and Rib Bone	Tender. Use dry heat.
Short Loin Cuts	Back Bone (T-Shape) T-Bone	Tender. Use dry heat.
Hip (Sirloin) Cuts (Cross Sections of Hip Bone)	Pin Bone (near short loin) Flat Bone (center cuts) Wedge Bone (near round)	Tender. Use dry heat.
Leg or Round Cuts	Leg or Round Bone	Tender, except in beef. Use dry heat; for beef use moist heat or liquid.
Breast, or Brisket Cuts	Breast and Rib Bones	Not tender. Use moist heat; liquid.

Adapted from the National Live Stock and Meat Board

A Meat Label Tells the Story

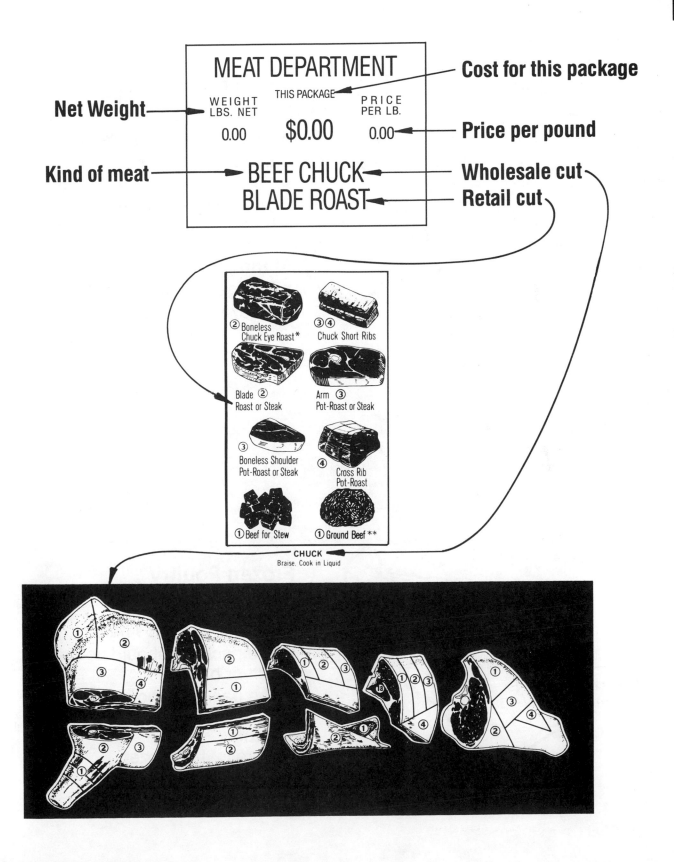

Net Weight

Kind of meat

MEAT DEPARTMENT

THIS PACKAGE

WEIGHT
LBS. NET

PRICE
PER LB.

0.00 $0.00   0.00

BEEF CHUCK

BLADE ROAST

Cost for this package

Price per pound

Wholesale cut
Retail cut

② Boneless
Chuck Eye Roast*

③④ Chuck Short Ribs

Blade ②
Roast or Steak

Arm ③
Pot-Roast or Steak

③ Boneless Shoulder
Pot-Roast or Steak

④ Cross Rib
Pot-Roast

① Beef for Stew

① Ground Beef **

CHUCK
Braise, Cook in Liquid

Buying and Storing Poultry

Fresh Poultry

Buying
- Read the label for class of bird.
- Look for the grade.
- The skin should be clear and bright with no blemishes, bruises, breaks, or feathers.

Storing
- Refrigerate for 1-2 days.
- Freeze for longer storage.

Frozen Poultry

Buying
- Poultry should be hard-frozen.
- The package should not be torn or broken.
- The package should be clean.

Storing
- Store in the freezer.

Buying Fresh Fish

Forms of Fresh Fish

Whole: Fish just as it is caught.

Dressed: Cleaned and scaled. Head, tail, and fins may be cut off.

Steaks: Slices cut across fish.

Fillets: Sides cut away from backbone.

Look for . . .

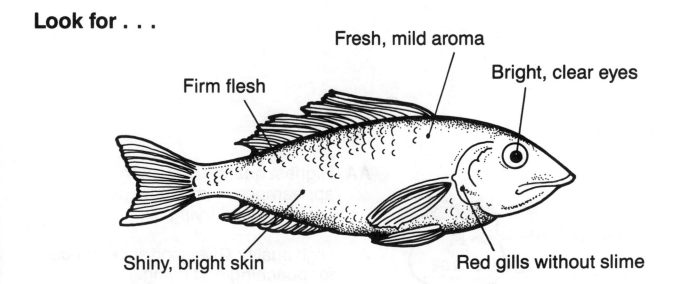

Fresh, mild aroma

Bright, clear eyes

Firm flesh

Shiny, bright skin

Red gills without slime

Cut edges should look fresh, firm, and clean.

Buying Eggs

Egg Sizes

Minimum Weight Per Dozen

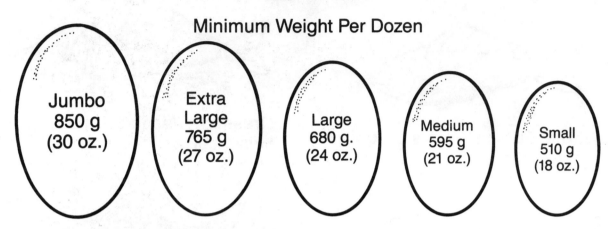

Jumbo
850 g
(30 oz.)

Extra
Large
765 g
(27 oz.)

Large
680 g.
(24 oz.)

Medium
595 g
(21 oz.)

Small
510 g
(18 oz.)

Buying Guidelines

- Buy only eggs stored in refrigerated cases.
- Open the carton to inspect the eggs. They should be clean and have no cracks.
- Buy the grade and size suitable for your needs.
- Look for the best price relative to the grade and size.

Grades

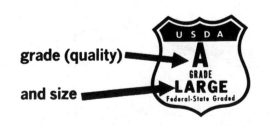

grade (quality)

and size

AA Highest quality. Buy when appearance is important (for poaching and frying).

A High quality. Give good appearance for poaching and frying.

B Good quality. Choose for general cooking and baking.

Storing Eggs

In the Refrigerator

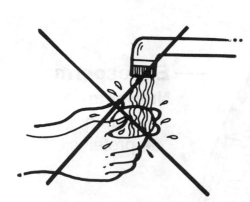

- Don't wash eggs before storing.

- Refrigerate in the original container.
- Eggs absorb aromas and must be stored in covered containers.

In the Freezer

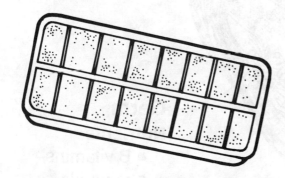

Whites
- Freeze each in a separate compartment of an ice cube tray.
- Store the frozen cubes in an airtight container.

Yolks
- Freeze in an airtight container.
- Add 1/8 teaspoon salt for every 4 yolks.

The Grain Kernel

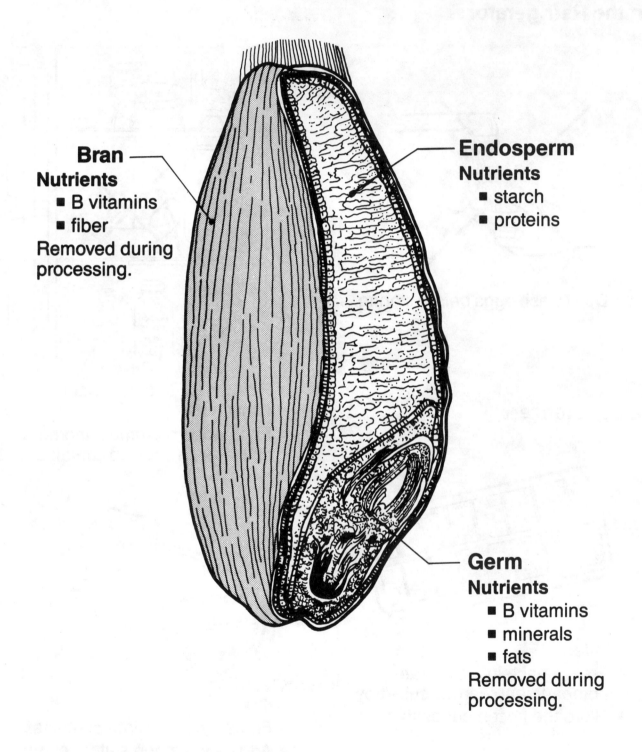

Bran
Nutrients
- B vitamins
- fiber

Removed during processing.

Endosperm
Nutrients
- starch
- proteins

Germ
Nutrients
- B vitamins
- minerals
- fats

Removed during processing.

Leavening Agents

How They Work

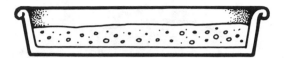 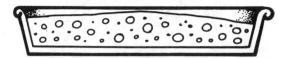

Air or gas bubbles in cold batter.

Heated bubbles expand and the batter rises.

Four Types of Leavening Agents

Air
Trapped in the mixture by:
- Sifting flour
- Creaming fat and sugar
- Beating egg whites
- Beating batter

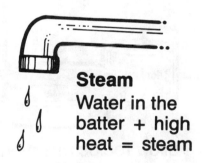

Steam
Water in the batter + high heat = steam

Chemical
Baking powder + liquid = carbon dioxide

Baking soda + acid = carbon dioxide

Yeast
Microscopic plant that grows, giving off carbon dioxide

Six Essential Steps in Baking

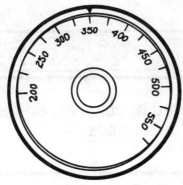

1. Use correct oven temperature.

2. Use the pan specified in the recipe.

3. Follow recipe directions for preparing the pan.

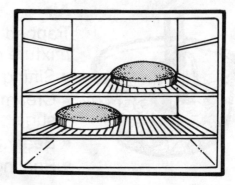

4. Place pans correctly in the oven.

5. Time the product according to recipe directions.

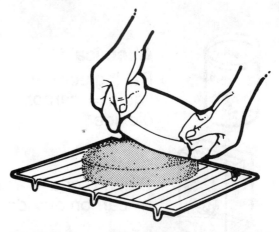

6. Remove from the pan carefully, following recipe directions.

How to Mix Shortened Cakes

Conventional Method

1. Cream fat and sugar.

2. Beat in eggs.

3. Sift dry ingredients together.

4. Add the dry ingredients and liquid alternately to the creamed mixture. Begin and end with the dry ingredients.

5. Mix until well blended.

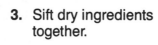

Quick Method

1. Combine the flour, sugar, shortening, and part of the liquid in a large bowl.

2. Blend until smooth.

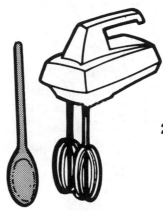

3. Mix in the remaining ingredients.

How to Thicken With . . .

Flour

- Food looks opaque and pasty when thickened with flour.
- To thicken . . .
  1. Add a small amount of *cold* liquid to flour to make a thin paste.
  2. Slowly pour flour mixture into hot liquid.
  3. Cook, stirring constantly, until mixture thickens.

Cornstarch

- Has twice the thickening power of flour and food remains clear.
- To thicken . . .
  1. Cool a small amount of liquid to be thickened and add to cornstarch. Stir to make a smooth paste.
  2. Slowly pour cornstarch mixture into hot liquid, stirring constantly.
  3. Cook, stirring constantly, until mixture thickens and becomes clear.

Tapioca

- Usually used for puddings and pies. As tapioca cooks, part of each granule dissolves to thicken liquid and part turns to a jelly-like bead.
- To thicken . . .
  1. Add tapioca to mixture as directed in recipe. Avoid over-stirring.

Eggs

- Used in custards, puddings, cream pie fillings, and sauces.
- Eggs can curdle if they are added improperly to a hot mixture or over-cooked.
- To thicken a hot or acidic mixture . . .
  1. Break eggs into bowl and beat lightly.
  2. Slowly pour small amount of hot or acidic liquid into eggs, stirring constantly.
  3. Pour diluted mixture gradually into remaining liquid, stirring constantly.

Vegetables

- Vegetables high in starch, such as cooked potatoes and legumes, can be used to thicken liquid.
- To thicken . . .
  1. Add vegetables to food. Puree or mash when cooked. Or add cooked, pureed vegetable to food.

Fruit Juices and Beverages

Fruit Juice
To be labeled "juice," product must be 100% juice.

Fruit Beverages
Read labels carefully to see what you are buying.

The pH Guide to Canning

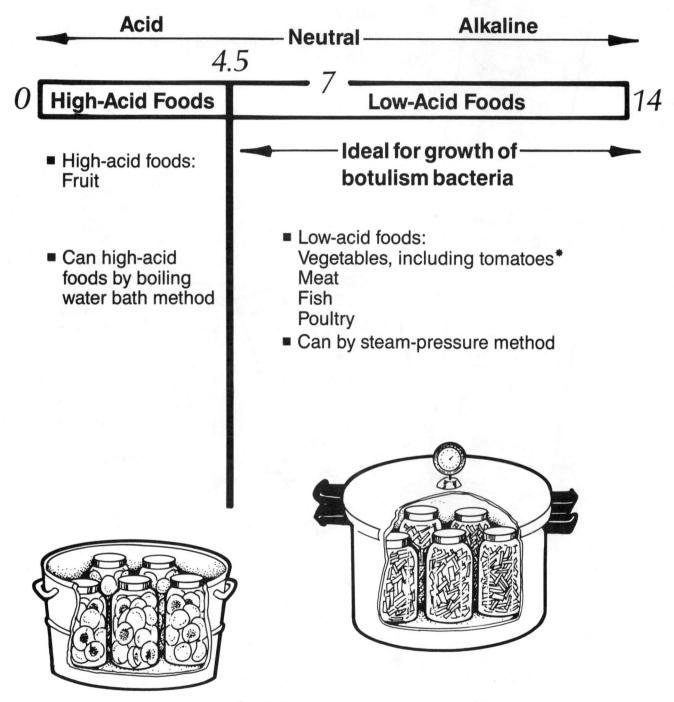

Acid ←——— **Neutral** ———→ **Alkaline**

4.5

7

0 **High-Acid Foods** **Low-Acid Foods** *14*

←——— **Ideal for growth of botulism bacteria** ———→

- High-acid foods:
  Fruit

- Can high-acid
  foods by boiling
  water bath method

- Low-acid foods:
  Vegetables, including tomatoes*
  Meat
  Fish
  Poultry
- Can by steam-pressure method

*NOTE: To can tomatoes by boiling water bath
method, add lemon juice or citric acid.

Foods of the World — Eastern Hemisphere

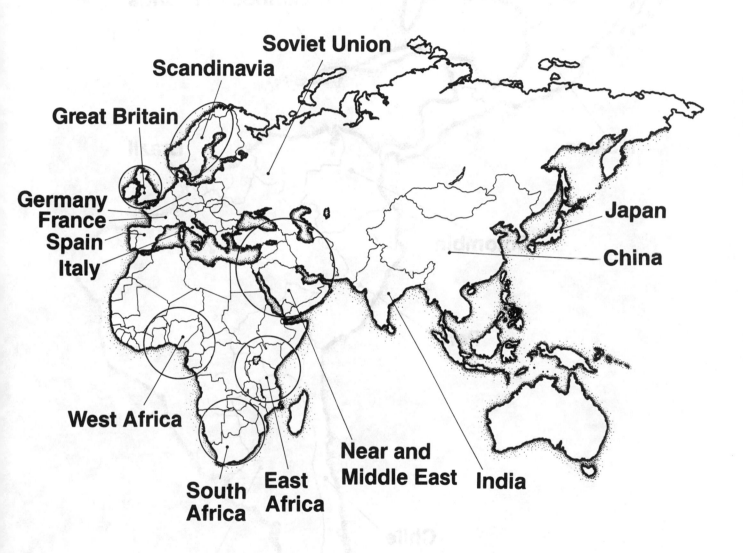

Soviet Union

Scandinavia

Great Britain

Germany
France
Spain
Italy

Japan

China

West Africa

South
Africa

East
Africa

Near and
Middle East

India

Foods of the World — Latin America

Caribbean Islands

Mexico

Brazil

Colombia

Peru

Chile

Argentina

Regional Foods — Northeast, South, Midwest

Midwest

Corn
Wheat
Beef
Pork
Dairy products
Fruits
Vegetables

Northeast

Shellfish
Fish
Wild game
Fruits
Corn
Beans
Squash
Pumpkins
Chowder

South

Shellfish
Fish
Ham
Rice
Corn
Grits
Sweet potatoes
Okra
Greens
Pecans
Gumbo
Hush puppies

Regional Foods —
Southwest, Pacific Coast and Northwest, Hawaii

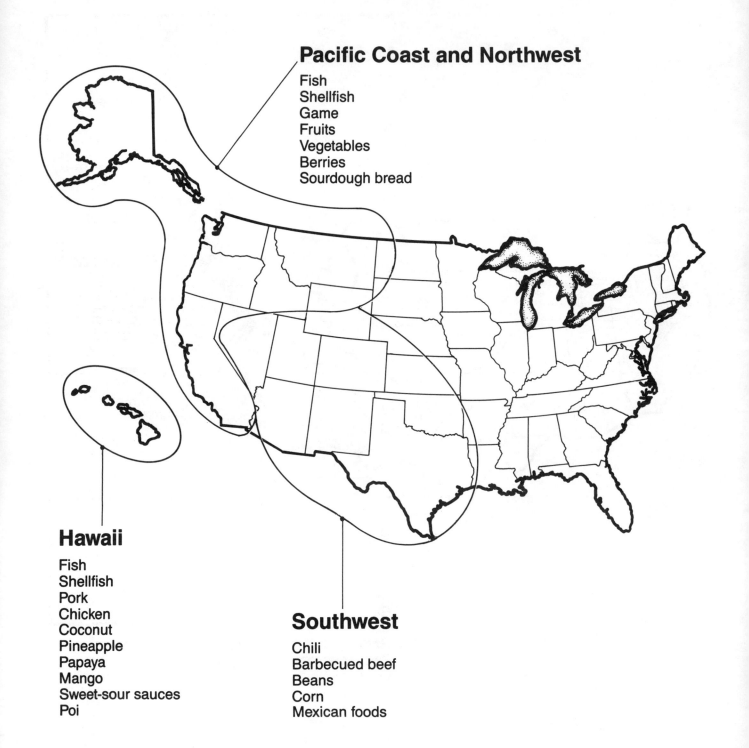

Pacific Coast and Northwest

Fish
Shellfish
Game
Fruits
Vegetables
Berries
Sourdough bread

Hawaii

Fish
Shellfish
Pork
Chicken
Coconut
Pineapple
Papaya
Mango
Sweet-sour sauces
Poi

Southwest

Chili
Barbecued beef
Beans
Corn
Mexican foods

Finishing Touches

Radish Daisy

- Cut round radish into 5-6 crosswise slices, each about ¹/₈″ thick.
- Cut the stem off another radish and cut 5-6 V-shaped notches around the outside.
- Insert the slices into the notches to form a daisy.

Celery Flutes

  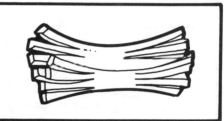

- Cut celery into 3″ lengths. Make short, straight cuts in each end, from the center out.
- Make cuts from each outside end toward the middle. Do not cut through the middle.
- Refrigerate in ice water until celery flutes curl.

Carrot Zigzags

 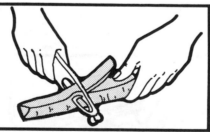 

- Have carrot at room temperature. Cut about ¹/₂″ from the root end.
- Holding the carrot firmly, cut thin, strips lengthwise from the carrot using a peeler.
- Thread the carrot strips onto toothpicks in a zigzag arrangement. Refrigerate in ice water. Remove toothpicks before serving.

More Finishing Touches

Onion Mum

- Peel a medium, round onion, leaving the root end intact.
- With sharp knife, cut down from top of onion to 1/2" from root.
- Make cuts all around the onion.

- Place the onion in bowl of hot water for 5 minutes to remove odor.

- Add food coloring to a bowl of ice water.
- Place the onion in ice water to cover. Soak until onion absorbs food coloring and separates into petals.

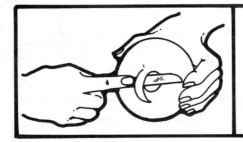
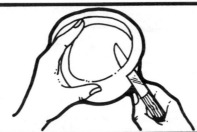
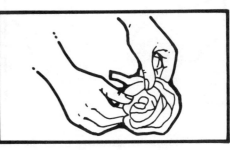

Tomato Rose

- With a sharp knife, pare tomato beginning at the *blossom* end.

- Pare skin as thinly as possible in one continuous strip.

- Beginning with the blossom end, cut side toward the center, roll strip to form a rose. It will almost form itself.

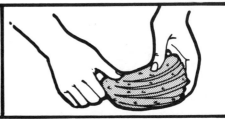

Pickle Fan

- With a sharp knife, cut a plump 3" gherkin lengthwise. Begin the cut 1/2" from one end.

- Make 3-4 more cuts the same way.

- Spread the slice apart to form a fan.

How to Choose a Career

Talents?

Interests?

HOW TO CHOOSE A CAREER

Working alone or with people?

Helping people?

Travel?

Security?

30 Year Employee

Retirement

Health Plan

Employees' Day-Care Center

Flexible Hours?

Are You an Entrepreneur?

☑ **Checklist for Qualities Needed to Run a Business**

☑ Self-starter

☑ Accept responsibility

☑ Well-organized

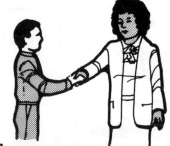

☑ Can be trusted

☑ Get along well with people

☑ Make decisions easily

☑ Do your best all the time

☑ Willing to learn

How Do You Spend Your Day?

1 **Evaluate how you spend time.**
Write down your activities and time spent on each for a week.

2 **Learn to manage time.**
Prioritize your activities.

3 **Be flexible.**
Rearrange your schedule when the unexpected happens.

4 **Don't be a perfectionist.**
Not every task needs to be done perfectly.

5 **Learn to say "NO" to activities that don't interest you.**

A Plan for Managing Your Time

Things to do this week

1. Finish term paper--English.
2. My turn to cook supper—Saturday Night.
3. Go to Jan's party.
4. Hem Mom's dress.
5. Plan Jerry's birthday party.
6. Repot plants.

Calendar for Week

Monday
School - 8-3
Work - 3:30 - 6:00
Homework - 7:30 - ?

Tuesday
School - 8-3
Basketball Practice - 3:30 - 6:00
Homework - 7:30 - ?

Wednesday
School - 8-3
Work - 3:30 - 6:00
Homework - 7:30 - ?

Thursday
School - 8-3
Work - 3:30 - 5:00
Piano Lesson 5:30 - 6:30

Friday
School - 8-3
Work - 3:30 - 6:00
Jan's Party - 7:30

Saturday
Work - 9-1
Hem Mom's dress
Work on term paper
Cook Supper

Sunday
Finish term paper
Repot plants
Homework - 6:30 - ?

Handout Masters

TABLE OF CONTENTS

Handout Masters (HO)

No.	Title	Page

TOPICAL INDEX

Handout Masters (HO)

Commonly Used Additives and What They Do

Additives	Used In	Purpose
NUTRIENTS B vitamins, beta carotene, iodine, potassium iodide, iron, alpha tocopherols (vitamin E), vitamins A, D, and C, ascorbic acid.	Refined grains and grain products; margarine; milk and dairy products; beverages.	Replace vitamins and minerals lost in processing or add nutrients that may be lacking in the diet.
PRESERVATIVES Ascorbic acid, benzoic acid, butylparaben, calcium lactate, calcium propionate, calcium sorbate, citric acid, heptylparaben, lactic acid, methylparaben, potassium propionate, potassium sorbate, propionic acid, propylparaben, sodium benzoate, sodium diacetate, sodium erythorbate, sodium nitrate, sodium nitrite, sodium propionate, sodium sorbate, sorbic acid.	Fruit products; acidic foods; margarine; cheeses; frozen desserts; baked goods; cured meats, fish, poultry; processed meats; syrups; beverages; mayonnaise.	Prevent food spoilage from bacteria, molds, fungi, and yeast; extend shelf life; protect natural color and flavor.
EMULSIFIERS Carrageenan, lecithin, mono- and diglycerides, polysorbates, sorbitan monostearate, dioctyl sodium sulfosuccinate.	Milk drinks; margarine; dressings; baked goods; desserts; ice cream; toppings; chocolate; cocoa; nondairy creams; whipped toppings; peanut butter; cereals.	Help distribute tiny particles of one liquid into another so they do not separate; improve homogeneity, consistency, stability, texture.
COLORS Annatto extract, beta-apo-8, carotenal, beta carotene, canthaxanthin, caramel, carrot oil, citrus red No. 2, cochineal extract, dehydrated beets, blue No. 1, red No. 3, red No. 40, yellow No. 5, grape skin extract, paprika, riboflavin, saffron, titanium dioxide, toasted and partially defatted cooked cottonseed flour, turmeric (oleoresin), fruit and vegetable juices.	Foods where color is needed or desired.	Increase consumer appeal and product acceptance by giving a desired, appetizing, or characteristic color; may not be used to cover up an unwholesome food or used in excessive amounts.

Additives	Used In	Purpose
STABILIZERS; THICKENERS; TEXTURIZERS Alginates (ammonium, calcium, potassium or sodium), carrageenan, cellulose, gelatin, flour, furcelleran, modified food starch, pectin, propylene glycol, various vegetable gums (guar, arabic, locust bean, tragacanth).	Baked goods; dairy products; frozen desserts; fruit products; sauces; soups; pie fillings; canned meals; snack foods; puddings; ice cream; diet foods.	Impart body; improve consistency or texture; stabilize emulsions; affect food texture.
ANTIOXIDANTS Ascorbic acid, BHA (butylated hydroxyanisole), BHT (butylated hydroxytoluene), citric acid, EDTA (ethylenediaminetetraacetic acid), propyl gallate, TBHQ (tertiary butylhydroquinone), tocopherols (vitamin E).	Processed fruits; baked goods; cereals; snack foods; fats and oils; dressings; sauces; instant potatoes.	Delay and prevent rancidity and browning or discoloration due to oxidation.
pH CONTROL AGENTS Acetic acid, adipic acid, citric acid, lactic acid, phosphates, phosphoric acid, sodium acetate, sodium citrate, tartaric acid, fumaric acid.	Baked goods; beverages; fruits; vegetables; oils; frozen desserts; confections; sauces; dressings; relishes; dry/condensed milk.	Change/maintain acidity or alkalinity; can affect texture, taste, wholesomeness.
MATURING AND BLEACHING AGENTS; DOUGH CONDITIONERS Acetone peroxide, azodicarbonamide, benzoyl peroxide, calcium bromate, hydrogen peroxide, potassium bromate, sodium stearyl fumarate.	Flour; baked goods; cereals; instant potatoes.	Accelerate the aging process (oxidation) to develop the gluten characteristics of flour, improve baking qualities.
SWEETENERS *Natural* — corn syrup, dextrose, fructose, glucose, invert sugar, mannitol, sorbitol, sucrose. *Low- or non-caloric* — aspartame, saccharin, acesulfame potassium.	Candies; gum; confections; baked goods; cereals; processed foods including meats; beverages; special dietary foods and beverages.	Make aroma or taste of food more agreeable or pleasurable.

Know Your Nutrients

Nutrients	Best Sources	Benefits	If You Get Too Little	If You Get Too Much
Carbohydrates	■ *Starches:* Breads, cereals, macaroni products, corn, potatoes, dried beans and peas. ■ *Sugars:* Natural sources — fruits, vegetables, and milk. ■ *Fiber:* Whole-grain breads and cereals, fresh fruits and vegetables.	■ Supply energy. Most economical source of energy you can buy. ■ Help your body use protein and fats efficiently. ■ Fiber essential for digestion.	■ Poor vitality. ■ Fatigue. ■ Digestive problems.	■ Overweight problems and related diseases.
Fats	■ *Unsaturated Fats:* Fish, vegetable oils, and soft and semisolid margarines. ■ *Saturated Fats:* All animal foods, oil from coconut, olive, and palm. *Note: Fat consumption should be limited.*	■ Supply energy, twice as much ounce for ounce as carbohydrates and proteins. ■ Some supply essential fatty acids for normal growth and skin health. ■ Carry fat-soluble vitamins A, D, E, K.	■ Dermatitis or skin inflammation, caused by lack of essential fatty acids.	■ Overweight problems and related diseases. ■ High cholesterol levels from saturated fats. ■ Possible increased risk of developing certain cancers.
Proteins	■ *Complete Proteins:* Most animal foods — meat, fish, poultry, eggs, and dairy products. ■ *Incomplete Proteins:* All plant foods — legumes, cereals, grains, and vegetables.	■ Help make antibodies to fight disease. ■ Help regulate some body processes. ■ Help maintain the body's water balance. ■ Help keep blood neutral (not too acid or alkaline). ■ Provide amino acids used to build body proteins. ■ Provide essential amino acids that cannot be totally supplied by the body.	■ Poor vitality. ■ Poor muscle tone. ■ More apt to get infections and diseases. ■ Slow recovery from illness, injuries, or surgery. ■ Extreme deficiency in children: stunted growth, low resistance to disease, mental retardation.	■ Waste of money since excess stored as fat and can never be used for building and repairing cells.
Vitamin A (Retinol) (Fat soluble)	■ Liver. ■ Deep yellow fruits and vegetables: carrots, pumpkin, sweet potatoes, winter squash, apricots, cantaloupe, papayas, peaches. ■ Dark green vegetables: broccoli, spinach, greens. ■ Milk, cheese, eggs.	■ Helps eyes adjust to dim light. ■ Keeps skin healthy. ■ Helps promote growth. ■ Helps you resist infection by keeping linings of mouth, nose, throat, and digestive tract healthy.	■ Eyes become oversensitive to light. ■ Night blindness may develop. ■ Skin becomes rough and cracked. ■ Resistance to infections lowered.	■ Headache; nausea. ■ Dry, itchy skin. ■ Skin may turn yellow. ■ Stunted growth in children.

(Continued on next page)

Nutrients	Best Sources	Benefits	If You Get Too Little	If You Get Too Much
Vitamin D (Calciferol) (Fat soluble)	■ Made on skin in sunlight. ■ Fortified milk. ■ Cod liver oil.	■ Helps body use calcium and phosphorus. ■ Needed for healthy, strong bones and teeth. ■ Helps keep nervous system and heart working properly.	■ Bones become soft and deformed. ■ Teeth become soft. ■ Body cannot absorb calcium properly. ■ Phosphorus is retained in kidneys.	■ Nausea, loss of appetite, diarrhea. ■ Kidney stones. ■ Fragile bones. ■ Deafness.
Vitamin E (Tocopherols) (Fat soluble)	■ Vegetable oils: corn, cottonseed, soybean; margarine. ■ Wheat germ. ■ Whole-grain cereals and bread. ■ Liver. ■ Green leafy vegetables.	■ Protects vitamin A and fatty acids from oxidation. ■ Helps form red blood cells, muscles, and other tissues.	■ Blood cells may rupture. ■ Muscles may become wasted. ■ (Shortage is very rare among humans.)	■ Nausea, dizziness, blurred vision. ■ Extreme fatigue and muscle weakness.
Vitamin K (Fat soluble)	■ Made by bacteria in human intestine. ■ Green leafy vegetables. ■ Cabbage. ■ Cauliflower. ■ Potatoes. ■ Liver.	■ Helps form the substances needed for blood clotting.	■ In infants, hemorrhage (bleeding). ■ In adults, loss of calcium from bones. ■ (Shortage is very rare. People on antibiotics for a long time or those with impaired fat absorption may need extra vitamin K.)	■ In infants, jaundice.
Vitamin B$_1$ (thiamin) (water soluble)	■ Pork. ■ Liver. ■ Oysters. ■ Whole-grain and enriched breads and cereals. ■ Wheat germ. ■ Legumes.	■ Helps body obtain energy from carbohydrates. ■ Helps brain, nerves, and muscles function.	■ Mental confusion. ■ Swelling of the heart. ■ Numbness of hands and feet. ■ Leg cramps.	Symptoms unknown.
Vitamin B$_2$ (riboflavin) (water soluble)	■ Milk, cheese. ■ Liver, kidneys. ■ Eggs. ■ Dried beans and peas. ■ Enriched breads and cereals.	■ Helps break down carbohydrates, proteins, and fats to release energy. ■ Keeps lining of mouth, nose, and digestive tract healthy.	■ Cracked lips. ■ Sore tongue. ■ Skin disorders. ■ Eyes become sensitive to light.	Symptoms unknown.
Niacin (water soluble)	■ Liver. ■ Fish. ■ Poultry. ■ Enriched breads and cereals. ■ Peanuts, dried peas and beans.	■ Helps break down food to provide energy.	■ Sore, cracked skin. ■ Sore mouth. ■ Diarrhea. ■ Mental confusion, anxiety.	■ Ulcers in the duodenum (tube leading from stomach to small intestine). ■ Liver abnormalities. ■ Increased level of blood sugar.

(Continued on next page)

Know Your Nutrients

Nutrients	Best Sources	Benefits	If You Get Too Little	If You Get Too Much
Vitamin B$_6$ (pyridoxine) (water soluble)	■ Meats, fish, poultry. ■ Liver. ■ Whole-grain cereals and bread. ■ Wheat germ. ■ Oatmeal. ■ Potatoes. ■ Green leafy vegetables. ■ Avocados, bananas. ■ Nuts.	■ Helps the body utilize proteins and fats. ■ Helps form red blood cells.	■ Skin disorders. ■ Dry, cracked lips. ■ Nausea, dizziness. ■ Anemia. ■ Kidney stones. ■ Depression.	■ High doses can lead to dependency. Symptoms of shortage appear when dose is decreased to normal. ■ Some evidence that high doses cause joint stiffness.
Vitamin B$_{12}$ (cobalamins) (water soluble)	■ Meats, fish, oysters. ■ Liver, kidneys. ■ Eggs. ■ Dairy products. ■ (Not available from plant sources.)	■ Helps form red blood cells. ■ Needed for healthy nerves. ■ Helps form genetic material.	■ B$_{12}$ deficiency anemia: paleness, fatigue, heart fluttering. ■ Numbness and tingling in hands and feet, loss of balance.	Symptoms unknown.
Pantothenic acid (water soluble)	■ Liver, kidneys. ■ Eggs. ■ Whole-grain cereals and bread. ■ Nuts. ■ Dark green vegetables. ■ Made by bacteria in human intestines.	■ Helps the body utilize proteins, carbohydrates, and fats. ■ Assists in production of hormones.	■ Abdominal cramps, vomiting. ■ Fatigue. ■ Restlessness, inability to sleep. ■ Tingling in hands and feet. ■ (Shortage is very rare.)	■ Body's need for thiamin increases; symptoms of a thiamin shortage could develop.
Biotin (water soluble)	■ Egg yolk. ■ Liver, kidneys. ■ Mushrooms. ■ Peanuts. ■ Dark green vegetables. ■ Made by bacteria in human intestine.	■ Helps body make fatty acids. ■ Helps release energy from carbohydrates.	■ Loss of appetite, nausea, vomiting. ■ Fatigue, muscle pain. ■ Depression. ■ (Shortages unknown except in people who eat large amounts of raw egg white. The raw egg white destroys biotin.)	Symptoms unknown.
Folic acid (water soluble)	■ Liver, kidneys. ■ Eggs. ■ Dark green leafy vegetables. ■ Dried peas and beans. ■ Wheat germ.	■ Helps produce red blood cells. ■ Helps in forming genetic material.	■ Anemia. ■ In pregnant women, shortage can cause loss of baby or abnormalities in baby.	■ Could mask the symptoms of a B$_{12}$ shortage.
Vitamin C (ascorbic acid) (water soluble)	■ Citrus fruits: oranges, grapefruit, tangerines, lemons. ■ Strawberries, papayas, cantaloupes. ■ Broccoli, raw cabbage, mustard and turnip greens, collards.	■ Works with calcium to build and maintain healthy bones and teeth. ■ Keeps blood vessels strong. ■ Protects other vitamins from oxidation. ■ Helps form collagen. ■ Helps body fight infection.	■ Bleeding gums. ■ Loss of appetite, weight loss. ■ Weakness. ■ Thick, roughened skin.	■ Diarrhea. ■ Dependency on high doses. ■ Kidney and bladder stones.

Nutrients	Best Sources	Benefits	If You Get Too Little	If You Get Too Much
Calcium and Phosphorus	■ Milk. ■ Dairy products — cheese, ice cream. ■ Green leafy vegetables. ■ Canned sardines and other processed fish eaten with bones. ■ Egg yolks. ■ Meat, fish, poultry. ■ Whole-grain breads and cereals.	■ Helps build and maintain healthy bones and teeth. ■ Helps blood clot during bleeding. ■ Helps heart, nerves and muscles work properly. ■ Helps body produce energy.	■ Weak bones and teeth. ■ Osteoporosis — adult bones become fragile and may break.	■ Difficult to get an excess of calcium. ■ Excess of phosphorus forces body to remove calcium from bones.
Iron	■ Liver, kidney, heart. ■ Meat. ■ Egg yolk. ■ Dried beans and peas. ■ Spinach. ■ Dried fruit. ■ Whole-grain and enriched breads, cereals. ■ Nuts.	■ Helps make hemoglobin. ■ Helps cells use oxygen.	■ Anemia: Poor appetite, pale skin, tired feeling, weakness.	■ Can damage the liver and other body tissues.
Iodine	■ Iodized table salt. ■ Salt water fish and shellfish. ■ Almost all animal foods.	■ Helps thyroid gland work properly.	■ Goiter: Swelling in neck due to enlarged thyroid gland.	Symptoms unknown.
Zinc	■ Meat. ■ Seafood. ■ Eggs. ■ Milk.	■ Helps body use carbohydrates, proteins, and fat. ■ Important in growth, reproduction, and healing wounds.	■ Loss of sense of taste. ■ Wounds heal slowly.	■ Fever. ■ Nausea.
Magnesium	■ Organ meats. ■ Whole-grain cereals. ■ Nuts. ■ Dried beans and peas. ■ Green leafy vegetables. ■ Egg yolks. ■ Milk.	■ Keeps the nervous system healthy. ■ Helps maintain healthy nerves and muscles.	■ Muscle tremors.	■ Disturbed nervous system function.
Chlorine, Potassium, and Sodium	■ Most foods. ■ Table salt. ■ *Potassium:* fish, meat, bananas, citrus fruit, and milk.	■ Responsible for maintaining water balance in body. ■ Help maintain normal muscle action. ■ Help to balance acids and alkalies in body. ■ Help the nervous system work properly.	■ Fainting. ■ Vomiting.	■ *Potassium:* muscular paralysis. ■ *Sodium:* edema, may increase likelihood of high blood pressure.

Your Personal Wellness Plan

Developing your own wellness plan isn't difficult. Your first step is to decide to be responsible for your own health. That means you make a decision to improve or maintain your health. Then you carry out that decision. You have many resources to help you, including your family, your physician, other health professionals, and reliable books and magazines. Here's a checklist to help you develop your own personal wellness plan.

✔ **Eat nutritious food.** Base your daily food choices on health guidelines, such as the Dietary Guidelines for Americans on page 67 and the Daily Food Guide on pages 77-80 of the text.

Ask yourself: What foods that are not healthful do I eat too often? How can I improve my daily food habits?

✔ **Get regular exercise.** How much exercise you need depends on your lifestyle. People who are active during the day will need less exercise than those who lead sedentary lives. Even such ordinary activities as climbing stairs can be considered exercise. Begin by determining how active you are during the day.

Ask yourself: How much time do I spend sitting? What can I do to get more regular exercise?

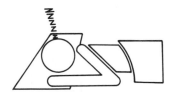

✔ **Get plenty of sleep.** The average person needs about 7 hours of sleep, but some people need more while others may need less.

Ask yourself: How much sleep do I need? What can I do to make sure I get the rest I need every night?

✔ **Learn to cope with emotions and stress.** Read the information on pages 70-73 in the text. Experiment with the suggestions and select several that work for you. List three methods that you can use to help you control your emotions and cope with stress.

Ask yourself: What methods could I use to help control my emotions and cope with stress?

✔ **Avoid harmful habits such as smoking and the use of alcohol and other drugs.** Any drugs, including nicotine and alcohol, can have a harmful effect on the body. If you don't begin using drugs, you won't get caught in the drug trap and become addicted.

Ask yourself: What methods could I use to avoid the use of drugs?

Diet Analysis Worksheet

Using the blank chart below, fill in all the foods and amounts you eat in one day. Then, using Appendix D, "Nutrients in Food," pages 591-611 of FOOD FOR TODAY, fill in the rest of the columns with the percentages of each nutrient. Add the figures in each column and write the totals at the bottom in the spaces provided. Fill in the bottom row with the recommended figures given in Appendix C, "Percentages of U.S. RDA," for your age group. How do the figures compare? If you are lacking in any nutrients, which foods could you eat to help balance your diet?

Food	Amount Eaten	Calories	Protein	Vitamin A	Vitamin C	Thia-min	Ribo-flavin	Niacin	Cal-cium	Iron
TOTAL										
U.S. RDA GOAL										

The "Percentage of U.S. RDA" heading spans the Protein through Iron columns.

Vegetarian Meals

Vegetarians who eat only fruits, vegetables, grains, and nuts run the risk of not getting enough high-quality proteins in their diet. By properly combining incomplete proteins, however, they can get the complete proteins they need.

Grains, legumes (dried beans, peas, lentils, and peanuts), nuts, and seeds each lack a few essential amino acids. Each group, however, lacks different ones. Therefore, if foods from these groups are properly combined, the body will get all the essential amino acids that are needed.

Protein complementarity means combining legumes with grains, nuts, or seeds to get all of the essential amino acids. The foods do not have to be mixed together, but they should be eaten on the same day.

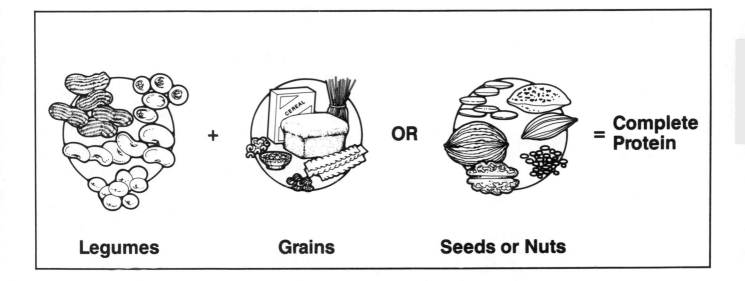

Legumes + Grains OR Seeds or Nuts = **Complete Protein**

What Food Combinations Provide Protein Complementarity?

- Beans and Rice
- Baked Beans and Boston Brown Bread
- Lentil-Rice Soup
- Hummus (Mashed Garbanzo Beans and Ground Sesame Seeds)

- Tofuburger on a Bun
- Split Pea Soup and Nut Bread
- Blackeyed Peas and Cornbread
- Peanut Butter Sandwich

How to Compute the Percentage of Calories from Nutrients

Total Calories

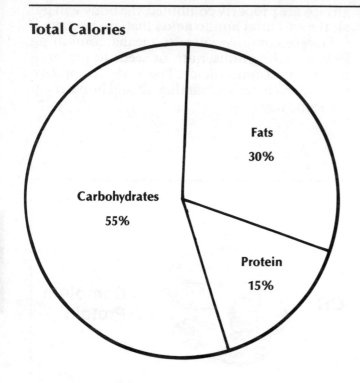

Health experts recommend that of the total calories consumed each day, 30 percent or less should be from fats, about 15 percent from proteins, and about 55 percent from carbohydrates. With some simple calculations, you can determine whether or not your diet fits these guidelines. Use the steps that follow.

1. Keep track of the food you eat in one day.
2. Add up the total number of calories consumed. Use food labels and nutrition charts to find the calorie count for each food.
3. Add up the total grams of fat consumed during the day. Again, use labels and charts to find the grams of fat in each food. Repeat this process for carbohydrates and proteins.
4. Calculate the percentages. A gram of fat has 9 calories, a gram of protein has 4 calories, and a gram of carbohydrate also has 4 calories. So to figure the percentage of calories that come from each nutrient, the formulas are:

   Grams of fat × 9 ÷ total calories × 100
   = % of calories from fat

   Grams of carbohydrate × 4 ÷ total calories × 100 = % of calories from carbohydrate

   Grams of protein × 4 ÷ total calories × 100 = % of calories from protein

5. Compare the percentages to the recommended ones. (These three numbers should total about 100 percent. The total may not be exact due to rounded numbers.)

This procedure may also be used to find the percentages for a meal or a single food or recipe. Only by looking at a whole day's intake, however, can you get a general idea about your diet.

Using the Formulas

During one day, Alex kept track of everything he ate. After determining the calorie count for each item, he added these figures to get the total number of calories consumed for the day. This total was 3300 calories. Using charts and labels to help him, Alex also figured nutrient totals: 128 grams of fat, 372 grams of carbohydrates, and 165 grams of protein. Using the formulas, he next found the calorie percentage for each nutrient.

128 grams of fat × 9 = 1152
1152 ÷ 3300 = .35
.35 × 100 = **35% of calories from fats**

372 grams of carbohydrate × 4 = 1488
1488 ÷ 3300 = .45
.45 × 100 = **45% of calories from carbohydrates**

165 grams of protein × 4 = 660
660 ÷ 3300 = .20
.20 × 100 = **20% of calories from protein**

Alex consumed higher percentages of fat and protein than are recommended. By cutting down on fats and proteins, he could improve all three percentages.

Hints for Controlling Weight

Here are a few hints to help you control your weight and make it fun.

- Weight control can be fun, not just a chore. To make it enjoyable, choose a variety of foods to avoid monotony.

- Learn to use herbs and spices to give different flavors to foods.

- Stretch your meals without adding calories. Use low-calorie vegetables, such as asparagus, green and wax beans, bean sprouts, broccoli, cabbage, cauliflower, celery, cucumbers, okra, green and red peppers, radishes, summer squash, tomatoes, and zucchini.

- Drink a large glass of water before meals. It helps fill the stomach so you won't feel like overeating.

- Take small servings of food and use a luncheon or salad plate instead of a large dinner plate. It makes the food portions look larger.

- Don't skip meals. Every meal is important. If you skip a meal, you may get so hungry that you will snack and eat more food than you would have otherwise. Be sure to have a breakfast that includes protein, so your body will have a good supply of amino acids.

- Try eating five or six small meals during the day instead of just three large ones. Don't increase your total intake; just divide it into more meals.

- Eat slowly and chew food thoroughly. It takes 20 minutes from the start of a meal for the stomach to signal the brain that it's feeling full. Also, if you eat slowly, you get a sense of satisfaction from every bite. That will help you have less desire for second helpings.

- Processed snack foods are usually high in calories. Instead, choose nutritious low-calorie foods, such as fresh fruits and vegetables. Prepare unflavored gelatin with fruit juice. Cut it into cubes. Serve it with fresh fruit in a sherbet or parfait glass for a low-calorie dessert or snack.

- Put a sign on the refrigerator, such as "Think Thin."

- If you have a special occasion like a party, budget your calories to prepare for it. Eat only very low-calorie foods during the day so you have a few calories saved up for the special event. Remember, though, do not drastically cut back on calories one day to use them the next. If you do, you will rob your body of the nutrients needed every day.

- Don't start a diet just before a holiday season. Wait until after the holidays.

- Some people like to keep weight loss charts. If you keep one, do not weigh yourself more than once a week. Your body retains water, which causes day-to-day differences in weight. Weighing yourself too often can be discouraging. You may also want to keep a chart of your body measurements from week to week. It will help you "see" yourself getting thinner.

Use Electricity Safely

Electrical Safety Tips

- Disconnect portable appliances when not in use.
- Never yank on an electrical cord to disconnect it. Grasp the plug and pull gently.
- Be sure appliances are grounded.
- Don't overload wall outlets by connecting a number of appliances to one receptacle.
- Try to avoid using extension cords. If you must use one, be sure it is the correct type. Appliances that heat, such as toasters, roasters, and waffle irons, require heavy-duty extension cords.
- Don't run electrical cords near hot objects or under rugs. Never place an object directly on top of an electrical cord. The cord could become damaged and unsafe.

- Keep electrical devices away from water and moisture. Do not use appliances if your hands are wet or if you are standing on a moist surface.
- When operating electrical appliances, be careful not to touch any plumbing, such as a sink or faucet. If you do, an undetected defect in the appliance could result in a severe shock.
- Never bring metal objects in contact with the working parts of an electrical appliance while it is connected.
- Turn off the main power supply before replacing a fuse. Be sure you are not in contact with water, moisture, or plumbing.
- Never replace a fuse with a penny or a piece of foil. Always use the correct size fuse. (The size is marked on the fuse, such as "20 amperes.")

How Does Electricity Work?

Electricity from a power plant enters your home through a main supply line. The main line goes to a service panel in your house, and from there electricity is circulated throughout your home by many smaller wires called circuits. Each circuit supplies power to a limited number of lights and wall outlets. Appliances that draw a lot of power, such as an electric range or a clothes dryer, are connected to special circuits of their own.

You don't see the circuits in your home because they are usually hidden inside walls and ceilings. These wires are covered with insulation to protect you from shock and death and to help prevent fires. Each circuit is designed to carry a certain amount of electricity. If too much electricity were to flow through one of the circuits, it would overheat and burn. To prevent that, safety devices are usually installed in homes.

The Grounding System

One safety feature built into newer electrical systems is a grounding wire. In homes with this feature, wall receptacles have three holes. These are designed to be used with modern appliances that have a plug with three prongs. The third prong is connected by a wire in the cord to the appliance's metal housing. This provides grounding for the appliance. If the electrical system was properly installed in the home, the third prong connects to the home's grounding wire. This wire provides an alternate path for the electricity in case of a defect in the appliance. Without the protection of a grounding wire, a defective appliance could give you a severe shock or kill you when you touch the appliance.

For safety, all appliances should be grounded. If the receptacles in your home do not have three holes, an electrician can tell you how to ground your appliances. Even if the receptacles in your

(Continued on next page)

home have three holes, it is best to have them checked by a qualified electrician to make sure they are properly grounded.

Fuses and Circuit Breakers

What would happen if too many appliances were drawing power from a circuit at once? They could cause the circuit to carry too much electricity and start a fire. With a fuse or circuit breaker, that does not happen. These devices are another safety feature of electrical systems. They are designed to stop the flow of electricity. They allow only a limited amount of electricity to pass through each circuit — no more than the wire was intended to handle.

Fuses and circuit breakers are found in the home's service panel. A fuse is a disk or cartridge that screws or snaps into place. It has a glass surface through which you can see a metal strip. If too many appliances are being used on one circuit or if there is a defect in an appliance, the fuse "blows." This means the metal strip melts and breaks the circuit. Then no electricity can flow through the wire, and a fire is prevented. After the problem is corrected (by shutting off some of the appliances or repairing the defective appliance), the fuse must be replaced.

A circuit breaker is a switch that does the same job as a fuse. If a problem develops, the switch automatically opens, or "trips." Circuit breakers do not have to be replaced. They are simply reset after the problem is corrected.

Service Panels

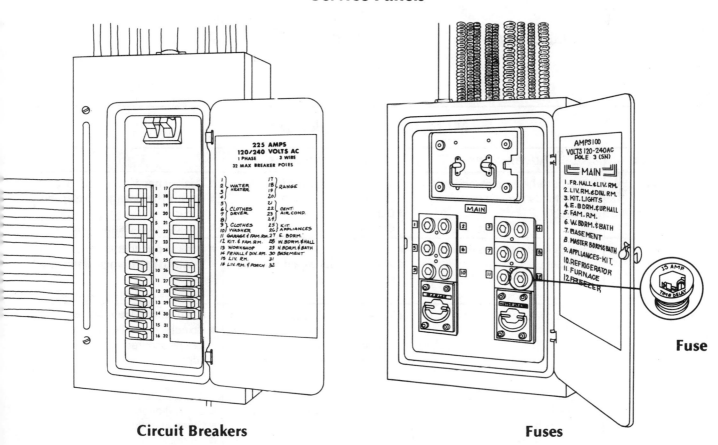

Circuit Breakers   **Fuses**   **Fuse**

Features to Look for When Buying Pans

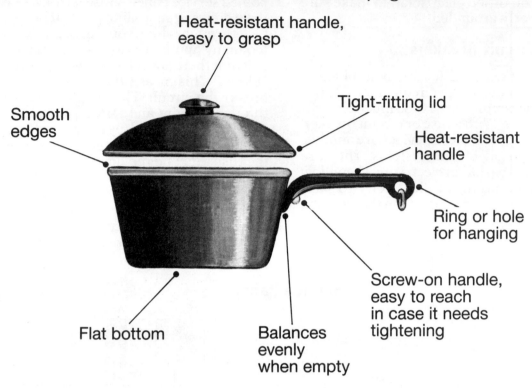

Heat-resistant handle, easy to grasp

Tight-fitting lid

Smooth edges

Heat-resistant handle

Ring or hole for hanging

Screw-on handle, easy to reach in case it needs tightening

Flat bottom

Balances evenly when empty

Materials for Cookware

Material	Advantages	Disadvantages	Care
Aluminum	■ Conducts heat rapidly and evenly. ■ Acid foods remove darkening. ■ Durable.	■ Minerals in water and food cause darkening and pitting. ■ Dishwasher detergent stains and darkens.	■ Soak, if needed. ■ Clean in hot detergent water and scour. ■ Do not put in dishwasher.
Cast Iron	■ Holds heat well and distributes it evenly.	■ Heavy. ■ Will rust if not wiped dry when stored.	■ Soak, if needed. ■ Wash in hot detergent water; dry well. ■ Never scour.
Copper	■ Good conductor of heat.	■ When heated, copper reacts with food to form poisonous compounds. Do not use for cooking unless lined with tin or chrome.	■ Clean in hot detergent water. ■ Do not scour — lining is thin and can be scoured away, exposing copper. ■ Clean outsides with copper cleaner.
Earthenware	■ Attractive. ■ Retains heat so food is kept hot after being removed from oven.	■ Conducts heat slowly and unevenly. ■ Chips and breaks easily.	■ Soak, if needed. ■ Clean in hot detergent water. ■ Do not scour.

(Continued on next page)

Materials for Cookware (continued)

Material	Advantages	Disadvantages	Care
Stoneware	■ Retains heat so food stays at perfect serving temperature. ■ Can use in oven and microwave. ■ Use to cook and serve. ■ Dishwasher safe.	■ Breaks and chips easily.	■ Dishwasher safe. ■ Do not use abrasive cleaners. ■ Wash in hot, sudsy water.
Clay Cookers	■ Cooks at high heat. ■ Cook without additional fat or liquid. ■ No basting needed. ■ Can use in conventional or microwave oven.	■ Breaks and chips easily. ■ Cannot be used to refrigerate or freeze food. ■ Cannot withstand extreme temperature changes.	■ Never use soap, detergent, or cleaners; clay can absorb. ■ Scrub with a stiff brush in plain hot water. ■ Use salt or baking soda as a cleaning aid.
Microwave-Safe Plastic	■ Can go from freezer to oven. ■ Will not warp or melt from heat of food. ■ Dishwasher safe.	■ Some cannot be used in conventional ovens.	■ Clean in hot detergent water. ■ Do not scour with metal pads or abrasive powders.
Enamel Glass baked on metal	■ Attractive decorator patterns. ■ Maintains heat distribution of base metal.	■ Chips easily. ■ May be heavy if iron is base metal.	■ Soak, if needed. ■ Clean in hot detergent water. ■ Do not scour.
Glass	■ Can see food in container. ■ Attractive designs.	■ Chips and breaks easily. ■ Conducts heat unevenly. ■ Cannot hold up under extreme temperature changes.	■ Soak, if needed. ■ Wash in hot detergent water. ■ Do not scour.
Glass-Ceramic	■ Can see through some types. ■ Goes right from refrigerator to range. ■ Goes from range to soak while still hot. ■ Can be used under broiler (not lids). ■ Can use in microwave. ■ Durable and attractive.	■ Breakable if dropped. ■ Heats slowly, but holds heat well; preheating helps. ■ Heats unevenly with hottest area over element or flame. ■ Tends to stick; preheating and low heat settings help.	■ Dishwasher safe. ■ Soak, if needed. ■ Clean in hot detergent water. ■ Do not scour with abrasive products.
Nonstick Surface	■ Keeps food from sticking to pan. ■ Durable if used properly.	■ May be damaged by metal spoons or forks, or metal scouring pads.	■ Soak, if needed. ■ Clean in hot detergent water. ■ Do not scour with metal pads or abrasive powders.
Stainless Steel	■ Will not rust, corrode, or stain. ■ Keeps brightness under normal care. ■ Durable and attractive.	■ Conducts heat slowly and unevenly. ■ Develops hot spots. ■ May darken if overheated.	■ Soak, if needed. ■ Clean in hot detergent water. ■ Scour.
Stainless Steel with copper- or aluminum-clad bottom	■ Heats quickly and evenly. ■ Combines advantages of both metals. ■ Durable and attractive.	■ Copper discolors and needs to be cleaned regularly.	■ Soak, if needed. ■ Clean in hot detergent water. ■ Use copper cleaner on bottom. ■ Scour aluminum bottom.

When You Have a Complaint

Sometimes, no matter how carefully you shop, you may buy poor-quality or inedible food. When you have a complaint, return the item to the store immediately. Speak to the manager. If your complaint is valid, the manager should replace the product or refund your money. You may want to write a letter of complaint to the manufacturer. For guidelines on what to include in such a letter, see the sample below.

If you find foreign food particles in packaged foods, report it to the FDA. Look in the telephone book under "United States Government" or "U.S. Department of Health and Human Services" for the number and address of the FDA office nearest you.

Being a good consumer means shopping with care. It also means being a responsible shopper.

1000 Adams St.
River City, OH 11111
Phone: 101-555-3333
May 10, 19____

INCLUDE YOUR NAME,
FULL ADDRESS,
PHONE NUMBER,
AND DATE OF LETTER

Mr. Jack Grain
President
XYZ Food Co.
333 First St.
Main, OH 55555

Dear Mr. Grain:

SPECIFIC NAME
OF PRODUCT

DATE OF PURCHASE

On May 1, 19____ I purchased three loaves of your Home Baked bread for my family from Your Neighborhood Grocery Store, 2000 Adams St., River City for $1.39 a loaf. The product code on the packages was 1110324 and the sell date for each loaf was May 6.

NAME AND ADDRESS OF STORE WHERE PURCHASED

PRODUCT CODE AND OTHER PERTINENT INFORMATION

THE PRICE PAID FOR PRODUCT. IF POSSIBLE, INCLUDE A COPY OF THE SALES SLIP

In the store, the bread looked fine. At home that day, though, when I was making a sandwich I noticed mold on a slice of the bread. When I looked closely at the loaf, I found that three-fourths of the slices were moldy. The other two loaves also had a lot of mold on them. I have not had this problem with your product before, so I hope this is an isolated incident.

WHAT THE PROBLEM IS IN DETAIL

I contacted the manager at Your Neighborhood Grocery Store, but she is unwilling to replace the bread or refund my money. Therefore I find it necessary to write to you for a refund. I am enclosing a copy of my sales slip for this purpose.

WHAT ACTION YOU EXPECT

I hope you can resolve this problem. Thank you.

Sincerely,

Bob Consumer

Food Storage Times

Dry Storage Times*

VEGETABLES AND FRUITS
Onions, potatoes, sweet potatoes	1-2 weeks
Dried fruits	6 months

GRAIN PRODUCTS, NUTS, AND SEEDS
Flour (all-purpose or cake)	1 year
Dried bread crumbs	6 months
Noodles, macaroni	2 years
Rice, white	2 years
Dried beans and peas	1 year

SWEETENERS, SEASONINGS, BAKING NEEDS
Granulated sugar	2 years
Honey	1 year
Herbs, ground spices	6 months
Salad oil	3 months
Shortening	8 months

BAKED GOODS
Cookies and crackers (store-bought)	3-4 months
Breads and rolls	3 days

PACKAGED MIXES
Cake mixes, pudding mixes	1 year
Nonfat dry milk	6 months

CANNED FOODS
All types	1 year

OTHER
Peanut Butter	
Unopened	6 months
Opened	2 months
Barbecue sauce, catsup, chili sauce	
Unopened	1 year
Opened	1 month

Refrigerator Storage Times*

DAIRY PRODUCTS
Milk, cream	1 week
Butter, buttermilk, sour cream, yogurt	2 weeks
Margarine	4 weeks
Eggs	4 weeks
Cottage cheese, fresh	3 days
Cheese, natural	3-6 months

MEAT
Ground or cooked meat	1-2 days
Fresh steaks, roasts, chops	3-5 days
Cold cuts	3-5 days
Bacon, frankfurters, smoked sausage, whole ham	7 days

POULTRY
Fresh or cooked poultry	1-2 days

FISH AND SHELLFISH
Fresh fish or leftover canned	1 day

FRUITS
Fresh	2-5 days
Leftover canned fruits	1 week
Citrus fruits	2 weeks
Apples	1 month

VEGETABLES
Leftover canned vegetables	3 days
Broccoli, brussels sprouts, green onions, leafy greens, lima beans, peas, zucchini	5 days
Cabbage, cauliflower, celery, cucumbers eggplant, green beans, peppers, tomatoes	1 week
Beets, carrots, parsnips, radishes, turnips	2 weeks

Freezer Storage Times*

MEAT
Beef roasts and steaks	6-12 months
Pork, veal, and lamb roasts	4-8 months
Ground meat, Pork chops	3-4 months
Ham	1-2 months
Bacon	1 month
Cooked meats and meat dishes, gravies, meat broth	2-3 months

POULTRY
Whole chicken or turkey	12 months
Chicken pieces	9 months
Turkey pieces	6 months
Cooked poultry dishes	4-6 months

FISH AND SHELLFISH
Fresh	3-6 months
Cooked fish dishes	3 months
Home-frozen shellfish	3 months
Commercially frozen shellfish	3 months

FRUITS AND VEGETABLES
Most fruits and vegetables	8-12 months
Juices and concentrates	12 months

DAIRY PRODUCTS
Cheese (cheddar, Swiss, etc.)	3 months
Butter, margarine	9 months
Ice cream, ice milk, sherbet	1 month

OTHER
Bread	3 months
Unbaked bread dough	1 month
Cakes	2-6 months
Cookies and cookie dough	3 months
Sandwiches	2-4 weeks
Commercially frozen dinners and main dishes	3-6 months

*Eating quality drops after times shown.

Home from the Supermarket

When arriving home from the supermarket, you must store the food in the right places — and in the right order. Some foods require quick refrigeration or freezing in order to prevent spoilage. Other foods can simply be stored at room temperature and will keep that way for a long time. The pictures below will give you an idea about how to categorize the foods you buy so that you can store them in the correct order. Can you think of additional items that would go in each category?

STORE THESE IMMEDIATELY

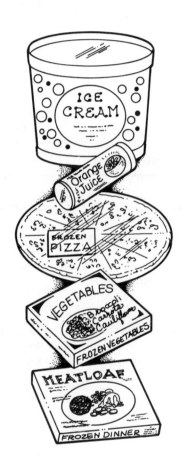

STORE THESE NEXT

STORE THESE LAST

Accidents — Prevention and First Aid

Fires and Burns

Prevention

Watch for things that could catch fire

- Keep all flammable materials such as towels, curtains, paper, pot holders, and plastics away from the top of the range. Also keep them away from portable appliances that heat, such as toasters.
- Clothing can catch fire easily. Avoid loose garments and long sleeves when working in the kitchen.
- Use a pot holder, not a towel, to remove a pan from the range. A towel could catch on fire.
- Never use or store flammable substances such as cleaning fluid, adhesives, or aerosol sprays near any source of heat.
- Use a metal container for trash. If a fire occurs, it will not spread as quickly as it would in a plastic container.
- Clean range exhaust hoods and ducts frequently. Grease from cooking can build up and catch fire easily.

Use electrical cords correctly

- Do not run electrical cords near hot objects.
- Avoid the electrical octopus — one outlet with a number of cords plugged into it.
- If you must use an extension cord, use a heavy-duty one designed for appliances.

Use gas appliances safely

- If you have to light gas burners with a match, strike the match first and then turn the burner on. Otherwise there may be an explosion.
- If you smell gas, turn off all range and oven controls and open a window or door. Alert others and leave the home immediately. Call your gas company right away from a neighbor's house.

Avoid burns from steam, hot liquids, and hot surfaces

- Keep pan handles turned away from the edge of the range so the pan will not be knocked off.
- When cooking, always remove pan lids by tilting them away from you. This allows steam to escape safely at the back of the pot, away from your face.
- If you are cooking with a portable appliance, be sure that it won't tip or be knocked over. Keep the cord out of the way.
- Pull out the oven rack when you remove a pan. Avoid reaching into the oven.
- Use both hands to remove baking pans. Wear oven mitts.
- Be sure pot holders and oven mitts are well padded and dry. A damp pot holder on a hot pan creates steam. Steam can cause serious burns.
- When you're through cooking, always check to be sure that the range or portable appliance is turned off. Be especially careful with electric ranges. You may not be able to tell whether a surface unit is turned on unless you check the controls.
- Deep-fat frying requires special care. Always lower the food into the fat gently with a spoon or other utensil. That way your fingers won't touch the hot oil and it won't splash on you.

In Case of Fire

Quick action may be able to keep a small fire from becoming a big one.

- If a grease fire starts, turn off the burner or appliance. Cover the pan with a lid or pour baking soda over the fire. Do not try to carry the pan of burning grease to the sink or outside. Do not throw cold water on the fire — it will spatter with explosive force.
- You may be able to put out a small fire with a fire extinguisher. But remember that fire spreads quickly. If you can't put out the fire right away, get out and call the fire department.
- If your clothing ever catches on fire, don't run. Drop to the ground and roll to smother the flames.
- Smoke can be as dangerous as fire. Don't try to stay in a smoke-filled room. Drop to your hands and knees and crawl to safety. The smoke will be thinner near the floor.

First Aid

Burns

- Cool the burn with cold water. Cover with a dry, clean bandage if needed. Do not put grease, ointments, or oil on a burn — they can make it worse. Do not clean a burn or break blisters. If the burn is large or serious, get medical help.

Smoke Inhalation

- Get the person to a safe area. If the person is not breathing, begin rescue breathing. Do not stop until the person can breathe unaided or until professional medical help arrives.

Falls

Prevention

- Don't leave objects on the floor. Someone could trip over them.
- Use a sturdy stepstool or ladder to reach high places. Do not stand on a chair or box.
- Wipe spills off the floor immediately.
- Be sure rugs have a nonskid backing.

✚ First Aid

- If you think a bone is broken, do not move the person unless absolutely necessary, as in a fire. Call for medical help.
- Head injuries can be serious. Look for symptoms such as a headache, dizziness, vomiting, speech difficulty, or unconsciousness. If any of these develop, call for medical help.
- Check for cuts or scrapes. Follow the instructions on this page for treating cuts.
- Treat mild bumps, bruises, and sprains by applying a cold cloth or ice bag. Elevate the injured area if possible.

Cuts

Prevention

- Keep knives sharp. Sharp knives are safer than dull ones.
- When cutting, always slant the blade of the knife away from you. Use a cutting board for all cutting jobs.
- If a knife starts to fall, do not try to catch it in midair. Get out of the way.
- Wash knives separately and dry them immediately.
- Store knives in a knife rack or separate container. Do not store them loose in a drawer.
- Use knives and other sharp tools only for the jobs they are meant to do.
- Keep your fingers away from the blades when using a mixer or any appliance with sharp blades. If the blades jam or you need to remove food from them, first turn the appliance off. Unplug the appliance so it does not turn on accidentally.
- Sweep up broken glass and china immediately. Never pick up pieces with bare fingers. Use several thicknesses of damp paper towel to pick up small pieces safely.
- Never grope for broken glass in a sink filled with water. Wrap your hand in a towel and open the drain. When the water has drained, use a towel to pick up the pieces.
- When you open a can, cut the lid off completely and throw it away. Do not leave it partly attached to the can.

✚ First Aid

- Stop severe bleeding, if any, by covering the wound with a thick pad of cloth and pressing firmly. Keep the person lying down and warm. Get medical help.
- For minor cuts and scrapes, wash the wound with soap and water. Blot the area around the wound with a sterile pad until dry. Apply a dry, clean bandage.

Electric Shock

Prevention

- Disconnect portable appliances when not in use.
- Disconnect appliances before cleaning them. Never put electrical parts in water unless the part is stamped "immersible."
- If portable appliances have detachable cords, connect the cord to the appliance first. Then plug the cord into the wall outlet. When you disconnect it, remove the cord first from the wall outlet, then from the appliance. Do not yank on the cord.
- Do not use appliances with electrical cords that are damaged in any way. The same goes for extension cords.
- Electricity travels easily through water. Do not use appliances if your hands are wet, if you are perspiring, or if you are standing on a moist surface. You could get a shock. Be especially careful when operating appliances near the kitchen sink or other source of water.
- Do not use appliances if you are in contact with plumbing, such as a sink or faucet. If there is a defect in the appliance, leaking electricity will flow to the plumbing if it can. It will flow through you to get there.
- Never use an ordinary vacuum cleaner on wet surfaces or to pick up wet material. If you have carpeting in the kitchen, be sure it is dry before you vacuum.
- Do not bring metal objects in contact with the working parts of an electrical appliance while it is connected. People who used forks to get toast out of electric toasters have had to be hospitalized for severe shock and burns.

✚ First Aid

- Do not touch a person who is still in contact with electricity — you will get just as severe a shock. Try to stop the shock by pulling out the plug or turning off the house current. If you can't stop the current, use a rope, wooden broom handle, or loop of dry cloth to pull the person away.
- Start rescue breathing if needed. Call for medical help or the fire or police department immediately.

(Continued on next page)

Poisoning

Many common household substances can be poisonous. These include medicines; products for cleaning, grooming, gardening, automotive uses, and pest control; and craft, hobby, and workshop supplies.

Prevention

- Keep all poisonous substances in their original containers. The labels contain essential information on use, storage, and what to do in case of an accident.
- Close all containers securely. If children live in or visit the household, buy products in childproof containers.
- Avoid spilling hazardous products. Clean up spills immediately.
- Store household cleaners and other chemicals in a locked cabinet out of children's reach.
- Never store poisonous substances in the same cabinet with food. Someone could accidentally pick up the wrong container.
- Before you use any cleaning product or other household chemicals, read the label for directions and warnings. Follow label directions carefully.
- Never mix two or more cleaning products together, such as bleaches, chlorine, ammonia, toilet bowl cleaners, rust removers, and oven cleaners. Do not even mix different brands of the same kind of product. Chemicals in the mixtures may interact and explode or release poisonous gases.
- Use spray products only in well-ventilated areas.
- When using a spray container, be sure to point the nozzle in the right direction. Never point sprays toward your face or another person. Some chemicals can cause serious eye injuries and skin burns.
- When using pesticides, follow package directions carefully. You may have to cover or remove food, cookware, and dishes from the area to be sprayed.
- Never use a charcoal grill or hibachi inside the home or garage. Burning charcoal gives off large amounts of **carbon monoxide** (KAR-bun muh-NOX-ide), an odorless gas that is deadly in just a short time.
- Don't use old products. They may contain chemicals that are now considered unsafe.

✚ First Aid

Swallowed poisons

- Call a hospital emergency room or your local or regional poison control center. Have the container of poison with you. Tell the kind of poison taken, how much you think was taken, and the victim's approximate age and weight. Follow the instructions you are given.

Skin contact poisons

- Rinse the affected area immediately and thoroughly with plain water. Use gloves or a towel to protect your own skin.
- Try to remove any clothing that has the poisonous chemical on it. Do not remove any clothing that is stuck to the skin.
- Call for medical help.

Eye contact poisons

- Flush the eyes with large amounts of water. Call for medical help.

Inhaled poisons

- Get the person to a well-ventilated area away from the source of fumes. Start rescue breathing if needed. Continue as long as necessary. Call for medical help.

Choking

Prevention

- Eat small portions slowly and chew food thoroughly.
- Don't talk with food in your mouth.
- Do not give small children foods that they may easily choke on, such as raisins, nuts, sliced hot dogs, or tough pieces of meat.

✚ First Aid

- If the person can cough, speak, or breathe, don't do anything. Be ready to take action if needed.
- If the person cannot cough, speak, or breathe, use the airway passage first aid technique. (Many restaurants display a poster describing these techniques.) Have someone call for medical help or the police or fire department.

CONSCIOUS VICTIM:

1 Ask the victim: "Are you choking?" If the victim CAN speak or cough, do NOT interfere.

Victim may be using the "Universal Distress Signal" of choking: clutching the neck between the thumb and index finger. Continually check whether the victim is able to speak, breathe, or cough.

2 If the victim CANNOT speak or cough, apply abdominal thrusts (the Heimlich maneuver) until the obstruction is expelled or the victim becomes unconscious.

THE HEIMLICH MANEUVER: Stand behind the victim and wrap your arms around the victim's waist. Grasp one fist with your other hand. Place the thumb side of your fist on the middle of the victim's abdomen, slightly above the navel. Press your fist into the abdomen with quick inward and upward thrusts. **CAUTION:** The Heimlich maneuver (abdominal thrusts) can cause injury. Do **NOT** practice on persons who are not choking.

IF VICTIM BECOMES UNCONSCIOUS:

1 Open the victim's mouth and perform a finger sweep.

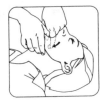

Sweep deeply into the victim's mouth to remove the obstruction. This can only be done on an unconscious victim.

2 Open the victim's airway and try to ventilate.

Use the head-tilt/chin-lift method of opening the victim's airway. Attempt rescue breathing. (See guidelines on next page.)

3 If unsuccessful, apply 6-10 abdominal thrusts (the Heimlich maneuver).

THE HEIMLICH MANEUVER: Straddle the victim's thighs. Place the heel of one hand slightly above the victim's navel. Place your other hand directly on top of the first. Press with quick upward thrusts.

4 Activate the Emergency Medical Services system as soon as possible. Repeat the sequence until EMS help arrives.

Know your local EMS telephone number.

Rescue Breathing

1. **Tap or shake the victim's shoulder. Shout "Are you OK?" Call out "Help!"**

Determine unresponsiveness and get help if possible.

2. **Turn the victim flat on his or her back, supporting the head and neck. Open the airway using the head-tilt/chin-lift.**

Kneel beside the victim's shoulder. Gently lift the chin up with one hand while pushing down on the forehead with the other to tilt the victim's head back.

3. **Maintain an open airway. Turn your head toward the victim's chest with your ear directly over and close to the mouth. Look, listen, and feel for breathing.**

LOOK at the chest for movement. **LISTEN** for sounds of breathing. **FEEL** for breath on your cheek.

4. **If breathing is absent, give the victim two full breaths.**

Pinch off the victim's nostrils with the thumb and forefinger of your upper hand while keeping the head tilted. Open your mouth wide, take a deep breath, make a tight seal, and breathe into the victim's mouth. Repeat. Watch for the victim's chest to rise.

5. **Check to see if the victim has a pulse.**

Place 2-3 fingers on the victim's voice box just below the chin. Slide your fingers into the groove between the voice box and the muscle on the side nearest you. Maintain the head-tilt with your other hand. Feel for the carotid pulse.

6. **Activate the Emergency Medical Services system.**

Know your local EMS telephone number.

7. **If you are trained in CPR, begin the first cycle of cardiopulmonary resuscitation. Continue until EMS help arrives.**

WARNING: Cardiopulmonary Resuscitation (CPR) should only be performed by trained persons. Contact your local American Red Cross or American Heart Association regarding CPR training.

Dealing with Household Chemicals

When people buy such common household products as scouring powder, furniture polish, and aerosol hairspray, they often assume the products are safe to use. Yet many household products contain hazardous chemicals that, if improperly handled, may be a threat to your health or the environment.

Just how dangerous are household chemicals? Usually, the more powerful the product, the more hazardous it is. But any household chemical should be used, stored, and disposed of with care — if it's necessary to use it at all.

Here are some of the problems related to household chemicals:

- Many household chemicals require that directions and precautions be followed exactly. Otherwise you may run the risk of poisoning yourself or someone else or causing chemical burns, fire, or an explosion.
- Household chemicals contribute to indoor air pollution, a growing problem.
- Long-term use of some hazardous chemicals is known to cause serious health problems. Not all products have been tested for long-term health effects. Nor is it known what effects many of these products may have on pregnant women and their unborn babies.
- Over time, the widespread use of certain types of household chemicals can seriously damage the environment. An example is the harm done to the ozone layer in the atmosphere by certain types of aerosol sprays. Scientists still do not know all of the long-range effects of the damage or whether there is a solution.
- Disposal of leftover hazardous products has also become a problem. Dumping hazardous chemicals into the sink, toilet, or storm drain has caused sewers to explode or sewage treatment plants to be damaged. Tossing half-empty containers into the trash can is no better. Such trash is usually crushed, then buried in landfills. Containers have exploded, setting garbage trucks on fire and causing workers to be burned or blinded. In the landfill, hazardous chemicals can leak from crushed containers, polluting the soil, the air, and water supplies.

What Can Be Done?

As more and more people become aware of these problems, the search for solutions is bound to grow. How can you help? One place to begin is by improving your knowledge about household chemicals. Then develop some new habits.

First, think before using household chemicals. Look for safer alternative products and methods that will serve the same purpose.

When you must use household chemicals, use them responsibly. Follow these guidelines:

- Only buy products you need.
- Read labels before you buy.
- Buy quantities you can use quickly.
- Follow all instructions carefully. Never mix products together.
- Follow proper procedures for storing household chemicals. (See page 200 of the *Food for Today* textbook.)
- When you must dispose of household chemicals, do so in the correct manner.

All of the substances listed on the next two pages can cause long-range problems to the environment if disposal is not handled properly. **TO DISPOSE OF ALL OF THESE MATERIALS, TAKE THEM TO YOUR LOCAL HAZARDOUS WASTE COLLECTION/TRANSFER STATION OR RECYCLING CENTER (IF AVAILABLE).**

Read the following pages carefully to learn about the danger of many common household products. The products are divided into categories depending on the type of chemicals they contain. The chart describes some of the hazards of each category, then suggests safer alternatives for the products listed.

(Continued on next page)

CAUSTICS AND CORROSIVES

These substances are effective cleaners, but they can cause severe eye and skin damage. Any acid or alkaline product is corrosive and is also poisonous if ingested. Try the alternatives suggested below.

- **Drain Openers and Cleaners:** Pour boiling water down your drain twice weekly as a preventive. Unclog drains with a metal snake or plunger.

- **Rug and Upholstery Cleaners:** Sprinkle corn meal or cornstarch on rug. Use club soda or soap-based, non-aerosol rug shampoos. Vacuum when dry.

- **Toilet Bowl, Window, and Surface Cleaners:** Clean often so that harsh chemicals are not necessary. For windows and mirrors, use vinegar and water (two teaspoons vinegar to one quart water) and rub with newspaper. For bathroom, coffee pots, chrome, copper, and tile, use dissolved baking soda.

- **Abrasive Scouring Powders:** Use baking soda instead.

- **Oven Cleaners:** Keep your oven clean as you use it, with baking or washing soda. Mix three tablespoons of soda with one cup of warm water.

- **Chlorine Bleach:** Use dry bleach, borax, or soda to whiten. Borax is a good grease cutter.

AEROSOL SPRAYS

These contain a high proportion of organic solvents. Mist particles enter the lungs and blood stream. They can be a major source of pollution in the home. There is a danger of exploding cans for refuse workers. Try the alternatives suggested below.

- **Aerosol Sprays:** Use non-aerosol deodorants. Use setting lotions or gels. Use shaving soaps and brush. Purchase other necessary products in non-aerosol containers, such as pump spray bottles.

- **Air Fresheners:** (These work by masking one odor with another, coating the nasal passages with an oil film, or diminishing the sense of smell with a nerve-deadening agent.) Ventilate instead. Set vinegar out in an open dish. Use an opened box of baking soda in enclosed areas, such as refrigerators or closets. Add cloves and cinnamon to boiling water and let simmer.

PESTICIDES AND HERBICIDES

These are poisons that may cause serious damage to skin, eyes, or internal organs; some are flammable. They contribute to environmental contamination when used improperly or in excess. Chemical fertilizers may deplete soil's growing capacity with extended use. They may also be corrosive, flammable, or toxic. Try to use alternative methods of solving the problem.

- **House Plant Insecticide:** Wash leaves with soapy water and rinse. Swab insects with rubbing alcohol.

- **Ant Control Products:** Pour a line of cream of tartar, red chili powder, paprika, or dried peppermint at point of entry.

- **Roach Control Products:** Place bay leaves around cracks in the room. Set out a dish of equal parts of baking soda and powdered sugar, or equal parts of oatmeal flour and plaster of paris, or chopped bay leaves and cucumber skins.

- **Chemical Fertilizers:** Use peat moss, compost, blood and fish meal, or steer manure instead.

- **Garden Insecticides:** Use organic gardening techniques. Strong hosing washes insects from plants. Avoid standing water, which allows mosquitoes to breed. Pull weeds instead of using herbicides. Cover garden with plastic in fall to prevent weed germination.

- **Snail and Slug Killer:** Overturn clay pots, and snails will seek shelter in them from the heat; collect and destroy. Lay boards between rows of planted vegetables; snails often attach themselves to the underside of the boards.

- **Pet Care Products:** Give pets brewer's yeast or vitamin B as a preventive. Use herbal baths.

SOLVENTS

These substances are used to dissolve other substances. Breathing the vapors or accidental drinking can be harmful or even fatal. Long-term exposure to some solvents may cause liver and kidney problems, birth defects, central nervous system disorders, or cancer. Many solvents are flammable. Avoid products containing highly toxic ingredients, such as nitrobenzene, trichloroethane, dinitrobenzene (carcinogens), and oil or cedar (central nervous system stimulant). Try the alternatives suggested below.

- **Furniture and Floor Polish:** Dissolve one teaspoon lemon oil into one pint mineral oil. Or use light, soapy water to clean and soft cloth to shine. Rub toothpaste on wood furniture to remove water marks.

- **Silver Polish:** Soak silver in one quart warm water with one teaspoon baking soda, one teaspoon salt, and a small piece of aluminum foil.

- **Spot Removers:** Use club soda, immediate cold water, corn meal and water paste, lemon juice, or salt.

- **Shoe Polish:** Use polishes that do NOT contain trichloroethylene, methylene chloride, or nitrobenzene.

- **Moth Balls:** Use cedar chips, newspaper, dried lavender, or peppercorns.

Chart adapted from "Volunteers' Voice for Community Safety and Health,"
National Safety Council, Sept.-Oct., 1988.

How Would You Make This Kitchen Safe?

The kitchen is the most hazardous room in the house. There are 18 safety and sanitation hazards in the kitchen pictured here. How many can you identify? What would you do to correct each hazardous situation?

Checklist for Food Service Sanitation

Local health officials regularly inspect food service establishments in order to protect the public. The partial report form below shows what is checked by the inspectors.

Food Service Establishment Inspection Report

Based on an inspection this day, the items circled below identify the violations in operations or facilities which must be corrected by the next routine inspection or such shorter period of time as may be specified in writing by the regulatory authority. Failure to comply with any time limits for corrections specified in this notice may result in cessation of your Food Service operations.

FOOD

*01	Source; sound condition, no spoilage
02	Original container; properly labeled

FOOD PROTECTION

*03	Potentially hazardous food meets temperature requirements during storage, preparation, display, service, transportation
*04	Facilities to maintain product temperature
05	Thermometers provided and conspicuous
06	Potentially hazardous food properly thawed
*07	Unwrapped and potentially hazardous food not re-served
08	Food protection during storage, preparation, display, service, transportation
09	Handling of food (ice) minimized
10	In use, food (ice) dispensing utensils properly stored

PERSONNEL

*11	Personnel with infections restricted
*12	Hands washed and clean, good hygienic practices
13	Clean clothes, hair restraints

FOOD EQUIPMENT & UTENSILS

14	Food (ice) contact surfaces: designed, constructed, maintained, installed, located
15	Non-food contact surfaces: designed, constructed, maintained, installed, located
16	Dishwashing facilities; designed, constructed, maintained, installed, located, operated
17	Accurate thermometers, chemical test kits provided, gauge cock (1/4″ IPS valve)
18	Pre-flushed, scraped, soaked
19	Wash, rinse water: clean, proper temperature
*20	Sanitization rinse: clean, temperature, concentration, exposure time; equipment, utensils sanitized
21	Wiping cloths: clean, use restricted
22	Food-Contact surfaces of equipment and utensils clean, free of abrasives, detergents
23	Non-food contact surfaces of equipment and utensils clean
24	Storage, handling of clean equipment/utensils
25	Single-service articles, storage, dispensing
26	No re-use of single service articles

WATER

*27	Water source, safe: hot & cold under pressure

SEWAGE

*28	Sewage and waste water disposal

PLUMBING

29	Installed, maintained
*30	Cross-connection, back siphonage, backflow

TOILET & HANDWASHING FACILITIES

*31	Number, convenient, accessible, designed, installed
32	Toilet rooms enclosed, self-closing doors; fixtures, good repair, clean: hand cleanser, sanitary towels/hand-drying devices provided, proper waste receptacles

GARBAGE & REFUSE DISPOSAL

33	Containers or receptacles, covered: adequate number insect/rodent proof, frequency, clean
34	Outside storage area enclosures properly constructed, clean; controlled incineration

INSECT, RODENT, ANIMAL CONTROL

*35	Presence of insects/rodents — outer openings protected, no birds, turtles, other animals

FLOORS, WALLS & CEILINGS

36	Floors, constructed, drained, clean, good repair, covering installation, dustless cleaning methods
37	Walls, ceiling, attached equipment: constructed, good repair, clean, surfaces, dustless cleaning methods

LIGHTING

38	Lighting provided as required, fixtures shielded

VENTILATION

39	Rooms and equipment — vented as required

DRESSING ROOMS

40	Rooms, area, lockers provided, located, used

OTHER OPERATIONS

*41	Toxic items properly stored, labeled, used
42	Premises maintained free of litter, unnecessary articles, cleaning maintenance equipment properly stored. Authorized personnel
43	Complete separation from living/sleeping quarters. Laundry.
44	Clean, soiled linen properly stored

*Critical Items Requiring Immediate Attention.

Recipe Helpers

How Foods Change in Volume When Prepared*

Before	After
Apple, 1 medium-size	250 mL (1 cup) sliced
Beans, dried, 250 mL (1 cup)	500-690 mL (2-2³/₄ cups) cooked
Bread, 1 slice	75 mL (¹/₃ cup) bread crumbs
Cabbage, 1 small, 500 g (1 lb.)	1250 mL (5 cups) shredded
Carrots, raw, 500 g (1 lb.)	750 mL (3 cups) shredded
Cheese, American, Swiss, or cheddar, 500 g (1 lb.)	1 L (4 cups) grated
Crackers, 14 graham	250 mL (1 cup) finely crushed
Eggs, 6-7 large	250 mL (1 cup) egg whites
Fruit, dried, 500 g (1 lb.)	About 1 L (4 cups) cooked
Lemon, 1 medium-size	45 mL (3 Tbsp.) juice 10 mL (2 tsp.) grated peel
Macaroni, 250 mL (1 cup)	500-575 mL (2-2¹/₄ cups) cooked
Noodles or Spaghetti, 250 mL (1 cup)	450-500 mL (1³/₄-2 cups) cooked
Nuts, shelled walnuts or pecans, 500 g (1 lb.)	1 L (4 cups) chopped
Orange, 1 medium-size	75 mL (¹/₃ cup) juice 20 mL (4 tsp.) grated peel
Potato, 1 medium-size	250 mL (1 cup) sliced raw potato
Rice, regular, 250 mL (1 cup)	750 mL (3 cups) cooked

*Note that volumes indicated are only approximate.

Equivalents

Customary Measure	Customary Equivalent	Approx. Metric Equivalent
¹/₈ teaspoon		0.5 mL
¹/₄ teaspoon		1 mL
¹/₂ teaspoon		3 mL
1 teaspoon		5 mL
1 tablespoon	3 teaspoons ¹/₂ fluid ounce	15 mL
¹/₈ cup	2 tablespoons 1 fluid ounce	30 mL
¹/₄ cup	4 tablespoons	50 mL
¹/₃ cup	5¹/₃ tablespoons	75 mL
¹/₂ cup	8 tablespoons	125 mL
²/₃ cup	10²/₃ tablespoons	150 mL
³/₄ cup	12 tablespoons	175 mL
1 cup	16 tablespoons 8 fluid ounces	250 mL
1 pint	2 cups	500 mL
1 quart	2 pints	1000 mL 1 L
1 gallon	4 quarts	4 L
1 peck	8 quarts	8 L
1 bushel	4 pecks	32 L
¹/₄ pound	4 ounces	125 g
¹/₂ pound	8 ounces	250 g
1 pound	16 ounces	500 g
2 pounds	32 ounces	1000 g (1 kg)

Understanding Metrics

Using metrics will put you in step with the rest of the world. (Every other major country has officially adopted the metric system of measure-ment.) So give the metric system a try — it's easy to learn and simple to use! Begin by learning the common units.

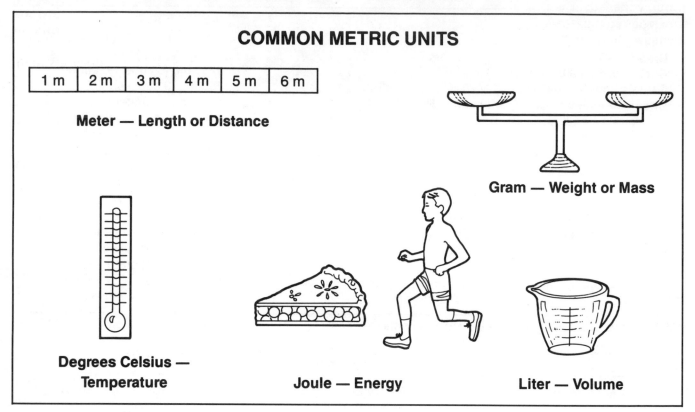

COMMON METRIC UNITS

| 1 m | 2 m | 3 m | 4 m | 5 m | 6 m |

Meter — Length or Distance

Gram — Weight or Mass

Degrees Celsius — Temperature

Joule — Energy

Liter — Volume

Prefixes

Sometimes you need larger or smaller units than the common units shown in the box above. For example, it would be awkward to express the distance from Los Angeles to San Diego as 203 000 meters. A larger unit of measurement is needed. In the metric system it's easy to remember the names of larger or smaller units because they are formed by simply adding prefixes to the original word. It's easy to convert a measurement because each prefix stands for a multiple or submultiple of 10.

For example, "kilo" is the prefix which means "1000." Thus, a kilometer would be 1000 meters. The distance from Los Angeles to San Diego could therefore be stated as 203 kilometers.

Besides kilo, the most common prefixes are "centi," meaning "1/100," and "milli," which means "1/1000." Here are some examples:

- one milligram = one-thousandth of a gram
- one centigram = one-hundredth of a gram
- one kilogram = one thousand grams

Symbols

Just as there are abbreviations for units of customary measurements (such as *in.* for *inch*), the metric system uses symbols for units and prefixes. The symbols are:

Common Units	**Prefixes**
meter — m	centi — c
gram — g	milli — m
liter — L	kilo — k
degrees Celsius — °C	
joule — j	

Here are some examples of metric symbols when a prefix and a common unit are combined:

- kilogram — kg
- centimeter — cm
- kilometer — km
- milligram — mg
- milliliter — mL

Notice that periods are not used after the metric symbols. That is because they are symbols and not abbreviations. (A period is used after a symbol at the end of a sentence.)

(Continued on next page)

Metric Equivalents

How does the metric system compare to customary measurements? Since each of the common metric units is used for a different type of measurement, such as weight or volume, they can be used to replace the customary measurements. Let's look at how they compare, using the approximate equivalents that are commonly accepted rather than exact conversions.

The Meter

The meter replaces length measurements, such as inch, foot, yard, and mile. The meter is actually a little longer than a yard.

Approximate equivalents:

- 1 inch = 2.54 centimeters
- 1 foot = 30 centimeters
- 1 yard = 1 meter
- 1 mile = 1.6 kilometers

The Liter

The liter replaces volume measurements, such as gallons, quarts, pints, fluid ounces, and cups. The liter is actually a little larger than a quart.

Approximate equivalents:

- 1 teaspoon = 5 milliliters
- 1 tablespoon = 15 milliliters
- 1 fluid ounce = 30 milliliters
- 1 cup = 250 milliliters
- 1 pint = 500 milliliters
- 1 quart = 1 liter
- 1 gallon = 4 liters

The Gram

The gram replaces weight measurements, such as the ounce, pound, and ton. A gram is a very small unit, equal to 1/28th of an ounce. The kilogram is a little more than 2 pounds.

Approximate equivalents:

- ¼ pound = 125 grams
- ½ pound = 250 grams
- 1 pound = 500 grams
- 2 pounds = 1 kilogram

Degrees Celsius

Temperatures are read on the Celsius scale. On the Celsius scale, water freezes at 0°C and boils at 100°C. How does that compare to the Fahrenheit scale? Water freezes at 32°F and boils at 212°F.

Here are some common temperatures given in both Fahrenheit and degrees Celsius:

	Fahrenheit	Celsius
Normal body temperature	98.6°F	37°C
Average room temperature	68°F	20°C
Temperature in freezer	0°F	−18°C
Oven temperatures	150°F	60°C
	275°F	140°C
	300°F	150°C
	350°F	180°C
	450°F	230°C

Joules

In metrics, calories are measured in joules (JEWLS). One calorie equals 4.2 joules. A 1200 calorie diet, for instance, becomes a 5040 joule diet.

A Few Rules to Remember

- Never use commas to separate digits in metrics. If a number has more than four digits, such as 10 000 m, put a space where a comma normally would be. The reason for this is that some European countries use the comma in place of the decimal point. To use commas in metrics, therefore, would create confusion.
- If no number appears to the left of the decimal point, use a zero. For instance, write 0.5 liter, not .5 liter. This is to verify that the amount is accurate and that the number to the left of the decimal point has not been forgotten or accidently removed.
- Always use the decimal feature of the system. Never use fractions. For example, write 0.5 liter or 500 milliliters, never ½ liter.

How to Read Electric and Gas Meters

ELECTRIC METER

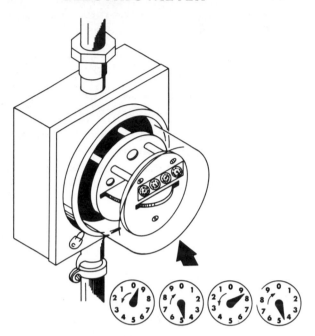

GAS METER

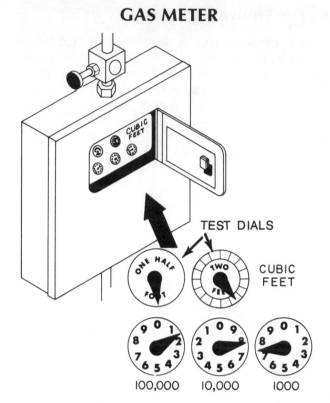

The electricity you use is measured in kilowatt-hours (kwh). A watt is a measure of electricity. A kilowatt is 1000 watts. You will use 1 kwh of electricity if you leave a 100-watt light bulb burning for 10 hours.

An electric meter has four or five dials. Some of the dials run clockwise, while others run counterclockwise. Each dial represents one digit of a number that tells how many kwh of electricity have been used. A four-dial meter can register up to 9,999 kwh before beginning again.

When reading an electric meter, begin with the dial on the left. If the pointer is between two numbers, always read the lower number. In the illustration, the first dial reads as 9. Write this number down. Continue to read the dials, writing each number down to the right of the last number recorded. What is the reading on the meter? If you read 9484, you are correct.

You can determine how many kwh of electricity you have used since your last billing. First, read your meter. Then look up the meter reading on your last electric bill. Subtract this reading from the current one to find out how many kwh of electricity you have used.

Natural gas is measured in cubic feet. Since natural gas varies slightly in heating value, some companies sell gas by the therm. This is a measurement of the heating value of gas.

A residential gas meter generally has from three to five dials for measuring the cubic feet of gas you use. The other dials on the meter — here, the two on the top line — are the test dials used by the gas company to check the accuracy of the meter. Do not read test dials when you read the meter.

The gas meter is read in the same manner as the electric meter. Begin on the left. The first dial reads as 1, the second 7, and the third 7. Note that the dials show the hundred-thousands, ten-thousands, and thousands positions. What is the meter reading? This meter shows a reading of 177,000 cubic feet.

You can determine how much gas you have used since your last billing. Follow the same procedure as for electricity usage. Subtract last month's reading on your gas bill from the current reading on the meter.

How to Set a Table

How often do you set the table for a family meal or a dinner for guests? Are you aware of how all the pieces should be placed? The arrangement of the items was developed over a period of time and is generally considered to be the most convenient for the person eating.

The arrangement of dishes, flatware, glasses, and linen for one person is called a cover. The tableware used will depend on the food served. Follow these general guidelines for arranging a cover:

- Position the plate so that it will be directly in front of the diner. If food is served on plates from the kitchen, allow enough empty space on the cover for the plate.

- Knives are at the right of the plate, with the blades facing toward the plate.

- Spoons are to the right of the knives.

- Forks are to the left of the plate.

- Each type of flatware is placed in order of its use. For instance, the fork to be used first is farthest from the plate.

- Place the water glass just above the tip of the largest knife. Other glasses are placed to the right of the water glass. A coffee cup is placed to the right of the spoons.

- A bread and butter plate is placed above the forks. The butter knife is placed on the edge of the bread and butter plate, horizontally or vertically. The blade should be facing toward the plate. For informal family meals, the bread can be placed on the dinner plate, if there is space.

- The salad plate can be placed either to the left of the forks or above them, depending on the space. Sometimes for a first course, the salad plate is placed on the dinner plate and is then removed after the salad is eaten.

- The napkin goes to the left of the forks, with the folded edge farthest from the forks. This makes it easier for the user to pick up the corner, unfold the napkin, and pull it down on the lap. If you are short of space, you can also place the napkin on the dinner plate or just above it, horizontally, on the table. Napkins can also be tucked into glasses or tied into a knot.

Nutritious Table Decorations

Melon Magic

Food can be more than something to eat. With a bit of imagination, it can decorate your table too! One large melon, for example, can become a spectacular edible table decoration. Here's how:

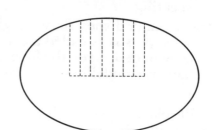

1. With the tip of a sharp knife, draw a horizontal line across the center of the melon, as shown in the drawing. The line should stop within 7.5 to 12.5 cm (3 to 5 in.) of each end of the melon. Do the same on the other side of the melon.

2. Make vertical cuts about 4 cm (1½ in.) apart above the horizontal line only. Slice down to the horizontal line on each cut.

3. Cut through the melon on the horizontal line. This releases the slices on the top.

4. Pull the first slice halfway to the right, second slice to the left, and so on.

5. For extra flair, add a few fresh flowers secured with toothpicks.

Festive Orange Cups

Here's a refreshing idea! Turn oranges into individual cups. Each orange makes two cups.

1. Using a small, sharp knife, make a small V-shaped cut at the middle of the orange.

2. Repeat, circling the orange.

3. Pull the two halves apart. (Use your knife, if necessary, to cut through the center.)

4. Use a grapefruit knife to carefully remove the orange pulp. (A grapefruit knife has a flexible, curved blade with serrated edges.) You now have two cups with zigzag edges.

5. Cut a small slice off the bottom of each cup, so the cups will sit securely.

6. Fill each cup as desired. Choose something light and refreshing, such as fresh berries, melon balls, sherbet, ice milk, or frozen yogurt. Garnish with a whole fresh strawberry.

Reception Table

Buffet service is the easiest way to serve a large group, and formal buffet service is used at most teas and receptions. Even with today's casual lifestyle, you may have occasion to give a tea or a reception. Club groups often have such events to introduce new members. You may want to have a reception for a special occasion, such as a wedding anniversary or a graduation.

Usually a large table is used for the food, with coffee served at one end and tea at the other. If you wish, you may also serve a fruit punch. In that case, the coffee and tea are at one end of the table and the punch at the other. Small fancy sandwiches, cakes, cookies, candies, and nuts are arranged attractively on plates and trays.

If you expect a large group, divide the table in half lengthwise and offer the same food on both sides. This will enable people to move in two lines instead of just one.

Punch Bowl

Cups

Nuts and Mints

Cookies

Sandwiches

Spoons

Plates

Napkins

Napkins

Plates

Spoons

Sandwiches

Cookies

Nuts and Mints

Cups

Coffee, Tea, Cream,
Sugar, Lemon Slices

Buying Guidelines for Fresh Fruit

Fruit and Time When Available	Description	Look For	Avoid
Apples All year	*Eating raw:* Delicious, Golden Delicious, McIntosh, Stayman, Jonathan, Winesap, Cortland. *Cooking and Baking:* McIntosh, Jonathan, Northern Spy, York, Golden Delicious, Rhode Island Greening, Wealthy, Stayman.	■ Good color, bright, sparkly. ■ Firm to touch. ■ Uniform shape, smooth skin. ■ Red apples — background color just slightly green.	■ Bruises, decay. ■ Softness — means overripe, damage, or fruit has frozen and thawed. ■ Shriveled. ■ Red apples — too green background color means immature.
Bananas All year	Picked green; must ripen to full yellow color. *Plantain* — greenish banana; rough skin and many blemishes; starchy; used as vegetable in tropics in place of potato; never eaten raw.	■ Firm, plump. ■ Stage of ripeness: *Green tips* — full flavor not developed. *Yellow specked with brown* — best eating quality.	■ Bruises or splits. ■ Discoloration. ■ Dull, grayish, aged look — means bananas have been exposed to cold and will not ripen properly.
Berries April-August	Blackberries, blueberries, boysenberries, gooseberries, raspberries, strawberries.	■ Firm, plump. ■ Full color for variety. ■ Only strawberries should have cap as a sign of maturity; all others should be free of hull.	■ Strawberries without hulls. ■ Other berries with hulls — will be immature. ■ Mold. ■ Decay or damage.
Cantaloupes May-September	Buy only ripe melons. If firm, soften them at room temperature. Unripe melons will never develop full flavor.	■ Smooth shallow base where stem was. ■ Thick, coarse veining that stands out over at least part of surface. ■ Yellow or gray skin between netting. ■ Should yield slightly to thumb pressure on *blossom end.*	■ Part of stem left on — means immaturity. ■ Green skin between netting. ■ Excess rattling of seed when shaken — overripe. ■ Softness, deep yellow color — overripe. ■ Large bruised areas or mold.
Cherries May-August	*Bing* — large, round, plump, deep mahogany color. *Lambert* — same color as Bing, but longer and heart-shaped.	■ Good color. ■ Good shape. ■ Firm. ■ Fresh.	■ Soft or sticky — overripe. ■ Damage, decay — usually brown discoloration. ■ Hard with light color — immature.
Grapefruit All year	*White* — light yellow pulp with tangy, tartsweet flavor. *Pink* — slightly sweeter than white; pink pulp.	■ Firm, springy to touch. ■ Well-shaped, round. ■ Heavy for size.	■ Softness, wilting, puffiness; loose skin. ■ Point at stem end — means thick skin. ■ Decay — soft, discolored areas.
Grapes All year	*Thompson seedless* — green, olive-shaped, small berries, sweet, seedless. *Cardinals* — dark red, large. *Emperor* — red, large. *Tokay* — red, large, round. *Concord* — blue.	■ Grapes firmly attached to stem. ■ Good color for variety. ■ Fresh. ■ Smooth skins. ■ Plump.	■ Fruit falling off stem. ■ Sticky fruit — sign of damage, decay. ■ Discoloration.
Mangos May-August	Tropical fruit; green with yellow to red; round to oval; weight ½-1 lb.; apricot-pineapple flavor.	■ Good color. ■ Firm but allow to ripen till very soft.	■ Wilting. ■ Gray discoloration of skin. ■ Pitting, black spots, decay.

(Continued on next page)

Fruit and Time When Available	Description	Look For	Avoid
Nectarines May-September	Yellowish with a hint of red; smooth skin.	■ Bright-looking. ■ Plump. ■ Firm to moderately hard.	■ Hard. ■ Slightly shriveled. ■ Cracked or punctured skin. ■ Bruises or decay.
Oranges All year	*Navel* — seedless, easy to peel and eat out of hand. *Valencia* — good for juice and as sections; deep color; few seeds; thin skin. *Tangerine* — deep color; distinctive flavor; easy to peel. *Tangelo* — cross between tangerine and grapefruit; sweet flavor; tender. *Temple* — rich flavor; easy to peel.	■ Good color; ignore greening. ■ Firm. ■ Heavy for size. ■ Reasonably smooth skin for variety. ■ Fresh and bright looking.	■ Lightweight — lack juice. ■ Puffiness, sponginess. ■ Unusually rough skin — means thick skin, less flesh. ■ Damage, decay, discoloration, soft areas especially around stem end or button.
Peaches June-September	*Freestone* — fruit can be easily separated from pit; preferred for eating raw or freezing. *Clingstone* — fruit sticks tightly to pit; sold mainly for canning.	■ Firm or slightly soft. ■ Yellow creamy color between red areas.	■ Very firm or hard — immature. ■ Green color. ■ Bruises or decay. ■ Overripe, too soft.
Pears August-March	*Bartlett* — summer pear; bellshaped; pale to rich yellow. *Bosc* — long tapering neck; dark yellow skin overlaid with brown russet; sweet, juicy. *Anjou* — yellow to green color; sweet, spicy flavor. *Comice* — large, almost round; yellow with some red; juicy.	■ Color typical of variety. ■ Firm texture, but not unusually hard.	■ Wilting, shriveling, softness, dull skin — immature, will never ripen. ■ Dark spots on side or blossom ends — means hard corky tissue may be underneath.
Pineapple March-September	Pineapple cannot ripen after it is picked; growers test sugar content to decide when pineapple is ripe enough to pick; the ease with which leaves pull out is no sign of quality.	■ Large. ■ Plump. ■ Fresh-looking. ■ Fresh, deep-green leaves. ■ Pleasant fragrance.	■ Brown leaves or other signs of dryness. ■ Discolored or soft spots. ■ Slight decay at base or on sides with dark, soft, watery spots.
Plums, Prunes June-September	*Plums* — many varieties; color ranges from yellow to purple. *Prunes* — blue-black; oval; firm; good for eating and cooking.	■ Good color for variety. ■ Firm to slightly soft.	■ Skin breaks. ■ Brownish discoloration. ■ Immature — hard, poor color, green. ■ Excessively soft, leaking, decay.
Watermelon May-September	Best way to judge is to cut it. When you buy whole one, first look for a cut one that has good quality signs; try to find a whole one to match its outside appearance. Thumping a melon proves nothing.	*Cut melon:* ■ Firm juicy flesh. ■ Good red color. ■ Dark brown or black seeds. *Whole melon:* ■ Firm, symmetrical. ■ Creamy color on underside. ■ Ends rounded out.	*Cut melon:* ■ Pale-colored flesh. ■ White streaks and whitish seeds — immature. ■ Dry, mealy, watery — overmature. *Whole melon:* ■ White or pale green underside. ■ Very hard to the touch.

Storing Fresh Fruit

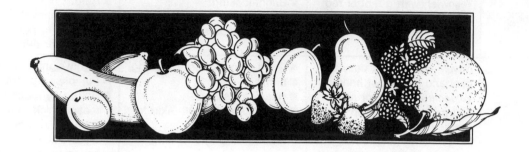

UNDERRIPE FRUITS

Allow underripe fruits to stand at room temperature to ripen. If desired, speed the ripening process by putting the fruit in a brown paper bag.

BANANAS

Bananas can be refrigerated after they ripen. The skin turns dark, but the bananas keep their eating quality.

CITRUS FRUITS

Store these fruits at room temperature. Refrigerate if you want to keep them for a long time.

MELONS AND PINEAPPLE

Refrigerate these fruits. Wrap them in plastic or foil to keep their aroma from flavoring other foods.

BERRIES, CHERRIES, AND GRAPES

Remove damaged and decayed fruit and discard. Refrigerate the remainder in the crisper, in a plastic bag, or in a covered, shallow container. Use the fruit as soon as possible. Wash just before serving.

CUT FRUITS

Fruits that have been cut should be refrigerated in an airtight container or wrapped in foil or plastic. To keep them from turning brown, sprinkle with lemon juice or ascorbic acid before storing.

ALL OTHER RIPE FRUITS

Wash them before storing. Dry well. Then refrigerate the fruit in the crisper or loosely wrapped.

Buying and Cooking Legumes

Common Legumes

Variety	Description	Uses
Black beans (turtle beans)	Black beans from yellow pod Rich, meaty flavor	Side dish; black bean soup Popular in Latin American, oriental, and Mediterranean cooking
Black-eyed peas (black-eyed beans or cow peas)	Small white beans with black spots	Main dish; casseroles
Dried peas	May be yellow or green, whole or split	Soups
Garbanzos (chick-peas)	Nut-flavored, round seeds Available canned	Salads; soups; main dish
Kidney beans	Large, dark red, kidney-shaped	Chili; salads; Mexican dishes; some baked bean recipes
Lentils	Size of pea with disc shape Quick cooking	Soups Combine well with other foods
Lima beans (butter beans)	Broad and flat Available in different sizes (size does not affect quality)	Main dish; casseroles; soups
Navy beans (usually includes Great Northern and pea beans)	Small white beans with bland flavor	Baked beans Combine well with other foods
Pinto beans	Oval with small pink dots	Salads; chili
Red and pink beans	More delicate flavor than kidney beans	Mexican dishes; chili
Soybeans	Distinct nutlike flavor Most nutritious of all beans	Meat extender or substitute Combine well with other foods

Cooking Guide for Legumes

Legume 250 mL (1 cup)	Amount of Water		Approximate Simmering Time*	Yield	
	mL	Cups	Hours	mL	Cups
Black beans	750	3	2	500	2
Black-eyed peas (black-eyed beans, cow peas)	625	2½	½	625	2½
Kidney beans	750	3	2	690	2¾
Lentils	500	2	½	625	2½
Lima beans, large	625	2½	1	625	2½
Lima beans, small	625	2½	1	500	2
Navy beans	750	3	1½ to 2	625	2½
Peas, whole	625	2½	1	625	2½
Pinto beans	750	3	2	625	2½
Soybeans	750	3	2½	625	2½
Split peas	500	2	⅓	625	2½

*Soak peas and beans before cooking.

Standards Scorecard:
Vegetables Cooked in Liquid

Student Name: _____ **Class:** _____ **Date:** _____

Recipe Prepared: _____

Evaluation:

	Excellent (4)	Good (3)	Fair (2)	Poor (1)
Color bright, characteristic of vegetable.	_____	_____	_____	_____
Texture firm but tender. Not too soft, mushy, or too hard.	_____	_____	_____	_____
Unless mashed, vegetable retains its shape.	_____	_____	_____	_____
Flavor mild, characteristic of vegetable. Not too strong or watered down.	_____	_____	_____	_____
Seasoning just right to bring out natural flavor of vegetable.	_____	_____	_____	_____
Total Score (20 for Excellent)	_____			

Comments: _____

_____

_____

_____

_____

_____

_____

_____

_____

_____

_____

_____

_____

How Do Seeds Sprout?

Have you ever eaten sprouts on your salad? A sprout is the first tender shoot that pokes out of a seed as it starts to grow. Sprouts of many seeds are quite good to eat. They add flavor, texture, and color to salads, sandwiches, oriental stir fry, and other dishes. And sprouts are very nutritious. They contain healthy amounts of vitamin C, B vitamins, protein, and iron.

From Seed to Sprout

A dry seed contains everything a plant needs to start life. That includes a built-in supply of protein and starch.

In moist surroundings, seeds absorb water, swell, and start to grow. This sprouting is called *germination*. The sprout uses the food stored in the seed for growth until it is big enough to make its own food.

A sprout that started underground eventually pushes up out of the soil. Once in the open air, a plant uses sunlight to produce food. In the process called *photosynthesis*, plants capture the energy in light and use it to make carbohydrates.

Sprouts from Many Seeds

You can grow sprouts from the seeds of most common vegetables and grains grown in North America. Their tastes are as varied and interesting as the plants from which they came. A few of those you could try are wheat, rice, alfalfa, rye, radish, cabbage, and many kinds of beans and peas.

Caution: The sprouts of tomato and potato seeds are highly poisonous. Also, make sure you use seeds labeled for human consumption. Many seeds intended for garden or field planting are coated with pesticides and should not be eaten.

How to Grow Your Own Alfalfa Sprouts

You will need the following supplies:
- 1 L (1 qt.) jar
- 30 mL (2 Tbsp.) alfalfa seeds
- Cheesecloth

1. Remove any debris. Rinse seeds in lukewarm water.

2. Place seeds in jar; add 500 mL (2 cups) warm water. Cover with cheesecloth. Let stand 4 to 6 hours at room temperature.

3. Drain water from jar, rinse seeds gently, and drain again. Place jar on its side in a warm, dark place. Rinse and drain seeds twice a day.

4. When seeds have sprouted, place the jar in indirect sunlight so seeds will "green up." Continue to rinse and drain until sprouts are 2.5 to 5 cm (1 to 2 in.) long and ready to eat.

Tofu, also known as bean curd, is made from soybeans, one of the most complete plant sources of protein. It is a good source of calcium, potassium, and iron. It is low in fat and calories and contains no cholesterol. Because of its bland flavor and custard-like texture, tofu can be substituted for eggs, dairy products, meat, fish, and poultry. It absorbs other flavors easily and blends well with other foods.

Buying Tofu

Tofu can be bought in a variety of forms, from soft to a dense, hard curd. The form depends on how the tofu was made and the amount of liquid in the curd. Soft tofu is best for blending, mashing, and crumbling. The firm form is best for slicing and cubing.

Tofu is most commonly sold as a square block, weighing from 250 to 500 g (8 ounces to a pound). It is packed in water and sealed in a plastic container or pouch. You can find it in the refrigerated or produce sections of health food stores and supermarkets. You can also buy tofu in aseptic packages in the packaged foods section. Although tofu is often purchased plain, it is also available seasoned with assorted Oriental spice blends.

When buying tofu, look at the package date to be sure you are buying a fresh product. Fresh tofu has a very mild, delicate scent that is almost unnoticeable. As it ages, it begins to sour. Only fresh tofu should be eaten raw. If tofu has a slightly sour aroma, it can be used but should be parboiled first. If it has a pronounced sour odor, return it to the store.

Tofu is commonly sold in block form.

Storing Tofu

Tofu is highly perishable and must be refrigerated. If any portion is left over, store in a container, cover with water, and then cover the container with a lid. Change the water daily to keep the tofu fresh.

Freezing tofu gives it sponge-like properties. To use frozen tofu, thaw it first. Squeeze out the water, and then follow recipe directions. The tofu will have a tougher, meatier, and chewier consistency than tofu that has not been frozen. It will also absorb liquids more readily.

Preparing Tofu

You can use tofu as is, right out of the container. If you need firm tofu for slicing or cubing and have been able to buy only the soft, you can still use it. Simply press out the excess liquid with this method:

- Slice the tofu into uniformly thick slices.
- Place several thicknesses of towels on a flat surface and arrange tofu slices on the towels.
- Cover with several thicknesses of towels.
- Set a cutting board or cookie sheet on top of the towels.
- Place a heavy weight of several pounds on top of the board to press out the liquid.
- Let stand for about 20 to 30 minutes. The towels will absorb the excess liquid as it is pressed out.

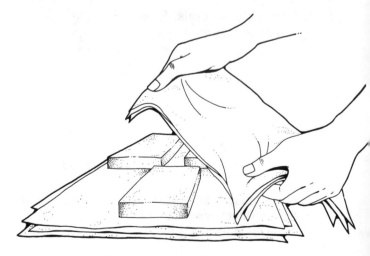

Towels can be used to absorb
excess liquid from tofu.

(Continued on next page)

If you plan to crumble or mash the tofu, you can reduce the liquid by squeezing it. Use this method:
- Place the tofu in the center of a clean dish towel.
- Twist the towel closed.
- Squeeze the tofu for several minutes. The liquid will drain through the towel. **Be careful** not to squeeze so hard that the tofu is also squeezed out through the towel.

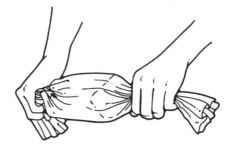

Squeezing is another way to remove liquid from tofu.

If tofu is slightly soured, it can be sweetened by parboiling. This also firms the tofu slightly, making it harder and chewier, and increases its ability to absorb flavors. To parboil:
- Place the tofu in a pan. If the piece is too large, cut it into several smaller pieces.
- Cover with water.
- Bring the liquid to a boil and simmer for about 20 minutes.

Measuring Tofu

To measure tofu for slicing or cubing, use the water displacement method described in the text on page 232. Use a 1 liter (4-cup) glass measuring cup. Mashed or crumbled tofu can be measured in a dry measuring cup.

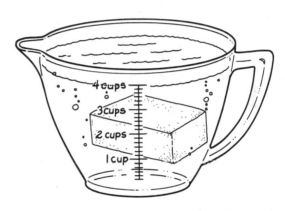

The water displacement method can be used to measure tofu.

Tofu Ideas

Tofu can be prepared in many different ways, such as scrambled, grilled, sauteed, fried, baked, boiled, barbecued, marinated in sauces, and stir-fried. If it is fresh, it can also be eaten raw.

Here are a few ideas for using tofu in daily meals:
- Substitute for part or all of the cheese or meat in recipes such as lasagne, spaghetti, manicotti, tacos, pizza, crepes, and casseroles.
- Marinate and stir-fry with assorted vegetables.
- Blend with seasonings and vegetables to use as a dip, sauce, or a salad dressing.

One way to use tofu is stir-frying with vegetables.

Standards Scorecard: Roast Meat

Student Name: _____ **Class:** _____ **Date:** _____

Recipe Prepared: _____

Evaluation:

	Excellent (4)	Good (3)	Fair (2)	Poor (1)
Exterior				
Nicely browned. Not charred.	_____	_____	_____	_____
Firm, tender crust. May be crisp, but not tough.	_____	_____	_____	_____
Flavorful with no burned or bitter taste.	_____	_____	_____	_____
Interior				
Cooked to desired doneness.	_____	_____	_____	_____
Tender, firm. Not tough, stringy, chewy, or mushy.	_____	_____	_____	_____
Moist.	_____	_____	_____	_____
Characteristic meat flavor.	_____	_____	_____	_____
Total Score (28 for Excellent)	_____			

Comments: _____

_____

_____

_____

_____

_____

_____

_____

_____

_____

_____

Standards Scorecard: Meat Cooked with Moist Heat or Liquid

Student Name: _____ Class: _____ Date: _____

Recipe Prepared: _____

Evaluation:

	Excellent (4)	Good (3)	Fair (2)	Poor (1)
Meat				
Firm but tender. Not stringy, chewy, tough, or mushy.	_____	_____	_____	_____
Moist.	_____	_____	_____	_____
Holds shape. Does not fall apart.	_____	_____	_____	_____
Characteristic meat flavor.	_____	_____	_____	_____
Sauce (If Any)				
Flavorful. Just enough seasoning to bring out natural flavor of meat.	_____	_____	_____	_____
Desired consistency — not too thick or too thin.	_____	_____	_____	_____
Total Score (24 for Excellent)	_____			

Comments: _____
_____
_____
_____
_____
_____
_____
_____
_____
_____
_____

How to Cut Up a Chicken

1. With the chicken breast side up, pull a leg out from the body and slice through the skin.

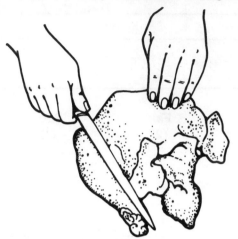

2. Lift the chicken and bend the leg until the joint cracks. Cut through the hip joint to remove the leg from the body. Repeat for the other leg. Remove the wings in the same manner.

3. If you wish to separate the drumstick from the thigh, bend the leg to crack the joint. Cut through the joint.

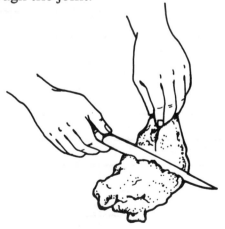

4. To remove the breast, use kitchen shears to cut from the leg joint to the backbone and along the backbone to the neck. Repeat on the other side.

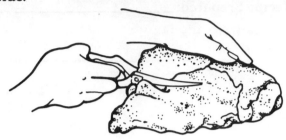

5. To divide the breast in two, hold it skin side down and bend it back until the breastbone snaps.

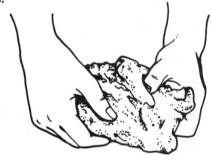

6. Cut the breast in half using a knife. Leave the breastbone on one half of the breast.

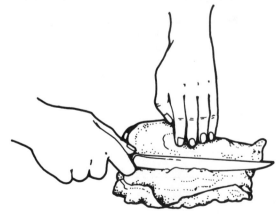

How to Carve a Turkey

1. To remove the drumstick and thigh, pull the leg away from the body. The joint connecting the leg to the backbone oftentimes will snap free. If not, sever it with a knife point. Cut the dark meat completely away from the body by following the body contour with the knife. Repeat for the other drumstick and thigh.

2. Place the drumstick and thigh on a separate plate and cut through the connecting joint. Both pieces may be individually sliced. Tilt the drumstick to a convenient angle, slicing toward the plate as shown in the illustration. Repeat for the other drumstick.

3. To slice thigh meat, hold the thigh firmly on the plate with a fork. Cut even slices parallel to the bone. Repeat for the other thigh.

4. Next the breast is prepared. In preparing the breast for easy slicing, place the knife parallel and as close to the wing as possible. Make a deep cut into the breast, cutting right to the bone. This is your base cut. All breast slices will stop at this vertical cut. Repeat on the other side.

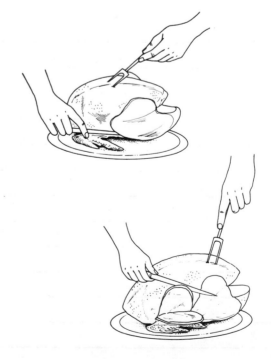

5. After the base cut, begin to slice the breast. Carve downward, ending at the base cut. Start each new slice slightly higher up on the breast. Keep the slices thin and even.

Standards Scorecard: Roast Poultry

Student Name: _____ **Class:** _____ **Date:** _____

Recipe Prepared: _____

Evaluation:

	Excellent (4)	Good (3)	Fair (2)	Poor (1)
Exterior				
Golden brown color. No charred or undercooked areas.	_____	_____	_____	_____
Crisp but not dry or chewy.	_____	_____	_____	_____
Firm, tender crust. Not tough or falling apart.	_____	_____	_____	_____
Flavorful. No burned taste.	_____	_____	_____	_____
Interior				
Firm, tender texture. Not dry or tough.	_____	_____	_____	_____
Moist.	_____	_____	_____	_____
Flavor typical of kind of poultry.	_____	_____	_____	_____
Total Score (28 for Excellent)	_____			

Comments: _____

_____

_____

_____

_____

_____

_____

_____

_____

_____

_____

_____

Standards Scorecard:
Fish Cooked in Dry Heat

Student Name: _____ **Class:** _____ **Date:** _____

Recipe Prepared: _____

Evaluation:

	Excellent (4)	Good (3)	Fair (2)	Poor (1)
Golden brown exterior. No charred or underdone areas.	_____	_____	_____	_____
Crisp exterior. Not tough or dry.	_____	_____	_____	_____
Tender and flaky inside. Not tough or mushy.	_____	_____	_____	_____
Slightly moist.	_____	_____	_____	_____
Natural flavor well developed.	_____	_____	_____	_____
Well seasoned to bring out natural fish flavor.	_____	_____	_____	_____
Total Score (24 for Excellent)	_____			

Comments: _____

_____

_____

_____

_____

_____

_____

_____

_____

_____

_____

_____

_____

Common Pasta Shapes

Pasta comes in many different shapes. Here are some of the more common ones.

Cannelloni (can-nel-LOAN-ee): "large reeds," flat squares that are rolled around filling.

Elbow: small semicircles of hollow tubed pasta.

Farfalle (far-FAL-lee): "butterfly"; also called bows.

Fettuccine (fet-two-CHEE-nee): "small ribbons" or straight strips of pasta.

Fusilli (fu-SEE-lee): spaghetti twisted like a corkscrew.

Giant shells: large, shell-shaped pasta; they are stuffed and baked in a sauce.

Lasagne (le-ZON-ya): wide, flat pasta; they are boiled, layered with a sauce and cheese, and baked.

Linguine (lin-GWEE-knee): narrow, thin, flat noodles.

Macaroni: general term for hollow pasta products.

Manicotti (mah-ni-COT-tee): giant tubes of pasta that are stuffed and baked in a sauce.

Ravioli (rah-vee-O-lee): squares of pasta with a hollow center pocket; they are stuffed, boiled, and served in a sauce.

Rigatoni (rig-a-TOE-nee): large, grooved, round tubes of pasta.

Ruote (rue-O-tay): "wagon wheels"; a fancy shape.

Spaghetti: long rods of pasta.

Vermicelli (ver-mi-CHEL-lee): "little worms," very thin spaghetti.

Ziti (zee-TEE): large round tubes of hollow pasta.

cannelloni

elbow

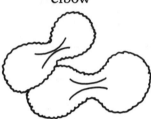
farfalle

fettuccine

fusilli

giant shells

lasagne

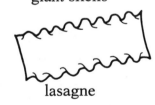
linguine

macaroni

manicotti

ravioli

rigatoni

ruote

spaghetti

vermicelli

ziti

Before you shape yeast rolls, you will need to grease and flour a muffin tin or baking sheet. Use a muffin tin for cloverleaf rolls and fan tails. Use a baking sheet for crescents and sailor's knots.

When shaping yeast rolls, begin by turning the punched-down dough out on your work surface. With a sharp knife or scissors, cut the dough into two or three equal pieces, depending on the amount of dough you have. Work with one piece. Cover the others with a towel to keep them from drying out. Shape the dough according to one of the procedures on this handout.

After shaping the rolls, allow them to rise until double in size. Then bake according to recipe directions.

CLOVERLEAF ROLLS	CRESCENTS
Use both hands to shape the dough into a roll about 2.5 cm (1 in.) thick. Do this by rolling the dough as you would a stick. To keep the roll even in thickness, start rolling with both hands at the center of the piece. Roll toward the ends. 	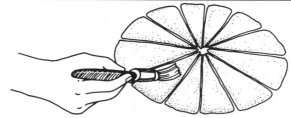 Roll the dough into an even circle, about 30 cm (12 in.) in diameter. Spread the dough with a little melted margarine or butter. Let the dough rest for a few minutes and then cut the circle into 16 pie-shaped pieces.
With a sharp knife or scissors, cut the dough into pieces 2.5 cm (1 in.) long. Shape into balls. 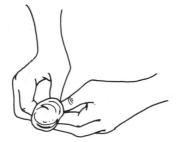	Roll each wedge up tightly, beginning at the wide end. Seal the points firmly to the dough so the crescent does not unroll. 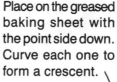
Place three balls in each greased muffin cup. Brush with melted butter or margarine. 	Place on the greased baking sheet with the point side down. Curve each one to form a crescent. 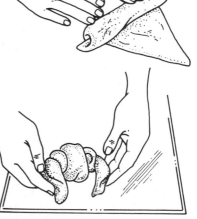

FAN TAILS	SAILOR'S KNOTS
Roll a portion of the dough into a thin rectangle. Spread with melted butter or margarine. Cut lengthwise into six strips.	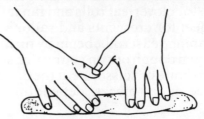 Cut one portion of the dough into nine equal pieces. Roll each piece under your hands, as if you were rolling a twig, until it is about 15 cm (6 in.) long. Roll all the pieces before shaping.
Stack the strips.	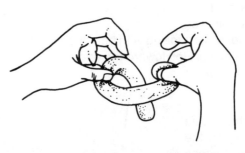 Pick up the first piece and tie it into a loose knot. Do not pull the knot tight. If you do, the rolls will not keep their shape as they rise.
Slice the stack into pieces 2.5 cm (1 in.) wide.	
Place the strips, cut side down, in the greased muffin cups.	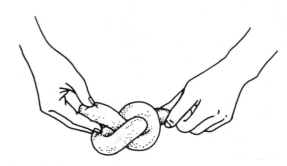 Put the knots on the prepared baking sheet about 5 cm (2 in.) apart.

Standards Scorecard: Biscuits

Student Name: _____ Class: _____ Date: _____

Recipe Prepared: _____

Evaluation:

	Excellent (4)	Good (3)	Fair (2)	Poor (1)
Exterior				
Uniform shape with straight sides and level tops.	_____	_____	_____	_____
Uniform size. Twice the size of unbaked biscuits.	_____	_____	_____	_____
Uniform golden brown tops and bottoms. Free from yellow or brown spots.	_____	_____	_____	_____
Tender crust, smooth, and free from excess flour.	_____	_____	_____	_____
Interior				
Creamy white, free from yellow or brown spots.	_____	_____	_____	_____
Flaky grain, pulling off in thin sheets.	_____	_____	_____	_____
Tender texture, slightly moist, light.	_____	_____	_____	_____
Pleasing, well-blended flavor.	_____	_____	_____	_____
Total Score (32 for Excellent)	_____			

Comments: _____

_____

_____

_____

_____

_____

_____

Problem Solvers: Biscuits

Student Name: _____ Class: _____ Date: _____

 After preparing biscuits, check them for the problems listed below. Place a check mark beside each problem you discover. Then try to determine why the problems occurred, placing check marks beside the causes that apply. Ask your teacher for help if the cause of any problem is not clear.

Exterior

_____ **Irregular shape:**

 _____ Too much liquid used.

 _____ Dough not rolled or cut properly.

 _____ Uneven oven heat.

 _____ Too much shortening used.

 _____ Dough overmixed or overhandled.

_____ **Too pale:**

 _____ Oven temperature too low.

_____ **Too dark:**

 _____ Oven too hot.

 _____ Baked too long.

_____ **Poor color:**

 _____ Dough not rolled or cut properly.

 _____ Pans not placed in oven correctly.

 _____ Uneven oven heat.

 _____ Ingredients not well mixed.

_____ **Rough:**

 _____ Too much liquid used.

 _____ Dough not kneaded or rolled correctly.

_____ **Excess flour on crust:**

 _____ Not enough liquid used.

 _____ Too much flour on working surface.

Interior

_____ **Poor color:**

 _____ Too much shortening used.

 _____ Poor quality ingredients used.

 _____ Ingredients not well mixed.

_____ **Not flaky:**

 _____ Not enough shortening used.

 _____ Shortening mixed either too much or too little with flour mixture.

_____ **Coarse texture:**

 _____ Overmixed.

_____ **Too dry:**

 _____ Dough too stiff.

 _____ Overbaked.

_____ **Too moist:**

 _____ Underbaked.

_____ **Crumbly:**

 _____ Too much shortening used.

_____ **Tough:**

 _____ Not enough shortening used.

 _____ Overmixed.

_____ **Heavy:**

 _____ Too much shortening used.

 _____ Overmixed.

 _____ Underbaked.

_____ **Poor flavor:**

 _____ Wrong proportion of ingredients used.

 _____ Ingredients not mixed properly.

Standards Scorecard:
Muffins and Quick Breads

Student Name: _____ Class: _____ Date: _____

Recipe Prepared: _____

Evaluation:

	Excellent (4)	Good (3)	Fair (2)	Poor (1)
Exterior				
Uniform shape. Well-rounded top free from peaks and cracks. (Note: loaf bread should have crack down the center.)	_____	_____	_____	_____
Uniform size. Large in proportion to weight.	_____	_____	_____	_____
Uniform golden brown color.	_____	_____	_____	_____
Tender crust, slightly rough and shiny.	_____	_____	_____	_____
Interior				
Color characteristic of muffin or bread type, free from streaks.	_____	_____	_____	_____
Rounded, even grain, free from tunnels.	_____	_____	_____	_____
Tender texture, moist and light.	_____	_____	_____	_____
Pleasing, well-blended flavor.	_____	_____	_____	_____
Total Score (32 for Excellent)	_____			

Comments: _____
_____
_____
_____
_____

Problem Solvers:
Muffins and Quick Breads

Student Name: _____ **Class:** _____ **Date:** _____

After preparing quick bread or muffins, check them for the problems listed below. Place a check mark beside each problem you discover. Then try to determine why the problems occurred, placing check marks beside the causes that apply. Ask your teacher for help if the cause of any problem is not clear.

Exterior

_____ **Irregular shape:**

　_____ Too much flour used.

　_____ Not enough liquid used.

　_____ Batter overmixed.

　_____ Too much or not enough batter in pans.

　_____ Oven temperature too hot.

　_____ Too much shortening used.

_____ **Too pale:**

　_____ Batter overmixed.

　_____ Oven temperature not hot enough.

_____ **Too dark:**

　_____ Too much sugar used.

　_____ Oven too hot.

　_____ Overbaked.

_____ **Tough:**

　_____ Too much flour used.

　_____ Not enough shortening used.

　_____ Batter overmixed.

　_____ Overbaked.

_____ **Too smooth:**

　_____ Too much liquid used.

　_____ Batter overmixed.

Interior

_____ **Poor color:**

　_____ Poor quality ingredients used.

　_____ Egg and milk not well blended.

_____ **Coarse texture:**

　_____ Egg insufficiently beaten.

　_____ Batter overmixed.

_____ **Tunnels:**

　_____ Too much flour used.

　_____ Not enough liquid used.

　_____ Batter overmixed.

　_____ Too much batter in pan.

　_____ Oven temperature too high.

_____ **Too dry:**

　_____ Too much flour used.

　_____ Overbaked.

_____ **Too moist:**

　_____ Eggs not beaten sufficiently.

　_____ Underbaked.

_____ **Crumbly:**

　_____ Too much flour used.

　_____ Oven temperature too low.

_____ **Heavy:**

　_____ Overmixed.

　_____ Underbaked.

_____ **Poor flavor:**

　_____ Wrong proportion of ingredients used.

　_____ Poor quality ingredients used.

Standards Scorecard:
Yeast Breads and Rolls

Student Name: _____ **Class:** _____ **Date:** _____

Recipe Prepared: _____

Evaluation:

	Excellent (4)	Good (3)	Fair (2)	Poor (1)
Exterior				
Well-proportioned, even shape with rounded top.	_____	_____	_____	_____
Large size, but not airy in proportion to weight.	_____	_____	_____	_____
Even, rich, golden brown color.	_____	_____	_____	_____
Tender, crisp crust, even thickness, and free from cracks.	_____	_____	_____	_____
If break and shred is present — rough area between top and sides of product — it should be even.	_____	_____	_____	_____
Interior				
Creamy white (unless using flour such as whole wheat), free from streaks.	_____	_____	_____	_____
Fine, thin-walled cells, evenly distributed.	_____	_____	_____	_____
Tender, soft texture, slightly moist.	_____	_____	_____	_____
Sweet, nutty flavor.	_____	_____	_____	_____
Total Score (36 for Excellent)	_____			

Comments: _____

_____

_____

_____

Problem Solvers:
Yeast Breads and Rolls

Student Name: _____ Class: _____ Date: _____

After preparing yeast bread or rolls, check them for the problems listed below. Place a check mark beside each problem you discover. Then try to determine why the problems occurred, placing check marks beside the causes that apply. Ask your teacher for help if the cause of any problem is not clear.

Exterior

_____ **Poor shape:**

    _____ Loaf not shaped properly.

    _____ Too much dough for pan.

    _____ Insufficient rising time.

_____ **Too small:**

    _____ Too much salt used.

    _____ Not enough yeast used.

    _____ Insufficient rising period.

    _____ Oven temperature too high.

_____ **Too large:**

    _____ Not enough salt used.

    _____ Too much yeast used.

    _____ Rising period too long.

    _____ Oven temperature too low.

_____ **Too pale:**

    _____ Not enough sugar used.

    _____ Temperature of dough too high during mixing and rising.

    _____ Oven temperature too low.

_____ **Too dark:**

    _____ Too much sugar used.

    _____ Insufficient rising time.

    _____ Oven temperature too high.

_____ **Crust too thick:**

    _____ Crust dried during rising time.

    _____ Oven temperature too low.

    _____ Overbaked.

Interior

_____ **Streaks:**

    _____ Crust dried during rising.

    _____ Dough not mixed properly.

    _____ Too much flour used during kneading and shaping.

    _____ Dough too soft.

    _____ Improper punching and shaping.

_____ **Poor texture:**

    _____ Too much flour used.

    _____ Other types of flour substituted for wheat flour.

    _____ Temperature of dough too high during mixing and rising.

    _____ Rising time too long.

    _____ Overkneading.

_____ **Poor flavor:**

    _____ Wrong proportions of ingredients used.

    _____ Rising time too long.

Standards Scorecard: Cookies

Student Name: _____ **Class:** _____ **Date:** _____

Evaluation:

Cookie Type	Excellent (4)	Good (3)	Fair (2)	Poor (1)
Drop Cookies				
Fairly uniform mound shape.	_____	_____	_____	_____
Delicately browned exterior.	_____	_____	_____	_____
Slightly moist, tender texture.	_____	_____	_____	_____
Flavor characteristic of ingredients.	_____	_____	_____	_____
Total Score (16 for Excellent)	_____			
Bar Cookies				
Uniform, well-cut shape.	_____	_____	_____	_____
Thin, delicate, tender crust.	_____	_____	_____	_____
Rich, moist texture.	_____	_____	_____	_____
Flavor characteristic of ingredients.	_____	_____	_____	_____
Total Score (16 for Excellent)	_____			
Refrigerator Cookies				
Uniform, thin slices.	_____	_____	_____	_____
Lightly browned texture.	_____	_____	_____	_____
Crisp and crunchy texture.	_____	_____	_____	_____
Flavor characteristic of ingredients.	_____	_____	_____	_____
Total Score (16 for Excellent)	_____			

Student Name: _____ Class: _____ Date: _____

Evaluation:

Cookie Type	Excellent (4)	Good (3)	Fair (2)	Poor (1)
Rolled Cookies				
Retain shape of cutter.	_____	_____	_____	_____
Lightly browned surface.	_____	_____	_____	_____
Texture crisp and thin or soft and thick, depending on variety.	_____	_____	_____	_____
Rich flavor, depending on ingredients.	_____	_____	_____	_____
Total Score (16 for Excellent)	_____			
Molded Cookies				
Uniform, well shaped.	_____	_____	_____	_____
Delicately browned.	_____	_____	_____	_____
Crisp and tender texture.	_____	_____	_____	_____
Pleasing flavor characteristic of ingredients.	_____	_____	_____	_____
Total Score (16 for Excellent)	_____			
Pressed Cookies				
Well-shaped and well-defined pattern of cookie press.	_____	_____	_____	_____
Delicately browned edges.	_____	_____	_____	_____
Very tender and crisp texture.	_____	_____	_____	_____
Rich and buttery flavor.	_____	_____	_____	_____
Total Score (16 for Excellent)	_____			

Problem Solvers: Cookies

Student Name: _____ Class: _____ Date: _____

    After preparing cookies, check them for the problems listed below. Place a check mark beside each problem you discover. Then try to determine why the problems occurred, placing check marks beside the causes that apply. Ask your teacher for help if the cause of any problem is not clear.

Drop Cookies

_____ **Irregular size and shape:**

    _____ Dough not dropped on baking sheet properly.

_____ **Dark, crusty edges:**

    _____ Overbaked.

    _____ Baking sheet too large for oven.

_____ **Too dry, hard:**

    _____ Overbaked.

_____ **Doughy:**

    _____ Underbaked.

_____ **Excessive spreading:**

    _____ Ingredients not measured properly.

    _____ Dough dropped on hot baking sheet.

    _____ Dough not peaked when dropped.

    _____ Incorrect oven temperature used.

Bar Cookies

_____ **Dry, crumbly:**

    _____ Overbaked.

_____ **Hard, crusty top:**

    _____ Overmixed.

_____ **Crumbles when cut:**

    _____ Bars cut while too warm.

Refrigerator Cookies

_____ **Irregular shape:**

    _____ Dough not rolled into uniform shape.

    _____ Dough not chilled enough to be sliced uniformly.

    _____ Dull knife used for slicing.

_____ **Too brown:**

    _____ Overbaked.

Rolled Cookies

_____ **Tough:**

    _____ Excessive rerolling.

_____ **Loose flour visible on top:**

    _____ Too much flour used when rolling dough.

_____ **Dry:**

    _____ Dough rolled in too much flour or rerolled.

Molded Cookies

_____ **Misshapen:**

    _____ Molded incorrectly.

_____ **Too brown:**

    _____ Overbaked.

_____ **Crumbly:**

    _____ Not shaped well.

    _____ Ingredients not measured properly.

Pressed Cookies

_____ **Misshapen:**

    _____ Cookie press not used correctly.

    _____ Dough in press too moist, cold, or warm.

    _____ Dough placed on hot baking sheet.

    _____ Oven temperature too low.

_____ **Too brown:**

    _____ Overbaked.

Standards Scorecard:
Shortened Cakes

Student Name: _____ **Class:** _____ **Date:** _____

Recipe Prepared: _____

Evaluation:

	Excellent (4)	Good (3)	Fair (2)	Poor (1)
Exterior				
Uniform shape with slightly rounded top. No peaks or cracks.	_____	_____	_____	_____
Uniform size. Light in weight in proportion to size.	_____	_____	_____	_____
Uniform golden brown color. (Color, however, may be affected by flavoring such as spices or chocolate.)	_____	_____	_____	_____
Tender, smooth crust.	_____	_____	_____	_____
Interior				
Uniform color, characteristic of type of cake.	_____	_____	_____	_____
Fine, even grain, free from tunnels.	_____	_____	_____	_____
Velvety, moist, and tender texture.	_____	_____	_____	_____
Not soggy or too dry.	_____	_____	_____	_____
Pleasing flavor, well blended, and characteristic of kind of cake.	_____	_____	_____	_____
Total Score (36 for Excellent)	_____			

Comments: _____
_____
_____
_____
_____

Standards Scorecard:
Unshortened Cakes

Student Name: _____ Class: _____ Date: _____

Recipe Prepared: _____

Evaluation:

	Excellent (4)	Good (3)	Fair (2)	Poor (1)
Exterior				
Uniform shape, free from cracks.	_____	_____	_____	_____
Large volume. Very light in weight in proportion to size.	_____	_____	_____	_____
Uniform light brown color.	_____	_____	_____	_____
Tender crust, free from moist, shiny spots.	_____	_____	_____	_____
Interior				
Uniform color, characteristic of kind of cake.	_____	_____	_____	_____
Small, uniform grain. No large air spaces or compact layer.	_____	_____	_____	_____
Tender, feathery texture. Moist and light, not compact or soggy.	_____	_____	_____	_____
Pleasing, delicate flavor, characteristic of type of cake.	_____	_____	_____	_____
Total Score (32 for Excellent)	_____			

Comments: _____

_____

_____

_____

_____

_____

_____

Problem Solvers: Shortened Cakes

Student Name: _____ Class: _____ Date: _____

    After preparing a shortened cake, check it for the problems listed below. Place a check mark beside each problem you discover. Then try to determine why the problems occurred, placing check marks beside the causes that apply. Ask your teacher for help if the cause of any problem is not clear.

Exterior

_____ **Peaked or cracked:**

    _____ Too much flour used.

    _____ Oven too hot.

_____ **Pale color:**

    _____ Not enough sugar used.

    _____ Underbaked.

    _____ Wrong size pan used.

_____ **Too brown:**

    _____ Too much sugar used.

    _____ Overbaked.

    _____ Oven too hot.

_____ **Poor volume:**

    _____ Too much shortening or liquid used.

    _____ Wrong size pan used.

    _____ Oven too hot.

_____ **Sunken in center:**

    _____ Too much sugar or shortening used.

    _____ Not enough liquid used.

    _____ Underbaked.

Interior

_____ **Uneven grain:**

    _____ Not enough liquid used.

    _____ Undermixed.

    _____ Oven too cool.

    _____ Too much shortening used.

_____ **Crumbly:**

    _____ Too much shortening or sugar used.

    _____ Undermixed.

_____ **Tunnels:**

    _____ Too many eggs used.

    _____ Not enough sugar used.

    _____ Poorly mixed.

_____ **Dry:**

    _____ Not enough sugar used.

    _____ Overbaked.

_____ **Soggy:**

    _____ Undermixed.

    _____ Underbaked.

    _____ Too much shortening used.

_____ **Solid:**

    _____ Too much flour, shortening, or liquid used.

_____ **Flavor poor; not characteristic of ingredients:**

    _____ Poor quality ingredients used.

    _____ Wrong proportion of ingredients used.

Problem Solvers: Unshortened Cakes

Student Name: _____ Class: _____ Date: _____

After preparing an unshortened cake, check it for the problems listed below. Place a check mark beside each problem you discover. Then try to determine why the problems occurred, placing check marks beside the causes that apply. Ask your teacher for help if the cause of any problem is not clear.

Exterior

_____ **Pale color:**

_____ Wrong size pan used.

_____ Underbaked.

_____ **Too brown:**

_____ Too much sugar used.

_____ Overbaked.

_____ Oven too hot.

_____ **Poor volume:**

_____ Incorrect baking temperature used.

_____ Not baked long enough.

_____ Wrong size pan used.

_____ Pan was greased.

_____ Poor quality eggs used.

_____ Eggs at too high or too low a temperature while being beaten.

_____ Eggs not beaten sufficiently.

_____ Mixture overfolded.

_____ **Sunken:**

_____ Pan was not inverted to cool cake.

_____ Cake removed from pan before cool.

Interior

_____ **Uneven grain:**

_____ Mixture overfolded.

_____ Eggs not beaten enough.

_____ **Coarse grain:**

_____ Mixture underfolded.

_____ **Dry:**

_____ Overbaked.

_____ Not enough liquid used.

_____ **Soggy:**

_____ Underbaked.

_____ Mixture not mixed enough.

_____ **Solid:**

_____ Too much flour or liquid used.

_____ Eggs not beaten sufficiently.

_____ **Tough:**

_____ Mixture overmixed.

_____ Overbaked.

_____ Not enough sugar used.

_____ **Flavor poor; not characteristic of ingredients.**

_____ Poor quality ingredients used.

_____ Wrong proportions of ingredients used.

When making a piecrust, divide the dough into two portions. Make one slightly larger and use it for the bottom crust. It must fill the pie pan with enough left to cover the rim.

Roll the Dough

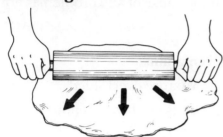

Sprinkle a small amount of flour on the working surface. Pat the larger ball of dough out into a circle. Using a light pressure on the rolling pin, roll the dough from the center out in all directions. Keep the dough as even as possible. Always roll the dough out toward the shortest part of the circle so it spreads evenly in all directions. Flour the rolling pin and surface as needed to keep the dough from sticking.

Place Dough in the Pan

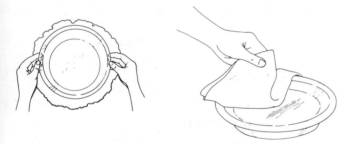

Measure the pie pan against the dough. Be sure the dough is wide enough to fill the depth of the pan. Fold the dough in half and transfer it to the pie pan. Center the dough in the pan carefully and unfold it. Push it down gently so it fits into all areas, but do not stretch it. Be careful not to poke your fingers through the dough.

Trim the Dough

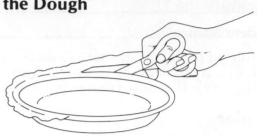

Let the dough rest for a few minutes. Then, using scissors or a sharp knife, trim the dough off even with the edge of the pan. Fill the pie.

Prepare the Top Crust

Roll out the second ball of dough. Fold it in half and place it over half of the filled pie. Unfold. Trim the top crust to about 1.3 cm (½ in.) larger than the pie pan.

Finish the Crust

Very slightly moisten the top of the bottom crust along the edge. Fold the remaining 1.3 cm (½ in.) of the top crust under the bottom crust. This will seal the two crusts together to keep in the juices. Press both crusts together, and decorate the edge, as shown on the next page. Cut slits in the top crust with a sharp knife to allow steam to escape and to keep juices from boiling out around the edge.

(Continued on next page)

Decorate the Edge

The edge of the pie crust should have an attractive finish. Choose one of these edging techniques to achieve a pleasing look.

Fluted Edge

Place the thumb and index finger of one hand against the edge of the crust. With one finger of the other hand, push the dough gently between the thumb and index finger to make a V-shape. Be careful not to break the dough.

Rope Edge

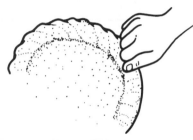

Using the thumb and knuckle of your index finger, gently pinch the edge of the crust at an angle. Repeat around the edge to make a rope design.

Ridges

Gently press the tines of a floured fork into the edge to make a ridge design. Do not poke the fork through the crust.

Lattice Crust

To make a lattice crust, roll out the top crust after the pie is filled. Be sure the crust is large enough to fit the top of the pie. With a pastry cutter or sharp knife, cut the crust into 1.3 cm (½ in.) strips. Arrange half the strips on the pie, parallel to each other. Place them about 1.3 cm (½ in.) or more apart.

Weave in the crosswise strips. To do this, first fold alternate strips back halfway. Then place a crosswise strip down the center of the pie. Bring the folded strips back across the pie and over the crosswise strip.

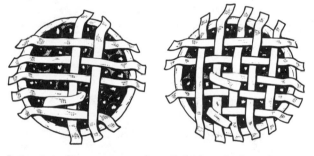

Repeat the process, but fold back the alternate strips that were not folded the first time. Add a second crosswise strip before unfolding the second set of strips. Continue this process on both sides of the pie to give a woven effect. By starting at the center, you need only pull the strips back halfway. Work carefully so you do not break them.

When all the strips are in place, proceed as with a full top crust. Trim the strips 1.3 cm (½ in.) beyond the edge of the pan. Moisten the bottom crust slightly under each strip. Fold the strips under the bottom crust. Make a fluted edge.

Standards Scorecard: Pies and Tarts

Student Name: _____ **Class:** _____ **Date:** _____

Recipe Prepared: _____

Evaluation:

	Excellent (4)	Good (3)	Fair (2)	Poor (1)
Exterior				
Crust even in thinness all over with neat, even edges.	_____	_____	_____	_____
Fits pan well.	_____	_____	_____	_____
Light golden brown color with darker brown edges.	_____	_____	_____	_____
Crust with slightly blistered, rough texture; not smooth or leathery looking.	_____	_____	_____	_____
Crust Interior				
Delicate, crispy, flaky texture. Not compact or soggy.	_____	_____	_____	_____
Tender — easily cut, but not crumbly or tough.	_____	_____	_____	_____
Rich, delicate flavor. No scorched fat or salty taste. Does not overpower flavor of filling.	_____	_____	_____	_____
Filling				
Fits pastry well.	_____	_____	_____	_____
Color and flavor characteristic of ingredients used.	_____	_____	_____	_____
Delicate, tender texture. Thick, but not sticky.	_____	_____	_____	_____
Total Score (40 for Excellent)	_____			

Comments: _____

_____

_____

Problem Solvers: Pies and Tarts

Student Name: _____ Class: _____ Date: _____

After preparing a pie or tart, check it for the problems listed below. Place a check mark beside each problem you discover. Then try to determine why the problems occurred, placing check marks beside the causes that apply. Ask your teacher for help if the cause of any problem is not clear.

_____ **Tough or solid crust:**

_____ Not enough shortening used.

_____ Too much water used.

_____ Dough overmixed when water added.

_____ Excess flour used when rolling.

_____ Dough overhandled or kneaded.

_____ Shortening and flour overmixed.

_____ Oven temperature too low.

_____ **Too pale:**

_____ Dough overmixed.

_____ Oven temperature too low.

_____ Pie not baked long enough.

_____ **Too dark:**

_____ Oven temperature too high.

_____ Pie baked too long.

_____ **Soggy lower crust:**

_____ Pastry overhandled.

_____ Filling too moist.

_____ Oven temperature too low.

_____ **Crust thick, soft, doughy:**

_____ Not enough shortening used.

_____ Too much water used.

_____ Water not cold enough.

_____ Pastry rolled too thick.

_____ Oven temperature too low.

_____ **Dry, mealy crust:**

_____ Shortening cut in too finely.

_____ Not enough liquid used.

_____ **Crust too tender, falls apart:**

_____ Dough undermixed.

_____ Not enough liquid used.

_____ Too much shortening used.

_____ **Crust thin, brittle; burns easily:**

_____ Too much shortening used.

_____ Pastry rolled too thin.

_____ **Pastry shell blisters:**

_____ Pastry not pricked enough.

_____ Oven temperature too low.

_____ **Pastry shell shrinks in pan:**

_____ Wrong proportion of ingredients used.

_____ Pastry overhandled when fitted into pan.

_____ Pastry stretched when fitted into pan.

_____ Oven temperature too low.

_____ **Poor flavor:**

_____ Wrong proportion of ingredients used.

_____ Poor quality ingredients used.

_____ **Filling boils over in oven:**

_____ Slits not cut properly in top crust.

_____ Too much filling used.

_____ Overbaked.

_____ Edges not sealed completely.

Standards Scorecard: Thickened Foods

Student Name: _____ **Class:** _____ **Date:** _____

Recipe Prepared: _____

Evaluation:

	Excellent (4)	Good (3)	Fair (2)	Poor (1)
Correct consistency, neither too thick nor too thin.	_____	_____	_____	_____
Smooth and free from lumps.	_____	_____	_____	_____
Not curdled or separated.	_____	_____	_____	_____
Well seasoned.	_____	_____	_____	_____
Good flavor, typical of the foods used.	_____	_____	_____	_____
Total Score (20 for Excellent)	_____			

Comments: _____

_____

_____

_____

_____

_____

_____

_____

_____

_____

_____

_____

_____

_____

Standards Scorecard: Beverages

Student Name: _____ **Class:** _____ **Date:** _____

Recipe Prepared: _____

Evaluation:

	Excellent (4)	Good (3)	Fair (2)	Poor (1)
Hot beverage piping hot; cold beverage well chilled.	_____	_____	_____	_____
Pleasing, rich flavor.	_____	_____	_____	_____
Not too strong.	_____	_____	_____	_____
Not too weak.	_____	_____	_____	_____
Total Score (16 for Excellent)	_____			

Comments: _____

_____

_____

_____

_____

_____

_____

_____

_____

_____

_____

_____

_____

_____

_____

_____

How to Freeze Fresh Fruit

Before fruit can be frozen, the enzyme action must be stopped. This is done by using ascorbic acid or sugar or both. To use the ascorbic acid, follow the directions on the package. Drain fruit thoroughly. Sugar can be added either dry or as a syrup:

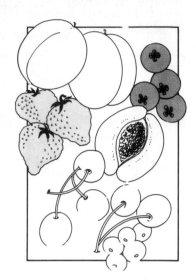

- **Dry Sugar Method.** This works well with juicy berries or fruits cut into small pieces. Coat fruit with ascorbic acid and drain. Add dry sugar, about 250 mL (1 c.) for 450 g (1 lb.) of fruit. Mix fruit and sugar lightly until the fruit is completely coated. Allow mixture to stand. In a short time, the sugar draws the juice from the fruit and dissolves into a thick syrup. When packing, cover the fruit with syrup. If there is not enough syrup, add just enough cold water to bring the liquid level to the top of the food.

- **Syrup Method.** The syrup may be thin, medium, or heavy, depending on the percentage of sugar to water. As a rule, medium syrup is used for most fruits. Heavy syrup is used for sour fruits, such as plums, and thin syrup for sweet fruits, such as peaches. Prepare the syrup ahead of time and chill it thoroughly. Add ascorbic acid according to manufacturer's directions. When packing fruit into containers, add enough syrup to cover the top of the fruit.

- **Unsweetened Pack Method.** Fruit may be packed without sugar or syrup. Coat with ascorbic acid. You can also add water or juice from the fruit without sweetening. Pack into containers.

Syrup for Freezing and Canning Fruit

For every 1 L (1 qt.) of water add . . .				
Type of Syrup	**Sugar**		**Yield**	
	Cups	mL	Cups	L
Light	2	500	5	1.2
Medium	3	750	5½	1.3
Heavy	7	1750	7¾	1.8

1. Combine water and sugar in a saucepan.
2. Cook, stirring frequently, until mixture boils and the sugar dissolves.

Adapted from USDA "Home Freezing of Fruits and Vegetables."

How to Use an Outdoor Grill

Most people really enjoy the flavor of foods cooked on an outdoor grill. Foods just seem to taste better. Many of your cooking skills can be used for cooking with a grill. When building a fire and cooking over it, however, keep safety uppermost in mind. Just a second's carelessness can turn a cookout into a tragedy.

SAFETY TIPS

- Know your local regulations before using a grill. Usually an outdoor grill can be on a balcony, porch, or patio, but in some areas laws restrict the use of grills to certain places.

- Never use an outdoor grill indoors — whether in a house or garage. Charcoal gives off deadly carbon monoxide, an odorless gas. Even if a window is open, enough fumes can accumulate to kill you.

- Read the directions in the owner's manual accompanying your grill. The instructions given here are general. Your grill may have special instructions that must be followed for safe and proper cooking.

- Make yourself as fire resistant as possible. Wear a heavy-duty apron without sashes or frills. Don't wear plastic aprons; some ignite easily. Be sure you don't have long dangling sleeves or shirttails that could easily catch fire. Tie long hair back in a ponytail to keep it from catching fire.

- Keep pets away from the outdoor cooking area. They can easily knock over the grill or work table.

- Keep a container of water handy for flareups. You can use a plastic spray bottle or a bowl of water with a baster. A flareup occurs when fat drippings accumulate on the coals and ignite. Squirt water on it to douse the flame. Otherwise, the food will burn.

- Place the grill in the open, away from anything that might catch fire. If the grill is movable, test the wind. Place the grill so the wind will not blow smoke or hot ashes toward you as you work. Remember, wind-swept coals can catch a garage, a house, or an apartment building on fire.

- If you must step away from the grill, appoint someone as fire tender. Never leave a fire unattended.

Using the Grill

Using the grill properly is not only essential for your safety, but it also helps ensure that food is properly cooked. Follow these guidelines:

- Line the bottom of the fire bowl with heavy-duty aluminum foil, shiny side up. If the bowl has vents, cut out openings in the foil to fit the vents. A layer of gravel on the bottom of the bowl will keep it from burning out. It also helps the fire "breathe" and give more heat for cooking.

- Read the instructions on the package of charcoal briquets. Start the fire early enough so the coals are ready when you need them. NOTE: When you cook with charcoal, you do not cook over flaming coals. It takes time for the coals to burn to the point that they are usable for cooking. The package should give guidelines. Be sure to make allowances for the time needed.

- Put the charcoal briquets in the bowl. Stack the briquets in a pyramid so they will burn more quickly. Use enough briquets to give you one layer of coals covering the area under the food.

- Ignite the coals. Self-lighting briquets will ignite quickly. The others will light easily if they are dry. If the weather is humid, however, they may take longer to light.
- If you use a fire starter fluid, be sure to keep other people, especially children, away from the grill. Use the fire starter according to directions on the container. Never apply more fire starter fluid on the fire after it has been started. It may explode. Never use gasoline, kerosene, alcohol, or cigarette lighter fluid to start a fire.
- Briquets do not burn with a visible flame unless there is a considerable draft. Instead, the fire creeps around the surface to form a fine gray ash that hides the glow of the burning briquets.
- When the briquets are covered with a gray ash, they are ready for cooking. Separate them with long-handled tongs, and space them according to the type of food you are preparing.
- For extra flavor, sprinkle wood chips over the coals. The smoke gives food an added flavor. If the wood is dry, soak it in water first so it will burn slowly and create smoke. You can also throw orange and lemon peels on the coals as well as herbs, spices, onions, and garlic. A small bunch of fresh herbs placed on the coals adds a wonderful flavor to food.
- Cook food according to a recipe. Douse any flareups to prevent your food from burning.

When you are through cooking, allow the briquets to cool in the fire bowl. They retain heat for a long time, so do not discard them in an area where people or animals might walk on them. Do not dump them into a combustible box, such as cardboard or plastic. It could ignite.

Also, never remove the grid from the grill until it is cool. Someone could step on it with bare feet and suffer serious burns.

Food for Grilling

Keep the menu simple. You might want to include one food, however, that is special. For instance, you might make up a special barbecue sauce for the meat.

Since grilling is a dry-heat method of cooking, tender cuts of meat should be used. Less tender cuts can be grilled if they are tenderized with a meat tenderizer. Besides beef, other foods, such as lamb, poultry, fish, and veal, may also be grilled. Pork is delicious when grilled, but be sure fresh pork is well done throughout before serving.

Meat cooked on the grill is usually basted with a sauce to keep it from drying out. A tomato-based barbecue sauce is most popular. You can also make other sauces using juices, such as citrus or apple, and honey or a fruit preserve.

Kabobs can be made up in a wide variety of combinations. Select foods that take about the same time to cook. Leave a little space between each food on the skewer so it will cook faster. You might combine chunks of turkey breast with fresh pineapple cubes. Combine pieces of fish with zucchini squash, green peppers, and onions.

Other foods besides meat can also be cooked on the grill. Use a skillet or pan or wrap the foods in heavy-duty foil and place on the grill. You can cook vegetables, such as corn and potatoes, and you can warm buns and biscuits.

The outdoor atmosphere and aroma of cooking foods seems to increase appetites. Be sure to allow a little more food per person than you would normally.

Remember to keep hot food hot and cold food cold. Bring out only enough food to serve everyone once and keep the rest stored at proper temperatures. If seconds are wanted, more food can be brought out later.

Application for Employment

PERSONAL DATA:

Name:	LAST	FIRST	MIDDLE	Home Phone: Business Phone:

Permanent Address:	NUMBER	STREET	CITY	STATE	ZIP

Social Security Number: If under 18 years of age, state your age:

If not a U.S. citizen, do you have a visa permitting you to work?   Yes   No   Number:

WORK INTERESTS:
Position Desired: Willing to Relocate?   Yes ☐   No ☐

Referred By: Salary Desired: Willing to Travel?   Yes ☐   No ☐

EDUCATION:					
	NAME & ADDRESS OF SCHOOL	MAJOR COURSE	LAST GRADE COMPLETED	GRADUATED/DEGREE	STILL ATTENDING
GRAMMAR SCHOOL					
HIGH SCHOOL					
COLLEGE					
GRADUATE SCHOOL					
OTHER					

U.S. MILITARY SERVICE:

Have you ever served in the Armed Forces?   Yes   No   If Yes: Active Duty From _____ To _____

This Company is an equal opportunity employer. All applicants for employment will be considered on the basis of merit and job qualifications without regard to race, national origin, sex, or physical handicap. Employment is terminable at the will of either party.

EMPLOYMENT:		
LIST BELOW YOUR FORMER EMPLOYERS. BEGIN WITH THE PRESENT EMPLOYERS. NOTE ANY PERIODS OF UNEMPLOYMENT.		

1. EMPLOYER:	DATE EMPLOYED:	POSITION:
	FROM: TO:	
ADDRESS:		MAJOR JOB DUTIES:
	SALARY:	
SUPERVISOR:		
MAY WE CONTACT?	$ TO $	
REASON FOR LEAVING:		

2. EMPLOYER:	DATE EMPLOYED:	POSITION:
	FROM: TO:	
ADDRESS:		MAJOR JOB DUTIES:
	SALARY:	
SUPERVISOR:		
MAY WE CONTACT?	$ TO $	
REASON FOR LEAVING:		

Have you ever been convicted of a crime, offense, or violation, other than parking violations, within the last five years that was not sealed or annulled by a court?   YES ☐   NO ☐

If yes, list all convictions, showing date, court, and name of offense. Conviction of a crime is not necessarily a bar to employment.

_____

I agree that the company may, as part of the verification of this application, contact the educational institutions and references above. I understand that falsification of any part of this application is justifiable grounds for immediate dismissal. If employed, I understand that the first ninety (90) days of my employment constitute a probationary period and, if employed, I understand that I am employed at the will of management, and management retains the right to alter the terms and conditions of my employment at any time.

Date: _____ Signature: _____

(DO NOT WRITE IN THIS SPACE)		COMMENTS:
INTERVIEWED BY:	REFERRED TO:	
EMPLOYED BY:	POSITION: GRADE:	
EMPLOYMENT DATE:	STARTING SALARY: JOB CODE:	

THIS APPLICATION IS NOT AN EMPLOYMENT AGREEMENT

Recipe Worksheets

TABLE OF CONTENTS

Recipes (R)

No.	Title	Page

FOOD AND INGREDIENT INDEX

Recipes (R)

C — **Conventional cooking directions**
M — **Microwave cooking directions**
★ — **Appears in textbook with photo**

Foods Lab Safety and Sanitation

With your parent(s) or legal guardian, read the following safety and sanitation procedures for working in the kitchen. Then have one of your parents or your legal guardian sign the blank on the next page stating that you have read the procedures. Return the signed portion to your teacher by _____.

(date)

SAFETY PROCEDURES

To prevent falls . . .

1. Wipe up all spills at once.
2. To reach items stored in high places, use a sturdy stepstool or ladder. *Don't* use a chair, box, or counter top.
3. Close cabinet doors and drawers after opening them.

To prevent cuts . . .

1. Keep sharp knives sharp. They are less likely to cause an accident than dull ones.
2. Cut away from you with the knife blade slanted.
3. For peeling vegetables such as carrots or potatoes, use a peeler instead of a knife.
4. Cut, chop, and dice foods on a cutting board.
5. If a knife, kitchen scissors, or ice pick starts to fall, get out of the way. Do not try to catch it in midair.
6. Wash, dry, and store knives separately from other dishes and utensils.
7. Keep your fingers away from the beaters in mixers and away from the blades in other appliances.
8. Use knives and other sharp tools only for their intended purpose.
9. Sweep up broken glass immediately.
10. Wrap your hand in a towel to pick up broken glass.
11. When opening cans, cut the lids completely off.

To prevent fires and burns . . .

1. Use baking soda, *not water*, to put out a grease fire.
2. Keep flammable materials away from the top of the range and away from portable appliances that heat.

3. Use a dry potholder, *not* a towel or the corner of an apron, to remove pans from the range.
4. Store flammable substances such as cleaning fluid or aerosol sprays away from heat sources.
5. Use a metal trash can when disposing of hot or smoldering items.
6. Keep the range exhaust hood and ducts clean.
7. Keep pan handles turned inward on the range.
8. When removing a pan lid, tilt the lid away from you and do not hold your face directly over the pan.
9. When removing a pan from the oven, pull the oven rack out. *Don't* reach into a hot oven.
10. Wear an oven mitt on each hand and use both hands to remove pans from the oven.
11. Check to be sure the range and all appliances are turned off when you are finished with them.
12. Use a spoon or tongs, *not your fingers*, to remove food from hot liquids.
13. When lighting gas burners with a match, strike the match first, then turn the burner on.
14. If you smell gas, turn off all range and oven controls and tell your teacher.

To prevent electric shock . . .

1. Read appliance booklets before using appliances.
2. Keep electrical cords away from water and hot objects.
3. Do not plug several cords into an electrical outlet at one time.
4. Unplug portable appliances after you have used them.
5. Disconnect appliances before cleaning them. Do not put them in water unless the appliance is labeled "immersible."
6. Before using an appliance, make sure your hands are dry and that you are standing on a dry surface.
7. Unplug appliances before bringing metal objects in contact with any working parts.
8. Plug the cord of portable appliances into the appliance first, then into the wall.

To prevent microwave accidents . . .

1. Never damage the door of a microwave or use a microwave if the door appears damaged.
2. Never turn on the microwave if there is no food inside.
3. Do not heat sealed jars, cans, or bottles in the microwave.
4. Do not heat home-canned foods in the microwave. Use a conventional range.
5. Use potholders to remove food containers from the microwave.
6. Remove lids and plastic wrap carefully to avoid steam burns.
7. Distribute the heat by stirring foods prepared in the microwave before serving them.

Sanitation Procedures

1. Place books, purses, and other personal items in an area of the classroom not used for food preparation.
2. Wear appropriate, clean clothing on lab days. Avoid long, loose sleeves, sashes, and dangling jewelry.
3. Wear a clean apron during food preparation and cleanup.
4. Pull hair back and secure it so that it stays away from your face and shoulders.
5. Avoid working with food if you have an open cut, sore, or other wound on your hands.
6. Wash your hands with soap before beginning the lab. Dry your hands on paper towels or on cloth towels not used for drying dishes.
7. While working with food, avoid touching your hair, skin, face, or other unclean objects.
8. Repeat hand washing when necessary — especially after coughing, sneezing, or using the restroom.
9. Be sure you have clean dish towels, dish cloths, potholders, and oven mitts before beginning the lab. Obtain additional clean items as they are needed.
10. Wipe all counter tops and tables at the beginning and end of each lab.

11. Use *hot* water for washing dishes.
12. Fill the sink with hot soapy water at the beginning of the lab. Soak dirty dishes, pots, and pans in the water as you are through with them. (*Don't* leave sharp knives in the water.)
13. Wash dishes, pans, and utensils as you use them, allowing them to dry on the drain board when possible.
14. When tasting foods, use a spoon other than the one used for stirring. Use a clean spoon for each person tasting and for each time food is tasted.
15. After working with raw animal foods, scrub all areas and utensils used with hot soapy water.
16. When possible use a kitchen tool, *not* your hands, to complete tasks.
17. Thoroughly cook foods to be served hot. Keep them hot until they are served.
18. Foods to be served cold should be kept cold until serving time.
19. Cover leftover foods and store them in the refrigerator immediately.

EMERGENCY INFORMATION

The fire extinguisher in our classroom is located

_____

_____.

The fire blanket in our classroom is located

_____

_____.

Phone numbers:

Fire Department _____

Ambulance _____

Poison Control Center _____

Police _____

- -

We have read the safety and sanitation procedures for working in the foods lab.

_____   _____
(Student's signature)   (Parent's signature)

_____   _____
(Date)   (Date)

Foods Lab Work Plan

A work plan can help you manage your time in the foods lab. Good planning and organization will help your group work as a team to finish the lab in the time allowed. Here's how:

1. Read the recipe carefully. As a group, discuss what steps are involved in preparing the recipe. Remember that the first step is always to wash your hands and get ready to work in the lab. The second step is always to gather your ingredients and equipment. What other steps are listed in the recipe? Are there any not listed, such as washing vegetables, chopping or slicing, measuring, setting the table? Using a separate sheet of paper, make a list of all the steps.

2. Next, discuss how you will be able to complete all the steps in the time available. How many minutes should you allow for each step? Which steps would go faster if two people shared the job? Which steps can be "dovetailed" so that both are going on at the same time? You may want to have one member of the group take notes.

3. Use the chart on the second page of this handout to develop your work plan. Write each group member's name in one of the columns. Under each name, show which job that person will do first, next, and so on. You can read across the chart to see what everyone will be doing at any given time. If the plan doesn't "come out right" the first time, make adjustments until everyone in the group is satisfied with it. Remember, your plan will work best if:

   ▪ Everyone has a job to do at all times.
   ▪ Each job can be done without getting in the way of other jobs.
   ▪ The plan lets your group finish in the shortest possible time.

4. On lab day, make sure everyone knows what he or she is to do. Post a copy of the work plan where everyone in the group can see it. Keep track of what time you start and finish the lab.

5. After the lab, complete the evaluation (below) to see how well your plan worked. The more experience you gain, the easier it will be to develop a successful work plan.

Lab Group _____

Recipe Name _____ Lab Date _____

Time started _____ Time finished _____ Total minutes _____

Rate your lab experience on the following: (circle one)

Efficiency (Did you finish on time? Was time wasted?)	Good	Fair	Needs Improvement
Cooperation (Did group members work as a team?)	Good	Fair	Needs Improvement
Safety (Were safety rules followed?)	Good	Fair	Needs Improvement
Cleanliness (Were sanitation rules followed? Did you leave the lab clean?)	Good	Fair	Needs Improvement
Accuracy (Were the recipe directions correctly followed?)	Good	Fair	Needs Improvement
Finished product (How well did it turn out?)	Good	Fair	Needs Improvement

If you were going to repeat this lab experience, what changes would you make in your work plan?

_____

_____

_____

WORK PLAN CHART

Minutes	(Name)	(Name)	(Name)	(Name)
0				
5				
10				
15				
20				
25				
30				
35				
40				
45				
50				

JOGGER'S SNACK PAK

Equipment

___ 15-cm (6-in.) Square microwave-safe dish	___ Spatula
	___ Kitchen shears
___ Dry measuring cups	___ Fork
___ Measuring spoons	___ Rubber scraper

Metric	Customary	Ingredients
50 mL	3 Tbsp.	___ Butter or margarine
7 mL	1$\frac{1}{2}$ tsp.	___ Celery salt
7 mL	1$\frac{1}{2}$ tsp.	___ Chili powder
7 mL	1$\frac{1}{2}$ tsp.	___ Onion powder
1250 mL	5 cups	___ Mixed, chopped dried apricots, raisins, sunflower seeds, nuts, and whole-wheat cereal squares

Microwave Directions

___ 1. **Place** butter, celery salt, chili powder, and onion powder in dish.

___ 2. **Microwave** on high (100%) until butter melts, about 30 seconds.

___ 3. **Add** fruit-seed-nut-cereal mix and toss with fork until coated.

___ 4. **Microwave** on Medium Low (30%) until toasted, about 30 seconds, stirring three times.

___ 5. **Cool** and serve or store in airtight container.

Yield: 1250 mL (5 cups)

Per $\frac{1}{2}$ cup: 255 calories; 7 g protein; 28 g carbohydrate; 15 g fat; 334 mg sodium; 9 mg cholesterol

Percentage of U.S. RDA:

Vitamin A:	24%	Niacin:	20%
Vitamin C:	4%	Calcium:	4%
Thiamin:	9%	Iron:	12%
Riboflavin:	5%		

Kitchen Management Tip

■ Dried fruits, such as apricots, are sticky and difficult to chop with a knife. They can be "chopped" more easily by snipping them with kitchen shears. Rinse the shears occasionally in warm water to wash off apricot pulp as it accumulates.

Thinking About . . . Jogger's Snack Pak (R-1)

Questions

1. Using the formula in Appendix E of *Food for Today*, determine the following:

   a. Percentage of calories from fat _____

   b. Percentage of calories from carbohydrate _____

   c. Percentage of calories from protein _____

2. Which ingredient(s) do you think contributed the most fat? _____

   _____

3. Why is it important to stir the nuts, seeds, and dried fruits during Step 4 of the directions? ____

   _____

4. List three food preparation skills used in this recipe.

   a. _____

   b. _____

   c. _____

5. Name one microwave precaution you should follow when preparing this recipe. _____

   _____

6. How would the appearance differ if you toasted the ingredients in a conventional oven rather than

   in the microwave oven? _____

   _____

7. If you were planning to serve this snack to guests, what other nutritious foods might you serve

   with it? _____

   _____

Evaluation

Complete the following after preparing the recipe:

1. How did the snack look and taste? _____

   _____

2. How could you change or improve the recipe? _____

   _____

3. List any difficulties you had in preparing the recipe. _____

   _____

4. How would you solve the problem(s) next time? _____

   _____

NACHOS — PRONTO!

Equipment

____ Microwave-safe plate, 30-cm (12-in.)	____ 2 teaspoons	____ Paper towel
____ Dry measuring cups	____ Grater	____ Waxed paper
____ Spatula	____ Rubber scraper	____ Pot holders
	____ Can opener	

Metric	Customary	Ingredients
12	12	____ Tortilla chips
113 g can	4 oz. can	____ Chopped green chilies
50 mL	$\frac{1}{4}$ cup	____ Coarsely shredded Monterey Jack or Cheddar cheese
1 pkg. (35 g)	1 pkg. ($1\frac{1}{4}$ oz.)	____ Taco seasoning mix

Microwave Directions

____ 1. **Line** plate with paper towel and arrange tortilla chips on the towel.

____ 2. **Top** each chip with a bit of chopped green chilies. (See tip below.)

____ 3. **Cover** with cheese and sprinkle with taco seasoning.

____ 4. **Microwave** on High (100%) for 15 seconds. Rotate the plate one-half turn. Microwave 15 to 30 seconds more.

____ 5. **Serve** hot!

Yield: 12 nachos

Per nacho (using Monterey Jack cheese):
31 calories; 1 g protein; 3 g carbohydrate; 1.5 g fat; 167 mg sodium; 2 mg cholesterol

Percentage of U.S. RDA:

Vitamin A:	18%	Niacin:	0.5%
Vitamin C:	6%	Calcium:	2%
Thiamin:	0.2%	Iron:	0.3%
Riboflavin:	0.8%		

Kitchen Management Tip

■ Be careful when using chilies. They contain capsaicin, a volatile oil that gives them their characteristic "hot" spiciness. It also makes them irritating to the skin and particularly the eyes. Handle chilies with a utensil whenever possible. When you must touch chilies, you can remove most of the oil by washing your hands with soap and warm water. But traces of capsaicin may remain for as long as an hour. Avoid touching the eye area until the oil has evaporated.

Thinking About . . . Nachos — Pronto! (R-2)

Questions

1. Using the formula in Appendix E of *Food for Today*, determine the following:

   a. Percentage of calories from fat _____

   b. Percentage of calories from carbohydrate _____

   c. Percentage of calories from protein _____

2. Which ingredient(s) do you think contributed the most fat? _____

   _____

3. List three safety guidelines to follow in preparing this recipe.

   a. _____

   b. _____

   c. _____

4. Name one food preparation skill used in this recipe. _____

5. If you were preparing this recipe at home and discovered that you had all the ingredients but the

   Taco seasoning mix, what could you substitute? _____

   _____

6. If you were serving this recipe as part of a Mexican party menu, what other foods would you serve?

   _____

   _____

7. How might you decorate the table to give the party a festive atmosphere? _____

   _____

   _____

Evaluation

Complete the following after preparing the recipe:

1. How did the nachos look and taste? _____

   _____

2. How could you change or improve the recipe? _____

   _____

3. List any difficulties you had in preparing the recipe. _____

   _____

4. How would you solve the problem(s) next time? _____

   _____

SNACK-A-PIZZA

Equipment

___ Cutting board	___ Bread knife	___ Grater
___ Set measuring spoons	___ Chef's knife	___ Paper towel
___ Fork	___ Rubber scraper	___ Waxed paper

Metric	Customary	Ingredients
$\frac{1}{2}$	$\frac{1}{2}$	___ English muffin or bagel
30 mL	2 Tbsp.	___ Pizza sauce
30 mL	2 Tbsp.	___ Pepperoni slices
30 mL	2 Tbsp.	___ Shredded mozzarella cheese
5 mL	1 tsp.	___ Parmesan cheese
Dash	Dash	___ Dried Italian herbs

Microwave Directions

___ 1. **Place** muffin half on paper towel, crust-side down.

___ 2. **Spread** with sauce; then arrange pepperoni slices on top.

___ 3. **Cover** with mozzarella cheese.

___ 4. **Sprinkle** with Parmesan cheese and Italian herbs.

___ 5. **Cover** pizza loosely with waxed paper.

___ 6. **Microwave** on High (100%) until hot and cheese is melted, about $1\frac{1}{2}$ minutes.

Yield: One 12.5-cm (5-in.) pizza

Per pizza: 241 calories; 13 g protein; 20 g carbohydrate; 12 g fat; 687 mg sodium; 25 mg cholesterol

Percentage of U.S. RDA:

Vitamin A:	6%	Niacin:	12%
Vitamin C:	3%	Calcium:	19%
Thiamin:	13%	Iron:	7%
Riboflavin:	12%		

Kitchen Management Tips

- The serrated edge of a bread knife slices easily through breads and rolls. To slice a bagel, hold it with one hand and stand it on end on a cutting board. Begin slicing at the top, cutting with a back-and-forth sawing motion.

- Break an English muffin in half with a fork. Insert the fork tines into the edge of the muffin at the middle. Push the fork tines to the center of the muffin. Repeat the process around the muffin, then gently separate the two halves.

Thinking About . . . Snack-A-Pizza (R-3)

Questions

1. Using the formula in Appendix E of *Food for Today,* determine the following:

    a. Percentage of calories from fat _____

    b. Percentage of calories from carbohydrate _____

    c. Percentage of calories from protein _____

2. Which ingredient(s) do you think contributed the most fat? _____
   _____

3. How could you alter the recipe to reduce the amount of fat? _____
   _____

4. How could you alter the recipe so that you could serve the pizza snack to someone on a strict low-salt diet? _____
   _____

5. What could you do to shorten the preparation time? _____
   _____

6. If you wanted to broil the snack pizza in a conventional oven, what rule-of-thumb would you use to figure the approximate cooking time? _____
   _____

7. What foods would you serve with this recipe for lunch? _____
   _____

Evaluation

Complete the following after preparing the recipe:

1. How did the pizza look and taste? _____
   _____

2. How could you change or improve the recipe? _____
   _____

3. List any difficulties you had in preparing the recipe. _____
   _____

4. How would you solve the problem(s) next time? _____
   _____

LEMONY POACHED PEARS

Equipment

- Baking dish, 30 × 20 × 5 cm (12 × 8 × 2 in.)
- Oven cooking bag, 35 × 50 cm (14 × 20 in.)
- Electric mixer
- Medium bowl
- Dry measuring cups
- Liquid measuring cup
- Measuring spoons
- Spatula
- Paring knife
- Apple corer (optional)
- Kitchen shears
- Rubber scraper
- Mixing spoon
- Pot holder

Metric	Customary	Ingredients
175 mL	³/₄ cup	Light brown sugar (firmly packed)
375 mL	1¹/₂ cups	Water
75 mL	¹/₃ cup	Grapefruit juice
10 mL	2 tsp.	Lemon juice
1	1	Cinnamon stick
3	3	Whole cloves
6	6	Medium-size, firm pears
250 mL	1 cup	Low-fat milk
1 pkg. (99-g)	1 pkg. (3¹/₂-oz.)	Instant lemon pudding and pie filling mix
10 mL	2 tsp.	Grated lemon rind

Directions

1. **Preheat** oven to 180°C (350°F).
2. **Place** oven cooking bag in baking dish.
3. **Combine** brown sugar, water, grapefruit juice, lemon juice, cinnamon, and cloves in bag. Turn bag gently until sugar dissolves.
4. **Pare** pears. Core from blossom end, leaving on the stems. If necessary, cut a thin slice off bottom of each pear so it will stand up.
5. **Roll** each pear in syrup and stand up in bag, arranging in a circle.
6. **Close** bag with a nylon tie.
7. **Make** six 1.5-cm (¹/₂-in.) slits in top.
8. **Bake** in oven at 180°C (350°F) for 30 minutes or until tender. Cool.
9. **Make custard sauce:** Combine milk and 250 mL (1 cup) syrup from bag in mixing bowl. Add pudding mix and beat with electric mixer on low speed 2 minutes or until well blended. Chill until ready to serve. Custard will thicken, but not set.
10. **Spoon** custard sauce over warm or chilled pears. Sprinkle with grated lemon rind.

Yield: 6 servings

Per serving: 274 calories; 2 g protein; 67 g carbohydrate; 1.5 g fat; 252 mg sodium; 3 mg cholesterol

Percentage of U.S. RDA:

Vitamin A:	2%	Niacin:	1%
Vitamin C:	13%	Calcium:	9%
Thiamin:	4%	Iron:	8%
Riboflavin:	8%		

Microwave Directions

Same as above except for Step 8.

8. **Microwave** on High (100%) for 6 to 10 minutes, rotating dish periodically. Let stand 4 minutes.

Thinking About . . . Lemony Poached Pears (R-4)

Questions

1. Using the formula in Appendix E of *Food for Today*, determine the following:

   a. Percentage of calories from fat _____

   b. Percentage of calories from carbohydrate _____

   c. Percentage of calories from protein _____

2. Since the recipe is relatively low in fat, how do you account for the high caloric content of one serving?

   _____

3. What basic cooking method is used in this recipe? _____

   _____

4. List two safety guidelines to follow when using a plastic cooking bag in a conventional oven.

   a. _____

   b. _____

5. List two additional safety guidelines to follow when preparing this recipe in a microwave oven.

   a. _____

   b. _____

6. List three basic food preparation skills used in this recipe.

   a. _____

   b. _____

   c. _____

Evaluation

Complete the following after preparing the recipe:

1. How did the pears look and taste? _____

   _____

2. How could you change or improve the recipe? _____

   _____

3. List any difficulties you had in preparing the recipe. _____

   _____

4. How would you solve the problem(s) next time? _____

   _____

SAUTÉED APPLE RINGS

Equipment

____ Large skillet
(for conventional cooking)
____ Microwave-safe casserole
with lid, 1.5 L or 1½ qt.
(for microwave cooking)

____ Measuring spoons
____ Spatula
____ Cutting board
____ Chef's knife

____ Paring knife
____ Turner
____ Pot holders

Metric	Customary	Ingredients
3	3	____ Cooking apples, medium size
50 mL	¼ cup	____ Butter or margarine
50 mL	¼ cup	____ Finely chopped onion
1 mL	¼ tsp.	____ Crushed dried marjoram
1 mL	¼ tsp.	____ Crushed dried thyme

Conventional Directions

____ 1. **Wash** apples thoroughly.
____ 2. **Remove** core from apples carefully.
____ 3. **Slice** horizontally about 1.3 cm (½ in.)
____ 4. **Melt** butter or margarine in skillet.
____ 5. **Add** onion, marjoram, and thyme.
____ 6. **Sauté,** turning occasionally, until onions soften.
____ 7. **Add** apple slices.
____ 8. **Sauté,** turning occasionally, until apples soften.
____ 9. **Serve** as an accompaniment for broiled fish or chicken; roast pork, lamb, or veal; or pancakes.

Yield: 9-15 slices

Per serving (1/9 of recipe): 74 calories;
0.2 g protein; 7 g carbohydrate; 5 g fat;
53 mg sodium; 14 mg cholesterol

Percentage of U.S. RDA:

Vitamin A:	4%	Niacin:	0.2%
Vitamin C:	5%	Calcium:	0.7%
Thiamin:	0.7%	Iron:	1%
Riboflavin:	0.5%		

Microwave Directions

Follow Conventional Directions for Steps 1 to 3.

____ 4. **Melt** butter or margarine in casserole on High (100%) for 30 to 45 seconds.
____ 5. **Add** chopped onion, marjoram, and thyme.
____ 6. **Microwave** on High (100%) for 1½ to 2 minutes or until onions are soft and translucent.
____ 7. **Add** apple slices.
____ 8. **Cover** and microwave on High (100%) for 3 minutes.
____ 9. **Rearrange** slices to coat with butter-onion mixture.
____ 10. **Continue** to microwave, covered on High (100%) for another 1½ to 2½ minutes or until apples are just tender.
____ 11. **Let stand** for 3 to 5 minutes.
____ 12. **Serve** as in Step 9 of Conventional Directions.

Kitchen Management Tips

■ Select firm cooking apples, such as Rome Beauty, that hold their shape when cooking.
■ To keep sliced apples from turning dark before they are cooked, sprinkle them with an ascorbic acid mixture.

Thinking About . . . Sautéed Apple Rings (R-5)

Questions

1. Using the formula in Appendix E of *Food for Today,* determine the following:

    a. Percentage of calories from fat _____

    b. Percentage of calories from carbohydrate _____

    c. Percentage of calories from protein _____

2. Which ingredients do you think contributed the most fat? _____ _____

3. What is the basic conventional cooking method used in this recipe? _____ _____

4. List two safety guidelines to follow when sautéing.

    a. _____

    b. _____

5. List two additional safety guidelines to follow when preparing the recipe in the microwave oven.

    a. _____

    b. _____

6. List two different steps you must take if you prepare the apple rings in the microwave oven rather than the conventional oven.

    a. _____

    b. _____

7. Do you think cooking the apples in the microwave oven would require more or less work? Give reasons for your answer. _____ _____

Evaluation

Complete the following after preparing the recipe:

1. How did the apple rings look and taste? _____ _____

2. How could you change or improve the recipe? _____ _____

3. List any difficulties you had in preparing the recipe. _____ _____

4. How would you solve the problem(s) next time? _____ _____

BROCCOLI-ONION CASSEROLE

Equipment

___ Medium saucepan with lid (for conventional cooking)
___ Small saucepan (for conventional cooking)
___ Casserole with lid, 1.5 L (1½ qt.)

___ Glass measuring cup, 500 mL or 2 cup (for microwave cooking)
___ Liquid measuring cup
___ Measuring spoons
___ Fork
___ Spatula

___ Tongs
___ Mixing spoon
___ Rubber scraper
___ Can opener
___ Pot holders
___ Cooling rack

Metric	Customary	Ingredients
1 pkg. (248-g)	1 pkg. (10-oz.)	___ Frozen broccoli spears
125 mL	½ cup	___ Water (Conventional Directions)
6 mL	1¼ tsp.	___ Salt (Conventional Directions)
½ of 43-g can	½ of 1½-oz. can	___ Canned French-fried onion rings
250 mL	1 cup	___ Low-fat milk
1 pkg.	1 pkg.	___ Cheese sauce mix
Dash	Dash	___ Paprika

Conventional Directions

___ 1. **Simmer** broccoli in salted water until tender.
___ 2. **Drain.**
___ 3. **Arrange** half of broccoli in casserole.
___ 4. **Sprinkle** with half of the onion rings.
___ 5. **Stir** milk into cheese sauce mix gradually in saucepan.
___ 6. **Bring** sauce to a boil and cook until it thickens.
___ 7. **Pour** half of sauce over broccoli and onions.
___ 8. **Arrange** remaining broccoli over first layer.
___ 9. **Pour** remaining sauce over broccoli.
___ 10. **Top** with remaining onions.
___ 11. **Sprinkle** with paprika.
___ 12. **Bake** at 160°C (325°F) for 5 to 8 minutes.

Yield: 6 servings

Per serving: 81 calories; 4 g protein; 7 g carbohydrate; 4 g fat; 734 mg sodium; 6 mg cholesterol

Percentage of U.S. RDA:

Vitamin A:	18%	Niacin:	1%
Vitamin C:	20%	Calcium:	12%
Thiamin:	3%	Iron:	2%
Riboflavin:	8%		

Microwave Directions

___ 1. **Place** broccoli in casserole. Arrange with heads toward center of dish. Cover.
___ 2. **Microwave** on High (100%) for 4 minutes.
___ 3. **Rearrange** stalks so heads point outward. Continue microwaving for 3 to 3½ minutes or until stalks are tender.
___ 4. **Prepare** cheese sauce by combining milk and cheese sauce mix in a 500-mL (2-cup) glass measure, stirring to blend.
___ 5. **Microwave** sauce on High (100%) for 3 to 3½ minutes or until mixture comes to a boil and thickens.
___ 6. **Remove** half of the broccoli from the casserole.
___ 7. **Pour** half of the cheese sauce over the broccoli remaining in the casserole.
___ 8. **Top** with half of the onion rings.
___ 9. **Add** the remaining broccoli.
___ 10. **Cover** with the remaining cheese sauce.
___ 11. **Top** with remaining onions.
___ 12. **Sprinkle** with paprika.
___ 13. **Microwave** on High (100%) for 5 to 7 minutes or until thoroughly heated. Rotate the dish one-half turn after half of the cooking time.

Thinking About ... Broccoli-Onion Casserole (R-6)

Questions

1. Using the formula in Appendix E of *Food for Today,* determine the following:

   a. Percentage of calories from fat _____

   b. Percentage of calories from carbohydrate _____

   c. Percentage of calories from protein _____

2. What is one way you could change this recipe to reduce the fat content? _____
_____

3. List two safety guidelines you should follow when opening a can.

   a. _____

   b. _____

4. List two sanitation guidelines to follow when opening a can.

   a. _____

   b. _____

5. List three basic food preparation skills used in this recipe.

   a. _____

   b. _____

   c. _____

6. List three different steps you must follow if you prepare this recipe in the microwave oven rather than in the conventional oven.

   a. _____

   b. _____

   c. _____

Evaluation

Complete the following after preparing the recipe:

1. How did the casserole look and taste? _____
_____

2. How could you change or improve the recipe? _____
_____

3. List any difficulties you had in preparing the recipe. _____
_____

4. How would you solve the problem(s) next time? _____
_____

SAUTÉED COLLARD GREENS

Equipment

___ Large skillet with cover (for conventional cooking)	___ Measuring spoons	___ Mixing spoon
	___ Cutting board	___ Tongs
___ Large microwave-safe casserole with lid (for microwave cooking)	___ Chef's knife	___ Fork
	___ Spatula	___ Paper towels
	___ Paring knife	___ Pot holders
___ Small bowl		

Metric	Customary	Ingredients
2 strips	2 strips	___ Bacon
1 kg	2 lb.	___ Fresh collards, washed, drained, and cut into 2.5-cm (1-in.) strips
1 mL	¼ tsp.	___ Ground black pepper
15 mL	1 Tbsp.	___ Lemon juice
1	1	___ Small onion, thinly sliced

Conventional Directions

___ 1. **Fry** bacon in a large skillet until crisp.
___ 2. **Drain** bacon on a paper towel.
___ 3. **Break** bacon into bits and place in a bowl.
___ 4. **Place** collards in the same skillet with the bacon grease.
___ 5. **Cover** and cook until tender, about 15 to 20 minutes.
___ 6. **Stir** and turn frequently with tongs.
___ 7. **Season** with ground black pepper and lemon juice.
___ 8. **Add** crisp bacon and onion slices.
___ 9. **Toss** together lightly with fork and serve at once.

Microwave Directions

___ 1. **Microwave** bacon in a large microwave-safe casserole on High (100%) for 2 to 3 minutes, or until bacon is crisp.
___ 2. **Remove** bacon from casserole and drain on paper towel.
___ 3. **Crumble** bacon.
___ 4. **Place** collards in casserole and cover.
___ 5. **Microwave** on High (100%) for 12 to 14 minutes, stirring often.
___ 6. **Season** with ground black pepper and lemon juice.
___ 7. **Add** crumbled bacon and onion slices.
___ 8. **Toss** together lightly with fork and serve at once.

Yield: 6 servings

Per serving: 74 calories; 3 g protein; 7 g carbohydrate; 5 g fat; 98 mg sodium; 5 mg cholesterol

Percentage of U.S. RDA:

Vitamin A:	101%	Niacin:	4%
Vitamin C:	45%	Calcium:	18%
Thiamin:	5%	Iron:	6%
Riboflavin:	6%		

Thinking About . . . Sautéed Collard Greens (R-7)

Questions

1. Using the formula in Appendix E of *Food for Today*, determine the following:

   a. Percentage of calories from fat _____

   b. Percentage of calories from carbohydrate _____

   c. Percentage of calories from protein _____

2. Which ingredient(s) do you think contributed the most fat? _____
   _____

3. How should collard greens be stored before using them? _____
   _____

4. List three safety guidelines to follow when frying bacon and collards.

   a. _____

   b. _____

   c. _____

5. List four basic food preparation skills used in this recipe.

   a. _____

   b. _____

   c. _____

   d. _____

6. Give two advantages of microwave cooking over conventional when preparing this recipe.

   a. _____

   b. _____

Evaluation

Complete the following after preparing the recipe:

1. How did the greens look and taste? _____
   _____

2. How could you change or improve the recipe? _____
   _____

3. List any difficulties you had in preparing the recipe. _____
   _____

4. How would you solve the problem(s) next time? _____
   _____

TOFUBURGERS

Equipment

___ Large skillet	___ Large mixing bowl	___ Mixing spoon
___ 39 × 30 cm or 15¹/₂ × 12 in. Baking sheet (for conventional cooking)	___ Dry measuring cups	___ Rubber scraper
	___ Measuring spoons	___ Spatula
___ Microwave-safe plate or glass pie pan (for microwave cooking)	___ Cutting board	___ Turner
	___ Chef's knife	___ Brush
	___ Utility knife	___ Clean dish towel
___ Large strainer	___ Garlic press	___ Pot holders

Metric	Customary	Ingredients
375 mL	Two 10-oz. pkgs.	___ Firm tofu, drained and squeezed
15 mL	1 Tbsp.	___ Vegetable oil
250 mL	1 cup	___ Finely chopped onion
2 cloves	2 cloves	___ Garlic, pressed
2	2	___ Eggs
125 mL	¹/₂ cup	___ Dried bread crumbs
30 mL	2 Tbsp.	___ Tamari sauce
1 mL	¹/₄ tsp.	___ Lemon pepper
Dash	Dash	___ Crushed dried marjoram
Dash	Dash	___ Crushed dried thyme
		___ Vegetable oil

Yield: 6 patties

Per patty: 165 calories; 11 g protein; 11 g carbohydrate; 9 g fat; 312 mg sodium; 97 mg cholesterol

Percentage of U.S. RDA:

Vitamin A:	3%	Niacin:	3%
Vitamin C:	3%	Calcium:	15%
Thiamin:	8%	Iron:	15%
Riboflavin:	7%		

Conventional Directions

___ 1. **Drain** and squeeze tofu before measuring. Drain in a large strainer for about 15 to 20 minutes. Squeeze out remaining liquid by wrapping tofu in a clean dish towel and squeezing out the liquid.

___ 2. **Preheat** oven to 200°C (400°F).

___ 3. **Heat** 15 mL (1 Tbsp.) vegetable oil in a large skillet. Add the onions and pressed garlic. Sauté until the onions are soft and translucent.

___ 4. **Crumble** the tofu into a large bowl. Press out large lumps with the back of a mixing spoon.

___ 5. **Add** the sautéed onion and garlic, eggs, bread crumbs, tamari sauce, lemon pepper, marjoram, and thyme.

___ 6. **Mix** well so mixture is blended and holds together.

___ 7. **Oil** baking sheet lightly.

___ 8. **Form** the tofu mixture into 6 patties 1 cm to 1.3 cm (³/₈ to ¹/₂ in.) thick. Mixture is soft, so handle carefully.

___ 9. **Brush** the tops of the patties lightly with oil.

___ 10. **Bake** at 200°C (400°F) for 10 to 12 minutes or until lightly browned on the bottom.

___ 11. **Turn** the patties over carefully with a wide turner.

___ 12. **Bake** at 200°C (400°F) for an additional 10 minutes.

___ 13. **Serve** as you would a hamburger.

Microwave Directions

Follow Conventional Directions for Steps 1-8.

___ 9. **Place** 1 burger on a lightly oiled plate or glass pie pan.

___ 10. **Brush** top lightly with oil.

___ 11. **Microwave** on High (100%) for 1 minute.

___ 12. **Turn** patty over carefully with a turner.

___ 13. **Microwave** on High (100%) for 1 minute.

___ 14. **Serve** as you would a hamburger.

___ 15. **Repeat** for the other burgers.

Thinking About . . . Tofuburgers (R-8)

Questions

1. Using the formula in Appendix E of *Food for Today*, determine the following:

   a. Percentage of calories from fat _____

   b. Percentage of calories from carbohydrate _____

   c. Percentage of calories from protein _____

2. What two conventional cooking methods are used in this recipe?

   a. _____

   b. _____

3. List two safety guidelines to follow in preparing this recipe by the conventional method.

   a. _____

   b. _____

4. List two sanitation guidelines to follow when mixing and shaping the burgers.

   a. _____

   b. _____

5. List three food preparation skills used in this recipe.

   a. _____

   b. _____

   c. _____

6. If the recipe were made without eggs, would it still supply complete proteins? Explain your answer.

   _____

   _____

7. What other foods would you serve with this recipe to make a nutritious meal? _____

   _____

Evaluation

Complete the following after preparing the recipe:

1. How did the tofuburgers look and taste? _____

   _____

2. How could you change or improve the recipe? _____

   _____

3. List any difficulties you had in preparing the recipe. _____

   _____

4. How would you solve the problem(s) next time? _____

   _____

VEGETARIAN PIZZA

Equipment

- ____ Pizza pan, 30 cm or 12 in. (for conventional cooking)
- ____ Small saucepan (for conventional cooking)
- ____ Microwave-safe plate, 30 cm or 12 in. (for microwave cooking)
- ____ Small bowl (for microwave cooking)
- ____ Waxed paper (for microwave cooking)
- ____ Cutting board
- ____ Cooling rack
- ____ Dry measuring cups
- ____ Measuring spoons
- ____ Paring knife
- ____ Chef's knife
- ____ Spatula
- ____ Mixing spoon
- ____ Can opener
- ____ Grater
- ____ Pot holders

Metric	Customary	Ingredients
227-g can	8-oz. can	____ Refrigerated crescent rolls
227-g can	8-oz. can	____ Tomato sauce
1 mL	1/4 tsp.	____ Crushed dried oregano
1 mL	1/4 tsp.	____ Crushed dried basil
1 mL	1/4 tsp.	____ Ground black pepper
3 mL	1/2 tsp.	____ Crushed dried parsley
10 mL	2 tsp.	____ Minced onion
1 clove	1 clove	____ Garlic, minced
30 mL	2 Tbsp.	____ Olive oil
500 mL	8 oz.	____ Mozzarella cheese, sliced or shredded
50 mL	1/4 cup	____ Grated Parmesan cheese

Yield: 12-inch pizza (8 slices) or 2 9-inch pizzas

Per slice: 234 calories; 12 g protein; 17 g carbohydrate; 13 g fat; 718 mg sodium; 18 mg cholesterol

Percentage of U.S. RDA:

Vitamin A:	56%	Niacin:	6%
Vitamin C:	17%	Calcium:	27%
Thiamin:	9%	Iron:	6%
Riboflavin:	11%		

Conventional Directions

- ____ 1. **Preheat** oven to 190°C (375°F).
- ____ 2. **Unwrap** rolls and press dough into pizza pan. Seal perforations and form crust with a 1.3-cm (1/2-in.) rim.
- ____ 3. **Bake** for 15 minutes.
- ____ 4. **Remove** from oven.
- ____ 5. **Combine** tomato sauce, oregano, basil, pepper, parsley, onion, garlic, and olive oil in a small saucepan and simmer for 5 minutes to blend flavors.
- ____ 6. **Spread** sauce over crust.
- ____ 7. **Top** with mozzarella cheese.
- ____ 8. **Sprinkle** with grated Parmesan cheese.
- ____ 9. **Bake** at 190°C (375°F) for 10 to 12 minutes.

Microwave Directions

- ____ 1. **Cut** two pieces of waxed paper into 30-cm (12-in). circles.
- ____ 2. **Divide** can of rolls in half. Press half onto each sheet of waxed paper to form a 23-cm (9-in.) round crust. Seal perforations. A rim is not needed.
- ____ 3. **Brush** top of each crust lightly with 5 mL (1 tsp.) olive oil.
- ____ 4. **Place** waxed paper with dough for one pizza on a microwave-safe plate.
- ____ 5. **Microwave** on Medium (50%) for 4 minutes.
- ____ 6. **Hold** waxed paper with microwaved crust and flip dough over onto plate. Carefully peel off waxed paper.
- ____ 7. **Microwave** again on Medium (50%) for about 3 to 5 minutes or until the dough is set and crisp. There will be some brown spots.
- ____ 8. **Repeat** with second crust.
- ____ 9. **Mix** together in a small bowl the tomato sauce, remaining oil, oregano, basil, black pepper, parsley, onion, and garlic.
- ____ 10. **Spread** half of sauce on each cooked pizza crust, spreading to edges.
- ____ 11. **Top** with mozzarella cheese.
- ____ 12. **Sprinkle** with Parmesan cheese.
- ____ 13. **Microwave** one at a time, Medium (50%) for 4 to 6 minutes. Rotate plate 1/2 turn after 2 minutes.
- ____ 14. **Remove** immediately from plate onto cooling rack for crisper crust.

Thinking About . . . Vegetarian Pizza (R-9)

Questions

1. Using the formula in Appendix E of *Food for Today*, determine the following:

   a. Percentage of calories from fat _____

   b. Percentage of calories from carbohydrate _____

   c. Percentage of calories from protein _____

2. Which ingredient(s) do you think contributed the most fat? _____

   _____

3. List four food preparation skills used in this recipe.

   a. _____

   b. _____

   c. _____

   d. _____

4. List four different procedures you would use to prepare this recipe in the microwave oven rather than the conventional oven.

   a. _____

   b. _____

   c. _____

   d. _____

5. In analyzing both conventional and microwave directions, which method would you want to try? Why?

   _____

   _____

6. What other vegetarian foods could you use as toppings? _____

   _____

Evaluation

Complete the following after preparing the recipe:

1. How did the pizza look and taste? _____

   _____

2. How could you change or improve the recipe? _____

   _____

3. List any difficulties you had in preparing the recipe. _____

   _____

4. How would you solve the problem(s) next time? _____

   _____

AT-HOME SALAD BAR

Equipment

____ Large salad bowl   ____ Dry measuring cups   ____ Spoon
____ Large serving platter   ____ Cutting board   ____ Can opener
____ Small bowl for croutons   ____ Chef's knife   ____ Plastic wrap
____ Measuring spoons

Metric	Customary	Ingredients
2 L	8 cups	____ Torn salad greens (spinach, and lettuce — iceberg, leaf, and romaine), cleaned, drained, and chilled
500 mL	2 cups	____ Cherry tomatoes, washed and chilled
453-g can	16-oz. can	____ Garbanzo beans, drained and chilled
500 mL	2 cups	____ Fresh broccoli and cauliflower pieces, washed
175 g	6 oz.	____ Cooked ham, cut into 1.3-cm ($^1/_2$-in.) cubes
175 g	6 oz.	____ Cooked turkey breast, cut into 1.3-cm ($^1/_2$-in.) cubes
175 g	6 oz.	____ Cheddar cheese, cut into julienne strips
175 g	6 oz.	____ Swiss cheese, cut into julienne strips
1	1	____ Large avocado, peeled, pitted and sliced (See tip below.)
15 mL	1 Tbsp.	____ Lemon juice (See tip below.)
125 mL	$^1/_2$ cup	____ Seasoned croutons

Directions

____ 1. **Place** salad greens in a large salad bowl. Keep chilled.

____ 2. **Arrange** cherry tomatoes, garbanzo beans, broccoli and cauliflower pieces, ham, turkey, and cheeses on a large serving platter. Sprinkle avocado with lemon juice and arrange on platter.

____ 3. **Place** croutons in small bowl in center of platter.

____ 4. **Cover** platter with plastic wrap and refrigerate until serving time.

____ 5. **Serve** with Green Goddess and Dilled Cottage Cheese dressings.

Yield: 8 servings

Per serving (without salad dressing):
361 calories; 27 g protein; 17 g carbohydrate; 21 g fat; 529 mg sodium; 69 mg cholesterol

Percentage of U.S. RDA:

Vitamin A:	60%	Niacin:	17%
Vitamin C:	48%	Calcium:	43%
Thiamin:	21%	Iron:	18%
Riboflavin:	23%		

Kitchen Management Tips

■ To peel an avocado easily, cut the avocado in half lengthwise. Remove the pit. Insert a teaspoon between the avocado flesh and skin. Gently run the spoon around the avocado, separating the flesh from the skin.

■ To extract juice from a lemon, place the whole lemon on the counter, then cover it with the palm of your hand. Using gentle pressure and a rolling motion, you can break the tissues inside the lemon so the juice is easier to squeeze.

Thinking About . . . At-Home Salad Bar (R-10)

Questions

1. Using the formula in Appendix E of *Food for Today*, determine the following:
   a. Percentage of calories from fat _____
   b. Percentage of calories from carbohydrate _____
   c. Percentage of calories from protein _____
2. Which ingredient(s) do you think contributed the most fat? _____
   _____
3. If a vegan (someone who does not eat meat, eggs, or dairy products) made a salad from the salad bar, could it contain complete protein? Explain. _____
   _____
   _____
4. List four sanitation guidelines to follow when setting up a salad bar.
   a. _____
   b. _____
   c. _____
   d. _____
5. To make the salad bar a complete meal, what other foods would you add? _____
   _____
   _____
6. To add more variety to the selection, what would you add to the salad bar? _____
   _____
   _____
7. If you wanted a hot food on the salad bar, what would you serve? _____
   _____

Evaluation

Complete the following after preparing the recipe:

1. List any difficulties you had in preparing the salad bar. _____
   _____
2. How would you solve the problem(s) next time? _____
   _____

DILLED COTTAGE CHEESE DRESSING

Equipment

___ Small mixing bowl	___ Dry measuring cups	___ Vegetable peeler
___ Blender or electric mixer	___ Measuring spoons	___ Mixing spoon
___ Cutting board	___ Spatula	___ Rubber scraper
___ Strainer	___ Paring knife	___ Plastic wrap
___ Grater	___ Chef's knife	

Metric	Customary	Ingredients
375 mL	1¹/₂ cups	___ Creamed cottage cheese
250 mL	1 cup	___ Peeled, seeded, shredded and well-drained cucumber
45 mL	3 Tbsp.	___ White wine vinegar
10 mL	2 tsp.	___ Instant minced onion
3 mL	¹/₂ tsp.	___ Dill weed

Directions

___ 1. **Blend** cottage cheese in blender until almost smooth or beat in small mixing bowl with electric mixer at high speed.

___ 2. **Fold** in remaining ingredients.

___ 3. **Cover** and refrigerate 1 to 2 hours to allow flavors to blend.

Yield: 550 mL (2¹/₄ cups)

Per serving (1 Tbsp.): 11 calories; 1 g protein; 0.6 g carbohydrate; 0.5 g fat; 38 mg sodium; 1.5 g cholesterol

Percentage of U.S. RDA:

Vitamin A:	0.3%	Niacin:	0.1%
Vitamin C:	0.4%	Calcium:	0.7%
Thiamin:	0.2%	Iron:	0.2%
Riboflavin:	1%		

Kitchen Management Tips

- To clean the blender easily, pour a little detergent into the container, add hot water, cover, and turn the blender on to loosen food. Remove the container and use a dishcloth to wipe away any particles still sticking to the sides or blades. Rinse well and let air dry.
- If you use an electric beater, rinse the blades off in warm water immediately after using.
- To prepare cucumber, peel and cut lengthwise into quarters. Cut away the seeds with a sharp knife. Shred with a grater or a food processor. Put into strainer and let drain. Press down on the pulp to remove as much liquid as possible.

Thinking About . . . Dilled Cottage Cheese Dressing (R-11)

Questions

1. Using the formula in Appendix E of *Food for Today*, determine the following:

    a. Percentage of calories from fat _____

    b. Percentage of calories from carbohydrate _____

    c. Percentage of calories from protein _____

2. List three safety guidelines to follow when preparing this recipe.

    a. _____

    b. _____

    c. _____

3. List three food preparation skills used in this recipe.

    a. _____

    b. _____

    c. _____

4. Why should the shredded cucumber be drained? _____

    _____

5. Why should the cucumber seeds be removed? _____

    _____

6. If you were preparing the dressing at home and discovered that the cottage cheese carton was nearly empty, what could you use in its place? _____

    _____

Evaluation

Complete the following after preparing the recipe:

1. How did the dressing look and taste? _____

    _____

2. How could you change or improve the recipe? _____

    _____

3. List any difficulties you had in preparing the recipe. _____

    _____

4. How would you solve the problem(s) next time? _____

    _____

GREEN GODDESS DRESSING

Equipment

___ Small mixing bowl	___ Cutting board	___ Mixing spoon
___ Dry measuring cups	___ Chef's knife	___ Rubber scraper
___ Measuring spoons	___ Spatula	___ Plastic wrap

Metric	Customary	Ingredients
30 mL	2 Tbsp.	___ Tarragon wine vinegar
50 mL	1/4 cup	___ Chopped parsley
15 mL	1 Tbsp.	___ Anchovy paste
15 mL	1 Tbsp.	___ Lemon juice
15 mL	1 Tbsp.	___ Minced green onion
Dash	Dash	___ Garlic powder
375 mL	1 1/2 cups	___ Sour cream

Directions

___ 1. **Combine** vinegar, parsley, anchovy paste, lemon juice, onion, and garlic powder in a small mixing bowl.

___ 2. **Fold** in sour cream.

___ 3. **Cover** and refrigerate 1 to 2 hours to allow flavors to blend.

Yield: About 500 mL (2 cups)

Per serving (1 Tbsp.): 25 calories; 0.5 g protein; 0.7 g carbohydrate; 2 g fat; 99 mg sodium; 5 mg cholesterol

Percentage of U.S. RDA:

Vitamin A:	2%	Niacin:	0.1%
Vitamin C:	1%	Calcium:	2%
Thiamin:	0.3%	Iron:	0.4%
Riboflavin:	1%		

Kitchen Management Tips

- The anchovy is a small Mediterranean fish with a sharp flavor. It is used in appetizers, sauces, and dressings, and as a garnish. It can be purchased canned as fillets or as a paste.
- To extract juice easily from a lemon, place the whole lemon on the counter, then cover it with the palm of your hand. Using gentle pressure and a rolling motion, you can break the tissues inside the lemon so the juice is easier to squeeze.

Thinking About . . . Green Goddess Dressing (R-12)

Questions

1. Using the formula in Appendix E of *Food for Today*, determine the following:

    a. Percentage of calories from fat _____

    b. Percentage of calories from carbohydrate _____

    c. Percentage of calories from protein _____

2. How could you reduce the fat content in this recipe? _____
   _____

3. List four food preparation skills used in this recipe.

    a. _____

    b. _____

    c. _____

    d. _____

4. Why is vinegar such a common ingredient in salad dressings? _____
   _____

5. What other flavored vinegars might be used in this dressing? _____
   _____

Evaluation

Complete the following after preparing the recipe:

1. How did the dressing look and taste? _____
   _____

2. How could you change or improve the recipe? _____
   _____

3. List any difficulties you had in preparing the recipe. _____
   _____

4. How would you solve the problem(s) next time? _____
   _____

CHICKEN AND RICE SALAD

Equipment

___ Saucepan with lid, 2 L or 2 qt.	___ Dry measuring cups	___ Chef's knife
___ Large mixing bowl	___ Measuring spoons	___ Paring knife
___ Cutting board	___ Spatula	___ Mixing spoon
	___ Can opener	___ Rubber scraper

Metric	Customary	Ingredients
500 mL	2 cups	___ Cooked rice
Two (142-g) cans	Two (5-oz.) cans	___ Chicken
241-g can	8½-oz. can	___ Green peas, drained
125 mL	½ cup	___ Chopped onion
500 mL	2 cups	___ Sliced celery
2 mL	½ tsp.	___ Ground black pepper
Dash	Dash	___ Hot pepper sauce
125 mL	½ cup	___ Mayonnaise
8	8	___ Whole tomatoes
		___ Salad greens
		___ Avocado Dressing

Directions

___ 1. **Mix** rice with chicken, peas, onion, celery, black pepper, hot pepper sauce, and mayonnaise.

___ 2. **Chill.**

___ 3. **Cut** out blossom ends of tomatoes. Cut tomatoes into sixths or eighths, but do not cut all the way through. This should give a petal effect.

___ 4. **Fill** tomatoes with rice-chicken.

___ 5. **Top** with Avocado Dressing (Recipe #14).

Yield: 8 servings

Per serving (without dressing):
254 calories; 11 g protein; 21 g carbohydrate; 14 g fat; 334 mg sodium; 30 mg cholesterol

Percentage of U.S. RDA:

Vitamin A:	28%	Niacin:	18%
Vitamin C:	37%	Calcium:	4%
Thiamin:	11%	Iron:	11%
Riboflavin:	8%		

Kitchen Management Tips

- Leftover cooked chicken or peas can be used in place of the canned. For variety, you can use any leftover cooked vegetable or combination of vegetables.
- Substitute brown rice for white and the dish will provide more nutrients. Long-grain rice remains loose and fluffy after cooking; medium- and short-grain rice get sticky and compact when cooked.

Thinking About . . . Chicken and Rice Salad (R-13)

Questions

1. Using the formula in Appendix E of *Food for Today*, determine the following:
   a. Percentage of calories from fat _____
   b. Percentage of calories from carbohydrate _____
   c. Percentage of calories from protein _____

2. Which ingredient(s) do you think contributed the most fat? _____
   _____

3. One serving of this recipe, without the dressing, provides more than a third of the daily RDA requirement for vitamin C. Which ingredient(s) do you think contributed the most vitamin C? _____
   _____

4. List three safety guidelines to follow when preparing this recipe.
   a. _____
   b. _____
   c. _____

5. List three sanitation guidelines to follow when preparing this recipe.
   a. _____
   b. _____
   c. _____

6. If you didn't have cooked chicken on hand, what other foods might you substitute in this recipe?
   _____

7. What other foods could you serve with this recipe to make a nutritious lunch? _____
   _____

Evaluation

Complete the following after preparing the recipe:

1. How did the salad look and taste? _____
   _____

2. How could you change or improve the recipe? _____
   _____

3. List any difficulties you had in preparing the recipe. _____
   _____

4. How would you solve the problem(s) next time? _____
   _____

AVOCADO DRESSING

Equipment

___ Small bowl	___ Spatula	___ Rubber scraper
___ Blender (optional)	___ Mixing spoon	___ Teaspoon
___ Dry measuring cups	___ Paring knife	___ Plastic wrap
___ Measuring spoons	___ Cutting board	

Metric	Customary	Ingredients
1	1	___ Avocado, peeled, seeded, mashed (See tips below.)
250 mL	1 cup	___ Mayonnaise
250 mL	1 cup	___ Sour cream
3-4 drops	3-4 drops	___ Hot pepper sauce
3 mL	1/2 tsp.	___ Worcestershire sauce
3 mL	1/2 tsp.	___ Onion juice
1 mL	1/4 tsp.	___ Garlic powder

Directions

___ **1. Combine** ingredients in a mixing bowl or in a blender.

___ **2. Blend** until smooth.

___ **3. Cover** with plastic wrap and chill for several hours.

Yield: About 625 mL (2 1/2 cups)

Per serving (1 Tbsp.): 62 calories; 0.4 g protein; 0.9 g carbohydrate; 6 g fat; 36 mg sodium; 6 mg cholesterol

Percentage of U.S. RDA:

Vitamin A:	2%	Niacin:	0.6%
Vitamin C:	0.8%	Calcium:	0.9%
Thiamin:	0.6%	Iron:	0.5%
Riboflavin:	1%		

Kitchen Management Tips

- Be sure the avocado is ripe or it will not mash well. To test for ripeness, press the avocado gently. If it feels soft, it is ready to use.
- To peel an avocado easily, cut the avocado in half lengthwise. Remove the pit. Insert a teaspoon between the avocado flesh and skin. Gently run the spoon around the avocado, separating the flesh from the skin.
- If you use a blender to make the dressing, you don't have to mash the avocado. Just cut it into small pieces and add it to the blender with the other ingredients.
- If you aren't using a blender, you can easily mash a ripe avocado with the back of a mixing spoon.

Thinking About . . . Avocado Dressing (R-14)

Questions

1. Using the formula in Appendix E of *Food for Today*, determine the following:

   a. Percentage of calories from fat _____

   b. Percentage of calories from carbohydrate _____

   c. Percentage of calories from protein _____

2. How could you reduce the fat content of this recipe? _____

   _____

3. List two safety guidelines to follow when preparing this recipe.

   a. _____

   b. _____

4. List three food preparation skills used in this recipe.

   a. _____

   b. _____

   c. _____

5. In what other ways could you serve this recipe besides as a salad dressing? _____

   _____

   _____

Evaluation

Complete the following after preparing the recipe:

1. How did the dressing look and taste? _____

   _____

2. How could you change or improve the recipe? _____

   _____

3. List any difficulties you had in preparing the recipe. _____

   _____

4. How would you solve the problem(s) next time? _____

   _____

FRESH SPINACH SALAD

Equipment

___ Salad bowl
___ Small bowl
___ Colander
___ Cutting board
___ Dry measuring cups

___ Measuring spoons
___ Paring knife
___ Chef's knife
___ Mixing spoon
___ Teaspoon

___ Rubber scraper
___ Spatula
___ Salad fork and spoon
___ Plastic wrap

Metric	Customary	Ingredients
2 L	2 qt. (about 10 oz.)	___ Fresh leaf spinach
1 medium	1 medium	___ Avocado
1 small	1 small	___ Bermuda onion
125 mL	½ cup	___ Plain yogurt
15 mL	1 Tbsp.	___ Cider or wine vinegar
30 mL	2 Tbsp.	___ Mayonnaise
15 mL	1 Tbsp.	___ Honey
30 mL	2 Tbsp.	___ Imitation bacon crumbles
30 mL	2 Tbsp.	___ Minced onion

Directions

___ 1. **Wash** spinach, remove large stems, and drain completely. (See tip below.)
___ 2. **Peel** avocado, remove pit, and slice.
___ 3. **Peel** Bermuda onion, slice and separate into rings.
___ 4. **Place** spinach, avocado slices, and onion rings in salad bowl and refrigerate, covered, until ready to serve.

___ 5. **Mix** together yogurt, vinegar, mayonnaise, honey, bacon crumbles, and minced onion. Cover and refrigerate until needed.
___ 6. **Pour** dressing over spinach salad and serve.

Yield: 6 servings

Per serving: 143 calories; 4 g protein; 11 g carbohydrate; 10 g fat; 145 mg sodium; 4 mg cholesterol

Percentage of U.S. RDA:

Vitamin A:	69%	Niacin:	6%
Vitamin C:	29%	Calcium:	10%
Thiamin:	6%	Iron:	11%
Riboflavin:	11%		

Kitchen Management Tip

■ Spinach is a low-growing plant, so its leaves come in contact with the soil. Wash it carefully to remove all dirt and grit. Remove stems and wilted or damaged leaves. Drain the spinach thoroughly in a colander.

Name _____   Class _____   Date _____

Thinking About . . . Fresh Spinach Salad (R-15)

Questions

1. Using the formula in Appendix E of *Food for Today,* determine the following:

   a. Percentage of calories from fat _____

   b. Percentage of calories from carbohydrate _____

   c. Percentage of calories from protein _____

2. Which ingredient(s) do you think contributed the most fat? _____
   _____

3. What is one way to reduce the calories and fat in the recipe? _____
   _____
   _____

4. List three sanitation guidelines to follow when preparing this recipe.

   a. _____

   b. _____

   c. _____

5. List four food preparation skills used in this recipe.

   a. _____

   b. _____

   c. _____

   d. _____

6. How could you turn this recipe into a main dish salad? _____
   _____

Evaluation

Complete the following after preparing the recipe:

1. How did the salad look and taste? _____
   _____

2. How could you change or improve the recipe? _____
   _____

3. List any difficulties you had in preparing the recipe. _____
   _____

4. How would you solve the problem(s) next time? _____
   _____

GELATIN SQUARES

Equipment

___ Medium saucepan	___ Liquid measuring cup
___ Square pan,	___ Knife
20 × 5 cm or 8 in.	___ Mixing spoon
___ Medium bowl	___ Pot holders

Metric	Customary	Ingredients
3	3	___ Envelopes unflavored gelatin
375 mL	1¹/₂ cups	___ Cold fruit juice (See tip below.)
375 mL	1¹/₂ cups	___ Fruit juice, heated to boiling (See tip below.)

Directions

___ 1. **Sprinkle** gelatin over cold juice in a medium bowl.

___ 2. **Let stand** 1 minute.

___ 3. **Add** hot juice.

___ 4. **Stir** until gelatin is completely dissolved.

___ 5. **Pour** into a 20- or 23-cm (8- or 9-in.) square pan.

___ 6. **Chill** until firm.

___ 7. **Cut** into 2.5-cm (1-in.) squares to serve.

Yield: About 6 dozen

Per serving (1 square): 6 calories; 0.3 g protein; 1 g carbohydrate; 0.1 g fat; 0.4 mg sodium; 0 cholesterol

Percentage of U.S. RDA:

Vitamin A:	0.2%	Niacin:	0.1%
Vitamin C:	3%	Calcium:	0.1%
Thiamin:	0.6%	Iron:	0.1%
Riboflavin:	0.1%		

Kitchen Management Tips

- Do not use fresh or frozen pineapple juice. Enzymes in the juice will keep gelatin from gelling.
- You can use the microwave oven to heat the fruit juice. Use a 2-liter (2-cup) glass measure. Heat 3-4 minutes on High or until juice starts to boil.
- If desired, the squares can be sprinkled with powdered sugar.
- Store the gelatin squares in the refrigerator.

Thinking About . . . Gelatin Squares (R-16)

Questions

1. Using the formula in Appendix E of *Food for Today,* determine the following:

   a. Percentage of calories from fat _____

   b. Percentage of calories from carbohydrate _____

   c. Percentage of calories from protein _____

2. List two safety guidelines to follow when preparing this recipe, either by the conventional or microwave method.

   a. _____

   b. _____

3. Why must the gelatin be completely dissolved? _____

   _____

4. Name two kinds of juice you could use in this recipe?

   a. _____

   b. _____

5. If you were preparing flavored gelatin and wanted to reduce the sweetness, what would you add?

   _____

   _____

6. List two ways you might garnish or decorate gelatin squares to serve at a 5-year-old's birthday party.

   a. _____

   b. _____

Evaluation

Complete the following after preparing the recipe:

1. How did the gelatin squares look and taste? _____

   _____

2. How could you change or improve the recipe? _____

   _____

3. List any difficulties you had in preparing the recipe. _____

   _____

4. How would you solve the problem(s) next time? _____

   _____

TACO SALAD TOSS

Equipment

- ___ Large skillet with lid (for conventional cooking)
- ___ Plastic colander and nonmetal plate (for microwave cooking)
- ___ Microwave-safe casserole, 2 L or 2 qt. (for microwave cooking)
- ___ Large bowl
- ___ Serving bowls or plates
- ___ Cutting board
- ___ Liquid measuring cup
- ___ Dry measuring cups
- ___ Measuring spoons
- ___ Spatula
- ___ Chef's knife
- ___ Mixing spoon
- ___ Can opener
- ___ Grater
- ___ Rubber scraper
- ___ Slotted spoon
- ___ Pot holders

Metric	Customary	Ingredients
1 head	1 head	___ Iceberg lettuce
150 mL	2/3 cup	___ Chopped onion
1 clove	1 clove	___ Garlic, minced
30 mL	2 Tbsp.	___ Salad oil
500 g	1 lb.	___ Ground beef
227-g can	8-oz. can	___ Tomato sauce
30 mL	2 Tbsp.	___ Water
5 mL	1 tsp.	___ Chili powder
125 mL	1/2 cup	___ Bottled French dressing (optional)
1 L	4 cups	___ Taco chips
3	3	___ Tomatoes, thinly wedged
125 mL	1/2 cup	___ Sliced green onion
125 mL	1/2 cup	___ Sour cream or shredded cheese
		___ Ripe olives for garnish
		___ Bottled taco sauce

Yield: 5 servings

Per serving (without French dressing or cheese): 472 calories; 21 g protein; 30 g carbohydrate; 30 g fat; 575 mg sodium; 72 mg cholesterol

Percentage of U.S. RDA:

Vitamin A:	35%	Niacin:	25%
Vitamin C:	39%	Calcium:	9%
Thiamin:	13%	Iron:	19%
Riboflavin:	16%		

Conventional Directions

1. **Core,** rinse, and thoroughly drain lettuce.
2. **Refrigerate** in crisper or plastic bag.
3. **Sauté** onion and garlic in oil in skillet over medium heat until tender-crisp.
4. **Add** beef and brown.
5. **Drain** fat from mixture.
6. **Stir** in tomato sauce, water, and chili powder.
7. **Simmer,** covered over low heat for 10 minutes.
8. **Shred** lettuce very fine to a measure of 1500 mL (6 cups)
9. **Toss** lettuce with French dressing if desired.
10. **Spread** taco chips on individual salad plates.
11. **Top** the chips with meat mixture, lettuce, tomato, green onion, and sour cream or shredded cheese.
12. **Garnish** with olives if desired.
13. **Serve** with taco sauce.

Microwave Directions

Follow Steps 1 and 2 of Conventional Directions.

3. **Place** plastic colander on nonmetal plate. Crumble ground beef into colander and add onion and garlic. Mix well.
4. **Microwave** on High (100%) 5 or 6 minutes, stirring once halfway through cooking time.
5. **Remove** from microwave oven when meat is still tinged with pink. Stir well until pink color disappears.
6. **Pour** into 2 L (2 qt.) casserole and stir in tomato sauce, water, and chili powder.
7. **Microwave** on High (100%) for 2 to 3 minutes or until sauce is heated through.

Continue with Steps 8-13 of Conventional Directions.

Thinking About . . . Taco Salad Toss (R-17)

Questions

1. Using the formula in Appendix E of *Food for Today*, determine the following:

   a. Percentage of calories from fat _____

   b. Percentage of calories from carbohydrate _____

   c. Percentage of calories from protein _____

2. List three food preparation skills that are used in this recipe.

   a. _____

   b. _____

   c. _____

3. What two conventional cooking methods are used in this recipe?

   a. _____

   b. _____

4. List three safety guidelines to follow when preparing this recipe by the conventional method.

   a. _____

   b. _____

   c. _____

5. List three sanitation guidelines to follow when preparing this recipe.

   a. _____

   b. _____

   c. _____

6. In analyzing the instructions for conventional and microwave cooking, which method would you prefer to use? Why? _____

   _____

Evaluation

Complete the following after preparing the recipe:

1. How did the salad look and taste? _____

   _____

2. How could you change or improve the recipe? _____

   _____

3. List any difficulties you had in preparing the recipe. _____

   _____

4. How would you solve the problem(s) next time? _____

   _____

CREPES

Equipment

___ Large skillet	___ Dry measuring cups	___ Rubber scraper
___ Medium bowl	___ Measuring spoons	___ Paper towels
___ Sifter	___ Spatula	___ Waxed paper
___ Rotary beater	___ Mixing spoon	___ Pot holders
___ Liquid measuring cup	___ Turner	

Metric	Customary	Ingredients
45 mL	3 Tbsp.	___ Butter or margarine
175 mL	3/4 cup	___ All-purpose flour, sifted
1 mL	1/4 tsp.	___ Salt
3	3	___ Eggs
250 mL	1 cup	___ Low-fat milk
		___ Cheese Filling for Crepes (Recipe #19)

Directions

___ 1. **Melt** butter or margarine in the skillet.

___ 2. **Combine** flour and salt in a medium bowl.

___ 3. **Add** eggs, milk, and melted butter or margarine to dry ingredients. Set skillet aside.

___ 4. **Beat** the batter with a rotary beater until smooth.

___ 5. **Heat** buttered skillet over medium heat. (Do not add more butter or margarine.)

___ 6. **Pour** a scant 30 mL (2 Tbsp.) batter in the skillet. Tilt the pan to spread the batter over the bottom. Work quickly, before the batter has a chance to set.

___ 7. **Cook** until top of crepe appears dry and bottom is light brown.

___ 8. **Turn** and brown the other side.

___ 9. **Remove** the crepe by turning the pan upside down over a plate or paper towel. It can also be removed with a turner, but be careful not to tear the crepe.

___ 10. **Stack** between sheets of paper toweling until ready to use.

Yield: About 8 crepes

Per serving (2 crepes without filling):
252 calories; 9 g protein; 21 g carbohydrate; 14 g fat; 297 mg sodium; 234 mg cholesterol

Percentage of U.S. RDA:

Vitamin A:	13%	Niacin:	7%
Vitamin C:	1%	Calcium:	10%
Thiamin:	14%	Iron:	10%
Riboflavin:	18%		

Kitchen Management Tips

- Crepe batter should be the consistency of heavy cream.
- Results are better if refrigerated and allowed to rest for about an hour. The resting time lets the flour absorb the moisture. In addition, air bubbles break up, making a smoother batter and crepes without tiny holes.

Name _____ Class _____ Date _____

Thinking About . . . Crepes (R-18)

Questions

1. Using the formula in Appendix E of *Food for Today,* determine the following:

    a. Percentage of calories from fat _____

    b. Percentage of calories from carbohydrate _____

    c. Percentage of calories from protein _____

2. List two safety guidelines to follow when preparing this recipe.

    a. _____

    b. _____

3. List three food preparation skills used in this recipe.

    a. _____

    b. _____

    c. _____

4. Name two other kinds of filling besides cheese that you could use in the crepes.

    a. _____

    b. _____

5. How does crepe batter differ from pancake batter? _____

   _____

6. What could you use as a garnish? _____

   _____

Evaluation

Complete the following after preparing the recipe:

1. How did the crepes look and taste? _____

   _____

2. How could you change or improve the recipe? _____

   _____

3. List any difficulties you had in preparing the recipe. _____

   _____

4. How would you solve the problem(s) next time? _____

   _____

CHEESE FILLING FOR CREPES

Equipment

___ Baking dish, 1.5 L or 1½ qt.	___ Strainer	___ Paring knife
___ Saucepan, 1 L or 1 qt (for conventional cooking)	___ Cutting board	___ Mixing spoon
___ Glass measuring cup, 500 mL or 2 c. (for microwave cooking)	___ Liquid measuring cup	___ Rubber scraper
	___ Dry measuring cups	___ Pot holders
	___ Measuring spoons	___ Cooling rack
	___ Spatula	

Metric	Customary	Ingredients
350 mL	1½ cups	___ Creamed cottage cheese
8	8	___ Cooked crepes (See Crepes recipe.)
2 mL	½ tsp.	___ Ground nutmeg
30 mL	2 Tbsp.	___ Sugar
5 mL	1 tsp.	___ Cornstarch
125 mL	½ cup	___ Orange juice
5 mL	1 tsp.	___ Butter or margarine
250 mL	1 cup	___ Fresh strawberries, sliced (or frozen strawberries)

Yield: 4 servings, 2 crepes each

Per serving (filling for 2 crepes):
149 calories; 11 g protein;
15 g carbohydrate; 5 g fat;
353 mg sodium; 15 mg cholesterol

Percentage of U.S. RDA:

Vitamin A:	4%	Niacin:	1%
Vitamin C:	39%	Calcium:	6%
Thiamin:	3%	Iron:	2%
Riboflavin:	10%		

Conventional Directions

___ 1. **Preheat** oven to 180°C (350°F).

___ 2. **Drain** excess liquid from cottage cheese.

___ 3. **Place** about 45 mL (3 Tbsp.) cottage cheese on each crepe.

___ 4. **Sprinkle** with nutmeg.

___ 5. **Roll.** (See tip below.)

___ 6. **Place** in 1.5-L (1½-qt.) baking dish.

___ 7. **Bake** at 180°C (350°F) for 15 to 20 minutes or until heated through.

___ 8. **Combine** sugar and cornstarch in a 1-L (1-qt.) saucepan.

___ 9. **Stir** in orange juice.

___ 10. **Cook** over medium heat, stirring constantly until thickened. Boil an additional 2 minutes.

___ 11. **Stir** in butter or margarine.

___ 12. **Remove** from heat.

___ 13. **Stir** in strawberries.

___ 14. **Serve** two crepes per serving with about 50 mL (¼ cup) strawberry sauce.

Microwave Directions

The microwave oven can be used to prepare the strawberry sauce. Follow the Conventional Directions for Steps 1-7.

___ 8. **Mix** the sugar and cornstarch in a 500-mL (2-cup) glass measure.

___ 9. **Add** the orange juice and blend well.

___ 10. **Microwave** on High (100%) for 3 to 5 minutes, stirring after each minute. Sauce should thicken slightly and become bubbly.

___ 11. **Stir** in butter and strawberries.

___ 12. **Heat** on High (100%) until mixture just begins to bubble, about ½ to 1½ minutes, depending on the original temperature of the strawberries..

___ 13. **Serve** two baked crepes with about 50 mL (¼ cup) strawberry sauce.

Kitchen Management Tip

■ Crepes can be rolled in two ways:
1. Place filling at one end and roll. The ends are left open.
2. Place filling at one end. Roll once, fold the two long ends over to make an envelope and continue rolling. With this method, the filling will not run out.

Thinking About . . . Cheese Filling for Crepes (R-19)

Questions

1. Using the formula in Appendix E of *Food for Today,* determine the following:
   a. Percentage of calories from fat _____
   b. Percentage of calories from carbohydrate _____
   c. Percentage of calories from protein _____

2. This recipe provides more than one-third of your daily requirement for vitamin C. Which food(s) do you think contributed the vitamin C? _____

   _____

3. List two conventional cooking methods that are used in this recipe.
   a. _____
   b. _____

4. List two safety guidelines to follow in preparing this recipe by the conventional method.
   a. _____
   b. _____

5. If you are making the sauce when strawberries are out of season, what other fruits might you use?

   _____

   _____

6. Looking over both the conventional and microwave directions, which cooking method would you prefer? Why? _____

   _____

Evaluation

Complete the following after preparing the recipe:

1. How did the filling and sauce look and taste? _____

   _____

2. How could you change or improve the recipe? _____

   _____

3. List any difficulties you had in preparing the recipe. _____

   _____

4. How would you solve the problem(s) next time? _____

   _____

HEARTY CHOWDER WITH TOAST

Equipment

- Heavy saucepan, 3 L or 3 qt. (for conventional cooking)
- Microwave-safe casserole or mixing bowl, 4 L or 4 qt. (for microwave cooking)
- Cutting board
- Toaster
- Grater
- Can opener
- Liquid measuring cup
- Dry measuring cups
- Measuring spoons
- Spatula
- Chef's knife
- Mixing spoon
- Rubber scraper
- Pot holders

Metric	Customary	Ingredients
50 mL	1/4 cup	Butter or margarine
50 mL	1/4 cup	Chopped onion
284-g pkg.	10-oz. pkg.	Frozen peas and carrots
30 mL	2 Tbsp.	All-purpose flour
1 mL	1/4 tsp.	Ground sage
1 mL	1/4 tsp.	Crushed dried thyme
Dash	Dash	Ground black pepper
750 mL	3 cups	Low-fat milk
305-g can	10 3/4-oz. can	Condensed cream of potato soup
3	3	Frankfurters, sliced
125 mL	1/2 cup	Shredded cheddar cheese
6 slices	6 slices	Rye bread
30 mL	2 Tbsp.	Butter or margarine
50 mL	1/4 cup	Shredded cheddar cheese

Yield: 6 servings

Per serving: 501 calories; 17 g protein; 34 g carbohydrate; 34 g fat; 1230 mg sodium; 87 mg cholesterol

Percentage of U.S. RDA:
Vitamin A: 95% Niacin: 13%
Vitamin C: 15% Calcium: 34%
Thiamin: 20% Iron: 13%
Riboflavin: 25%

Conventional Directions

1. **Melt** butter in a heavy 3-L (3-qt.) saucepan.
2. **Add** onion and frozen peas and carrots.
3. **Sauté** until tender, about 5 minutes.
4. **Stir** in flour, sage, thyme, and pepper.
5. **Remove** from heat.
6. **Add** milk and soup gradually, stirring to blend well.
7. **Cook** over medium heat, stirring constantly for about 20 minutes or until thickened.
8. **Add** frankfurters and cheese.
9. **Heat** to serving temperature, about 2 or 3 minutes.
10. **Toast** thick slices of rye bread on both sides.
11. **Butter** the toasted bread.
12. **Sprinkle** the bread with shredded cheddar cheese.
13. **Broil** until cheese is melted. Serve with soup.

Microwave Directions

1. **Place** butter in mixing bowl or casserole. Microwave on High (100%) for 30 to 45 seconds.
2. **Add** chopped onion and frozen peas and carrots.
3. **Microwave** on High (100%) until tender, about 4 to 5 minutes, stirring several times during cooking.
4. **Stir** in flour, sage, thyme, and pepper until well blended.
5. **Add** milk and soup gradually, stirring to blend well.
6. **Microwave** on High (100%) for 10 to 12 minutes, stirring several times.
7. **Add** frankfurters and cheese.
8. **Microwave** on High (100%) 2 or 3 minutes or until mixture reaches serving temperature.
9. **Prepare** toast according to Conventional Directions, Steps 10-13.

Thinking About . . . Hearty Chowder with Toast (R-20)

Questions

1. Using the formula in Appendix E of *Food for Today,* determine the following:

   a. Percentage of calories from fat _____

   b. Percentage of calories from carbohydrate _____

   c. Percentage of calories from protein _____

2. This dish supplies nearly 100% of the U.S. RDA of vitamin A and almost one-third of the calcium. Which ingredient(s) do you think supplies most of each?

   a. Vitamin A: _____

   b. Calcium: _____

3. List four safety guidelines to follow when preparing this recipe by the conventional method.

   a. _____

   b. _____

   c. _____

   d. _____

4. List three food preparation skills that are used in this recipe.

   a. _____

   b. _____

   c. _____

5. What would happen if you cooked the chowder without stirring it? _____
   _____

6. What would you serve with this recipe for a soup party? _____
   _____

Evaluation

Complete the following after preparing the recipe:

1. How did the soup look and taste? _____
   _____

2. How could you change or improve the recipe? _____
   _____

3. List any difficulties you had in preparing the recipe. _____
   _____

4. How would you solve the problem(s) next time? _____
   _____

CONEY ISLANDS

Equipment

- ___ Large skillet (for conventional cooking)
- ___ Medium bowl (for conventional cooking)
- ___ 2.5 L (2½ qt.) microwave-safe casserole (for microwave cooking)
- ___ Cutting board
- ___ Liquid measuring cup
- ___ Dry measuring cups
- ___ Measuring spoons
- ___ Can opener
- ___ Chef's knife
- ___ Tongs
- ___ Mixing spoon
- ___ Rubber scraper
- ___ Pot holder
- ___ Cooling rack

Metric	Customary	Ingredients
8	8	___ Frankfurters, slit lengthwise
30 mL	2 Tbsp.	___ Butter or margarine
Two (319-g) cans	Two (11¼-oz.) cans	___ Condensed chili beef soup
150 mL	⅔ cup	___ Water
8	8	___ Frankfurter rolls, split and toasted (See tip below.)
250 mL	1 cup	___ Chopped onion

Conventional Directions

- ___ 1. **Brown** frankfurters in butter or margarine in large skillet.
- ___ 2. **Mix** soup and water in a bowl. Add to the skillet.
- ___ 3. **Heat,** stirring occasionally.
- ___ 4. **Place** frankfurters in rolls.
- ___ 5. **Spoon** chili over frankfurters.
- ___ 6. **Top** with chopped onion.

Microwave Directions

- ___ 1. **Mix** soup and water in the casserole.
- ___ 2. **Microwave** on High (100%) for 3 minutes, stirring after 1½ minutes.
- ___ 3. **Add** frankfurters.
- ___ 4. **Microwave** on High (100%) for 6 to 8 minutes. Rearrange frankfurters halfway through cooking time.
- ___ 5. **Place** frankfurters in toasted rolls.
- ___ 6. **Spoon** chili over frankfurters.
- ___ 7. **Top** with chopped onion.

Yield: 8 sandwiches

Per sandwich: 438 calories; 14 g protein; 37 g carbohydrate; 26 g fat; 1448 g sodium; 38 g cholesterol

Percentage of U.S. RDA:

Vitamin A:	21%	Niacin:	17%
Vitamin C:	22%	Calcium:	7%
Thiamin:	16%	Iron:	18%
Riboflavin:	12%		

Kitchen Management Tips

- In preparing the recipe by the conventional method, be sure to use a skillet large enough to hold the full recipe. If you don't have a large skillet, use a large saucepan.
- To toast frankfurter rolls, split them lengthwise and spread with a little butter or margarine. Broil until lightly browned. Watch carefully because they brown quickly.

Name _____ Class _____ Date _____

Thinking About . . . Coney Islands (R-21)

Questions

1. Using the formula in Appendix E of *Food for Today,* determine the following:

   a. Percentage of calories from fat _____

   b. Percentage of calories from carbohydrate _____

   c. Percentage of calories from protein _____

2. Which ingredients do you think contributed the most fat? _____
   _____

3. Name two conventional cooking methods that are used in this recipe.

   a. _____

   b. _____

4. List three safety guidelines to follow when preparing this recipe by the conventional method.

   a. _____

   b. _____

   c. _____

5. Give two different steps that are followed when you use the microwave oven rather than the conventional oven to prepare this recipe.

   a. _____

   b. _____

6. What other foods would you serve with this recipe to make a nutritious lunch? _____
   _____

Evaluation

Complete the following after preparing the recipe:

1. How did the Coney Islands look and taste? _____
   _____

2. How could you change or improve the recipe? _____
   _____

3. List any difficulties you had in preparing the recipe. _____
   _____

4. How would you solve the problem(s) next time? _____
   _____

CREOLE SPAGHETTI

Equipment

____ Large saucepan
(for conventional cooking)
____ Large skillet
(for conventional cooking)
____ Large casserole or 2-L
(2-qt.) glass measuring cup
(for microwave cooking)
____ Plastic colander and
microwave-safe plate
(for microwave cooking)

____ Cutting board
____ Liquid measuring cup
____ Dry measuring cups
____ Measuring spoons
____ Spatula
____ Grater
____ Can opener
____ Chef's knife

____ Mixing spoon
____ Slotted spoon
____ Kitchen fork
____ Ladle
____ Waxed paper
____ Pot holders
____ Cooling racks

Metric	Customary	Ingredients
50 mL	$1/4$ cup	____ Butter or margarine
50 mL	$1/4$ cup	____ Minced green pepper
50 mL	$1/4$ cup	____ Minced onion
50 mL	$1/4$ cup	____ All-purpose flour
7 mL	$1 1/2$ tsp.	____ Salt
1 mL	$1/4$ tsp.	____ Ground pepper
794-g can	28-oz. can	____ Canned tomatoes
75 mL	$1/3$ cup	____ Grated cheddar cheese
500 g	1 lb.	____ Ground beef
225 g	8 oz.	____ Spaghetti, cooked

Yield: 6 servings

Per serving: 438 calories;
21 g protein; 39 g carbohydrate;
22 g fat; 900 mg sodium;
79 mg cholesterol

Percentage of U.S. RDA:

Vitamin A:	24%	Niacin:	33%
Vitamin C:	34%	Calcium:	11%
Thiamin:	32%	Iron:	23%
Riboflavin:	20%		

Conventional Directions

____ 1. **Melt** butter or margarine in large saucepan.
____ 2. **Sauté** green pepper and onion in butter.
____ 3. **Blend** in flour, salt, and pepper.
____ 4. **Cook** until thickened.
____ 5. **Add** tomatoes, stirring constantly.
____ 6. **Cook** about 5 minutes.
____ 7. **Add** grated cheese and stir until cheese is melted. Remove from heat.
____ 8. **Brown** ground beef in skillet and cook thoroughly. Drain off excess fat.
____ 9. **Add** meat to tomato mixture.
____ 10. **Cover** and simmer for 10 minutes over low heat or until mixture is piping hot.
____ 11. **Pour** tomato-meat mixture over cooked spaghetti. Stir to mix thoroughly.
____ 12. **Serve** hot.

Microwave Directions

____ 1. **Melt** butter or margarine on High (100%) for 30-45 seconds in large casserole or 2-L (2-qt.) glass measure.
____ 2. **Add** onion and green pepper. Microwave on High (100%) until vegetables begin to soften, about $1 1/2$-$2 1/2$ minutes.
____ 3. **Add** flour, salt, and pepper. Stir until well blended.
____ 4. **Add** tomatoes, blending well with flour mixture.
____ 5. **Microwave** on High (100%) for 5 to 7 minutes, stirring several times to blend. Remove from oven.
____ 6. **Add** cheese and stir until cheese is melted.
____ 7. **Place** ground beef in plastic colander and set on a microwave-safe plate or casserole to catch drippings.
____ 8. **Microwave** ground beef for 4 to 5 minutes on High (100%) or until most of the pink color disappears.
____ 9. **Add** the ground beef to the tomato mixture.
____ 10. **Microwave** on High (100%) 4 to 5 minutes or until bubbly.
____ 11. **Pour** tomato-meat mixture over cooked spaghetti. Mix well.
____ 12. **Serve** hot.

Thinking About . . . Creole Spaghetti (R-22)

Questions

1. Using the formula in Appendix E of *Food for Today*, determine the following:

   a. Percentage of calories from fat _____

   b. Percentage of calories from carbohydrate _____

   c. Percentage of calories from protein _____

2. List three basic food preparation skills that are used in this recipe.

   a. _____

   b. _____

   c. _____

3. Name two conventional cooking methods that are used in this recipe.

   a. _____

   b. _____

4. List two safety guidelines to follow when browning the meat by the conventional method.

   a. _____

   b. _____

5. List two additional safety guidelines to follow when preparing this recipe in the microwave oven.

   a. _____

   b. _____

6. Do you think preparing the recipe in the microwave oven would require more or less work? Give reasons for your answer. _____

   _____

Evaluation

Complete the following after preparing the recipe:

1. How did the spaghetti look and taste? _____

   _____

2. How could you change or improve the recipe? _____

   _____

3. List any difficulties you had in preparing the recipe. _____

   _____

4. How would you solve the problem(s) next time? _____

   _____

SWEET AND SOUR PORK

Equipment

____ Large skillet with lid
    (for conventional cooking)
____ 2-L (2-qt.) microwave-safe
    casserole or skillet
    (for microwave cooking)
____ Cutting board

____ Small bowl
____ Strainer and bowl
____ Dry measuring cups
____ Measuring spoons
____ Can opener
____ Spatula

____ Chef's knife
____ Mixing spoon
____ Slotted spoon
____ Rubber scraper
____ Pot holders

Metric	Customary	Ingredients
567-g can	20-oz. can	____ Crushed pineapple in syrup
500 g	1 lb.	____ Pork shoulder, cubed
30 mL	2 Tbsp.	____ Vegetable oil
250 mL	1 cup	____ Sliced carrots
125 mL	1/2 cup	____ Sliced green onions
125 mL	1/2 cup	____ Cubed green pepper
50 mL	1/4 cup	____ Plum jam
30 mL	2 Tbsp.	____ Red wine vinegar
30 mL	2 Tbsp.	____ Natural soy sauce
15 mL	1 Tbsp.	____ Cornstarch
3 mL	1/2 tsp.	____ Ground ginger

Yield: 4 servings

Per serving: 459 calories;
29 g protein; 51 g carbohydrate;
16 g fat; 597 mg sodium;
83 mg cholesterol

Percentage of U.S. RDA:
Vitamin A: 174%   Niacin: 30%
Vitamin C: 50%   Calcium: 5%
Thiamin: 78%   Iron: 13%
Riboflavin: 20%

Conventional Directions

____ 1. **Drain** pineapple, reserving syrup.
____ 2. **Brown** pork in oil.
____ 3. **Cover** and simmer for 20 minutes.
____ 4. **Remove** pork from skillet. Set aside.
____ 5. **Stir** carrots, onions, and pepper into pan drippings.
____ 6. **Sauté** until just tender.
____ 7. **Remove** vegetables from pan. Set aside.
____ 8. **Add** plum jam to skillet. Cook over low heat, stirring, until melted.
____ 9. **Add** reserved pineapple syrup, vinegar, and soy sauce to jam. Cook one minute.
____ 10. **Combine** cornstarch and ginger in a small bowl.
____ 11. **Stir** a little of the hot sauce from the skillet into the cornstarch and ginger.
____ 12. **Add** cornstarch mixture to skillet.
____ 13. **Cook,** stirring constantly, until mixture is clear and thickened.
____ 14. **Return** pork and vegetables to skillet and add crushed pineapple.
____ 15. **Toss** lightly to coat with sauce and heat to serving temperature.
____ 16. **Serve** with cooked rice, if desired.

Microwave Directions

____ 1. **Drain** pineapple, reserving syrup.
____ 2. **Combine** pineapple syrup, soy sauce, and cubed pork in a large microwave-safe casserole or skillet.
____ 3. **Microwave** on High (100%) for 25 to 30 minutes.
____ 4. **Remove** pork and set aside.
____ 5. **Add** carrots, onions, and green pepper to casserole.
____ 6. **Microwave** on High (100%) for 4 to 6 minutes or until just tender. Stir once during cooking.
____ 7. **Add** plum jam and vinegar to vegetable mixture. Stir well.
____ 8. **Microwave** on High (100%) 1 to 2 minutes or until jam melts.
____ 9. **Combine** cornstarch and ginger in a small bowl.
____ 10. **Stir** a little of the hot liquid from the casserole into the cornstarch.
____ 11. **Add** cornstarch mixture to the casserole.
____ 12. **Microwave** on High (100%) for 2 minutes or until clear and thickened.
____ 13. **Add** crushed pineapple and cooked pork to mixture. Stir well.
____ 14. **Microwave** on High (100%) 4 to 6 minutes or until heated through.
____ 15. **Serve** with cooked rice, if desired.

Thinking About . . . Sweet and Sour Pork (R-23)

Questions

1. Using the formula in Appendix E of *Food for Today*, determine the following:

   a. Percentage of calories from fat _____

   b. Percentage of calories from carbohydrate _____

   c. Percentage of calories from protein _____

2. This recipe provides almost twice the amount of vitamin A needed daily and half the vitamin C. What food(s) do you think contributed each?

   a. Vitamin A: _____

   b. Vitamin C: _____

3. This recipe provides more than three-fourths of the daily thiamin requirement. What food(s) do you think contributed most of the thiamin? _____

4. List three food preparation skills that are used in this recipe.

   a. _____

   b. _____

   c. _____

5. Name two conventional cooking methods that are used in this recipe.

   a. _____

   b. _____

6. List three safety guidelines to follow when preparing this recipe by the conventional method.

   a. _____

   b. _____

   c. _____

Evaluation

Complete the following after preparing the recipe:

1. How did the pork dish look and taste? _____
   _____

2. How could you change or improve the recipe? _____
   _____

3. List any difficulties you had in preparing the recipe. _____
   _____

4. How would you solve the problem(s) next time? _____
   _____

SURPRISE BURGERS

Equipment

___ Broiler pan
    (for conventional cooking)
___ Microwave roasting rack
    in baking dish or micro-
    wave bacon rack
    (for microwave cooking)

___ Large mixing bowl
___ Cutting board
___ Measuring spoons
___ Chef's knife
___ Paring knife
___ Mixing spoon

___ Spatula
___ Rubber scraper
___ Turner
___ Waxed paper
___ Pot holders
___ Cooling racks

Metric	Customary	Ingredients
1 mL	1/4 tsp.	___ Garlic powder
Dash	Dash	___ Ground black pepper
1	1	___ Egg
10 mL	2 tsp.	___ Worcestershire sauce
500 g	1 lb.	___ Ground beef
		___ Fillings: tomato slices, grated cheese, pickle relish, chopped onion, dill pickle slices, blue cheese

Conventional Directions

___ 1. **Add** the garlic powder, pepper, egg, and Worcestershire sauce to the ground beef and mix thoroughly.

___ 2. **Form** 8 very thin patties.

___ 3. **Top** 4 of the patties with the fillings, using any combination desired. Keep the fillings in the center of the patties.

___ 4. **Cover** the filled patties with the 4 remaining patties, sealing the edges well so the filling will not run out.

___ 5. **Broil** until done as desired.

Microwave Directions

Follow Conventional Directions Steps 1-4.

___ 5. **Place** patties on a microwave roasting rack in a baking dish or on a bacon rack.

___ 6. **Microwave** on High (100%) for 3 minutes on the first side.

___ 7. **Turn** patties over.

___ 8. **Microwave** on High (100%) for $3\frac{1}{2}$ to $4\frac{1}{2}$ minutes or until done.

Yield: 4 servings

Per serving (with cheese and tomato):
288 calories; 23 g protein; 2 g carbohydrate; 20 g fat; 139 mg sodium; 153 mg cholesterol

Percentage of U.S. RDA:

Vitamin A:	9%	Niacin:	23%
Vitamin C:	7%	Calcium:	7%
Thiamin:	7%	Iron:	17%
Riboflavin:	15%		

Kitchen Management Tips

■ For easier cleaning, line the *bottom* broiler pan with foil to catch the drippings. Do not line the top pan with foil because fat would accumulate and catch fire. And the food would fry in the fat instead of broiling.

■ To clean the top broiler pan easily, as soon as you remove the burgers, sprinkle the hot pan with a little liquid detergent and cover it with a wet dish cloth.

Thinking About . . . Surprise Burgers (R-24)

Questions

1. Using the formula in Appendix E of *Food for Today,* determine the following:

    a. Percentage of calories from fat _____

    b. Percentage of calories from carbohydrate _____

    c. Percentage of calories from protein _____

2. What ingredient(s) do you think contributed the most fat? _____

    _____

3. List two sanitation guidelines to follow when preparing this recipe.

    a. _____

    b. _____

4. List three safety guidelines to follow when broiling the burgers.

    a. _____

    b. _____

    c. _____

5. List two safety guidelines to follow when preparing the recipe in a microwave oven.

    a. _____

    b. _____

6. What foods, other than the ones suggested in the recipe, could you use for the filling? _____

    _____

Evaluation

Complete the following after preparing the recipe:

1. How did the burgers look and taste? _____

    _____

2. How could you change or improve the recipe? _____

    _____

3. List any difficulties you had in preparing the recipe. _____

    _____

4. How would you solve the problem(s) next time? _____

    _____

ORIENTAL CHICKEN

Equipment

___ Wok with lid	___ Measuring spoons	___ Chef's knife
___ Small bowl	___ Can opener	___ Utility knife
___ Cutting board	___ Spatula	___ Mixing spoon
___ Liquid measuring cup	___ Boning knife	___ Rubber scraper
___ Dry measuring cups		

Metric	Customary	Ingredients
2	2	___ Medium chicken breasts
45 mL	3 Tbsp.	___ Cooking oil
4	4	___ Green onions, cut in 2.5-cm (1-in.) lengths
2 mL	1/2 tsp.	___ Finely shredded fresh ginger root
375 mL	1 1/2 cups	___ Water
250 mL	1 cup	___ Celery, sliced thin on the diagonal
250 mL	1 cup	___ Sliced fresh mushrooms
125 mL	1/2 cup	___ Diced red or green bell pepper
75 mL	1/3 cup	___ Soy sauce
75 mL	1/3 cup	___ Unsweetened grapefruit juice
227-g can	8-oz. can	___ Bamboo shoots, drained
10 mL	2 tsp.	___ Sugar
10 mL	2 tsp.	___ Cornstarch
30 mL	2 Tbsp.	___ Cold water
500 mL	2 cups	___ Hot cooked rice

Yield: 4 servings

Per serving (with rice):
413 calories; 32 g protein;
39 g carbohydrate; 14 g fat;
1480 mg sodium; 72 mg cholesterol

Percentage of U.S. RDA:

Vitamin A:	23%	Niacin:	73%
Vitamin C:	53%	Calcium:	5%
Thiamin:	17%	Iron:	18%
Riboflavin:	15%		

Directions

___ 1. **Remove** skin from chicken breasts. With a very sharp knife, remove bones. Cut chicken into very thin slices, about 3 mm (1/8 in.) thick. Cut slices into thin strips, about 1.3 cm (1/2 in.) wide.

___ 2. **Heat** oil in wok.

___ 3. **Add** chicken, green onions, and ginger root. Stir-fry until chicken is just lightly browned.

___ 4. **Add** the 375 mL (1 1/2 cups) water, celery, mushrooms, red or green pepper, soy sauce, and grapefruit juice.

___ 5. **Cover.** Simmer for about 5 minutes.

___ 6. **Add** drained bamboo shoots and sugar. Stir well.

___ 7. **Cover** and cook just until heated through.

___ 8. **Measure** cornstarch into small bowl.

___ 9. **Add** the 30 mL (2 Tbsp.) cold water slowly to the cornstarch, stirring to make a smooth mixture.

___ 10. **Stir** cornstarch slowly into chicken mixture.

___ 11. **Cook** and stir until thick and bubbly.

___ 12. **Serve** over hot cooked rice.

Thinking About . . . Oriental Chicken (R-25)

Questions

1. Using the formula in Appendix E of *Food for Today,* determine the following:

    a. Percentage of calories from fat _____

    b. Percentage of calories from carbohydrate _____

    c. Percentage of calories from protein _____

2. This recipe supplies almost three-fourths of the daily requirement for niacin. What food(s) do you think contributed the niacin? _____

    _____

3. The recipe supplies half of the daily requirement for vitamin C. What food(s) do you think contributed that nutrient?_____

4. List three safety guidelines to follow in preparing this recipe.

    a. _____

    b. _____

    c. _____

5. List two food preparation skills that are used in this recipe.

    a. _____

    b. _____

6. List two sanitation guidelines to follow to prevent cross-contamination and possible spread of any salmonella bacteria.

    a. _____

    b. _____

7. Why do some recipes recommend fresh ginger root rather than ground ginger? _____

    _____

Evaluation

Complete the following after preparing the recipe:

1. How did the chicken look and taste? _____

    _____

2. How could you change or improve the recipe? _____

    _____

3. List any difficulties you had in preparing the recipe. _____

    _____

4. How would you solve the problem(s) next time? _____

    _____

CRISPY CATFISH

Equipment

___ Large heavy skillet	___ Dry measuring cups	___ Turner
___ 2 large shallow pans	___ Measuring spoons	___ Mixing spoon
___ Pot holders	___ Liquid measuring cup	___ Tongs
___ Platter	___ Spatula	___ Paper towels

Metric	Customary	Ingredients
6	6	___ Skinned, pan-dressed catfish
125 mL	1/2 cup	___ Evaporated milk
5 mL	1 tsp.	___ Salt
Dash	Dash	___ Ground black pepper
250 mL	1 cup	___ All-purpose flour
125 mL	1/2 cup	___ Yellow cornmeal
10 mL	2 tsp.	___ Ground paprika
12 slices	12 slices	___ Bacon

Directions

___ 1. **Thaw** fish, if frozen.

___ 2. **Clean,** wash, and dry fish.

___ 3. **Combine** milk, salt, and pepper in large, shallow pan.

___ 4. **Combine** flour, cornmeal, and paprika in another large, shallow pan.

___ 5. **Dip** fish in milk mixture and roll in flour mixture.

___ 6. **Fry** bacon in a large, heavy skillet until crisp.

___ 7. **Remove** bacon, reserving fat for frying.

___ 8. **Drain** bacon on paper towels.

___ 9. **Fry** fish in hot bacon fat for about 4 minutes.

___ 10. **Turn** carefully and fry for 5 to 6 minutes longer or until fish is brown and flakes easily when tested with a fork.

___ 11. **Drain** on paper towels.

___ 12. **Serve** with bacon.

Yield: 6 servings

Per serving: 511 calories; 29 g protein; 26 g carbohydrate; 32 g fat; 777 mg sodium; 99 mg cholesterol

Percentage of U.S. RDA:

Vitamin A:	13%	Niacin:	23%
Vitamin C:	18%	Calcium:	9%
Thiamin:	26%	Iron:	11%
Riboflavin:	15%		

Kitchen Management Tips

■ Most catfish sold in consumer markets is grown on fish farms.

■ Dry fish as thoroughly as possible after washing. Even a little moisture will keep the breading from sticking properly.

■ Before breading the fish, set up an assembly line so that you work in a logical sequence. If you work from right to left, place the washed-and-dried fish on the far left, then the pan for the liquid mixture, then a pan for the flour mixture, and on the right, a large platter or two to hold the breaded fish. Stacking will cause the breading to break off, so place the fish on the platter in a single layer.

Thinking About . . . Crispy Catfish (R-26)

Questions

1. Using the formula in Appendix E of *Food for Today*, determine the following:

   a. Percentage of calories from fat _____

   b. Percentage of calories from carbohydrate _____

   c. Percentage of calories from protein _____

2. List two food preparation skills that are used in this recipe.

   a. _____

   b. _____

3. What is the cooking method used in this recipe? _____

4. List three safety guidelines to follow when frying the fish.

   a. _____

   b. _____

   c. _____

5. Why is the fish fried in bacon fat? _____
_____

6. What would be the advantage of using a vegetable oil such as corn oil in place of bacon fat?
_____
_____

7. Why does fish require a shorter cooking time than beef, pork, and poultry? _____
_____

8. After preparing the fish, how can you get rid of the fish odors on your hands? _____
_____

Evaluation

Complete the following after preparing the recipe:

1. How did the fish look and taste? _____
_____

2. How could you change or improve the recipe? _____
_____

3. List any difficulties you had in preparing the recipe. _____
_____

4. How would you solve the problem(s) next time? _____
_____

ITALIAN TUNA BURGERS

Equipment

___ Broiling pan or cookie sheet (for conventional cooking)
___ Microwave-safe plate or platter (for microwave cooking)
___ Large mixing bowl
___ Cutting board
___ Grater
___ Dry measuring cups
___ Measuring spoons
___ Spatula
___ Chef's knife
___ Mixing spoon
___ Fork
___ Rubber scraper
___ Turner
___ Paper towels (for microwave cooking)
___ Pot holders

Metric	Customary	Ingredients
Two (184-g) cans	Two (6½-oz.) cans	___ Tuna, drained
125 mL	½ cup	___ Mayonnaise
15 mL	1 Tbsp.	___ Ketchup
1 mL	¼ tsp.	___ Crushed dried oregano
8 mL	1½ tsp.	___ Instant minced onion
1	1	___ Egg, slightly beaten
1 slice	1 slice	___ White bread (with crusts removed), crumbled
6	6	___ Hamburger buns
1	1	___ Tomato, cut into 6 thin slices
125 mL	½ cup	___ Shredded mozzarella cheese
50 mL	¼ cup	___ Grated Parmesan cheese

Yield: 6 servings

Per serving: 407 calories;
27 g protein; 26 g carbohydrate;
21 g fat; 1036 mg sodium;
106 mg cholesterol

Percentage of U.S. RDA:
Vitamin A:	9%	Niacin:	49%
Vitamin C:	4%	Calcium:	18%
Thiamin:	15%	Iron:	15%
Riboflavin:	15%		

Conventional Directions

___ 1. **Flake** tuna in a large bowl.
___ 2. **Stir** in mayonnaise, ketchup, oregano, and onion.
___ 3. **Stir** in egg.
___ 4. **Add** bread crumbs to the tuna and mix well.
___ 5. **Spoon** 75 mL (⅓ cup) mixture onto bottom half of each bun and spread to edges.
___ 6. **Broil** burgers 15 cm (6 in.) from heat for 3 minutes.
___ 7. **Top** with slice of tomato.
___ 8. **Sprinkle** with mozzarella and Parmesan cheeses.
___ 9. **Return** to broiler for 1 minute or until cheese is lightly browned.
___ 10. **Serve** as is or cover with top half of bun.

Microwave Directions

Follow Conventional Directions for Steps 1-5.

___ 6. **Place** burgers on double thickness of paper towel on a plate. Microwave on High (100%) according to the following table:
1 sandwich . . . . 1 to 1½ minutes
2 sandwiches . . . . 2 to 2½ minutes
4 sandwiches . . . . 2½ to 3½ minutes
For best results, microwave 2 to 4 sandwiches at one time and repeat with remaining sandwiches.
___ 7. **Top** with tomato slice when filling is heated through.
___ 8. **Sprinkle** with mozzarella and Parmesan cheeses.
___ 9. **Microwave** on Medium (50%) until cheese begins to soften (about 2 minutes). Let stand 1 minute before serving.
___ 10. **Serve** as is or cover with top half of bun.

Thinking About . . . Italian Tuna Burgers (R-27)

Questions

1. Using the formula in Appendix E of *Food for Today,* determine the following:

   a. Percentage of calories from fat _____

   b. Percentage of calories from carbohydrate _____

   c. Percentage of calories from protein _____

2. List two safety guidelines to follow in preparing this recipe by the conventional method.

   a. _____

   b. _____

3. List three food preparation skills that are used in this recipe.

   a. _____

   b. _____

   c. _____

4. What four different steps do you take in preparing this recipe in the microwave oven rather than the conventional oven?

   a. _____

   b. _____

   c. _____

   d. _____

5. Do you think preparing the recipe in the microwave oven rather than the conventional oven would require more or less work? Give reasons for your answer. _____

   _____

Evaluation

Complete the following after preparing the recipe:

1. How did the tuna burgers look and taste? _____

   _____

2. How could you change or improve the recipe? _____

   _____

3. List any difficulties you had in preparing the recipe. _____

   _____

4. How would you solve the problem(s) next time? _____

   _____

TUNA-CHEESE CASSEROLE

Equipment

____ Large saucepan with lid
(for conventional cooking)
____ Casserole, 1½ L or 1½ qt.
(for conventional cooking)
____ Microwave-safe casserole,
2 L or 2 qt.
(for microwave cooking)

____ Strainer
____ Cutting board
____ Can opener
____ Liquid measuring cup
____ Dry measuring cups
____ Measuring spoons

____ Spatula
____ Chef's knife
____ Mixing spoon
____ Rubber scraper
____ Pot holders

Metric	Customary	Ingredients
112 g	4 oz.	____ Crinkly egg noodles, uncooked
305-g can	10¾-oz. can	____ Condensed cream of celery soup
125 mL	½ cup	____ Low-fat milk
184-g can	6½-oz. can	____ Tuna, drained and flaked
113-g can	4-oz. can	____ Sliced mushrooms, drained
15 mL	1 Tbsp.	____ Lemon juice
75 mL	⅓ cup	____ Finely chopped onion
5 mL	1 tsp.	____ Worcestershire sauce
250 mL	1 cup	____ Shredded Cheddar cheese
50 mL	¼ cup	____ Grated Parmesan cheese
		____ Tomato slices, lemon slices, and parsley for garnish

Yield: 4 servings

Per serving: 393 calories;
29 g protein; 31 g carbohydrate;
17 g fat; 1408 mg sodium;
101 mg cholesterol

Percentage of U.S. RDA:
Vitamin A: 14% Niacin: 43%
Vitamin C: 4% Calcium: 37%
Thiamin: 23% Iron: 14%
Riboflavin: 22%

Conventional Directions

____ 1. **Cook** noodles in saucepan according to package directions; drain.
____ 2. **Combine** soup, milk, tuna, mushrooms, lemon juice, onion, Worcestershire sauce, and 175 mL (¾ cup) of the cheddar cheese.
____ 3. **Add** to cooked noodles and mix lightly.
____ 4. **Pour** into buttered 1.5-L (1½-qt.) casserole. Top with remaining Cheddar cheese and Parmesan cheese.
____ 5. **Bake** in oven at 190°C (375°F) for 25 to 30 minutes.
____ 6. **Garnish** with tomato slices, lemon slices, and parsley.

Microwave Directions

____ 1. **Place** noodles in a microwave-safe casserole.
____ 2. **Add** 1 L (1 qt.) boiling water. Cook uncovered for 6 minutes on High (100%).
____ 3. **Remove** from oven and stir. Cover and let stand 10 minutes.
____ 4. **Drain** and return noodles to casserole.
____ 5. **Stir** in soup, milk, tuna, mushrooms, lemon juice, onion, Worcestershire sauce, and 175 mL (¾ cup) of the Cheddar cheese. Mix lightly.
____ 6. **Cover** and cook on High (100%) for 5 minutes.
____ 7. **Stir.** Cover and heat another 3 minutes on High (100%).
____ 8. **Sprinkle** remaining Cheddar cheese and Parmesan cheese on top.
____ 9. **Cook,** uncovered, on High (100%) for 2 minutes.
____ 10. **Garnish** with tomato slices, lemon slices, and parsley.

Thinking About . . . Tuna-Cheese Casserole (R-28)

Questions

1. Using the formula in Appendix E of *Food for Today*, determine the following:

   a. Percentage of calories from fat _____

   b. Percentage of calories from carbohydrate _____

   c. Percentage of calories from protein _____

2. List three food preparation skills that are used in this recipe.

   a. _____

   b. _____

   c. _____

3. What conventional cooking methods are used in this recipe? _____

   _____

4. List two safety guidelines to follow when cooking the noodles by the conventional method.

   a. _____

   b. _____

5. When cooking noodles, how can you keep them from sticking together? _____

   _____

6. What other garnishes could you use for this casserole? _____

   _____

7. What other kinds of pasta could you use in place of the crinkly egg noodles? _____

   _____

Evaluation

Complete the following after preparing the recipe:

1. How did the casserole look and taste? _____

   _____

2. How could you change or improve the recipe? _____

   _____

3. List any difficulties you had in preparing the recipe. _____

   _____

4. How would you solve the problem(s) next time? _____

   _____

CHEESE OMELET

Equipment

___ 20-cm (8-in.) skillet
or omelet pan
(for conventional cooking)
___ 23-cm (9-in.) glass pie pan
(for microwave cooking)
___ Medium bowl

___ Dry measuring cups
___ Measuring spoons
___ Grater
___ Spatula
___ Fork

___ Turner
___ Rubber scraper
___ Plastic wrap
___ Pot holder
___ Serving plate

Metric	Customary	Ingredients
3	3	___ Eggs
45 mL	3 Tbsp.	___ Water
2 mL	1/2 tsp.	___ Salt
Dash	Dash	___ Ground black pepper
15 mL	1 Tbsp.	___ Butter or margarine
125 mL	1/2 cup	___ Shredded cheddar cheese

Yield: 2 servings

Per serving: 284 calories;
16 g protein; 1.5 g carbohydrate;
24 g fat; 881 mg sodium;
458 mg cholesterol

Percentage of U.S. RDA:
Vitamin A: 18%   Niacin: 0.4%
Vitamin C: 0%   Calcium: 25%
Thiamin: 5%   Iron: 10%
Riboflavin: 20%

Conventional Directions

___ 1. **Stir** together eggs, water, salt, and pepper in a bowl with a fork.
___ 2. **Heat** butter or margarine in a skillet until just hot enough to make a drop of water sizzle.
___ 3. **Pour** in egg mixture. The mixture should set at the edges at once.
___ 4. **Draw** edges of cooked portions toward the center using a turner so that uncooked mixture flows to the bottom.
___ 5. **Slide** pan rapidly back and forth over the heat to keep mixture in motion and sliding freely. Keep the mixture as level as possible.
___ 6. **Increase** heat to brown the bottom quickly when eggs are set and surface is still moist.
___ 7. **Place** 50 mL (1/4 cup) of the cheese on left half of omelet.
___ 8. **Fold** or roll right half of omelet over cheese.
___ 9. **Slide** omelet from pan onto serving plate.
___ 10. **Top** with remaining cheese.
___ 11. **Serve** immediately.

Microwave Directions

___ 1. **Stir** together eggs, water, salt, and pepper in a bowl with a fork.
___ 2. **Melt** butter or margarine in the pie pan on High (100%) for 30 to 45 seconds.
___ 3. **Pour** egg mixture into pie pan.
___ 4. **Cover** with plastic wrap.
___ 5. **Microwave** on Medium (50%) for 3 to 5 minutes. Stir once during the first minute. After eggs have set around the edges, lift the cooked portion with a turner to allow uncooked egg to spread evenly over dish. Do this several times during cooking. Eggs are done when the center is almost set.
___ 6. **Sprinkle** 50 mL (1/4 cup) of the cheese on left half of omelet and fold right half over the cheese.
___ 7. **Slide** omelet onto serving plate.
___ 8. **Top** with remaining cheese.
___ 9. **Serve** immediately.

Thinking About . . . Cheese Omelet (R-29)

Questions

1. Using the formula in Appendix E of *Food for Today,* determine the following:

    a. Percentage of calories from fat _____

    b. Percentage of calories from carbohydrate _____

    c. Percentage of calories from protein _____

2. How could you lower the fat content of the omelet? _____

    _____

3. List two food preparation skills used in this recipe.

    a. _____

    b. _____

4. List three safety guidelines to follow when frying the omelet on top of the range.

    a. _____

    b. _____

    c. _____

5. List three safety guidelines to follow when preparing this recipe in a microwave oven.

    a. _____

    b. _____

    c. _____

6. Read both the conventional and the microwave directions. Which method of cooking the omelet would you prefer to use. Why? _____

    _____

Evaluation

Complete the following after preparing the recipe:

1. How did the omelet look and taste? _____

    _____

2. How could you change or improve the recipe? _____

    _____

3. List any difficulties you had in preparing the recipe. _____

    _____

4. How would you solve the problem(s) next time? _____

    _____

EGG FOO YUNG

Equipment

- ___ Medium skillet
- ___ Medium saucepan (for conventional cooking)
- ___ Glass measuring cup, 1 L or 1 qt. (for microwave cooking)
- ___ Medium bowl
- ___ Small bowl
- ___ Cutting board
- ___ Can opener
- ___ Garlic press
- ___ Strainer
- ___ Dry measuring cups
- ___ Measuring spoons
- ___ Spatula
- ___ Chef's knife
- ___ Mixing spoon
- ___ Rubber scraper
- ___ Turner
- ___ Pot holders

Metric	Customary	Ingredients
6	6	___ Eggs
30 mL	2 Tbsp.	___ Natural soy sauce
454-g can	16-oz. can	___ Bean sprouts
250 mL	1 cup	___ Finely chopped onion
		___ Vegetable oil
		Sauce:
50 mL	1/4 cup	___ Butter or margarine
1 clove	1 clove	___ Garlic, pressed
30 mL	2 Tbsp.	___ Cornstarch
30 mL	2 Tbsp.	___ Natural soy sauce
400-mL can	13 1/2-oz. can	___ Chicken broth
2 mL	1/2 tsp.	___ Powdered or chopped ginger

Yield: 8 pancakes

Per serving (1 pancake with sauce):
178 calories; 8 g protein;
7 g carbohydrate; 14 g fat;
780 mg sodium; 222 mg cholesterol

Percentage of U.S. RDA:

Vitamin A:	8%	Niacin:	6%
Vitamin C:	6%	Calcium:	4%
Thiamin:	5%	Iron:	8%
Riboflavin:	11%		

Directions

___ 1. **Beat** eggs with 30 mL (2 Tbsp.) soy sauce in a medium-size bowl.

___ 2. **Drain** sprouts, then rinse twice under cold running water and drain again.

___ 3. **Add** sprouts and onion to eggs.

___ 4. **Heat** 30 mL (2 Tbsp.) oil in a medium skillet.

___ 5. **Add** 50 mL (1/4 cup) egg mixture.

___ 6. **Flatten** with a turner.

___ 7. **Fry** until brown.

___ 8. **Turn** and brown other side.

___ 9. **Keep** warm on serving platter.

___ 10. **Repeat** process until mixture is used up. Add oil to skillet as needed.

___ 11. **Melt** butter or margarine in a medium-size saucepan to make the sauce.

___ 12. **Sauté** pressed garlic.

___ 13. **Blend** the cornstarch with the 30 mL (2 Tbsp.) soy sauce in a small bowl.

___ 14. **Add** chicken broth to saucepan.

___ 15. **Stir** in cornstarch mixture.

___ 16. **Add** ginger and heat, stirring constantly, until mixture is thickened.

___ 17. **Serve** sauce over egg pancakes.

Microwave Directions (for sauce):

Prepare egg pancakes as directed. To prepare the sauce in the microwave oven, use the directions below, beginning with Step 11.

___ 11. **Place** butter or margarine and pressed garlic in the glass measuring cup.

___ 12. **Microwave** on High (100%) for 30 to 45 seconds.

___ 13. **Blend** cornstarch with the 30 mL (2 Tbsp.) soy sauce in a small bowl.

___ 14. **Add** cornstarch to butter mixture along with chicken broth and ginger. Mix well.

___ 15. **Microwave** on High (100%) for 3 to 5 minutes, stirring every minute until sauce is thick and bubbly.

___ 16. **Serve** sauce over egg pancakes.

Name _____ Class _____ Date _____

Thinking About . . . Egg Foo Yung (R-30)

Questions

1. Using the formula in Appendix E of *Food for Today,* determine the following:

   a. Percentage of calories from fat _____

   b. Percentage of calories from carbohydrate _____

   c. Percentage of calories from protein _____

2. Which ingredient(s) do you think contributed the most fat? _____
   _____

3. List two food preparation skills used in this recipe.

   a. _____

   b. _____

4. List three safety guidelines to follow when preparing this recipe using the conventional method.

   a. _____

   b. _____

   c. _____

5. Give one conventional cooking method used in this recipe. _____
   _____

6. What other foods would you serve with this recipe to make a complete meal? _____
   _____

Evaluation

Complete the following after preparing the recipe:

1. How did the egg foo yung look and taste? _____
   _____

2. How could you change or improve the recipe? _____
   _____

3. List any difficulties you had in preparing the recipe. _____
   _____

4. How would you solve the problem(s) next time? _____
   _____

HUEVOS RANCHEROS
(Ranch-Style Eggs)

Equipment

____ Large skillet
____ Medium saucepan
  (for conventional cooking)
____ Glass measuring cup,
  1 L or 1 qt.
  (for microwave cooking)

____ Cutting board
____ Dry measuring cups
____ Measuring spoons
____ Spatula
____ Chef's knife
____ Paring knife

____ Mixing spoon
____ Turner
____ Pot holders
____ Cooling rack
____ Serving plates

Metric	Customary	Ingredients
6	6	____ Tortillas
		____ Oil for frying
125 mL	½ cup	____ Chopped onion
1 clove	1 clove	____ Garlic, pressed
2	2	____ Small green chili peppers
Two 227-g cans	Two 8-oz. cans	____ Tomato sauce
6	6	____ Eggs
Dash	Dash	____ Hot pepper sauce (optional)

Conventional Directions

____ 1. **Fry** the tortillas quickly in a small amount of oil. Do not allow them to become hard or crisp.
____ 2. **Sauté** the onion, garlic, and peppers in the saucepan, using a small amount of oil. Add the tomato sauce (for spicy Mexican flavor, also add a dash of hot pepper sauce).
____ 3. **Simmer** for 5 minutes.
____ 4. **Fry** the eggs sunny-side up. Make certain the tops are cooked.
____ 5. **Place** each egg on a tortilla and pour tomato sauce over the top.
____ 6. **Serve** immediately.

Microwave Directions

Follow the Conventional Directions except for Steps 2 and 3.

____ 2. **Combine** the onions, garlic, and peppers in a small amount of oil in the glass measuring cup. Microwave on High (100%) for 1½ to 2 minutes or until the onions are soft and translucent. Add tomato sauce (for hot spiciness, also add a dash of hot pepper sauce).
____ 3. **Microwave,** uncovered, on High (100%) for 5 to 7 minutes.

Yield: 3 servings

Per serving: 585 calories; 18 g protein; 42 g carbohydrate; 40 g fat; 1212 mg sodium; 549 mg cholesterol

Percentage of U.S. RDA:

Vitamin A:	72%	Niacin:	13%
Vitamin C:	37%	Calcium:	21%
Thiamin:	19%	Iron:	29%
Riboflavin:	25%		

Kitchen Management Tip

■ Be careful when using chilies. They contain capsaicin, a volatile oil that gives them their characteristic "hot" spiciness. This also makes them irritating to the skin and the eyes. Handle chilies with a utensil whenever possible. If you must touch chilies, you can remove most of the oil by washing your hands with soap and warm water. But traces of capsaicin may remain for as long as an hour. Avoid touching the eye area until the oil has evaporated.

Thinking About . . . Huevos Rancheros (R-31)

Questions

1. Using the formula in Appendix E of *Food for Today,* determine the following:

   a. Percentage of calories from fat _____

   b. Percentage of calories from carbohydrate _____

   c. Percentage of calories from protein _____

2. List three food preparation skills used in this recipe.

   a. _____

   b. _____

   c. _____

3. What three conventional cooking methods are used in this recipe?

   a. _____

   b. _____

   c. _____

4. List three safety guidelines to follow when preparing this recipe by the conventional method.

   a. _____

   b. _____

   c. _____

5. Read through the conventional and microwave directions. Which method would you prefer to use? Explain. _____

   _____

6. Make up a brunch menu including this recipe. _____

   _____

Evaluation

Complete the following after preparing the recipe:

1. How did the eggs look and taste? _____

   _____

2. How could you change or improve the recipe? _____

   _____

3. List any difficulties you had in preparing the recipe. _____

   _____

4. How would you solve the problem(s) next time? _____

   _____

PUMPKIN CUSTARD

Equipment

___ Baking dish, 33 × 23 × 5-cm 13 × 9 × 2-in (for conventional cooking)	___ Medium bowl	___ Spatula
	___ Rotary beater	___ Knife
	___ Whisk	___ Mixing spoon
___ 6 custard cups	___ Liquid measuring cup	___ Rubber scraper
___ Microwave-safe medium bowl (for microwave cooking)	___ Dry measuring cups	___ Pot holders
	___ Measuring spoons	___ Cooling racks

Metric	Customary	Ingredients
3	3	___ Eggs
150 mL	2/3 cup	___ Cooked, mashed pumpkin
30 mL	2 Tbsp.	___ Honey
30 mL	2 Tbsp.	___ Sugar
Dash	Dash	___ Nutmeg
350 mL	1 1/2 cups	___ Skim milk
		___ Boiling water

Yield: 6 custard cups

Per serving (1/6th of recipe):
108 calories; 5 g protein;
15 g carbohydrate; 3 g fat;
68 mg sodium; 139 mg cholesterol

Percentage of U.S. RDA:

Vitamin A:	124%	Niacin:	1%
Vitamin C:	2%	Calcium:	10%
Thiamin:	3%	Iron:	5%
Riboflavin:	10%		

Conventional Directions

___ 1. **Preheat** oven to 160°C (325°F).

___ 2. **Beat** eggs thoroughly in large bowl.

___ 3. **Add** pumpkin, honey, sugar, and nutmeg. Blend well.

___ 4. **Add** milk, mixing until smooth.

___ 5. **Divide** mixture among 6 custard cups.

___ 6. **Place** cups in baking pan.

___ 7. **Pour** boiling water into pan around the custard cups to a depth of 2.5 cm (1 in.).

___ 8. **Bake** at 160°C (325°F) for 40 to 45 minutes or until a knife inserted near the center comes out clean.

___ 9. **Serve** at room temperature or chilled.

Microwave Directions

Follow Conventional Directions for Steps 1-4.

___ 5. **Place** mixing bowl with pumpkin mixture into microwave oven and cook on High (100%) for 3 minutes, stirring after 1 1/2 minutes.

___ 6. **Reduce** power to Medium (50%) and continue cooking for 6 to 9 minutes or until mixture is hot and beginning to thicken. Stir with whisk after first 2 minutes of cooking and then stir every minute during cooking.

___ 7. **Pour** hot mixture into custard cups.

___ 8. **Microwave** on Medium (50%) for 6 to 9 minutes or until edges begin to bubble and a knife inserted near the center comes out clean.

___ 9. **Serve** at room temperature or chilled.

Thinking About . . . Pumpkin Custard (R-32)

Questions

1. Using the formula in Appendix E of *Food for Today*, determine the following:

   a. Percentage of calories from fat _____

   b. Percentage of calories from carbohydrate _____

   c. Percentage of calories from protein _____

2. One serving of this recipe provides more than 100% of the daily requirement for vitamin A. What food do you think contributed the most vitamin A? _____

   _____

3. List two food preparation skills used in this recipe.

   a. _____

   b. _____

4. List two safety guidelines to follow when baking the custard in the conventional oven.

   a. _____

   b. _____

5. If you did not have custard cups, what could you use to bake the custard in the conventional oven?

   _____

6. Give two different steps that you follow when baking the custard in the microwave oven rather than the conventional?

   a. _____

   b. _____

7. After reading the directions for the two cooking methods, which would you prefer to use? Give reasons for your answer. _____

   _____

Evaluation

Complete the following after preparing the recipe:

1. How did the custard look and taste? _____

   _____

2. How could you change or improve the recipe? _____

   _____

3. List any difficulties you had in preparing the recipe. _____

   _____

4. How would you solve the problem(s) next time? _____

   _____

BROCCOLI AND CHEESE SPAGHETTI

Equipment

- ___ Large pot (for conventional cooking)
- ___ 3 L (3 qt.) saucepan with lid (for conventional cooking)
- ___ Glass measuring cup, 1 L or 1 qt. (for microwave cooking)
- ___ Microwave-safe casserole, 30 × 17.5 cm or 12 × 7 in. (for microwave cooking)
- ___ Colander or strainer
- ___ Grater
- ___ Can opener
- ___ Cutting board
- ___ Liquid measuring cup
- ___ Dry measuring cups
- ___ Measuring spoons
- ___ Spatula
- ___ Garlic press
- ___ Rubber scraper
- ___ Chef's knife
- ___ Paring knife
- ___ Mixing spoon
- ___ Turner
- ___ Pot holders
- ___ Cooling rack

Metric	Customary	Ingredients
196-g pkg.	7-oz. pkg.	___ Spaghetti, uncooked
283-g pkg.	10-oz. pkg.	___ Frozen chopped broccoli, thawed and well-drained
175 mL	¾ cup	___ Sliced onion
126-g jar	4½-oz. jar	___ Sliced mushrooms, drained
1 clove	1 clove	___ Garlic, pressed
45 mL	3 Tbsp.	___ Vegetable oil
250 mL	1 cup	___ Low-fat cottage cheese
250 mL	1 cup	___ Skim milk
5 mL	1 tsp.	___ Crushed dried basil leaves
Pinch	Pinch	___ Ground black pepper
125 mL	½ cup	___ Shredded Cheddar cheese

Yield: 6 servings

Per serving: 293 calories; 15 g protein; 33 g carbohydrate; 11 g fat; 323 mg sodium; 14 mg cholesterol

Percentage of U.S. RDA:
Vitamin A: 21% Niacin: 13%
Vitamin C: 22% Calcium: 19%
Thiamin: 25% Iron: 10%
Riboflavin: 19%

Conventional Directions

- ___ 1. **Cook** spaghetti in large pot of boiling, salted water until tender.
- ___ 2. **Drain** and set aside.
- ___ 3. **Combine** broccoli, onion, mushrooms, garlic, and oil in saucepan.
- ___ 4. **Sauté** until onion is tender.
- ___ 5. **Stir** in cooked spaghetti, cottage cheese, milk, crushed basil leaves, and pepper.
- ___ 6. **Cover.** Heat over low heat, stirring occasionally, until hot.
- ___ 7. **Stir** in shredded cheese and serve immediately.

Kitchen Management Tips

- 125 mL (½ cup) of sliced fresh mushrooms may be substituted for the canned mushrooms.
- Before discarding, rinse the empty jar and frozen food carton so no food residue remains to attract germs and pests and create unpleasant odors.

Microwave Directions

- ___ 1. **Place** spaghetti in baking dish. Add 1 L (1 qt.) boiling water. Cook 6 to 8 minutes on High (100%), stirring several times to separate spaghetti. Let stand 10 minutes covered. Drain and set aside.
- ___ 2. **Combine** broccoli, onion, oil, and garlic in microwave-safe casserole.
- ___ 3. **Microwave** 6 to 7 minutes on High (100%) or until onion is tender, stirring once or twice.
- ___ 4. **Add** cooked spaghetti, mushrooms, cottage cheese, milk, crushed basil, and pepper.
- ___ 5. **Microwave** on High (100%) 5 to 7 minutes or until heated through. Stir once or twice during cooking time.
- ___ 6. **Sprinkle** with grated cheese, cover, and let stand 2 to 3 minutes before serving.

Thinking About . . . Broccoli and Cheese Spaghetti (R-33)

Questions

1. Using the formula in Appendix E of *Food for Today,* determine the following:
   a. Percentage of calories from fat _____
   b. Percentage of calories from carbohydrate _____
   c. Percentage of calories from protein _____

2. Name two conventional cooking methods used in this recipe.
   a. _____
   b. _____

3. List three safety guidelines to follow when cooking the spaghetti and sauce on top of the range.
   a. _____
   b. _____
   c. _____

4. List two different steps you follow when preparing this recipe in the microwave oven rather than the conventional oven.
   a. _____
   b. _____

5. After reading the instructions, would you prefer to prepare the recipe by the conventional method or in the microwave oven? Give reasons for your answer. _____

6. What other vegetables could you use in this recipe besides broccoli? _____

Evaluation

Complete the following after preparing the recipe:

1. How did the spaghetti look and taste? _____

2. How could you change or improve the recipe? _____

3. List any difficulties you had in preparing the recipe. _____

4. How would you solve the problem(s) next time? _____

PIZZA WITH RICE CRUST

Equipment

____ 30-cm (12-in.) pizza pan	____ Grater	____ Chef's knife
____ 1.5 L (1½ qt.) saucepan	____ Dry measuring cups	____ Mixing spoon
____ Large skillet	____ Measuring spoons	____ Pizza cutter or sharp knife
____ Large mixing bowl	____ Spatula	____ Turner
____ Rotary beater	____ Garlic press	____ Pot holders
____ Can opener	____ Cutting board	

Metric	Customary	Ingredients
1 L	4 cups	____ Cooked rice
2	2	____ Eggs, beaten
250 mL	1 cup	____ Grated mozzarella cheese
125 mL	½ cup	____ Finely chopped onion
15 mL	1 Tbsp.	____ Oil
Two (227-g) cans	Two (8-oz.) cans	____ Tomato sauce
15 mL	1 Tbsp.	____ Vinegar
5 mL	1 tsp.	____ Crushed dried oregano
1 mL	¼ tsp.	____ Ground black pepper
1 clove	1 clove	____ Garlic, minced
250 g	½ lb.	____ Ground beef
125 mL	½ cup	____ Grated mozzarella cheese
125 mL	½ cup	____ Sliced stuffed olives
50 mL	¼ cup	____ Sliced canned mushrooms

Yield: 9 servings

Per serving: 264 calories;
14 g protein; 28 g carbohydrate;
11 g fat; 624 mg sodium;
88 mg cholesterol

Percentage of U.S. RDA:

Vitamin A:	14%	Niacin:	13%
Vitamin C:	8%	Calcium:	17%
Thiamin:	12%	Iron:	13%
Riboflavin:	10%		

Directions

____ 1. **Preheat** oven to 230°C (450°F).

____ 2. **Combine** rice, eggs, and 250 mL (1 cup) grated cheese in mixing bowl.

____ 3. **Press** into greased 30-cm (12-in.) pizza pan.

____ 4. **Bake** in oven at 230°C (450°F) for 15 minutes.

____ 5. **Sauté** onion in oil in the saucepan until transparent.

____ 6. **Add** tomato sauce, vinegar, oregano, pepper, and garlic to the onion.

____ 7. **Simmer** sauce for 20 minutes.

____ 8. **Brown** ground meat in skillet; drain.

____ 9. **Spread** sauce over baked rice crust to within 2.5 cm (1 in.) of edge.

____ 10. **Top** with browned meat, 125 mL (½ cup) grated cheese, olives, and mushrooms.

____ 11. **Bake** at 230°C (450°F) for about 10 minutes or until cheese melts and sauce is hot.

Note: For a thinner crust, use 750 mL (3 cups) cooked rice.

Kitchen Management Tip

■ Use a short grain rice for the pizza crust. Short grain rice sticks together and is easier to shape into a crust.

Thinking About . . . Pizza with Rice Crust (R-34)

Questions

1. Using the formula in Appendix E of *Food for Today,* determine the following:
   a. Percentage of calories from fat _____
   b. Percentage of calories from carbohydrate _____
   c. Percentage of calories from protein _____

2. List three food preparation skills used in this recipe.
   a. _____
   b. _____
   c. _____

3. Name two conventional cooking methods used in this recipe.
   a. _____
   b. _____

4. List three safety guidelines to follow when preparing this recipe.
   a. _____
   b. _____
   c. _____

5. How does simmering differ from boiling? _____

6. What other toppings could you use on the pizza? _____

Evaluation

Complete the following after preparing the recipe:

1. How did the pizza look and taste? _____

2. How do you rate the rice crust in comparison to a standard pizza crust? _____

3. How could you change or improve the recipe? _____

4. List any difficulties you had in preparing the recipe. _____

5. How would you solve the problem(s) next time? _____

TABBOULEH

Equipment

- ___ 2 medium mixing bowls
- ___ Cutting board
- ___ Liquid measuring cup, 1 L or 1 qt.
- ___ Dry measuring cups
- ___ Measuring spoons
- ___ Kitchen shears
- ___ Chef's knife
- ___ Paring knife
- ___ Mixing spoon
- ___ Rubber scraper
- ___ Spatula

Metric	Customary	Ingredients
250 mL	1 cup	___ Bulgur
750 mL	3 cups	___ Boiling water
1	1	___ Medium onion, diced
2	2	___ Medium tomatoes, chopped
250 mL	1 cup	___ Snipped parsley
5 mL	1 tsp.	___ Ground cinnamon
45 mL	3 Tbsp.	___ Vinegar and oil salad dressing
750 mL	3 cups	___ Torn lettuce
		___ Tomato wedges and parsley for garnish

Directions

- ___ 1. **Place** bulgur in mixing bowl.
- ___ 2. **Pour** boiling water over bulgur and stir.
- ___ 3. **Let** stand 30 minutes.
- ___ 4. **Squeeze** water out of bulgur with your hands and place bulgur in another mixing bowl. Discard water.
- ___ 5. **Add** diced onion, chopped tomatoes, snipped parsley, ground cinnamon, and salad dressing to bulgur.
- ___ 6. **Mix** gently with spoon only until ingredients are combined.
- ___ 7. **Serve** on bed of torn lettuce, garnished with sliced tomatoes and parsley.

Yield: 4 servings

Per serving: 215 calories; 6 g protein; 37 g carbohydrate; 6 g fat; 170 mg sodium; 0 mg cholesterol

Percentage of U.S. RDA:

Vitamin A:	29%	Niacin:	11%
Vitamin C:	42%	Calcium:	6%
Thiamin:	13%	Iron:	20%
Riboflavin:	6%		

Kitchen Management Tips

- This is a popular recipe in the Middle East. Serve cold as a salad or hot as a side dish.
- Before squeezing water out of the bulgur, wash hands carefully in warm water and soap and rinse well.
- Use ripe, firm tomatoes. Soft tomatoes will make the mixture watery.
- Because bulgur is made from whole wheat, it contains both germ and bran. Oils in the germ can become rancid at room temperature. Store dry bulgur in a closed container in the refrigerator.

Thinking About . . . Tabbouleh (R-35)

Questions

1. Using the formula in Appendix E of *Food for Today*, determine the following:

   a. Percentage of calories from fat _____

   b. Percentage of calories from carbohydrate _____

   c. Percentage of calories from protein _____

2. List two safety guidelines to follow when preparing this recipe.

   a. _____

   b. _____

3. List three sanitation guidelines to follow when preparing this recipe.

   a. _____

   b. _____

   c. _____

4. Why does the recipe call for torn rather than sliced lettuce? _____

   _____

5. What would you serve with this recipe to make a vegetarian meal with complete protein? _____

   _____

6. Make up a nutritious menu for supper, using this recipe as the salad. _____

   _____

   _____

Evaluation

Complete the following after preparing the recipe:

1. How did the tabbouleh look and taste? _____

   _____

2. How could you change or improve the recipe? _____

   _____

3. List any difficulties you had in preparing the recipe. _____

   _____

4. How would you solve the problem(s) next time? _____

   _____

OATMEAL MUFFINS

Equipment

- ____ Muffin pan with 12 medium-size cups (for conventional cooking)
- ____ Paper baking cups and microwave-safe muffin pan (for microwave cooking)
- ____ Medium bowl
- ____ Small bowl
- ____ Sifter
- ____ Rotary beater
- ____ Liquid measuring cup
- ____ Dry measuring cups
- ____ Measuring spoons
- ____ Spatula
- ____ Mixing spoon
- ____ Toothpicks
- ____ Pot holders
- ____ Cooling rack

Metric	Customary	Ingredients
250 mL	1 cup	____ Sifted all-purpose flour
50 mL	1/4 cup	____ Sugar
15 mL	1 Tbsp.	____ Baking powder
2 mL	1/2 tsp.	____ Salt
250 mL	1 cup	____ Quick or old-fashioned oats
125 mL	1/2 cup	____ Raisins
45 mL	3 Tbsp.	____ Oil
1	1	____ Egg, beaten
250 mL	1 cup	____ Low-fat milk
		Topping:
30 mL	2 Tbsp.	____ Sugar
5 mL	1 tsp.	____ Cinnamon

Yield: 12 muffins

Per muffin: 154 calories; 4 g protein; 25 g carbohydrate; 5 g fat; 183 mg sodium; 24 mg cholesterol

Percentage of U.S. RDA:

Vitamin A:	1%	Niacin:	3%
Vitamin C:	0.8%	Calcium:	9%
Thiamin:	9%	Iron:	6%
Riboflavin:	6%		

Conventional Directions

- ____ 1. **Preheat** oven to 220°C (425°F).
- ____ 2. **Grease** muffin cups.
- ____ 3. **Sift** together flour, 50 mL (1/4 c.) sugar, baking powder, and salt.
- ____ 4. **Stir** in oats and raisins.
- ____ 5. **Add** oil, beaten egg, and milk.
- ____ 6. **Stir** just until dry ingredients are moistened.
- ____ 7. **Fill** muffin cups 2/3 full.
- ____ 8. **Combine** 30 mL (2 Tbsp.) sugar and cinnamon. Sprinkle muffins with cinnamon sugar topping.
- ____ 9. **Bake** at 220°C (425°F) for 15 minutes or until toothpick inserted in the center of a muffin comes out clean.
- ____ 10. **Remove** from pan immediately and place on cooling rack so the bottoms do not become soggy.

Kitchen Management Tips

- Do not overbeat the batter. Stir only until the dry ingredients are moistened. Batter will be lumpy.
- Fill muffin cups with equal amounts of batter. If some of the cups have more batter than others, the muffins will not bake evenly.
- As soon as you put the muffins in the oven to bake, soak the mixing bowl to keep the batter from drying and sticking to the bowl.

Microwave Directions

Follow Steps 3-6 of the Conventional recipe, then use Steps 7 through 10 below.

- ____ 7. **Place** paper baking cups in the muffin pan. Since the pan has only 6 cups, you will be baking 6 muffins at a time.
- ____ 8. **Fill** muffin cups 1/2 full. (Muffins rise higher in the microwave than in a conventional oven.)
- ____ 9. **Combine** 30 mL (2 Tbsp.) sugar and cinnamon. Sprinkle muffins with cinnamon sugar topping.
- ____ 10. **Bake** at Medium High (70%) for 2 1/2 to 4 minutes. Test with a toothpick at end of minimum baking time. Muffins are done if toothpick inserted in center comes out clean. Muffins will appear barely set, and there may be moist spots on the surface. The muffins will not brown.

Note: If you don't have a microwave muffin pan, you can make muffin cups out of paper cups. Cut off the upper portion, leaving a bottom with 2.5-cm (1-in.) sides. Put the paper baking cups inside. Arrange the muffin cups in a ring on a flat, microwave-safe plate.

Thinking About . . . Oatmeal Muffins (R-36)

Questions

1. Using the formula in Appendix E of *Food for Today,* determine the following:

   a. Percentage of calories from fat _____

   b. Percentage of calories from carbohydrate _____

   c. Percentage of calories from protein _____

2. List two food preparation skills used in this recipe.

   a. _____

   b. _____

3. What mixing method is used in this recipe? _____

   _____

4. Why is this mixing method so important in making muffins? _____

   _____

5. What conventional cooking method is used in this recipe? _____

6. List two safety guidelines to follow when preparing this recipe.

   a. _____

   b. _____

7. List the three basic differences if you are preparing the muffins in the microwave oven rather than the conventional.

   a. _____

   b. _____

   c. _____

8. If you did not have a mixer or rotary beater, how would you beat the egg? _____

   _____

Evaluation

Complete the following after preparing the recipe:

1. How did the muffins look and taste? _____

   _____

2. List any difficulties you had in preparing the recipe. _____

   _____

3. How would you solve the problem(s) next time? _____

   _____

SPOON BREAD

Equipment

___ Casserole, 1.5 L or 1½ qt.	___ Liquid measuring cup	___ Paring knife
___ 3 L (3 qt.) saucepan	___ Dry measuring cups	___ Mixing spoon
___ Electric mixer	___ Measuring spoons	___ Rubber scraper
___ 2 small bowls	___ Spatula	___ Pot holders

Metric	Customary	Ingredients
500 mL	2 cups	___ Low-fat milk
125 mL	½ cup	___ White cornmeal
30 mL	2 Tbsp.	___ All-purpose flour
3	3	___ Eggs, separated
60 mL	4 Tbsp.	___ Butter or margarine, melted
		___ Shortening

Directions

___ 1. **Preheat** oven to 180°C (350°F).
___ 2. **Grease** the casserole.
___ 3. **Heat** milk in the saucepan over low heat.
___ 4. **Combine** cornmeal and flour.
___ 5. **Add** cornmeal mixture to milk gradually, stirring constantly to prevent lumps.
___ 6. **Simmer** 5 minutes or until mixture thickens.
___ 7. **Remove** from heat and cool.

___ 8. **Add** egg yolks and melted butter. Stir until smooth.
___ 9. **Beat** egg whites until stiff, but not dry.
___ 10. **Fold** egg whites into cornmeal mixture thoroughly.
___ 11. **Pour** into greased casserole.
___ 12. **Bake** at 180°C (350°F) for 45 minutes.
___ 13. **Serve** by spoonfuls onto plate.

Yield: 6 servings

Per serving (using butter in the recipe):
205 calories; 7 g protein; 14 g carbohydrate; 14 g fat; 167 mg sodium; 168 mg cholesterol

Percentage of U.S. RDA:
Vitamin A:	14%	Niacin:	2%
Vitamin C:	1%	Calcium:	12%
Thiamin:	7%	Iron:	5%
Riboflavin:	14%		

Kitchen Management Tips
- You can use yellow cornmeal in place of white to add more color and vitamin A to the recipe.
- Spoon bread can be served as a side dish in place of potatoes or rice.
- Watch milk carefully when heating so it does not overheat and scorch.
- As soon as you have poured the batter into the casserole, soak the saucepan so the batter does not dry and stick to the pan.

Thinking About . . . Spoon Bread (R-37)

Questions

1. Using the formula in Appendix E of *Food for Today,* determine the following:
   a. Percentage of calories from fat _____
   b. Percentage of calories from carbohydrate _____
   c. Percentage of calories from protein _____
2. Which ingredient(s) do you think contributed the most fat? _____
   _____
3. How could you lower the fat content of the bread? _____
   _____
4. List two food preparation skills used in this recipe.
   a. _____
   b. _____
5. What purpose do the beaten egg whites serve in this recipe? _____
   _____
6. Why should you be meticulous about keeping any yolk out of the egg white? _____
   _____
7. What two cooking methods are used in this recipe?
   a. _____
   b. _____
8. List three safety guidelines to follow when preparing this recipe?
   a. _____
   b. _____
   c. _____
9. Make up a supper menu that includes the spoon bread as a side dish. _____
   _____
   _____

Evaluation

Complete the following after preparing the recipe:
1. How did the bread look and taste? _____
   _____
2. List any difficulties you had in preparing the recipe. _____
   _____
3. How would you solve the problem(s) next time? _____
   _____

TORTILLAS

Equipment

___ Griddle or large skillet
___ Medium bowl
___ Rolling pin
___ Liquid measuring cup

___ Dry measuring cups
___ Spatula
___ Mixing spoon
___ Turner

___ Rubber scraper
___ Waxed paper
___ Pot holders

Metric	Customary	Ingredients
500 mL	2 cups	___ Masa harina (instant masa)
250 mL	1 cup	___ Water
15 mL	1 Tbsp.	___ Cooking oil

Directions

___ 1. **Combine** masa and water in a medium-size bowl.

___ 2. **Knead** to blend well. If necessary, add a little more water to make dough hold together. Mixture may appear dry, but it is quite workable. It should have the consistency of modeling clay.

___ 3. **Divide** dough into 12 parts and form into balls.

___ 4. **Roll** out or press each ball between two sheets of waxed paper or pat out by hand. Form a 15-cm (6-in.) circle.

___ 5. **Bake** on a lightly-oiled hot griddle until lightly browned.

___ 6. **Turn** and bake on other side until lightly browned.

Yield: 12 tortillas

Per tortilla: 84 calories; 2 g protein; 15 g carbohydrate; 2 g fat; 0.2 mg sodium; 0 mg cholesterol

Percentage of U.S. RDA:
Vitamin A:	2%	Niacin:	2%
Vitamin C:	0%	Calcium:	0.4%
Thiamin:	4%	Iron:	2%
Riboflavin:	1%		

Kitchen Management Tips

■ Tortillas are traditionally made with masa harina, a special corn flour that gives tortillas their characteristic flavor. Masa harina is sold in many supermarkets and in groceries specializing in Hispanic foods. Tortillas also can be made with wheat flour.

■ Tortillas can be used as a bread, and they are used in many dishes such as enchiladas, tostados, and tacos.

■ To fry tortillas, cook in about ½ inch of vegetable oil until crisp and lightly browned. Drain on paper towels.

■ Tortillas can be toasted in a moderate oven, broiler, or toaster oven until crisp.

Thinking About . . . Tortillas (R-38)

Questions

1. Using the formula in Appendix E of *Food for Today,* determine the following:

   a. Percentage of calories from fat _____

   b. Percentage of calories from carbohydrate _____

   c. Percentage of calories from protein _____

2. List four food preparation skills used in this recipe.

   a. _____

   b. _____

   c. _____

   d. _____

3. List three safety guidelines to follow when frying the tortillas.

   a. _____

   b. _____

   c. _____

4. Make up a nutritious Sunday brunch menu, using tortillas as part of the meal. _____

   _____

   _____

5. List four fillings you might put inside rolled-up tortillas.

   a. _____

   b. _____

   c. _____

   d. _____

Evaluation

Complete the following after preparing the recipe:

1. How did the tortillas look and taste? _____

   _____

2. List any difficulties you had in preparing the recipe. _____

   _____

3. How would you solve the problem(s) next time? _____

   _____

WHITE BREAD

Equipment

____ Two loaf pans, 22 × 11 × 6 cm or 8¹/₂ × 4¹/₂ × 2¹/₂ in. (For microwave rising, use glass pans.)
____ Medium saucepan
____ Large mixing bowl
____ Electric mixer
____ Rolling pin
____ Bread board or pastry cloth
____ Liquid measuring cup
____ Dry measuring cups
____ Measuring spoons
____ Spatula
____ Knife or kitchen shears
____ Mixing spoon
____ Rubber scraper
____ Clean dish towel
____ Plastic wrap or foil
____ Pot holders
____ Cooling racks

Metric	Customary	Ingredients
1.3 to 1.6 L	5¹/₂ to 6¹/₂ cups	____ Unsifted all-purpose flour
50 mL	3 Tbsp.	____ Sugar
10 mL	2 tsp.	____ Salt
1 pkg.	1 pkg.	____ Active dry yeast
250 mL	1 cup	____ Water
250 mL	1 cup	____ Low-fat milk
50 mL	3 Tbsp.	____ Butter or margarine

Yield: 2 loaves (16 slices each)

Per Slice: 97 calories;
3 g protein; 18 g carbohydrate;
1.5 g fat; 149 mg sodium;
4 mg cholesterol

Percentage of U.S. RDA:

Vitamin A:	1%	Niacin:	6%
Vitamin C:	0.1%	Calcium:	1%
Thiamin:	10%	Iron:	6%
Riboflavin:	7%		

Directions

____ 1. **Mix** in a large bowl thoroughly 500 mL (2 cups) flour with the sugar, salt, and undissolved dry yeast.
____ 2. **Combine** water, milk, and butter or margarine in a saucepan.
____ 3. **Heat** over low heat until the liquids are warm. Butter or margarine does not need to melt.
____ 4. **Add** warm liquid gradually to dry ingredients.
____ 5. **Beat** 2 minutes with electric mixer at medium speed, scraping bowl occasionally.
____ 6. **Add** 175 mL (³/₄ cup) flour, or enough to make a thick batter.
____ 7. **Beat** at high speed 2 minutes, scraping bowl occasionally.
____ 8. **Stir** in enough additional flour (about 625 mL, or 2³/₄ cup) to make a soft dough.
____ 9. **Turn out** onto lightly floured board.
____ 10. **Knead** until smooth and elastic, about 8 to 10 minutes.
____ 11. **Place** in greased bowl, turning to grease the top.
____ 12. **Cover** the dough lightly with plastic wrap or foil and then cover the bowl with a clean towel.
____ 13. **Let rise** in warm place, free from draft, until double in bulk, about 1 hour.
____ 14. **Punch** dough down.
____ 15. **Turn out** onto lightly floured board. Cover and let rest 15 minutes.
____ 16. **Divide** dough in half.
____ 17. **Shape** into loaves.
____ 18. **Place** in two greased 22 × 11 × 6 cm (8¹/₂ × 4¹/₂ × 2¹/₂ in.) loaf pans.
____ 19. **Cover** with a clean dish towel.
____ 20. **Let rise** in warm place until doubled in bulk, about 1 hour.
____ 21. **Preheat** oven to 200°C (400°F).
____ 22. **Bake** at 200°C (400°F) for about 25 to 30 minutes or until done.
____ 23. **Remove** from pans and cool on cooling racks.

Microwave Rising

A microwave oven can be used to speed the rising of yeast bread dough. Use glass loaf pans. Check the instructions in the owner's manual for your microwave oven for specific directions. The instructions differ from oven to oven. In some ovens, the dough is allowed to rise on Low (30%) power for 15 minutes or until double in bulk. In other ovens, hot water must be placed in the oven along with the bowl or pans of dough. Bake the bread in a conventional oven, lowering the temperature by 14°C (25°F) to compensate for the glass pans.

Thinking About . . . White Bread (R-39)

Questions

1. Using the formula in Appendix E of *Food for Today,* determine the following:

   a. Percentage of calories from fat _____

   b. Percentage of calories from carbohydrate _____

   c. Percentage of calories from protein _____

2. List four food preparation techniques used in preparing this recipe.

   a. _____

   b. _____

   c. _____

   d. _____

3. List three safety guidelines to follow when preparing the recipe.

   a. _____

   b. _____

   c. _____

4. List three differences in the recipe if you wanted to let the bread rise in the microwave oven.

   a. _____

   b. _____

   c. _____

5. List two possible results if you substituted water for the milk in this recipe.

   a. _____

   b. _____

Evaluation

Complete the following after preparing the recipe:

1. How did the bread look and taste? _____

   _____

2. List any difficulties you had in preparing the recipe. _____

   _____

3. How would you solve the problem(s) next time? _____

   _____

WHOLE WHEAT BREAD

Equipment

- ____ Two loaf pans, 22 × 11 × 6 cm or 8½ × 4½ × 2½ in. (For microwave rising, use glass pans.)
- ____ Medium saucepan
- ____ Large mixing bowl
- ____ Electric mixer
- ____ Rolling pin
- ____ Bread board or pastry cloth
- ____ Liquid measuring cup
- ____ Dry measuring cups
- ____ Measuring spoons
- ____ Spatula
- ____ Knife or kitchen shears
- ____ Mixing spoon
- ____ Rubber scraper
- ____ Clean dish towel
- ____ Plastic wrap or foil
- ____ Pot holders
- ____ Cooling racks

Metric	Customary	Ingredients
705 mL	3 cups	____ Whole-wheat flour
625 to 705 mL	2½ to 3 cups	____ Sifted all-purpose flour
50 mL	3 Tbsp.	____ Sugar
10 mL	2 tsp.	____ Salt
1 pkg.	1 pkg.	____ Active dry yeast
250 mL	1 cup	____ Water
250 mL	1 cup	____ Low-fat milk
50 mL	3 Tbsp.	____ Butter or margarine

Yield: 2 loaves (16 slices each)

Per Slice: 92 calories;
3 g protein; 17 g carbohydrate;
1.6 g fat; 149 mg sodium;
3.5 mg cholesterol

Percentage of U.S. RDA:

Vitamin A:	1%	Niacin:	6%
Vitamin C:	0.1%	Calcium:	2%
Thiamin:	9%	Iron:	5%
Riboflavin:	5%		

Directions

____ 1. **Mix** thoroughly in a large bowl 250 mL (1 cup) whole-wheat flour and 250 mL (1 cup) white flour with the sugar, salt, and undissolved dry yeast.

____ 2. **Combine** water, milk, and butter or margarine in a saucepan.

____ 3. **Heat** over low heat until the liquids are warm. Butter or margarine does not need to melt.

____ 4. **Add** warm liquid gradually to dry ingredients.

____ 5. **Beat** 2 minutes with electric mixer at medium speed, scraping bowl occasionally.

____ 6. **Add** 125 mL (½ cup) whole-wheat flour and 125 mL (½ cup) white flour.

____ 7. **Beat** at high speed 2 minutes, scraping bowl occasionally.

____ 8. **Stir** In 375 mL (1½ cups) whole-wheat flour and enough white flour (about 175 mL or ³/₄ cup) to make a soft dough.

____ 9. **Turn out** onto lightly floured board.

____ 10. **Knead** until smooth and elastic, about 8 to 10 minutes.

____ 11. **Place** in greased bowl, turning to grease the top.

____ 12. **Cover** the dough lightly with plastic wrap or foil and then cover the bowl with a clean dish towel.

____ 13. **Let rise** in warm place, free from draft, until double in bulk, about 1 hour.

____ 14. **Punch** dough down.

____ 15. **Turn out** onto lightly floured board. Cover with bowl and let rest 15 minutes.

____ 16. **Divide** dough in half.

____ 17. **Shape** into loaves.

____ 18. **Place** in two greased 22 × 11 × 6 cm (8½ × 4½ × 2½ in.) loaf pans.

____ 19. **Cover** with a clean dish towel.

____ 20. **Let rise** in warm place until doubled in bulk, about 1 hour.

____ 21. **Preheat** oven to 200°C (400°F).

____ 22. **Bake** at 200°C (400°F) for about 25 to 30 minutes or until done.

____ 23. **Remove** from pans and cool on cooling racks.

Microwave Rising

A microwave oven can be used to speed the rising of yeast bread dough. Use glass loaf pans. Check the instructions in the owner's manual for your microwave oven for specific directions. The instructions differ from oven to oven. In some ovens, the dough is allowed to rise on Low (30%) power for 15 minutes or until double in bulk. In other ovens, hot water must be placed in the oven along with the bowl or pans of dough. Bake the bread in a conventional oven, lowering the temperature by 14°C (25°F) to compensate for the glass pans.

Thinking About . . . Whole Wheat Bread (R-40)

Questions

1. Using the formula in Appendix E of *Food for Today,* determine the following:

   a. Percentage of calories from fat _____

   b. Percentage of calories from carbohydrate _____

   c. Percentage of calories from protein _____

2. List two food preparation techniques used in preparing the bread.

   a. _____

   b. _____

3. List three safety guidelines to follow when preparing this recipe.

   a. _____

   b. _____

   c. _____

4. List three sanitation guidelines to follow when preparing this recipe.

   a. _____

   b. _____

   c. _____

5. What two functions does the yeast serve in this recipe?

   a. _____

   b. _____

6. As you knead the bread, what indicator tells you when gluten is developing? _____

   _____

   _____

Evaluation

Complete the following after preparing the recipe:

1. How did the bread look and taste? _____

   _____

2. List any difficulties you had in preparing the recipe. _____

   _____

3. How would you solve the problem(s) next time? _____

   _____

BROWNIES

Equipment

- ____ 20 cm (8 in.) square baking pan (for microwave cooking, use microwave-safe pan)
- ____ Small saucepan or double boiler (for conventional cooking)
- ____ Large mixing bowl
- ____ Electric mixer
- ____ Cutting board
- ____ Sifter
- ____ 1-L or 1-qt. glass measuring cup or bowl (for microwave cooking)
- ____ Dry measuring cups
- ____ Measuring spoons
- ____ Spatula
- ____ Chef's knife
- ____ Utility knife
- ____ Mixing spoon
- ____ Rubber scraper
- ____ Waxed paper
- ____ Pot holders
- ____ Cooling rack

Metric	Customary	Ingredients
125 mL	¹/₂ cup	____ Butter or margarine
250 mL	1 cup	____ Sugar
5 mL	1 tsp.	____ Vanilla
2	2	____ Eggs
Two 28-g squares	Two 1-oz. squares	____ Unsweetened chocolate, melted
125 mL	¹/₂ cup	____ Sifted all-purpose flour (See increase for micro-wave cooking.)
125 mL	¹/₂ cup	____ Chopped walnuts

Yield: 16 brownies

Per serving (1 brownie without frosting): 174 calories; 2 g protein; 18 g carbohydrate; 12 g fat; 68 mg sodium; 50 mg cholesterol

Percentage of U.S. RDA:

Vitamin A:	5%	Niacin:	2%
Vitamin C:	0.2%	Calcium:	1%
Thiamin:	3%	Iron:	4%
Riboflavin:	3%		

Conventional Directions

- ____ 1. **Preheat** oven to 160°C (325°F).
- ____ 2. **Grease** and flour baking pan.
- ____ 3. **Cream** butter or margarine, sugar, and vanilla.
- ____ 4. **Add** eggs and beat well.
- ____ 5. **Blend** in melted chocolate.
- ____ 6. **Stir** in flour and nuts.
- ____ 7. **Pour** into greased and floured baking pan.
- ____ 8. **Bake** at 160°C (325°F) for 30 to 35 minutes.
- ____ 9. **Cool.**
- ____ 10. **Frost** with Double-Chocolate Frosting, if desired.
- ____ 11. **Cut** into squares or rectangles.

Microwave Directions

- ____ 1. **Melt** chocolate, butter or margarine, and sugar in glass measure or bowl on Medium (50%) for 2 to 4 minutes or until melted. Blend well.
- ____ 2. **Increase** flour to 175 mL (³/₄ cup).
- ____ 3. **Add** vanilla, eggs, flour and chopped nuts to chocolate mixture.
- ____ 4. **Beat** until well blended.
- ____ 5. **Spread** mixture into the microwave-safe baking dish.
- ____ 6. **Place** dish on an inverted saucer in the micro-wave oven.
- ____ 7. **Microwave** on High (100%) for 4 to 7 minutes or until done, rotating ¹/₄ turn after 2, 4, and 5 minutes.
- ____ 8. **Proceed** with Steps 9 through 11 of the Conventional Directions.

Kitchen Management Tips

- Melt chocolate over very low heat. Watch it carefully; chocolate scorches easily and that gives it an unpleasant flavor.
- Chocolate can also be melted in the microwave oven. Place the paper-wrapped squares seam-side up in the oven. Microwave on Medium (50%) for 1 minute per square or until the squares feel soft.
- Use a sharp knife to cut the brownies. For smooth cutting, rinse the knife occasionally in warm water to wash off accumulated crumbs and frosting.

Name _____ Class _____ Date _____

Thinking About . . . Brownies (R-41)

Questions

1. Using the formula in Appendix E of *Food for Today,* determine the following:

   a. Percentage of calories from fat _____

   b. Percentage of calories from carbohydrate _____

   c. Percentage of calories from protein _____

2. What type of cookie is this? _____

3. List two basic food preparation skills used in this recipe.

   a. _____

   b. _____

4. List two safety guidelines to follow when preparing this recipe by the conventional method.

   a. _____

   b. _____

5. List two additional safety guidelines to follow when preparing this recipe in a microwave oven.

   a. _____

   b. _____

6. Give four different steps that are followed when preparing this recipe in the microwave oven rather than the conventional oven?

   a. _____

   b. _____

   c. _____

   d. _____

7. If you were giving the brownies as a gift, how would you package them? _____

   _____

   _____

Evaluation

Complete the following after preparing the recipe:

1. How did the brownies look and taste? _____

   _____

2. List any difficulties you had in preparing the recipe. _____

   _____

3. How would you solve the problem(s) next time? _____

   _____

DOUBLE-CHOCOLATE FROSTING

Equipment

___ Medium saucepan
(for conventional cooking)
___ Sifter
___ 1-L or 1-qt. glass measuring
cup or bowl
(for microwave cooking)

___ Dry measuring cups
___ Measuring spoons
___ Spatula
___ Mixing spoon

___ Rubber scraper
___ Waxed paper
___ Pot holders

Metric	Customary	Ingredients
28-g square	1-oz. square	___ Unsweetened chocolate
30 mL	2 Tbsp.	___ Butter or margarine
30 mL	2 Tbsp.	___ Low-fat milk
350 mL	$1^1/_2$ cups	___ Sifted confectioners' sugar

Conventional Directions

___ 1. **Melt** chocolate with butter or margarine and milk over very low heat.
___ 2. **Stir** constantly until mixture melts and blends.
___ 3. **Remove** from heat.
___ 4. **Beat** in sifted confectioners' sugar. If too thin, add a little more sugar until mixture is of spreading consistency.

Microwave Directions

___ 1. **Combine** chocolate, butter and milk in the glass measuring cup or small bowl.
___ 2. **Microwave** on Medium (50%) for 3 or 4 minutes or until chocolate is soft and blends with other ingredients. Stir after $1^1/_2$ minutes.
___ 3. **Stir** in confectioners' sugar and beat until well blended. Add more milk if necessary.

Yield: Enough to cover the top of a 20-cm (8-in) pan of brownies or cake

Per serving ($^1/_{16}$th of recipe): 59 calories; 0.3 g protein; 10 g carbohydrate; 2.5 g fat; 16 mg sodium; 4 mg cholesterol

Percentage of U.S. RDA:

Vitamin A:	1%	Niacin:	0.1%
Vitamin C:	0%	Calcium:	0.4%
Thiamin:	0.1%	Iron:	0.7%
Riboflavin:	0.5%		

Kitchen Management Tips

■ If you don't have time to spread the frosting on the cake as soon as it is cool, cover the frosting with a clean damp cloth. This will prevent it from drying out and forming a crust.
■ If the frosting is either too thick or too thin, add more milk or confectioners' sugar, as needed, to get the proper spreading consistency.

Thinking About . . . Double-Chocolate Frosting (R-42)

Questions

1. Using the formula in Appendix E of *Food for Today*, determine the following:

   a. Percentage of calories from fat _____

   b. Percentage of calories from carbohydrate _____

   c. Percentage of calories from protein _____

2. List three food preparation skills used in this recipe.

   a. _____

   b. _____

   c. _____

3. List three safety guidelines to follow when preparing this recipe by the conventional method.

   a. _____

   b. _____

   c. _____

4. Do you think preparing the recipe in the microwave oven would require more or less work than preparing it on top of the range? Give reasons for your answer. _____

   _____

   _____

5. If you were taking brownies to a meeting but didn't have time to frost them with this chocolate frosting, what could you use instead? _____

   _____

Evaluation

Complete the following after preparing the recipe:

1. How did the frosting look and taste? _____

   _____

2. How could you change or improve the recipe? _____

   _____

3. List any difficulties you had in preparing the recipe. _____

   _____

4. How would you solve the problem(s) next time? _____

   _____

CARROT COOKIES

Equipment

___ Baking sheets
___ Medium bowl
___ Electric mixer or rotary beater
___ Grater

___ Dry measuring cups
___ Measuring spoons
___ Spatula
___ Teaspoon
___ Mixing spoon

___ Waxed paper
___ Pot holders
___ Turner
___ Cooling racks

Metric	Customary	Ingredients
500 mL	2 cups	___ Unsifted all-purpose flour
175 mL	3/4 cup	___ Regular wheat germ
5 mL	1 tsp.	___ Baking powder
5 mL	1 tsp.	___ Ground cinnamon
4 mL	3/4 tsp.	___ Salt
3 mL	1/2 tsp.	___ Ground nutmeg
1 mL	1/4 tsp.	___ Ground ginger
250 mL	1 cup	___ Butter or margarine
300 mL	1 1/4 cups	___ Brown sugar, packed
2	2	___ Eggs
375 mL	1 1/2 cups	___ Coarsely grated carrots
250 mL	1	___ Raisins

Directions

___ 1. **Preheat** oven to 190°C (375°F).
___ 2. **Combine** flour, wheat germ, baking powder, cinnamon, salt, nutmeg, and ginger on waxed paper.
___ 3. **Stir** dry ingredients on waxed paper gently to blend well.
___ 4. **Cream** butter or margarine and sugar thoroughly in a bowl.
___ 5. **Beat** in eggs.
___ 6. **Add** dry ingredients to creamed mixture alternately with carrots, beginning and ending with dry ingredients.
___ 7. **Blend** well.
___ 8. **Stir** in raisins.
___ 9. **Drop** by teaspoonfuls on a lightly greased baking sheet.
___ 10. **Bake** in preheated oven at 190°C (375°F) for 10-12 minutes or until golden brown.
___ 11. **Remove** from baking sheet and cool on rack.

Kitchen Management Tips

■ When dropping dough on a cookie sheet, make certain the mounds are rounded so the cookies are not too thin.
■ Soak beaters as soon as you are through with them so they will be easier to wash.
■ Unless a recipe specifies otherwise, cookies are easier to remove from a cookie sheet while they are still warm. As they cool, they may stick to the cookie sheet, making them harder to remove.

Yield: About 4 1/2 dozen cookies

Per Cookie: 83 calories; 1 g protein; 12 g carbohydrate; 4 g fat; 75 mg sodium; 19 mg cholesterol

Percentage of U.S. RDA:
Vitamin A: 20%　　Niacin: 2%
Vitamin C: 0.6%　　Calcium: 2%
Thiamin: 4%　　Iron: 4%
Riboflavin: 2%

Thinking About . . . Carrot Cookies (R-43)

Questions

1. Using the formula in Appendix E of *Food for Today*, determine the following:

    a. Percentage of calories from fat _____

    b. Percentage of calories from carbohydrate _____

    c. Percentage of calories from protein _____

2. What type of cookie is this? _____

3. One cookie provides 20% of the daily U.S. RDA requirement for vitamin A. What ingredient(s) do you think contributed the vitamin A? _____

4. Would three of these cookies be a nutritious snack? Explain. _____
_____

5. List five food preparation skills used in this recipe.

    a. _____

    b. _____

    c. _____

    d. _____

    e. _____

6. List two safety guidelines to follow when preparing this recipe for baking.

    a. _____

    b. _____

7. If the first batch of cookies came out of the oven looking like flat pancakes, how could you alter the dough so the next batch turns out nicely rounded? _____
_____

Evaluation

Complete the following after preparing the recipe:

1. How did the cookies look and taste? _____
_____

2. List any difficulties you had in preparing the recipe. _____
_____

3. How would you solve the problem(s) next time? _____
_____

SCANDINAVIAN SPICE COOKIES

Equipment

- ____ Cookie sheet (for micro-wave or conventional oven)
- ____ Large mixing bowl
- ____ Electric mixer
- ____ Bread board or pastry cloth
- ____ Rolling pin
- ____ Sifter
- ____ Grater
- ____ Dry measuring cups
- ____ Measuring spoons
- ____ Spatula
- ____ Mixing spoon
- ____ Rubber scraper
- ____ Cookie cutters
- ____ Turner
- ____ Waxed paper
- ____ Pot holders
- ____ Cooling racks

Metric	Customary	Ingredients
250 mL	1 cup	____ Butter or margarine
350 mL	1½ cups	____ Sugar
1	1	____ Egg
25 mL	1½ Tbsp.	____ Grated orange peel
30 mL	2 Tbsp.	____ Honey
15 mL	1 Tbsp.	____ Water
775 mL	3¼ cups	____ Sifted all-purpose flour
10 mL	2 tsp.	____ Baking soda
10 mL	2 tsp.	____ Ground cinnamon
5 mL	1 tsp.	____ Ground ginger
1 mL	¼ tsp.	____ Ground cloves

Yield: About 4 dozen cookies

Per Cookie: 94 calories;
1 g protein; 14 g carbohydrate;
4 g fat; 87 mg sodium;
16 mg cholesterol

Percentage of U.S. RDA:
Vitamin A:	3%	Niacin:	2%
Vitamin C:	0.5%	Calcium:	0.5%
Thiamin:	4%	Iron:	3%
Riboflavin:	2%		

Conventional Directions

____ 1. **Cream** the butter or margarine and sugar thoroughly.

____ 2. **Add** egg and beat until light and fluffy.

____ 3. **Add** orange peel, honey, and water. Mix well.

____ 4. **Sift** together flour, baking soda, cinnamon, ginger, and cloves.

____ 5. **Stir** dry ingredients into creamed mixture.

____ 6. **Chill** dough thoroughly. Can be chilled overnight.

____ 7. **Preheat** oven to 190°C (375°F).

____ 8. **Cut** off portion of dough. Knead a few times to make it pliable.

____ 9. **Roll** to 0.3 cm (⅛ in.) thick on lightly floured surface.

____ 10. **Cut** in desired shapes with floured cookie cutter.

____ 11. **Place** 2.5 cm (1 in.) apart on ungreased cookie sheet.

____ 12. **Sprinkle** with colored sugar or chopped nuts if desired.

____ 13. **Bake** at 190°C (375°F) for 6 to 8 minutes or until lightly browned.

____ 14. **Remove** from baking sheet and cool on cooling rack.

Microwave Directions

Follow Conventional Directions for Steps 1-10; omit Step 7 (preheating oven).

____ 11. **Place** waxed paper on microwave baking sheet, a large microwave-safe plate, or a piece of cardboard cut to fit the oven.

____ 12. **Arrange** cookies in a circle on the waxed paper. Bake 6 to 9 cookies at a time.

____ 13. **Sprinkle** with colored sugar or chopped nuts if desired.

____ 14. **Microwave** on high for 2 to 5 minutes or until cookies are dry, not moist and doughy.

____ 15. **Remove** waxed paper from plate and allow cookies to cool before removing from waxed paper.

Thinking About . . . Scandinavian Spice Cookies (R-44)

Questions

1. Using the formula in Appendix E of *Food for Today,* determine the following:

    a. Percentage of calories from fat _____

    b. Percentage of calories from carbohydrate _____

    c. Percentage of calories from protein _____

2. What type of cookie is this? _____

3. List three sanitation guidelines to follow when rolling out the dough.

    a. _____

    b. _____

    c. _____

4. List three different procedures you would use if preparing this recipe in the microwave oven rather than the conventional oven.

    a. _____

    b. _____

    c. _____

5. What other spices could be used in this recipe in addition to, or in place of, those already listed?

    _____

    _____

6. What could you do to use less flour when rolling out the cookie dough? _____

    _____

7. How could you decorate these cookies? _____

    _____

Evaluation

Complete the following after preparing the recipe:

1. How did the cookies look and taste? _____

    _____

2. List any difficulties you had in preparing the recipe. _____

    _____

3. How would you solve the problem(s) next time? _____

    _____

SWEDISH SPRITZ

Equipment

___ Large mixing bowl
___ Electric mixer
___ Cookie press
___ Sifter
___ Cookie sheet

___ Dry measuring cups
___ Measuring spoons
___ Spatula
___ Mixing spoon
___ Rubber scraper

___ Turner
___ Waxed paper
___ Pot holders
___ Cooling racks

Metric	Customary	Ingredients
250 mL	1 cup	___ Butter
5 mL	1 tsp.	___ Orange extract
125 mL	1/2 cup	___ Sugar
1	1	___ Egg yolk
500 mL	2 cups	___ Sifted all-purpose flour

Directions

___ 1. **Preheat** oven to 190°C (375°F).
___ 2. **Cream** the butter.
___ 3. **Blend** in the orange extract.
___ 4. **Add** the sugar and cream the mixture until fluffy.
___ 5. **Add** the egg yolk and mix well.

___ 6. **Mix** flour thoroughly into creamed mixture.
___ 7. **Put** dough through a cookie press, placing the cookies on an ungreased cookie sheet.
___ 8. **Bake** at 190°C (375°F) for 8 to 10 minutes. The cookies should be very light in color.

Yield: 5 dozen cookies

Per Cookie: 50 calories; 0.5 g protein; 5 g carbohydrate; 3 g fat; 32 mg sodium; 13 mg cholesterol

Percentage of U.S. RDA:

Vitamin A:	2%	Niacin:	1%
Vitamin C:	0%	Calcium:	0.2%
Thiamin:	2%	Iron:	1%
Riboflavin:	1%		

Kitchen Management Tips

- If the kitchen is warm, the dough may be too soft to maintain a shape. If so, refrigerate the dough in a covered bowl until it is firmer.
- Before reusing a cookie sheet, let it cool so the dough maintains its shape. Scrape off any crumbs from the cooled sheet and wipe the cookie sheet with a paper towel to remove traces of grease.
- To vary the flavor, substitute other extracts for the orange. Food coloring is often added to the dough to make holiday cookies. Cookies may also be decorated with nuts, colored sugar, or candy sprinkles.

Thinking About . . . Swedish Spritz (R-45)

Questions

1. Using the formula in Appendix E of *Food for Today,* determine the following:

   a. Percentage of calories from fat _____

   b. Percentage of calories from carbohydrate _____

   c. Percentage of calories from protein _____

2. What type of cookie is this? _____

3. List five food preparation skills used in this recipe.

   a. _____

   b. _____

   c. _____

   d. _____

   e. _____

4. List three safety guidelines to follow when preparing this recipe.

   a. _____

   b. _____

   c. _____

5. What color and flavoring would you use if you were preparing these cookies for a Halloween party?

   _____

   _____

6. If you wanted to give these cookies as a gift, how would you package them? _____

   _____

Evaluation

Complete the following after preparing the recipe:

1. Describe the texture, flavor, and appearance of the cookies. _____

   _____

2. List any difficulties you had in preparing the recipe. _____

   _____

3. How would you solve the problem(s) next time? _____

   _____

TWINKLE COOKIES

Equipment

____ Medium bowl
____ Two shallow pans
    (for egg white and nuts)
____ Cookie sheet (for microwave
    or conventional cooking)
____ Sifter

____ Dry measuring cups
____ Measuring spoons
____ Spatula
____ Mixing spoon
____ Rubber scraper
____ Fork

____ Teaspoon
____ Waxed paper
____ Pot holders
____ Turner
____ Cooling racks

Metric	Customary	Ingredients
125 mL	1/2 cup	____ Butter or margarine
75 mL	1/4 cup	____ Brown sugar
1	1	____ Egg, separated
1 mL	1/4 tsp.	____ Lemon extract
250 mL	1 cup	____ Sifted all-purpose flour
250 mL	1 cup	____ Chopped walnuts
		____ Strawberry jam or candied cherry halves

Conventional Directions

____ 1. **Preheat** oven to 190°C (375°F).

____ 2. **Mix** together the butter or margarine, brown sugar, egg yolk, and lemon extract. Stir in the flour.

____ 3. **Roll** dough into 2.5-cm (1-in.) balls.

____ 4. **Beat** egg white in shallow pan with a fork until foamy.

____ 5. **Dip** the balls in egg white. Then roll in the chopped walnuts in another shallow pan.

____ 6. **Place** about 5 cm (2 in.) apart on an ungreased cookie sheet.

____ 7. **Bake** in preheated oven at 190°C (375°F) for 5 minutes.

____ 8. **Remove** from the oven. Quickly press the tip of a teaspoon into the top of each cookie to make an indentation. Be careful not to poke through to the bottom of the cookie.

____ 9. **Return** to the oven. Continue baking for about 8 minutes longer. When browned, remove from oven.

____ 10. **Remove** from cookie sheet to a cooling rack.

____ 11. **Cool.**

____ 12. **Place** a little jam or a candied cherry half in the center of each cooled cookie.

Microwave Directions

Follow Conventional Directions for Steps 2-5. Do not preheat oven. Continue with Step 6 as follows:

____ 6. **Place** waxed paper on a microwave baking sheet, plate, or cardboard cut to fit the oven.

____ 7. **Arrange** cookies in a circle at least 5 cm (2 in.) apart.

____ 8. **Microwave** on Medium (50%) for 2 to 3 minutes. After the first minute, press the tip of a teaspoon into the top of each cookie to make an indentation.

____ 9. **Continue** baking until surface is dry.

____ 10. **Slide** waxed paper with cookies to a flat surface.

____ 11. **Cool.**

____ 12. **Remove** from waxed paper with a turner.

____ 13. **Place** a little jam or a candied cherry half in the center of each cooled cookie.

Yield: 2 dozen cookies

Per Cookie: 106 calories; 2 g protein; 9 g carbohydrate; 7 g fat; 45 mg sodium; 22 mg cholesterol

Percentage of U.S. RDA:

Vitamin A:	3%	Niacin:	2%
Vitamin C:	0.4%	Calcium:	1%
Thiamin:	4%	Iron:	3%
Riboflavin:	2%		

Name _____ Class _____ Date _____

Thinking About . . . Twinkle Cookies (R-46)

Questions

1. Using the formula in Appendix E of *Food for Today,* determine the following:

   a. Percentage of calories from fat _____

   b. Percentage of calories from carbohydrate _____

   c. Percentage of calories from protein _____

2. What type of cookie is this? _____

3. List two food preparation skills that are used to prepare the cookies for baking after the dough is mixed.

   a. _____

   b. _____

4. List four safety guidelines to follow when baking the cookies.

   a. _____

   b. _____

   c. _____

   d. _____

5. Read the conventional and microwave directions. Which method would you prefer to use? Why?

   _____

   _____

6. Why is it important to make all the cookies in a batch the same shape and thickness? _____

   _____

7. What other fillings could you use besides strawberry jam or candied cherries? _____

   _____

   _____

Evaluation

Complete the following after preparing the recipe:

1. How did the cookies look and taste? _____

   _____

2. List any difficulties you had in preparing the recipe. _____

   _____

3. How would you solve the problem(s) next time? _____

   _____

BANANA BUNDT CAKE

Equipment

- ____ 25-cm (10-in.) Bundt or tube cake pan (for microwave cooking, use a microwave-safe pan)
- ____ Large mixing bowl
- ____ Electric mixer
- ____ Cutting board
- ____ Liquid measuring cup
- ____ Chef's knife
- ____ Rubber scraper
- ____ Waxed paper
- ____ Pot holders
- ____ Cooling racks

Metric	Customary	Ingredients
1 pkg.	1 pkg.	____ Banana cake mix
99-g pkg.	3½ oz. pkg.	____ Instant banana or vanilla pudding mix
4	4	____ Eggs
125 mL	½ cup	____ Vegetable oil
2	2	____ Medium-size, overripe bananas
250 mL	1 cup	____ Hot water (Decrease for microwave cooking.)
		____ Confectioners' sugar
		____ Oil or nonstick vegetable spray and granulated sugar for microwave cooking

Conventional Directions

- ____ 1. **Preheat** oven to 180°C (350°F).
- ____ 2. **Grease** and flour pan.
- ____ 3. **Pour** cake mix and pudding mix into a large mixing bowl.
- ____ 4. **Add** eggs and oil.
- ____ 5. **Peel** and cut bananas into chunks and add to mixes.
- ____ 6. **Add** hot water.
- ____ 7. **Beat** with an electric mixer at low speed until ingredients are moistened.
- ____ 8. **Beat** at medium speed for 5 minutes, scraping bowl occasionally.
- ____ 9. **Pour** into greased and floured pan.
- ____ 10. **Bake** at 180°C (350°F) for approximately one hour, or until done. If top begins to brown too quickly, cover with aluminum foil.
- ____ 11. **Remove** from pan and cool.
- ____ 12. **Sprinkle** with confectioners' sugar.

Kitchen Management Tip

■ When beating with an electric mixer, scrape the bowl frequently with a rubber scraper to keep ingredients from sticking to the bowl and to insure a uniform blend.

Microwave Directions

Follow Conventional Directions for Steps 3-8. *However, reduce amount of hot water by 30 mL (2 Tbsp.).* Continue with the following steps.

- ____ 9. **Prepare** a nonmetal Bundt pan by oiling lightly or using a nonstick vegetable spray. Coat lightly with 30 mL (2 Tbsp.) granulated sugar.
- ____ 10. **Pour** batter into prepared pan.
- ____ 11. **Elevate** pan on a glass saucer or pie pan placed in center of microwave oven.
- ____ 12. **Microwave** on Medium (50%) for 10 minutes, rotating after 5 minutes.
- ____ 13. **Increase** power to High (100%) and microwave for 5 to 8 minutes or until top springs back when touched.
- ____ 14. **Let stand** on counter for 10 minutes before removing from pan.

Yield: 25-cm (10-in) cake (about 12 pieces)

Per slice: 351 calories; 4 g protein; 49 g carbohydrate; 16 g fat; 329 mg sodium; 92 mg cholesterol

Percentage of U.S. RDA:

Vitamin A:	2%	Niacin:	8%
Vitamin C:	3%	Calcium:	6%
Thiamin:	10%	Iron:	6%
Riboflavin:	8%		

Thinking About . . . Banana Bundt Cake (R-47)

Questions

1. Using the formula in Appendix E of *Food for Today,* determine the following:

   a. Percentage of calories from fat _____

   b. Percentage of calories from carbohydrate _____

   c. Percentage of calories from protein _____

2. List three food preparation skills used in this recipe.

   a. _____

   b. _____

   c. _____

3. List four safety guidelines to follow when using an electric mixer.

   a. _____

   b. _____

   c. _____

   d. _____

4. Give two different steps you would follow if you were preparing this recipe using the microwave directions rather than the conventional?

   a. _____

   b. _____

5. What advantage does the bundt pan have over cake pans with straight sides and no tube in the center?

   _____

   _____

6. Besides using the method suggested in the recipe, what other ways might you decorate this cake?

   _____

   _____

Evaluation

Complete the following after preparing the recipe:

1. How did the cake look and taste? _____

   _____

2. List any difficulties you had in preparing the recipe. _____

   _____

3. How would you solve the problem(s) next time? _____

   _____

PINEAPPLE UPSIDE DOWN CAKE

Equipment

- Skillet with heat-proof handle, 25 cm or 10 in. (for conventional cooking)
- 25-cm (10-in.) microwave-safe baking dish or 5-cm (2-in.) deep pie pan (for microwave cooking)
- Cupcake pan (for microwave cooking)
- Mixing bowl
- Small bowl (for pineapple juice)
- Electric mixer
- Can opener
- Liquid measuring cup
- Dry measuring cups
- Spatula
- Mixing spoon
- Rubber scraper
- Pot holders
- Cooling rack

Metric	Customary	Ingredients
567-g can	20-oz. can	Sliced pineapple in syrup
50 mL	1/4 cup	Butter or margarine
150 mL	2/3 cup	Packed brown sugar
10	10	Maraschino cherries (optional)
1 pkg.	1 pkg.	Pound cake mix

Yield: 25-cm (10-in) cake (12 slices)

Per slice: 295 calories; 3 g protein; 39 g carbohydrate; 15 g fat; 209 mg sodium; 101 mg cholesterol

Percentage of U.S. RDA:
Vitamin A:	12%	Niacin:	3%
Vitamin C:	8%	Calcium:	3%
Thiamin:	7%	Iron:	7%
Riboflavin:	5%		

Conventional Directions

1. **Preheat** oven to 180°C (350°F).
2. **Drain** pineapple, reserving syrup. You should have 175 mL (3/4 cup) syrup.
3. **Melt** butter or margarine in skillet.
4. **Stir** in brown sugar until just blended. Remove from heat.
5. **Arrange** drained pineapple slices in butter mixture. If desired, place a maraschino cherry in the center of each pineapple slice.
6. **Prepare** cake mix according to package directions, but use the reserved pineapple syrup for all or part of the milk.
7. **Pour** batter over pineapple in skillet.
8. **Bake** in preheated oven at 180°C (350°F) for 45 to 50 minutes or until cake tests done.
9. **Cool** in pan 5 minutes.
10. **Invert** on serving plate and serve warm.

Kitchen Management Tips

■ The pineapple slices can be cut and arranged in different designs.

Microwave Directions

1. **Drain** pineapple, reserving syrup. You should have 175 mL (3/4 cup) syrup.
2. **Put** butter or margarine in microwave-safe baking dish or pie pan and microwave on High (100%) for 30 seconds or until melted.
3. **Stir** in brown sugar until just blended.
4. **Arrange** drained pineapple slices in butter mixture. If desired, place a maraschino cherry in the center of each pineapple slice.
5. **Prepare** cake mix according to package directions, but substitute the reserved pineapple syrup for all or part of the milk. Decrease the liquid by 15 mL (1 Tbsp.)
6. **Fill** the baking dish or pie pan half full of batter. Make cupcakes from the remaining batter.
7. **Microwave** on Medium (50%) for 6 minutes, then on High (100%) for 6 1/2 minutes.
8. **Invert** on serving plate and serve warm.

■ After you bake the cake and invert the skillet on a serving plate, wait a few moments. Then gently and gradually begin to lift the skillet, allowing time for the cake and topping to separate from the pan.

Thinking About . . . Pineapple Upside Down Cake (R-48)

Questions

1. Using the formula in Appendix E of *Food for Today*, determine the following:

   a. Percentage of calories from fat _____

   b. Percentage of calories from carbohydrate _____

   c. Percentage of calories from protein _____

2. List four food preparation techniques used in this recipe.

   a. _____

   b. _____

   c. _____

   d. _____

3. List four safety guidelines to follow when preparing this recipe.

   a. _____

   b. _____

   c. _____

   d. _____

4. Name two different steps you would follow if preparing this recipe using the microwave instructions rather than the conventional?

   a. _____

   b. _____

5. Which method of cooking, microwave or conventional, would you prefer? Why? _____

   _____

6. If you didn't have a 10-inch skillet with a heat-proof handle, what could you use to bake the cake?

   _____

Evaluation

Complete the following after preparing the recipe:

1. How did the cake look and taste? _____

   _____

2. List any difficulties you had in preparing the recipe. _____

   _____

3. How would you solve the problem(s) next time? _____

   _____

APPLE PIE

Equipment

- ____ 23-cm (9-in.) pie pan
- ____ Large mixing bowl
- ____ Medium mixing bowl
- ____ Small mixing bowl
- ____ Cutting board
- ____ Bread board or pastry cloth
- ____ Rolling pin
- ____ Grater
- ____ Sifter
- ____ Liquid measuring cup
- ____ Dry measuring cups
- ____ Measuring spoons
- ____ Spatula
- ____ Vegetable peeler
- ____ Paring knife
- ____ Pastry blender or two knives
- ____ Fork
- ____ Mixing spoon
- ____ Kitchen shears
- ____ Plastic wrap or foil
- ____ Waxed paper
- ____ Pot holders
- ____ Cooling rack

Metric	Customary	Ingredients
500 mL	2 cups	____ All purpose flour, sifted
5 mL	1 tsp.	____ Salt
150 mL	$2/3$ cup	____ Shortening
75 to 100 mL	5 to 7 Tbsp.	____ Cold water
1500 mL	6 cups	____ Sliced apples (6 to 8 medium apples)
175 mL	$3/4$ cup	____ Sugar
30 mL	2 Tbsp.	____ All-purpose flour
5 mL	1 tsp.	____ Grated lemon rind
5 mL	1 tsp.	____ Ground cinnamon
1 mL	$1/4$ tsp.	____ Ground nutmeg
Dash	Dash	____ Ground mace
30 mL	2 Tbsp.	____ Butter or margarine

Yield: 23-cm (9-in) pie (8 pieces)

Per Piece: 413 calories;
4 g protein; 56 g carbohydrate;
20 g fat; 297 mg sodium;
8 mg cholesterol

Percentage of U.S. RDA:

Vitamin A:	3%	Niacin:	9%
Vitamin C:	4%	Calcium:	2%
Thiamin:	15%	Iron:	9%
Riboflavin:	8%		

Directions

- ____ 1. **Mix** together flour and salt in a medium bowl.
- ____ 2. **Cut in** 75 mL ($1/3$ cup) shortening until the mixture has the texture of fine cornmeal.
- ____ 3. **Cut in** the remaining 75 mL ($1/3$ cup) shortening until the particles are the size of small peas.
- ____ 4. **Add** water gradually, mixing with fork until the mixture forms a ball.
- ____ 5. **Cover** the dough and refrigerate while preparing the filling.
- ____ 6. **Pare** and core apples and slice thin; place in a large bowl.
- ____ 7. **Combine** sugar, flour, lemon rind, cinnamon, nutmeg, and mace in a small bowl. Mix well.
- ____ 8. **Sprinkle** the sugar mixture over the apples and toss gently until all apples are covered.
- ____ 9. **Preheat** oven to 200°C (400°F).
- ____ 10. **Divide** dough in half.
- ____ 11. **Cover** unused portion so it will not dry out.
- ____ 12. **Roll out** other half of dough on a lightly floured board.
- ____ 13. **Fit** into a 23-cm (9-in.) pie pan.
- ____ 14. **Fill** with apple mixture.
- ____ 15. **Dot** apples with butter or margarine.
- ____ 16. **Roll out** remaining half of dough and fit over pie.
- ____ 17. **Seal** edges so juices do not escape.
- ____ 18. **Slit** crust in center to allow steam to escape.
- ____ 19. **Bake** at 200°C (400°F) for 55 to 60 minutes or until lightly browned.

Thinking About . . . Apple Pie (R-49)

Questions

1. Using the formula in Appendix E of *Food for Today,* determine the following:

   a. Percentage of calories from fat _____

   b. Percentage of calories from carbohydrate _____

   c. Percentage of calories from protein _____

2. Which ingredient(s) contributed the most fat? _____

   _____

3. If you wanted to reduce the fat content, what could you do and still have a tasty dessert. _____

   _____

4. Break the process of preparing an apple pie into eight steps and list them below.

   a. _____

   b. _____

   c. _____

   d. _____

   e. _____

   f. _____

   g. _____

   h. _____

5. List four safety guidelines to follow when preparing this recipe.

   a. _____

   b. _____

   c. _____

   d. _____

6. What could you use on top of the pie in place of the top crust? _____

   _____

Evaluation

Complete the following after preparing the recipe:

1. How did the pie look and taste? _____

   _____

2. List any difficulties you had in preparing the recipe. _____

   _____

3. How would you solve the problem(s) next time? _____

   _____

PEA SOUP WITH HAM

Equipment

- ___ 3-L (3-qt.) saucepan with lid (for conventional cooking)
- ___ 3-L (3-qt.) microwave-safe casserole with lid (for microwave cooking)
- ___ Cutting board
- ___ Liquid measuring cup
- ___ Dry measuring cups
- ___ Chef's knife
- ___ Mixing spoon
- ___ Rubber scraper
- ___ Pot holders

Metric	Customary	Ingredients
226-g pkg.	10-oz. pkg.	___ Frozen green peas and potatoes in cream sauce
250 mL	1 cup	___ Chicken broth or bouillon
250 mL	1 cup	___ Half-and-half
15 mL	1 Tbsp.	___ Butter or margarine
375 mL	1½ cups	___ Diced cooked ham
500 mL	2 cups	___ Shredded romaine or iceberg lettuce

Conventional Directions

- ___ 1. **Place** green peas and potatoes, broth or bouillon, half-and-half, and butter in a large saucepan.
- ___ 2. **Cover.**
- ___ 3. **Bring** to a full boil over medium-high heat.
- ___ 4. **Remove** from heat and stir until sauce is smooth.
- ___ 5. **Add** ham and lettuce.
- ___ 6. **Simmer** about 5 minutes.

Microwave Directions

- ___ 1. **Combine** peas and potatoes, broth or bouillon, half-and-half, and butter in casserole.
- ___ 2. **Cover.**
- ___ 3. **Cook** on high power for 8 to 10 minutes.
- ___ 4. **Stir.**
- ___ 5. **Add** ham and lettuce.
- ___ 6. **Cook** on High (100%) 3 to 4 minutes longer.
- ___ 7. **Let** stand covered for 2 minutes.

Yield: About 750 mL (3 cups)

Per serving: (¼ of recipe): 288 calories; 17 g protein; 15 g carbohydrate; 18 g fat; 1167 mg sodium; 59 mg cholesterol

Percentage of U.S. RDA:

Vitamin A:	29%	Niacin:	19%
Vitamin C:	26%	Calcium:	11%
Thiamin:	37%	Iron:	10%
Riboflavin:	20%		

Kitchen Management Tips

- When a recipe calls for chicken broth or bouillon, you can use canned broth, bouillon made from a cube or granules, or leftover homemade chicken broth.
- To shred iceberg lettuce, break off a portion of the head instead of cutting it. If you cut it off, the leftover portion will turn brown quickly. After you tear off the amount you need, you can shred it with a sharp knife.

Thinking About . . . Pea Soup with Ham (R-50)

Questions

1. Using the formula in Appendix E of *Food for Today*, determine the following:

   a. Percentage of calories from fat _____

   b. Percentage of calories from carbohydrate _____

   c. Percentage of calories from protein _____

2. This recipe supplies more than one-fourth of the daily vitamin A requirement and more than one-third of the daily thiamin requirement. Which food(s) do you think contributed most of each?

   a. Vitamin A: _____

   b. Thiamin: _____

3. List three sanitation guidelines to follow *before* preparing the recipe.

   a. _____

   b. _____

   c. _____

4. List three safety guidelines to follow when cooking the food by the conventional method.

   a. _____

   b. _____

   c. _____

5. Name two general cleanup activities that should be carried out after the recipe is prepared.

   a. _____

   b. _____

6. What other foods would you serve with this soup to make a nutritious lunch? _____

   _____

Evaluation

Complete the following after preparing the recipe:

1. How did the soup look and taste? _____

   _____

2. List any difficulties you had in preparing the recipe. _____

   _____

3. How would you solve the problem(s) next time? _____

   _____

HOT TACO DIP

Equipment

- ____ 1.5-L (1½-qt.) saucepan (for conventional cooking)
- ____ 1.5-L (1½-qt.) microwave-safe bowl (for microwave cooking)
- ____ Blender or food processor (optional)
- ____ Can opener
- ____ Dry measuring cups
- ____ Measuring spoons
- ____ Spatula
- ____ Mixing spoon·
- ____ Rubber scraper
- ____ Fork
- ____ Pot holders

Metric	Customary	Ingredients
326-g can	11½-oz. can	____ Condensed bean with bacon soup
250 mL	1 cup	____ Sour cream
125 mL	½ cup	____ Shredded American or cheddar cheese
30 mL	2 Tbsp.	____ Dry taco seasoning mix
3 mL	½ tsp.	____ Instant minced onion
30 mL	½ Tbsp.	____ Chopped green chilies (optional)
		____ Corn or tortilla chips

Conventional Directions

- ____ 1. **Pour** soup into saucepan. Mash beans with a fork. For a smoother dip, purée soup in a blender or food processor.
- ____ 2. **Stir** in remaining ingredients, except for the chips, and mix well.
- ____ 3. **Cook** on medium-high heat until heated through, stirring to blend.
- ____ 4. **Serve** warm with corn or tortilla chips.

Microwave Directions

- ____ 1. **Pour** soup into a microwave-safe mixing bowl. Mash beans with a fork. For a smoother dip, purée soup in a blender or food processor.
- ____ 2. **Stir** in remaining ingredients, except for the chips, and mix well.
- ____ 3. **Cook,** uncovered, on High (100%) for 2½ minutes or until heated through. Stir occasionally.
- ____ 4. **Serve** warm with corn or tortilla chips.

Yield: About 750 mL (3 cups)

Per tablespoon: (chips not included): 24 calories; 0.8 g protein; 1.5 g carbohydrate; 2 g fat; 72 mg sodium; 3.5 mg cholesterol

Percentage of U.S. RDA:

Vitamin A:	2%	Niacin:	0.2%
Vitamin C:	0.2%	Calcium:	2%
Thiamin:	0.4%	Iron:	0.6%
Riboflavin:	0.8%		

Kitchen Management Tip

■ Be careful when using chilies. They contain capsaicin, a volatile oil that gives them their characteristic "hot" spiciness. It also makes them irritating to the skin and the eyes. Handle chilies with a utensil whenever possible. If you must touch chilies, you can remove most of the oil by washing your hands with soap and warm water. But traces of capsaicin may remain for as long as an hour. So it's wise to avoid touching the eye area until the oil has evaporated.

Thinking About . . . Hot Taco Dip (R-51)

Questions

1. Using the formula in Appendix E of *Food for Today*, determine the following:

   a. Percentage of calories from fat _____

   b. Percentage of calories from carbohydrate _____

   c. Percentage of calories from protein _____

2. How could you reduce the fat and calories in this recipe? _____

   _____

3. List four safety guidelines to follow when preparing this recipe by the conventional method.

   a. _____

   b. _____

   c. _____

   d. _____

4. Make up a menu for an informal get-together, using this recipe. _____

   _____

5. Why should you be careful when handling chilies? _____

   _____

Evaluation

Complete the following after preparing the recipe:

1. How did the dip look and taste? _____

   _____

2. How could you change or improve the recipe? _____

   _____

3. List any difficulties you had in preparing the recipe. _____

   _____

4. How would you solve the problem(s) next time? _____

   _____

NECTAR TEMPTER

Equipment

____ 2.5-L (2½-qt.) pitcher   ____ Bottle opener   ____ Spatula
____ Cutting board   ____ Liquid measuring cup   ____ Mixing spoon
____ Can opener   ____ Measuring spoons   ____ Utility knife

Metric	Customary	Ingredients
15 mL	1 tsp.	____ Instant tea
500 mL	2 cups	____ Cold water
Two 354-mL cans	Two 12-oz. cans	____ Apricot nectar, chilled
15 mL	1 Tbsp.	____ Lime juice
1-L bottle	1-qt. bottle	____ Ginger ale, chilled

Directions

____ 1. **Mix** together tea, water, apricot nectar, and lime juice.
____ 2. **Chill.**
____ 3. **Add** ginger ale just before serving. Serve over ice cubes.
____ 4. **Garnish** with lime slices, if desired.

Yield: About 2.3 L (2¼ qt.)

Per glass (¹/₁₀th of recipe): 72 calories; 0.3 g protein; 19 g carbohydrate; 0 fat; 2.3 mg sodium; 0 cholesterol

Percentage of U.S. RDA:

Vitamin A:	20%	Niacin:	1%
Vitamin C:	68%	Calcium:	0.5%
Thiamin:	0.5%	Iron:	2%
Riboflavin:	0.7%		

Kitchen Management Tips

- For easy serving, pour chilled tea-apricot mixture in tall glasses. Then add chilled ginger ale, stir, and serve.
- If the ginger ale is added and the mixture allowed to stand too long before serving, it will have a flat taste.
- Rinse ginger ale bottles before discarding or recycling them. Otherwise they may attract germs and insects.

Thinking About . . . Nectar Tempter (R-52)

Questions

1. This recipe provides about 20% of the daily vitamin A requirement and more than two-thirds of the daily vitamin C requirement. Which ingredient(s) supplied most of each?

   a. Vitamin A: _____

   b. Vitamin C: _____

2. What other carbonated beverages could you use in place of ginger ale? _____
   _____

3. If you had no instant tea, what could you use in its place? _____
   _____

4. If you were serving this beverage as a refreshment for a committee meeting, what else would you serve? _____
   _____

5. Besides lime slices, what other garnishes might you use? _____
   _____

6. How else might you give the nectar drink a festive look? _____
   _____

7. Imagine a springtime party at the local forest preserve. You've been asked to decorate a small buffet table where Nectar Tempter will be served. What might you use? _____
   _____

Evaluation

Complete the following after preparing the recipe:

1. How did the drink look and taste? _____
   _____

2. How could you change or improve the recipe? _____
   _____

3. List any difficulties you had in preparing the recipe. _____
   _____

4. How would you solve the problem(s) next time? _____
   _____

PEANUT BANANA COOLER

Equipment

____ Blender
____ Cutting board
____ Liquid measuring cup
____ Measuring spoons
____ Utility knife

Metric	Customary	Ingredients
250 mL	1 cup	____ Cold low-fat milk
1	1	____ Ripe banana, peeled and sliced
30 mL	2 Tbsp.	____ Peanut butter
15 mL	1 tsp.	____ Honey

Directions

____ 1. **Combine** milk, banana, peanut butter, and honey in blender jar.

____ 2. **Blend** well.

____ 3. **Pour** into 2 glasses.

____ 4. **Garnish** with banana slices rolled in chopped nuts if desired.

____ 5. **Serve** immediately. (See tip below.)

Yield: 2 servings

Per serving: 221 calories; 9 g protein; 25 g carbohydrate; 11 g fat; 137 mg sodium; 9 mg cholesterol

Percentage of U.S. RDA:

Vitamin A:	6%	Niacin:	13%
Vitamin C:	11%	Calcium:	16%
Thiamin:	7%	Iron:	3%
Riboflavin:	16%		

Kitchen Management Tips

- Make the cooler just before serving. If it is allowed to stand more than a few minutes, some of the ingredients may settle to the bottom. If this occurs, stir the drink before serving.
- To cut down on fat and calories, use skim milk instead of low-fat milk.
- For a special treat, add a little chocolate syrup to the mixture before blending.
- For a pleasing banana flavor, chose a ripe banana with brown specks on the skin. Bananas ripen easily at room temperature. Once they have ripened, refrigerate them to slow down the enzyme activity. The skin will turn dark, but the bananas will retain their flavor.

Thinking About . . . Peanut Banana Cooler (R-53)

Questions

1. Using the formula in Appendix E of *Food for Today*, determine the following:

   a. Percentage of calories from fat _____

   b. Percentage of calories from carbohydrate _____

   c. Percentage of calories from protein _____

2. List seven general safety guidelines to follow when using a small electric appliance, such as the blender.

   a. _____

   b. _____

   c. _____

   d. _____

   e. _____

   f. _____

   g. _____

3. How would you prepare this recipe if you didn't have a blender? _____
   _____

4. If you had no more bananas, what could you use to garnish the cooler? _____
   _____

5. If you were serving the cooler as a snack for guests, what else might you serve? _____
   _____
   _____

Evaluation

Complete the following after preparing the recipe:

1. How did the cooler look and taste? _____
   _____

2. How could you change or improve the recipe? _____
   _____

3. List any difficulties you had in preparing the recipe. _____
   _____

4. How would you solve the problem(s) next time? _____
   _____

FREEZING VEGETABLES

Equipment

- ___ 4-L (4-qt.) pot (for conventional preparation)
- ___ Strainer to fit pot (for conventional preparation)
- ___ 1.5- to 2-L (1½- to 2-qt.) microwave-safe casserole with lid (for microwave preparation)
- ___ Large pan for ice water
- ___ Cutting board
- ___ Liquid measuring cup
- ___ Chef's knife
- ___ Paring knife
- ___ Slotted spoon
- ___ Large spoon or tongs
- ___ Paper towels
- ___ Freezer containers or bags
- ___ Labels (if necessary)
- ___ Freezer marker

Metric	Customary	Ingredients
500 g	1 lb.	___ Green beans, broccoli, or carrots
3 L	3 qt.	___ Water
		___ Ice cubes

Conventional Directions

- ___ 1. **Heat** 3 L (3 qt.) water to boiling in a 4 L (4 qt.) pot.
- ___ 2. **Prepare** vegetables:
  Green beans: Wash, trim, and cut into 2.5 cm (1 in.) pieces.
  Broccoli: Wash and trim. Split stems lengthwise into pieces 2.5 cm (1 in.) thick or slices 2.5 cm (1 in.) long.
  Carrots: Wash, trim, and pare. Slice into "coins" of even thickness.
- ___ 3. **Fill** large pan with cold water. Add about a dozen ice cubes to keep water cold.
- ___ 4. **Place** vegetables in large strainer that will fit into 4-L (4-qt.) pot.
- ___ 5. **Lower** strainer of vegetables into boiling water. Set timer as follows:
  Green beans: 3 minutes
  Broccoli: 3 minutes
  Carrots: 2 minutes
- ___ 6. **Remove** strainer from boiling water as soon as timer rings.
- ___ 7. **Put** vegetables into ice water to stop further cooking.
- ___ 8. **Remove** cooled vegetables with slotted spoon and place on paper towels.
- ___ 9. **Drain** well. Pat dry, removing as much moisture as possible.
- ___ 10. **Divide** vegetables into desired number of servings.
- ___ 11. **Pack** into moisture- and vapor-proof freezer containers or plastic freezer bags.
- ___ 12. **Label** each container, giving the following information:
  - Type of vegetable and whether it is raw or cooked
  - Freezing date
  - Amount in container
- ___ 13. **Store** in freezer immediately.

Microwave Directions

Vegetables can be blanched in a microwave oven. Follow Conventional Directions through Step 3. Then proceed as follows:

- ___ 4. **Place** green beans or carrots in a 1.5-L (1½-qt.) casserole and broccoli in a 2-L (2-qt.) casserole. Add water in the following amounts:
  Green beans: 75 mL (⅓ cup)
  Broccoli: 75 mL (⅓ cup)
  Carrots: 50 mL (¼ cup)
- ___ 5. **Cover** casserole. Microwave on high for the following time:
  Green beans: 4 to 5 minutes
  Broccoli: 3½ to 4½ minutes
  Carrots: 3½ to 4½ minutes
  Halfway through the microwaving time, stir or rearrange the vegetables and then complete the microwaving for the minimum time. Check color of vegetables. They should have an evenly bright color throughout. If not, cover the casserole and continue microwaving to the maximum time.
- ___ 6. **Drain** vegetables.
- ___ 7. **Continue** with Step 7 of Conventional Directions.

Note: For loose-pack vegetables, spread blanched, drained vegetables in a shallow baking pan, one layer deep. Set pan in freezer for a few hours or until vegetables are frozen. Package vegetables in freezer containers or bags. Label and return to freezer.

Yield: 4 servings of frozen vegetables

Thinking About . . . Freezing Vegetables (R-54)

Questions

1. List three sanitation guidelines to follow before blanching vegetables.

    a. _____

    b. _____

    c. _____

2. List two safety guidelines to follow when blanching by the conventional method.

    a. _____

    b. _____

3. Read the conventional and microwave blanching directions. Which method would you prefer to use? Why? _____

    _____

4. Why are vegetables blanched before freezing? _____

    _____

5. What is the advantage of using the loose-pack method? _____

    _____

6. What can be done to insure that frozen vegetables don't get freezer burn? _____

    _____

7. Why should you leave head space between the top level of the food and the lid of the container?

    _____

8. After reading Chapter 34 of *Food for Today*, would you rather freeze or can vegetables? Why?

    _____

    _____

Evaluation

Complete the following after preparing the recipe:

1. List any difficulties you had in blanching and freezing the vegetable. _____

    _____

    _____

2. How would you solve the problem(s) next time? _____

    _____

CREATIVE CASSEROLES

Equipment

- ____ 1.5-L (1½-qt.) casserole
- ____ Small saucepan or glass measuring cup (for melting butter)
- ____ Colander
- ____ Can opener
- ____ Liquid measuring cup
- ____ Dry measuring cups
- ____ Measuring spoons
- ____ Spatula
- ____ Chef's knife
- ____ Kitchen shears
- ____ Mixing spoon
- ____ Rubber scraper
- ____ Other equipment as needed for particular choice of ingredients

---

Ingredient Groups

Ingredients from each group are combined as directed to make a unique casserole.

Group 1
250 mL (1 cup) flaked or diced:

Bacon, Canadian	Hamburger, browned
Bacon, cooked	Lobster, cooked
Bologna	Meat, canned or cooked
Cheese	Salmon, canned
Chicken, cooked	Sardines, canned
Chipped beef	Sausage, browned
Crab, cooked	Shrimp, cooked
Corned beef, cooked	Tuna, canned
Eggs, hard cooked	Turkey, cooked
Frankfurters	

Group 2
1 can condensed soup plus 125 mL (½ cup) liquid
Suggested soups: asparagus, celery, chicken, mushroom, shrimp, tomato, pea.

Group 3
250 mL (1 cup) cooked:

Macaroni	Rice
Noodles	Spaghetti

Group 4
Add any of these, if desired:

Almonds, slivered	Mustard
Bean sprouts	Olives, sliced or chopped
Catsup	Onions or chives, chopped and browned
Celery, chopped	Parsley, chopped
Cheese, grated	Pimiento, diced
Chili sauce	Tomatoes, slices or wedges
Chinese noodles	Vegetables, cooked
Green pepper, diced or in rings	French fried onion rings
Horseradish	
Mushrooms, browned	

Group 5
Add seasoning — herbs and spices — if desired. Begin with no more than 1 mL (¼ tsp.). Follow suggestions on any herb and spice chart. Do not add salt unless needed after tasting.

Group 6
Add topping to keep mixture from drying out:
Almonds, slivered
Bread or cracker crumbs with melted butter or margarine
Cornflakes, crushed and mixed with melted butter or margarine
Potato chips, crushed
Chinese noodles mixed with melted butter or margarine

Microwave Directions

Yield: 4 servings
Note: Microwave timing is based on foods that have been precooked. If foods need to be cooked first, follow directions for that particular food before using it in this recipe.

- ____ 1. **Select** one or more ingredients from each group.
- ____ 2. **Decrease** the liquid in Group 2 to 50 mL ¼ cup).
- ____ 3. **Combine** selected items from Groups 1 through 5 in the casserole. Note: Casserole does not need to be greased.
- ____ 4. **Microwave** on High (100%) for 7 to 13 minutes or to 60°C (150°F) with temperature probe. Stir twice during cooking.
- ____ 5. **Add** topping from Group 6 after the last stirring.
- ____ 6. **Use** a wider container if the recipe is doubled. Be sure the depth of the food remains the same as it would be in the regular size pan for one recipe. Increase cooking time to 11 to 17 minutes or to 60°C (150°F) with the temperature probe.

Conventional Directions

Yield: 4 servings
Note: Recipe may be doubled without increasing the baking time.

- ____ 1. **Grease** casserole.
- ____ 2. **Select** one or more ingredients from each of the groups.
- ____ 3. **Combine** the selected ingredients in the casserole.
- ____ 4. **Top** with ingredient from Group 6.
- ____ 5. **Bake** 30 minutes at 180°C (350°F).

Name _____ Class _____ Date _____

Thinking About . . . Creative Casseroles (R-55)

Questions

1. Under Group 2 of the ingredients, you are asked to select a condensed soup and add a liquid. What are three liquids you could add?

   a. _____

   b. _____

   c. _____

2. Describe a combination that sounds *unappealing*. Explain your answer. _____
_____
_____

3. Name two ingredients in Group 4 that might also be used as toppings.

   a. _____

   b ._____

4. Pick a theme (perhaps based on a country or region of the United States) and create a "designer casserole" to fit. Write down the theme and the ingredients, including the spices you would choose. Then describe how you would decorate the table to match the theme.

   a. Theme: _____

   b. Ingredients: _____

   c. Spices: _____

   d. Table decoration: _____

Evaluation

Complete the following after preparing the recipe:

1. How did the casserole look and taste? _____
_____

2. How could you change or improve the recipe? _____
_____

3. List any difficulties you had in preparing the recipe. _____
_____

4. How would you solve the problem(s) next time? _____
_____

MASTER BAKING MIX

Equipment

___ Large mixing bowl	___ Pastry blender or 2 knives
___ Dry measuring cups	___ Mixing spoon
___ Measuring spoons	___ Rubber scraper
___ Spatula	___ Airtight container for storage

Metric	Customary	Ingredients
500 mL	2 cups	___ All-purpose flour
20 mL	1 Tbsp. + 1 tsp.	___ Baking powder
5 mL	1 tsp.	___ Salt
10 mL	2 tsp.	___ Sugar
125 mL	1/2 cup	___ Nonfat dry milk
125 mL	1/2 cup	___ Shortening

Directions

___ 1. **Combine** flour, baking powder, salt, sugar and nonfat dry milk in large mixing bowl.

___ 2. **Cut in** shortening with a pastry blender or two knives.

___ 3. **Store** in airtight container.

___ 4. **Keep** in refrigerator 4 to 5 weeks. Freeze for longer storage periods.

Note: Use with recipes for Master Mix Biscuits, Master Mix Carrot Bread, and Master Mix Banana Bread.

Yield: 1 L (1 qt.) mix

Per 1 cup (1/4th of recipe): 506 calories; 11 g protein; 57 g carbohydrate; 26 g fat; 906 mg sodium; 3 mg cholesterol

Percentage of U.S. RDA:

Vitamin A:	6%	Niacin:	17%
Vitamin C:	1%	Calcium:	36%
Thiamin:	30%	Iron:	16%
Riboflavin:	28%		

Kitchen Management Tips

- Note that the flour is measured without sifting.
- Use this Master Baking Mix only with recipes designed for it. Although mixes may appear to be alike, the proportions of ingredients may differ, giving unsatisfactory results if used with other recipes.
- When freezing the Mix, freeze in amounts called for in recipes. For example, if you never make biscuits but plan to use the mix for the bread recipes, freeze it in 175-mL (3/4 cup) packages. Then you can defrost only the amount you need for the recipe.

Thinking About . . . Master Baking Mix (R-56)

Questions

1. List two food preparation techniques used in this recipe.

   a. _____

   b. _____

2. Describe how you would accurately measure the ½ cup of shortening called for in this recipe.

   _____

   _____

   _____

3. What are you really doing when you "cut" the shortening into the dry ingredients? _____

   _____

4. This mix can be used to make biscuits and carrot and banana breads. Name two other kinds of mixes you could prepare.

   a. _____

   b. _____

5. List two advantages a homemade mix offers over a store-bought equivalent.

   a. _____

   b. _____

6. If you wanted to prepare the mix for a child who would be making only the biscuits, how might you package it? _____

   _____

Evaluation

Complete the following after preparing the recipe:

1. List any difficulties you had in preparing the recipe. _____

   _____

2. How would you solve the problem(s) next time? _____

   _____

MASTER MIX BISCUITS

Equipment

___ Small baking sheet   ___ Spatula   ___ Rubber scraper
___ Mixing bowl   ___ Mixing spoon   ___ Pastry brush
___ Pastry cloth   ___ Fork   ___ Pot holders
___ Dry measuring cups   ___ Biscuit cutter or sharp knife   ___ Cooling rack
___ Measuring spoons   ___ Turner

Metric	Customary	Ingredients
250 mL	1 cup	___ Master Baking Mix
45 to 60 mL	3 to 4 Tbsp.	___ Low-fat milk

Directions

___ 1. **Preheat** oven to 230°C (450°F).

___ 2. **Measure** baking mix into a medium mixing bowl.

___ 3. **Add** milk slowly to the mix, stirring until dough leaves the sides of the bowl.

___ 4. **Turn** out onto floured surface.

___ 5. **Knead** lightly 10 strokes.

___ 6. **Roll** dough out 6 mm (¼ in.) thick.

___ 7. **Cut** into biscuits.

___ 8. **Place** on baking sheet.

___ 9. **Brush** tops with milk.

___ 10. **Bake** in the oven at 230°C (450°F) for 12 to 15 minutes or until golden brown.

Yield: 4 biscuits

Per biscuit: 132 calories; 3 g protein; 15 g carbohydrate; 7 g fat; 233 mg sodium; 1.4 mg cholesterol

Percentage of U.S. RDA:

Vitamin A:	2%	Niacin:	4%
Vitamin C:	0.5%	Calcium:	11%
Thiamin:	8%	Iron:	4%
Riboflavin:	8%		

Kitchen Management Tips

- Use a fork to mix the baking mix and milk until the dough forms a ball that leaves the sides of the bowl.
- Don't knead the dough more than ten strokes. If you over-knead, the biscuits will not be flaky.
- You can cut the biscuits into circles with a round biscuit cutter. Or you can save time and use all the dough by cutting the dough into squares using a sharp knife.
- Brushing the tops with milk aids browning.
- Biscuits taste best served hot from the oven.

Thinking About . . . Master Mix Biscuits (R-57)

Questions

1. List two advantages in having a mix available rather than preparing a biscuit recipe from scratch.

   a. _____

   b. _____

2. Give two reasons why you would make a homemade mix rather than buy a store-bought mix.

   a. _____

   b. _____

3. List six basic steps used in preparing biscuits.

   a. _____

   b. _____

   c. _____

   d. _____

   e. _____

   f. _____

4. List three sanitation guidelines to follow when preparing the biscuits.

   a. _____

   b. _____

   c. _____

5. In what ways could you use the biscuits as part of a main-dish or dessert recipe? _____
_____

Evaluation

Complete the following after preparing the recipe:

1. How did the biscuits look and taste? _____
_____

2. List any difficulties you had in preparing the recipe. _____
_____

3. How would you solve the problem(s) next time? _____
_____

MASTER MIX CARROT BREAD

Equipment

- ____ Loaf pan, 7.5 × 17 × 5 cm or 3 × 6³/₄ × 2 in.
- ____ Cutting board
- ____ Medium mixing bowl
- ____ Small mixing bowl
- ____ Grater
- ____ Rotary beater
- ____ Dry measuring cups
- ____ Measuring spoons
- ____ Spatula
- ____ Utility knife
- ____ Vegetable peeler
- ____ Mixing spoon
- ____ Rubber scraper
- ____ Pot holders
- ____ Cooling rack

Metric	Customary	Ingredients
175 mL	³/₄ cup	____ Master Baking Mix
50 mL	¹/₄ cup	____ Sugar
1 mL	¹/₄ tsp.	____ Ground cinnamon
1 mL	¹/₄ tsp.	____ Ground nutmeg
Dash	Dash	____ Ground cloves
1	1	____ Egg, well beaten
30 mL	2 Tbsp.	____ Orange juice
50 mL	¹/₄ cup	____ Grated carrots
30 mL	2 Tbsp.	____ Chopped nuts

Directions

- ____ 1. **Preheat** oven to 180°C (350°F).
- ____ 2. **Grease** the loaf pan.
- ____ 3. **Combine** baking mix, sugar, cinnamon, nutmeg, and cloves in a medium mixing bowl.
- ____ 4. **Mix** together egg and orange juice in a small bowl.
- ____ 5. **Stir** egg mixture into dry ingredients.
- ____ 6. **Blend** in carrots and nuts.
- ____ 7. **Pour** into prepared loaf pan.
- ____ 8. **Bake** in the oven at 180°C (350°F) for 35 to 45 minutes or until loaf tests done.
- ____ 9. **Cool** slightly.
- ____ 10. **Remove** from pan and cool on wire cooling rack.

Yield: One loaf

Per slice (¹/₆th of loaf): 130 calories; 3 g protein; 17 g carbohydrate; 6 g fat; 128 mg sodium; 46 mg cholesterol

Percentage of U.S. RDA:

Vitamin A:	28%	Niacin:	3%
Vitamin C:	4%	Calcium:	6%
Thiamin:	6%	Iron:	4%
Riboflavin:	5%		

Kitchen Management Tips

- You can use fresh, frozen, or canned juice. If you use frozen juice, reconstitute it first. If you are using fresh orange juice, grate the rind before squeezing the orange. Refrigerate or freeze the rind to save for another recipe.
- You can chop a whole bag of nuts, use what a recipe calls for, then store the remainder in a tightly closed container in the refrigerator or freezer. Besides using chopped nuts in recipes, you can sprinkle them on salads and desserts for added nutrition.

Thinking About . . . Master Mix Carrot Bread (R-58)

Questions

1. Using the formula in Appendix E of *Food for Today*, determine the following:

    a. Percentage of calories from fat _____

    b. Percentage of calories from carbohydrate _____

    c. Percentage of calories from protein _____

2. A slice of this bread provides slightly more than one-fourth of the daily vitamin A requirement. Which ingredient(s) do you think contributed the vitamin A? _____

    _____

3. List five food preparation skills used in this recipe.

    a. _____

    b. _____

    c. _____

    d. _____

    e. _____

4. List four safety guidelines to follow when preparing this recipe.

    a. _____

    b. _____

    c. _____

    d. _____

5. List three different ways to serve this bread.

    a. _____

    b. _____

    c. _____

6. How would you package the bread for storing in the freezer? _____

    _____

Evaluation

Complete the following after preparing the recipe:

1. How did the bread look and taste? _____

    _____

2. List any difficulties you had in preparing the recipe. _____

    _____

3. How would you solve the problem(s) next time? _____

    _____

MASTER MIX BANANA BREAD

Equipment

- ____ Loaf pan, 7.5 × 17 × 5 cm or 3 × 6³/₄ × 2 in.
- ____ Medium mixing bowl
- ____ Small mixing bowl
- ____ Cutting board
- ____ Rotary beater
- ____ Dry measuring cups
- ____ Measuring spoons
- ____ Spatula
- ____ Chef's knife
- ____ Paring knife
- ____ Mixing spoon
- ____ Rubber scraper
- ____ Fork
- ____ Pot holders
- ____ Cooling rack

Metric	Customary	Ingredients
175 mL	³/₄ cup	____ Master Baking Mix
50 mL	¹/₄ cup	____ Sugar
1 mL	¹/₄ tsp.	____ Ground cinnamon
1	1	____ Egg, well beaten
30 mL	2 Tbsp.	____ Low-fat milk
1 mL	¹/₄ tsp.	____ Vanilla
50 mL	¹/₄ cup	____ Mashed banana
30 mL	2 Tbsp.	____ Chopped nuts

Directions

- ____ 1. **Preheat** oven to 180°C (350°F).
- ____ 2. **Grease** the loaf pan.
- ____ 3. **Combine** baking mix, sugar and cinnamon in a medium bowl.
- ____ 4. **Mix** together egg, milk, and vanilla in a small bowl.
- ____ 5. **Stir** egg mixture into dry ingredients.
- ____ 6. **Blend** in banana and nuts.
- ____ 7. **Pour** mixture into prepared loaf pan.
- ____ 8. **Bake** in the oven at 180°C (350°F) for 35 to 45 minutes or until bread tests done.
- ____ 9. **Cool** slightly.
- ____ 10. **Remove** from pan and cool on wire rack.

Yield: One loaf

Per slice (¹/₆th of recipe): 136 calories; 3 g protein; 19 g carbohydrate; 6 g fat; 128 mg sodium; 47 mg cholesterol

Percentage of U.S. RDA:

Vitamin A:	2%	Niacin:	3%
Vitamin C:	2%	Calcium:	6%
Thiamin:	5%	Iron:	4%
Riboflavin:	6%		

Kitchen Management Tips

- Mix the dry and liquid ingredients only until moistened. The batter will be lumpy. When adding banana and nuts, stir just enough to blend the ingredients.
- You can mash and freeze overripe bananas in measurable quantities. Then you will have them on hand for whenever a recipe calls for mashed bananas.
- Small loaves of fruit bread make welcome gifts.

Name _____ Class _____ Date _____

Thinking About . . . Master Mix Banana Bread (R-59)

Questions

1. Using the formula in Appendix E of *Food for Today*, determine the following:

   a. Percentage of calories from fat _____

   b. Percentage of calories from carbohydrate _____

   c. Percentage of calories from protein _____

2. List three general sanitation guidelines to follow before preparing this recipe.

   a. _____

   b. _____

   c. _____

3. Make up a brown bag lunch menu, including the banana bread. _____

   _____

4. If you were giving the bread as a gift, how would you package it? _____

   _____

5. What are two spreads that you could use on the bread to make snacks?

   a. _____

   b. _____

6. If you wanted to make decorative open-face sandwiches, how would you garnish them? _____

   _____

Evaluation

Complete the following after preparing the recipe:

1. How did the bread look and taste? _____

   _____

2. List any difficulties you had in preparing the recipe. _____

   _____

3. How would you solve the problem(s) next time? _____

   _____

Food Science Material

TABLE OF CONTENTS

Food Science Material

Why Food Science?

How will home economics students benefit from the study of food science? Incorporating food science into foods and nutrition classes gives students an opportunity to develop many important skills and attitudes, including essential life management skills.

- **Critical thinking and related skills.** Science enhances students' abilities to observe, think about what they perceive, draw conclusions, solve problems, and make decisions. These same skills will help them make better choices, both in their daily activities and in planning and meeting their life's goals. By improving their skills in these areas, students can develop the self-confidence and self-esteem needed to reach their full potential.

- **Learning from trial and error.** People are so geared to success that any kind of failure often results in discouragement and loss of self-confidence. Yet when approached analytically, mistakes can provide valuable information and insights. R. H. Macy failed seven times before he finally hit on the right formula for his store in New York City — now one of the world's best known retail stores. Conducting food science experiments is one way to help students understand that "failures" provide an opportunity to learn. In a scientific experiment, ingredients and methods are varied in a deliberate trial-and-error process. Analyzing why one variation "failed" is often the only way to understand why others produce the desired results.

- **Consumer skills.** Understanding some basic scientific methods and principles can help students become better consumers in today's food marketplace. Science plays an increasingly larger role in the nation's food supply. A familiarity with scientific terms and methods will help students evaluate the rapid technological changes as they are reported in the media.

- **Food preparation skills.** The study of food science can introduce students to some of the natural laws that govern food preparation. Through simple experiments, they will have hands-on experience in observing these laws at work. Too often, these basic principles are ignored in food preparation. Yet once students understand that nutrition, aroma, flavor, color, and texture are all part of the chemical properties of food and cooking procedures, they can become more skilled in choosing and preparing nutritious meals.

- **Basic academic skills.** As part of conducting food science experiments, students learn to read carefully, measure accurately, and follow directions exactly. In making observations, they must find the right word to specifically describe the product and write down their description. They must reach conclusions and express them clearly in writing.

- **Career exploration.** Exposure to food science may encourage some students to consider food science as a career. Just the act of successfully conducting simple scientific experiments may be enough to spark an interest in the subject.

OVERCOMING SCIENCE "PHOBIAS"

In spite of the benefits of studying science, many people avoid it. Science is often viewed as a mysterious discipline requiring above-average intellect and a "scientific mind." For these and other reasons, students may be apprehensive about studying science or conducting experiments.

The truth is that science is not the complex, mysterious subject people believe it to be. It is a vital part of daily life. It involves simple natural laws or principles. And what is known as the "scientific method" (see *Food for Today* p. 34, "How Are Scientific Discoveries Made?") is nothing more than a specialized application of the basic life skills inherent in every human being. What makes science so mysterious and sometimes feared is not the subject itself but the attitude of people.

Few people think of science as an art. Yet to be successful, the scientist must look at the world differently, see beyond the obvious, and notice details that escape most people. Like the artist, the scientist relies on imagination, intuition, originality, courage, and creativity.

The story of Dr. Alexander Fleming and the discovery of penicillin in 1928 serves as an example of the creative aspects of science. Dr. Fleming was experimenting with the *staphylococci* bacteria. Unknown to him, a spore of the mold *penicillium* floated through the air, landed on a glass dish containing the bacteria, and began to grow.

When Dr. Fleming noticed that the bacteria around the mold was disappearing, he realized that something in the mold attacked the bacteria. His curiosity aroused, he turned his attention to the mold. Twelve years later, penicillin became a revolutionary medical treatment. But had Dr. Fleming not observed the action between the mold and the bacteria, had he not followed through with his curiosity and creativity, penicillin might never have been discovered.

Today, the nation is placing great emphasis on incorporating more science into the education process. Dr. Maxine Singer is president of the Carnegie Institution, Washington, D.C., which has taken the lead in such fields as extra-galactic astronomy, genetics, and the study of the earth's interior. A biochemist, Dr. Singer says the purpose of teaching science in elementary and high schools is not to have all students become scientists, but to give them a way of looking at the world.

The home economics laboratory is a natural place to introduce students to basic scientific concepts. Food science lets students experiment with familiar, everyday objects and ingredients. It takes advantage of students' natural interest in food to spark interest and curiosity in science. The discoveries students make will be of immediate practical benefit. More importantly, they will gain skills and attitudes that are applicable not only to the study of other sciences, but to many aspects of their lives.

Using the TRB Food Science Material

This section of the Teacher's Resource Book provides resources specifically designed to help you teach food science through hands-on experiences. Here you will find food science experiment worksheets as well as additional student handouts and teaching guidelines. This material, along with related food science material in the student text and Teacher's Wraparound Edition, is designed to make the study of food science an enjoyable and rewarding experience for both you and your students.

ORGANIZING YOUR APPROACH TO FOOD SCIENCE

To help you plan your approach to teaching food science concepts, a "Food Science Planning Chart" is provided on pages 350-356. For each chapter, the chart shows what information and resources relating to food science are available in the *Food for Today* student text, Teacher's Wraparound Edition, and Teacher's Resource Book.

How you use this chart will depend on your approach to food science. Many options are possible. For example, you can:

- Incorporate food science concepts into your day-to-day teaching of food and nutrition. On the chart, check off those topics and activities that you wish to emphasize in your lessons.
- Draw upon the food science activities and experiments listed in the chart when planning enrichment, independent study, or extra credit projects.
- Periodically devote one or more days to an in-depth treatment of food science — perhaps after completing "the basics" for a certain number of chapters. Use the chart to see what food science topics can be related to those chapters and what resources are available.
- Plan a separate food science unit, perhaps at the end of the course. Select topics and activities from the chart as a whole to design your own "mini-course."
- Plan the entire course around food science topics. Use this chart in conjunction with "Suggested Course Outlines" on page 50-51 to decide what chapters and topics to cover and how many days to devote to each.

For more planning aids that include other topics in addition to food science, refer to the Planning Charts section beginning on page 39.

USING THE FOOD SCIENCE EXPERIMENTS

Over 20 food science experiments are provided in this section of the TRB. These experiments will help students understand and apply some of the basic scientific principles that govern food preparation. The experiments offer a simple introduction to food science, using food items and equipment available in the typical home economics laboratory.

The Scientific Method

The experiments are based on the scientific method, a general set of ground rules for approaching scientific experiments. (You may wish to refer to the Food Science feature in the textbook, page 34, "How Are Scientific Discoveries Made?") The scientific method can be summarized as follows:
1. Observe a natural occurrence and state the problem.
2. Develop a hypothesis to explain the occurrence or solve the problem.
3. Test the hypothesis by conducting experiments and making observations.
4. Interpret the data from the experiments.
5. Draw conclusions based on the data and interpretations.

Rather than attempting to make new discoveries, which is beyond the scope of this course, students will be duplicating experiments that have already been successfully made. The experiments will give students experience in following laboratory procedures, observing results, and drawing their own conclusions. Performing the experiments themselves will help students understand and remember concepts more effectively than textbook reading.

Laboratory Safety

Safety is always of primary importance in any laboratory situation. The food science experiments in this section are designed for maximum safety. None of the experiments involve toxic chemicals or hazardous substances of any kind. Students will be working with ordinary food and equipment items such as vinegar, baking soda, saucepans, and measuring spoons. Other than basic rules of safety and sanitation — which should always be enforced in the foods lab — no special precautions need be taken when conducting these experiments. (You may wish to have students review the safety and sanitation principles found in Chapter 13 of the text and on TRB pages 221-222.)

Student Experiment Worksheets

Directions for conducting each experiment are found in the reproducible student experiment worksheets which begin on page 377. Each experiment worksheet includes nine sections:

- To help you to . . . (purpose of experiment)
- Look for these terms . . . (vocabulary)
- See also . . . (text references)
- Background Information
- Supplies
- Procedure
- Observations
- Conclusions
- Finishing Up

For more information on the content of these sections, see the reproducible student handout, "Conducting Food Science Experiments," pages 373-374.

Supplies listed on the experiment sheet are usually those needed by each lab group. The total number or amount of supplies needed will depend on how many lab groups will be working at one time.

In the "Finishing Up" section of the experiment worksheet, suggestions are given for using products resulting from the experiment. Every effort has been made to design the experiments so food is not wasted.

Guidelines and Answer Key

Beginning on page 357, teacher's guidelines (including an answer key) are provided for each experiment. The guidelines begin with a statement of the experiment's purpose. Under the heading *"Food for Today* Reference" is a list of chapters with which the experiment could be used. Page numbers of specific sections for suggested reading are also given. "Procedure Hints" gives suggestions that should help the experiment run smoothly. "Expected Results" summarizes the typical outcome of the experiment. This is followed by an answer key for the "Conclusions" section of the students' worksheet. The guidelines conclude with suggested "Discussion Questions" for classroom follow-up.

Getting Started

Before beginning the first experiment, have students read and discuss the handout, "Conducting Food Science Experiments" (pages 373-374). This handout will familiarize students with the format of the experiment worksheets. It also explains general procedures for conducting experiments and making observations. You may also wish to provide students with two additional handouts, "Vocabulary for

Sensory Evaluation" (page 371) and "Glossary of Selected Food Science Terms" (pages 375-376). Students will find it helpful to refer to these handouts throughout their study of food science.

You may wish to introduce students to food science with Experiment 21, "Taste-Testing Fruit Juice." This experiment gives students experience in judging products by taste and smell — observation skills that will be used in almost all of the experiments.

POINTERS FOR SUCCESS

Here are some general suggestions for successfully conducting the experiments.

- Before each experiment, read "Background Information" with students. Also review the information from the textbook pages shown on the worksheet.
- Go over the worksheet with students so they understand exactly what they are to do in the "Procedure," "Observations," and "Conclusions" sections.
- Emphasize the importance of writing down the data as it is observed. If students rely on their memories, they will likely forget what they observed.
- Stress the importance of following directions carefully. If a step is accidentally omitted or carried out improperly, the experiment will not have the best results.
- Encourage accurate labeling. If items are mislabeled or labels removed, students will be unable to make the necessary observations or the results of the experiment will be incorrect and misleading.
- Help students learn to develop their powers of observation. At first, students may have to make conscious efforts to actually see the details of what they are observing. Try this exercise: Give students five minutes to write a detailed description of the route they take to school each morning. Discuss how well they remember the details.
- When students are testing flavors, they should take a sip of water or rinse their mouths between samples. This removes traces of the previous sample which could affect the flavor of the next one.
- Encourage students to have the handout "Vocabulary for Sensory Evaluation" with them as they are observing the products of the experiments. Using the list will help students make concise, accurate observations.
- Emphasize that the purpose of food science experiments is to learn how and why specific ingredients or procedures create specific results. Nonstandard food products are expected in some experiment variations and should not be considered "wrong" or "failures."

Food Science References

Charley, Helen. *Food Science*. 2nd ed. New York: Wiley, 1982.

Edwards, Gabrielle I. *Biology the Easy Way*. Woodbury, N.Y.: Barron's Educational Series, 1984.

Fennema, Owen R. *Food Chemistry*. 2nd ed. New York: Marcel Dekker, 1985.

Grosser, Arthur E. *The Cookbook Decoder: or Culinary Alchemy Explained*. New York: Warner Books, 1981.

Hess, Fred C. *Chemistry Made Simple*. Garden City, N.Y.: Doubleday, 1984.

Hillman, Howard. *Kitchen Science: A Compendium of Essential Information for Every Cook*. Boston: Houghton Mifflin, 1983.

Mallow, Jeffry V. *Science Anxiety*. Asheboro, N.C.: H and H Publications, 1986.

Mascetti, Joseph A. *Chemistry the Easy Way*. Woodbury, N.Y.: Barron's Educational Series, 1983.

McGee, Harold. *On Food and Cooking: The Science and Lore of the Kitchen*. New York: Charles Scribner's Sons, 1984.

McWilliams, Margaret. *Food: Experimental Perspectives*. New York: Macmillan, 1989.

Mehas, Kay, and Sharon Rodgers. *Food Science and You*. Mission Hills, Calif.: Glencoe, 1989.

Potter, Norman N. *Food Science*. 4th ed. Westport, Conn.: AVI Publishing, 1982.

Food Science Planning Chart

There are many ways to incorporate food science concepts and activities into your foods and nutrition course. The following chart can serve as a guide and checklist, helping you plan a food science approach using the resources available in the *Food for Today* program.

The chart lists resources under three headings:

- **Textbook.** For each chapter of the text, a listing is given of topics which particularly relate to food science. Page numbers are given to help you locate the discussion in the text. In selecting topics to be listed, emphasis has been given to the biological aspects of nutrition, the physical and chemical changes involved in food preparation, and the field of food technology. However, "food science" can be defined broadly or narrowly, depending on your course outline and goals. Your particular classroom needs will also dictate the degree to which the text discussion should be supplemented by addi-

tional information and activities, such as those provided in the Teacher's Wraparound Edition and Teacher's Resource Book.

- **Teacher's Wraparound Edition (TWE).** Listed in this column are all "Focus on Food Science" boxes found in each chapter, including the page number and a brief description of each. These coral-colored boxes are found in the side margins of the TWE. The listing also includes many "More About" boxes — found in the bottom margins of the TWE — which include information related to food science.
- **Teacher's Resource Book (TRB).** Food science experiments are listed here. Note that many experiments logically relate to more than one chapter and therefore are listed more than once. The listing for each chapter also includes any transparency masters (TM), handout masters (HO), and color transparencies (CT) that relate to food science concepts.

Textbook	Teacher's Wraparound Edition (TWE)	Teacher's Resource Book (TRB)
Chapter 1: Your Food Choices ____ Sensory evaluation ("Enjoyment," p. 4) ____ Explore and Report #4, p. 15 (taste-testing vegetables)		____ Experiment 21, "Taste-Testing Fruit Juice"
Chapter 2: Food Facts and Fallacies ____ Food additives (pp. 20-25) ____ Sugar and fat substitutes (p. 22) ____ Irradiated food (p. 24) ____ Contaminants in food (pp. 25-26) ____ Explore and Report #4, p. 27 (chemical waste research)	____ Focus on Food Science, p. 21 (preservatives) ____ More About Contaminants, p. 25 (food web and bioconcentration)	____ TM-3, "Bioconcentration in the Food Web" ____ HO-1, "Commonly Used Additives and What They Do"
Chapter 3: The Science of Nutrition ____ Nutrition research (p. 35) ____ Food Science feature, "How Are Scientific Discoveries Made?" (p. 24) ____ Explore and Report #4, p. 36 (nutrient research)		
Chapter 4: The Nutrients You Need ____ Chemical nature of basic nutrients ____ Simple and complex carbohydrates (pp. 38-39) ____ Processed foods (p. 39) ____ Properties of saturated and unsaturated fats (p. 40) ____ Hydrogenation (p. 40) ____ Properties of cholesterol (p. 41) ____ Amino acids (p. 42) ____ Properties of fat-soluble and water-soluble vitamins (pp. 44-49) ____ Properties of minerals (pp. 49-53) ____ Hemoglobin (pp. 52-53) ____ Explore and Report #4, p. 54 (vitamin deficiencies and overdoses)	____ More About Fiber, pp. 38-39 (insoluble and soluble fibers) ____ More About Cholesterol, pp. 40-41 (LDLs and HDLs) ____ Focus on Food Science, p. 39 (breakdown of starch into simple sugars) ____ Focus on Food Science, p. 40 (identifying fat) ____ Focus on Food Science, p. 42 (identifying protein) ____ More About Vitamins, More About Vitamin A, More About the B Vitamins, pp. 44-49 (discovery of vitamins) ____ More About Minerals, pp. 52-53 (forms of sodium added to foods; foods affecting iron absorption)	____ Experiment 7, "Separating Fat from Cream" ____ CT-4, "Complete Protein from Plants"

Textbook	Teacher's Wraparound Edition (TWE)	Teacher's Resource Book (TRB)
Chapter 5: Food and Your Well-Being ____ Energy, calories, basal metabolism (pp. 58-60) ____ Food Science feature, "How Are Calories Measured?" (p. 59) ____ Chemistry of digestion, absorption, and metabolism (pp. 61-65) ____ Effect of drugs on digestion and nutrition (p. 73) ____ Explore and Report #4, p. 74 (digestive process)	____ "More About the Body," pp. 56-57 (energy in cells, Krebs cycle) ____ More About Oxygen, pp. 58-59 (composition of air in atmosphere) ____ More About Water, pp. 60-61 (lead contamination) ____ Focus on Food Science, p. 61 (pulse and respiration) ____ Focus on Food Science, p. 62 (villi) ____ More About Feeding the Cells, pp. 64-65 (osmosis, electrolytes)	____ Experiment 5, "Recrisping Celery" (osmosis) ____ CT-6, "How Food Is Digested" ____ CT-7, "How Cells Receive Nutrients"
Chapter 6: Plan Your Daily Food Choices ____ Combining amino acids in vegetarian diets (p. 84) ____ Explore and Report #4, p. 90 (nutrient chart)		____ HO-6, "How to Compute the Percentage of Calories from Nutrients"
Chapter 7: Controlling Your Weight ____ Calories and energy balance (pp. 94-95) ____ Complex carbohydrates in weight-control diets (p. 98) ____ Metabolic rate and setpoint (p. 99) ____ Explore and Report #4, p. 105 (diet evaluation)	____ Focus on Food Science, p. 94 (calories and energy balance) ____ More About the Seesaw Diet, pp. 96-97 (effects of seesaw dieting on metabolism) ____ Focus on Food Science, p. 103 (effects of anorexia nervosa)	____ Experiment 7, "Separating Fat from Cream" (invisible fat made visible) ____ TM-10, "Balance — The Key to Weight Control"
Chapter 8: Special Food Needs ____ Effects of alcohol and caffeine on pregnancy (p. 109) ____ Balancing food intake and energy output (pp. 114-117) ____ Diabetes and other medical conditions (p. 121) ____ Explore and Report #4, p. 123 (nutrient chart)	____ More About Lowering Cholesterol, p. 122 (polyunsaturated oils, monounsaturated oils, omega-3 fatty acids)	
Chapter 9: Your Kitchen		
Chapter 10: Kitchen Equipment and Appliances ____ Characteristics of cookware materials (pp. 142-143) ____ Scientific testing of appliances — AGA and UL (p. 146) ____ Microwave energy (p. 155) ____ Food Science feature, "How Do Appliances Heat Food?" (conduction, convection, radiation) (p. 159) ____ Explore and Report #4, p. 160 (microwave experiment)	____ Focus on Food Science, p. 143 (effects of saucepan materials on heating time) ____ More About Heat, p. 159 (changes in physical state; molecular energy; energy wavelength)	____ HO-9, "Buying Cookware"
Chapter 11: Buying Food ____ Processing and packaging of food (pp. 162-164) ____ Imitation foods (p. 168) ____ New food packaging technology (p. 176) ____ Explore and Report #4, p. 177 (taste testing imitation foods)	____ Focus on Food Science, p. 162 (food processing) ____ Focus on Food Science, p. 168 (imitation foods) ____ More About Packaging, p. 176 (controlled atmosphere packaging)	

Textbook	Teacher's Wraparound Edition (TWE)	Teacher's Resource Book (TRB)
Chapter 12: Storing Food ____ Enzymes and microorganisms that cause food spoilage (p. 179) ____ Effect of heat and moisture on stored food (p. 180) ____ Food Science feature, "What Happens When Food Is Frozen?" (p. 185) ____ Explore and Report #4, p. 189 (storage experiment)	____ Focus on Food Science, p. 179 (pH levels preferred by micro-organisms) ____ More About Microorganisms, p. 179 (food spoilage vs. food poisoning) ____ Focus on Food Science, p. 184 (freezing experiment) ____ More About Freezing, p. 185 (enzyme action)	____ Experiment 14, "Effects of Sugar and Salt on Yeast Growth" ____ Experiment 16, "Moisture Absorption by Cookies" ____ TM-21, "What Makes Food Spoil?"
Chapter 13: Safety and Sanitation ____ Poisons (p. 200) ____ Harmful bacteria and toxins in food (pp. 203-204) ____ Food-borne illness (pp. 203-204) ____ Effect of storage temperatures on bacterial growth in food (pp. 206-207) ____ Explore and Report #4, p. 208 (bacteria cultures)	____ More About Handling Poisons, pp. 200-201 (household chemicals) ____ More About Salmonella, p. 203 ____ Focus on Food Science, p. 205 (bacteria cultures)	____ CT-16, "Temperature Guide for Food Safety" ____ HO-14, "Dealing with Household Chemicals"
Chapter 14: Food Preparation Tools ____ Explore and Report #4, p. 222 (cookware and bakeware materials)	____ Focus on Food Science, p. 210 (using measuring cups; meniscus) ____ Focus on Food Science, p. 217 (calibrating thermometers) ____ Focus on Food Science, p. 219 (pressure cookers)	
Chapter 15: Food Preparation Techniques ____ Metrics in food science (p. 226) ____ Food substitutions (p. 227) ____ Increasing or decreasing recipes (p. 228) ____ Effect of high altitude on food preparation (p. 230) ____ Changes in food caused by different cooking methods (pp. 234-238) ____ Explore and Report #4, p. 239 (measuring experiment)	____ Focus on Food Science, p. 225 (food preparation as science) ____ Focus on Food Science, p. 232 (water displacement method) ____ Focus on Food Science, p. 233 (effects of cooking on food) ____ Focus on Food Science, p. 234 (boiling) ____ More About Basic Cooking Methods, p. 234 (effect of boiling on liquids) ____ More About Frying, p. 236 (smoking point of fat) ____ Focus on Food Science, p. 237 (effect of temperature in frying)	____ TM-27, "Cooking in Liquid and Moist Heat" ____ TM-28, "Cooking in Fat" ____ TM-30, "Cooking with Dry Heat" ____ HO-18, "Understanding Metrics"
Chapter 16: Microwave Cooking ____ How microwave ovens work (pp. 240-242) ____ Effects of food composition on microwaving time (pp. 245-246) ____ Solving microwave problems (p. 247) ____ Adapting standard recipes to microwave cooking (p. 251) ____ Explore and Report #4, p. 252 (adapting recipes)	____ More About the Microwave Oven, p. 241 (discovery of microwaves as a cooking method) ____ More About Containers, pp. 242-243 (effect of container shape on microwaving)	____ Experiment 4, "Cooking Vegetables by Conventional and Microwave Cooking Methods"
Chapter 17: Meal Management ____ Importance of sensory aspects in meal planning (pp. 255-256)	____ Focus on Food Science, p. 263 (food spoilage)	
Chapter 18: Serving and Eating Food		

Textbook	Teacher's Wraparound Edition (TWE)	Teacher's Resource Book (TRB)
Chapter 19: Fruits _____ Chemical and physical changes in fruit during the ripening process (p. 285) _____ Effect of cooking methods on physical and chemical properties of fruits (pp. 293-295) _____ Explore and Report #4, p. 296 (genetic engineering research)	_____ More About Fruit Facts, More About Fruits, pp. 285-287 (botanical and horticultural definitions and classifications of fruits) _____ Focus on Food Science, p. 289 (taste perception) _____ More About Ripening Fruits, p. 290 (ethylene gas) _____ Focus on Food Science, p. 291 (storage experiment) _____ Focus on Food Science, p. 292 (enzymatic browning) _____ More About Dried Fruit, p. 292 (use of sulfites) _____ More About Serving Fruits, p. 293 (chemical treatment of fresh fruits) _____ Focus on Food Science, p. 294 (reconstituting dried fruit)	_____ Experiment 1, "Oxidation of Fruit" _____ Experiment 21, "Taste-Testing Fruit Juice"
Chapter 20: Vegetables _____ Horticultural classifications of vegetables (p. 298) _____ Solanine in potatoes (p. 302) _____ Chemical changes caused by improper storage (p. 303) _____ Effects of cooking methods on physical and chemical properties of vegetables (pp. 306-313) _____ Effects of acids and bases when cooking vegetables (p. 308) _____ Explore and Report #4, p. 315 (nutrient chart)	_____ Focus on Food Science, p. 298 (scientific classification of vegetables) _____ Focus on Food Science, p. 302 (solanine) _____ More About Buying Vegetables, pp. 302-303 (commercial processing of fresh vegetables) _____ Focus on Food Science, p. 304 (storage of root vegetables) _____ Focus on Food Science, p. 308 (pigment changes when cooking vegetables)	_____ Experiment 2, "Effects of Acids and Bases on Vegetables" _____ Experiment 3, "The Effect of Vegetable Piece Size on Cooking Time" _____ Experiment 4, "Cooking Vegetables by Conventional and Microwave Methods" _____ Experiment 5, "Recrisping Celery"
Chapter 21: Salads and Salad Dressings _____ Food Science feature, "How Do Seeds Sprout?" (p. 327) _____ Explore and Report #4, p. 329 (emulsifier in salad dressing)	_____ Focus on Food Science, p. 318 (water content of lettuce) _____ Focus on Food Science, p. 320 (enzymes and gelatin) _____ More About Salad Dressings, pp. 322-323 (emulsions) _____ Focus on Food Science, p. 324 (browning of cut greens)	_____ Experiment 5, "Recrisping Celery" _____ HO-27, "How Do Seeds Sprout?"
Chapter 22: Dairy Foods _____ Pasteurization (p. 331) _____ Homogenization (p. 331) _____ Use of acids, bacteria, molds, yeasts, and enzymes in making dairy products (pp. 332-337) _____ Effect of cooking methods on chemical and physical properties of dairy products (pp. 341-343) _____ Dairy substitutes (p. 344) _____ Explore and Report #4, p. 345 (freezing milk experiment)	_____ More About Milk, p. 331 (acidophilus milk) _____ Focus on Food Science, p. 332 (coalescence of fat in buttermaking) _____ Focus on Food Science, p. 333 (lactose intolerance) _____ Focus on Food Science, p. 335 (making cottage cheese; bacteria in cheese-making) _____ Focus on Food Science, p. 337 (making ice cream) _____ Focus on Food Science, p. 339 (factors affecting cheese storage)	_____ Experiment 6, "The Effect of Acid on Protein" _____ Experiment 7, "Separating Fat from Cream" _____ Experiment 8, "The Effect of Gelatin on a Frozen Dessert"

Textbook	Teacher's Wraparound Edition (TWE)	Teacher's Resource Book (TRB)
Chapter 23: Meat ____ Meat composition — muscle, fat marbling, collagen, elastin (p. 347) ____ Processed meat (pp. 355-356) ____ Chemical and physical changes in spoiled meat (p. 356) ____ Effect of cooking methods on physical and chemical properties of meat (p. 357) ____ Mechanical and chemical tenderizers (p. 358) ____ Vegetable proteins (pp. 366-367) ____ Explore and Report #4, p. 368 (tenderizing experiment)	____ More About Meat, pp. 352-353 (myoglobin as cause of bloom; effect of aging) ____ More About Storing Meat, pp. 356-357 (effects of bacteria and molds) ____ Focus on Food Science, p. 357 (denatured protein) ____ Focus on Food Science, p. 358 (papain enzyme) ____ Focus on Food Science, p. 360 (infrared radiation)	____ Experiment 9, "Tenderizing Meat"
Chapter 24: Poultry ____ Effect of cooking on physical and chemical properties of poultry (p. 374) ____ Processed forms of poultry (p. 370-372) ____ Explore and Report #4, p. 381 (lunchmeat comparison)	____ Focus on Food Science, p. 371 (antibiotics and hormones in animal feed) ____ Focus on Food Science, p. 372 (pigments in feed formulas) ____ More About Poultry, pp. 372-373 (myoglobin as cause of light and dark meat) ____ Focus on Food Science, p. 374 (effect of high heat on barbecue sauce) ____ More About Poultry, pp. 374-375 (bacteria in poultry)	
Chapter 25: Fish and Shellfish ____ Classification of shellfish — mollusks and crustaceans (p. 384) ____ Fish farming (p. 387) ____ Effect of cooking methods on fish (p. 388) ____ Use of acidic foods to remove fish odors (p. 388) ____ Explore and Report #4, p. 393 (fish cooking experiment)	____ More About Shellfish, pp. 384-385 (imitation seafood made from surimi) ____ More About Aquaculture, p. 387 (ocean ranching)	
Chapter 26: Eggs ____ Eggs as thickeners, emulsifiers, binders (p. 395) ____ Egg substitutes (p. 396) ____ Salmonella bacteria in eggs (p. 397) ____ Effect of freezing on eggs (p. 397) ____ Effect of cooking methods on chemical and physical properties of eggs (p. 398) ____ Food Science feature, "What Happens When an Egg Cooks?" (p. 399) ____ Chemical and physical properties of egg white foams (pp. 403-405) ____ Explore and Report #4, p. 407 (test for hard-cooked egg)	____ Focus on Food Science, p. 398 (acids and protein coagulation; discoloration in hard-cooked eggs) ____ More About Eggs, p. 398 (characteristics of white and yolk) ____ More About Egg Protein, p. 399 (ovomucin) ____ Focus on Food Science, p. 400 (temperature of coagulation) ____ More About Cooking Eggs p. 400 (testing eggs) ____ Focus on Food Science, p. 403 (egg white foams) ____ Focus on Food Science, p. 404 (effects of bowl material on egg white foams)	____ Experiment 10, "Effects of Added Ingredients on Egg White Foams" ____ Experiment 20, "Heat and Protein Coagulation" ____ CT-26, "Eggs as Ingredients"
Chapter 27: Grain Products ____ Composition of grain kernel (p. 409) ____ Processed grains (p. 409) ____ Effects of cooking and stirring on grains (pp. 416-418) ____ Effect of minerals on cooking rice (p. 417) ____ Explore and Report #4, p. 421 (rice cooking comparison)	____ Focus on Food Science, p. 417 (gelatinization of starch granules)	____ TM-51, "The Grain Kernel"

Textbook	Teacher's Wraparound Edition (TWE)	Teacher's Resource Book (TRB)
Chapter 28: The Basics of Baking _____ Gluten development in dough (p. 423) _____ Food Science feature, "How Can Recipes Be Modified?" (p. 425) _____ Chemical and physical properties of leavening agents, fats, sweeteners, and other ingredients (pp. 426-431) _____ Effect of oven temperatures on baked products (p. 431) _____ Effect of pan materials on baked products (p. 432) _____ Differences in baking by conventional and microwave methods (p. 434) _____ Explore and Report #4, p. 435 (baking soda test)	_____ Focus on Food Science, p. 426 (baking powder) _____ Focus on Food Science, p. 427 (yeast experiment)	_____ Experiment 11, "The Effect of Gluten Development on Muffins" _____ Experiment 12, "Reaction Speed of Chemical Leavening Agents" _____ Experiment 13, "How Shortened Cakes Rise" _____ Experiment 14, "Effects of Sugar and Salt on Yeast Growth" _____ TM-52, "Leavening Agents"
Chapter 29: Quick and Yeast Breads _____ Effect of mixing methods on quick breads (pp. 438-439) _____ Role of food technologists in developing new products (p. 443) _____ Effect of temperature on yeast growth (pp. 444-445, 448) _____ Effect of kneading on physical and chemical properties of yeast dough (p. 445) _____ Explore and Report #4, p. 451 (bread comparison)	_____ Focus on Food Science, p. 438 (overmixing and gluten development) _____ Focus on Food Science, p. 444 (yeast experiment) _____ More About Kneading Dough, p. 444 (effect on molecular structure of dough) _____ Focus on Food Science, p. 446 (temperature of liquids) _____ More About Yeast Dough, p. 448 (chemical and physical changes as dough rises)	_____ Experiment 11, "The Effect of Gluten Development on Muffins" _____ Experiment 14, "Effects of Sugar and Salt on Yeast Growth" _____ Experiment 15, "Gluten Development in Yeast Bread" _____ HO-38, "Problem Solvers: Biscuits" _____ HO-40, "Problem Solvers: Muffins and Quick Breads" _____ HO-42, "Problem Solvers: Yeast Breads and Rolls"
Chapter 30: Cookies, Cakes and Frostings _____ Effect of humidity on cookie storage (p. 456) _____ Factors affecting foam cakes (p. 459) _____ Differing results of conventional and microwave baking (p. 462) _____ Explore and Report #4, p. 464 (cookie comparison)	_____ More About Cookies, pp. 454-455 (factors affecting texture of cookies) _____ Focus on Food Science, p. 458 (leavening agents in cakes) _____ Focus on Food Science, p. 460 (sugar/water concentration in frostings)	_____ Experiment 13, "How Shortened Cakes Rise" _____ Experiment 16, "Moisture Absorption by Cookies" _____ Experiment 17, "How Mixing Methods Affect a Shortened Cake" _____ HO-44, "Problem Solvers: Cookies" _____ HO-47, "Problem Solvers: Shortened Cakes" _____ HO-48, "Problem Solvers: Unshortened Cakes"
Chapter 31: Pies and Pastries _____ Factors affecting characteristics of pastry (p. 466) _____ Effects of mixing methods on fat and gluten in pastry (pp. 466-467) _____ Steam as a leavening agent (p. 473) _____ Explore and Report #4, p. 476 (microwave experiment)	_____ More About Piecrust, pp. 466-467 (effects of fat, water, mixing method, and dough temperature) _____ Focus on Food Science, p. 467 (piecrust comparison) _____ Focus on Food Science, p. 473 (cream puff batter)	_____ Experiment 18, "The Effects of Fats on Pastry" _____ HO-51, "Problem Solvers: Pies and Tarts"
Chapter 32: Stocks: Soups, and Sauces _____ Effect of starch on stock (p. 479) _____ Food Science feature, "Where Does Gelatin Come From?" (collagen in meat stock) (p. 483) _____ Chemical and physical properties of grain products, eggs, and starchy vegetables as thickeners (pp. 484-487) _____ Explore and Report #4, p. 489 (thickeners experiment)"	_____ Focus on Food Science, p. 481 (curdling in cream soups) _____ More About Gelatin, p. 483 (bound water; effect of enzymes) _____ Focus on Food Science, p. 484 (starches as thickeners)	_____ Experiment 19, "Creating a Smooth Sauce" _____ Experiment 20, "Heat and Protein Coagulation" _____ TM-55, "How to Thicken With . . ."

Textbook	Teacher's Wraparound Edition (TWE)	Teacher's Resource Book (TRB)
Chapter 33: Beverages ____ Chemical and physical properties of cocoa and chocolate (p. 491) ____ Effect of preparation methods on coffee (p. 492) ____ Soft drink ingredients (p. 495) ____ Effects of metal and ceramic on tea pigments (p. 496) ____ Explore and Report #4, p. 499 (tea taste-test)	____ Focus on Food Science, p. 494 (chemical composition of tea) ____ More About Herb Tea, p. 494 (toxicity in herbs) ____ More About Beverage Choices, p. 495 (USDA research — carbonated milk) ____ Focus on Food Science, p. 496 (sugar/tea solution)	____ Experiment 21, "Taste-Testing Fruit Juice"
Chapter 34: Preserving Food at Home ____ Effects of sugar, ascorbic acid, and heat on enzyme action in fresh fruits and vegetables (p. 502) ____ Destroying microorganisms and enzymes through heat processing methods (pp. 503-506) ____ Effect of acidity (pH) on selecting canning methods (p. 504) ____ Use of salt solution (brine) in food preservation (p. 507) ____ Food Science feature, "What Happens When You Make Jelly?" (p. 508) ____ Effect of acid and sugar on gelling properties of pectin (p. 509) ____ Dehydration as a home food preservation method (pp. 510-511) ____ Explore and Report #4, p. 513 (jam experiment)	____ More About Processing, pp. 504-505 (explanation of pH value) ____ More About Pickled Foods, pp. 506-507 (fermentation method) ____ More About Making Jelly, p. 508 (tests for gelling quality of pectin)	____ Experiment 1, "Oxidation of Fruit" ____ Experiment 22, "The Role of Pectin in Jelly" ____ TM-57, "The pH Guide to Canning"
Chapter 35: Foods of the World	____ Focus on Food Science, p. 521 (sauerkraut fermentation) ____ Focus on Food Science, p. 527 (effect of food piece size in Oriental cooking)	
Chapter 36: American Regional Foods ____ Explore and Report #4, p. 542 (recipe analysis)	____ Focus on Food Science, p. 537 (okra as thickener) ____ Focus on Food Science, p. 539 (effects of spices) ____ Focus on Food Science, p. 540 (fermentation of yeast)	
Chapter 37: Creative Cooking ____ Adapting recipes (p. 544) ____ Factors affecting the strength of herbs and spices (pp. 547-548) ____ Explore and Report #4, p. 553 (experimenting with herbs and spices)	____ Focus on Food Science, p. 549 (effect of water in cells)	
Chapter 38: Careers in Food and Nutrition ____ Careers in food technology (p. 560) ____ Foods used on space flights (p. 561) ____ Explore and Report #4, p. 568 (developments in food technology)		
Chapter 39: How to Get and Keep a Job		
Text Appendices ____ Appendix E: Calculating the Percentage of Calories from Each Nutrient ____ Appendix F: Metric System		

Guidelines and Answer Key
for Food Science Experiments

Experiment 1: Oxidation of Fruit

Purpose

This experiment tests the effectiveness of anti-oxidants on apple slices. One sample is coated with ascorbic acid solution, one with lemon juice, one with water, and one sample is left uncoated. Samples are compared to determine which substance best retards oxidation.

Food for Today Reference

Ch. 19, "Fruits" (p. 292, "Serving Fruits")

This experiment can also be used in Ch. 34 (p. 502, "How to Freeze Fruits"). Follow experiment procedure but freeze the fruit overnight before the students make their observations.

Procedure Hints

Students should work quickly but carefully when preparing the fruit and coating it. Some of the fruit may begin to brown almost immediately.

Variations: Use a fruit juice that is not acidic, such as apple juice. This juice could be used in addition to those specified or in place of sample D (water). Do not use a juice that will color the fruit and mask any browning, such as grape or cranberry. Peaches, pears, or bananas can also be used in conducting this experiment.

Expected Results

Ascorbic acid (B) and lemon juice (C) should prevent browning or delay it significantly. Water (D) should delay browning somewhat. The control sample (A) should begin browning almost immediately. Students will probably describe the browned samples as having poor texture and flavor.

"Conclusions" Answer Key

1. A — Control. Nothing to keep fruit from oxidizing. In sample D, water provides some antioxidant effect but not as much as the two acids.
2. B — Ascorbic Acid and C — Lemon Juice. Both liquids are antioxidants.
3. Normally, B. But results between B and C may be too close to notice.
4. It is an acid.
5. Any acidic juice: orange, grapefruit, lime.
6. Answers will vary.
7. When serving cut fresh fruit (or preparing fresh fruit for frozen storage).

Discussion Questions

1. How would you prepare fresh fruit for a two-hour reception? (Cut as close to serving time as possible and coat with ascorbic acid solution or lemon juice.)
2. What actually happens to a piece of cut fruit when it starts to turn brown? (It is exposed to oxygen in the air so it oxidizes.)
3. What other fruits or vegetables begin to brown when cut and exposed to air? (avocados, eggplant, potatoes.)

Experiment 2: Effects of Acids and Bases on Vegetables

Purpose

Orange, red, green, and white vegetables are cooked in an acid, a base, and water to determine the effects of the cooking liquid on the vegetables.

Food for Today Reference

Ch. 20, "Vegetables" (pp. 307-308, "Cooking in Liquid")

Procedure Hints

To conduct the complete experiment, at least four lab groups are needed. Assign each group to work with one kind of vegetable representing a specific color pigment. If it is not possible to have four lab groups working at one time, adapt the experiment accordingly. Each group may be able to complete more than one variation in the time allotted, or the experiment may be extended over more than one class period. You may also simply eliminate one or more kinds of vegetables from the experiment.

If you do not have enough saucepans to supply each group with three, have students cook one variation at a time. Make certain students wash equipment carefully after each variation.

After the experiment, have each group report its findings to the class. Let other students examine the vegetables to note differences.

Extend experiment by having students make a master chart, showing the characteristics of the four different colors of vegetables cooked under the various conditions.

To demonstrate the reversibility of the color change in pigments, have students treat the cooking liquids in the glass jars before the liquids are poured into the storage container. Have them add a base to "B —

Acid" and an acid to "C — Base" and observe any changes in color. The color change for anthocyanin and flavone is reversible, while the color change for chlorophyll is irreversible.

Expected Results

A — Cooked in water: all vegetables remained the same color, unless overcooked.

B — Cooked in acid (vinegar, lemon juice):

- *broccoli* — olive green; tough texture; little change in aroma.
- *red cabbage* — red-violet; tough texture; some change in aroma.
- *cauliflower* — light cream color; tough texture; little change in aroma.
- *carrots* — no color change; tough texture; no change in aroma.

C — Cooked in base (baking soda):

- *broccoli* — bright green; mushy-soft; little change in aroma.
- *red cabbage* — violet-blue; very mushy; little change in aroma.
- *cauliflower* — yellowish; mushy-soft; little change in aroma.
- *carrots* — darker orange color; softer texture; little change in aroma.

"Conclusions" Answer Key

1. Yes, if they contain the same color pigment, because the pigments react the same in acids and bases.
2. Bases should not be used because they affect texture and color adversely. Acids also affect color and texture and their use should be controlled.
3. Acids toughen texture; bases soften, making vegetables mushy.
4. Answers will vary.
5. Other ingredients in recipe can affect the vegetable color and texture.
6. a) Vegetables would be tough; b) Vegetables would be proper texture because they were cooked until tender before tomatoes added.
7. Hard water is basic; would get better results if acid added to vegetables when cooking. (However, if hardness is due to calcium or magnesium salts, vegetables will have a firm texture.)

Discussion Questions

1. Discuss the general effect acids have on vegetables. (Acids intensify color and toughen texture.)
2. Discuss the general effect bases have on vegetables. (Brighten green color of chlorophyll, but turn red of anthocyanins blue and white of flavones a more intense cream yellow. Give a mushy texture, which causes loss of nutrients from vegetable cells.)
3. Name other vegetables in the same color categories. (Green: beans, brussel sprouts, greens; White: potatoes, turnips, parsnips; Yellow/orange: winter squash. Beets, although red, do not have the anthocyanin pigment that red cabbage has.)

Experiment 3: The Effect of Vegetable Piece Size on Cooking Time

Purpose

In this experiment, carrots are cut into three different sizes and cooked for four different time periods to determine the effect of piece size on cooking time.

Food for Today Reference

Ch. 20, "Vegetables" (pp. 306-308, "Cooking Vegetables")

Procedure Hints

Uncooked carrots are edible, but they are hard and chewy. When cooked, carrots are easier to chew and digest and have a milder flavor.

When vegetables are overcooked, the walls of the vegetable cells break down. Nutrients and pigments escape through the cell membrane into the water. The color of the water indicates loss of nutrients.

Most people generalize as to the cooking time required for different kinds of vegetables. However, the cooking time for each kind of vegetable can vary greatly, depending on the size of the pieces. Thinly sliced carrots will take about half as long to cook as large pieces.

Because 12 different carrot samples are involved in this experiment, it is important that they be kept separate for observation and conclusions. Detailed instructions are given for identifying each sample.

Expected Results

The 12-mm ($^1/_2$-in.) slices should be properly cooked. The 3-mm ($^1/_8$-in.) slices will be overcooked, with a mushy texture and the greatest loss of color. The 2.5-cm (1-in.) slices will be undercooked and tough.

"Conclusions" Answer Key

1. Cell walls broke down in overcooked carrots; pigments escaped, coloring water.
2. When overcooked, pigments escaped. Carrots turned lighter color.
3. The 3-mm ($^1/_8$-in.) slices. Their small size means that heat can be quickly conducted to the center of the slices.

4. The 2.5-cm (1-in.) pieces. The pieces are so large they never got tender enough to cut with a fork. (However, if the carrot is thin, the 2.5-cm [1-in.] pieces may be cut with a fork after 20 minutes.)

5. Small thin pieces cook faster than larger and thicker ones, but they also overcook more easily.

6. If time is short, cut vegetables into small pieces. But small pieces lose nutrients more quickly. To cook evenly, vegetables should be cut into uniform sizes.

7. Can lower timing for vegetable recipes by cutting them into smaller pieces.

8. Decrease it because if pigments can escape into water, so can water-soluble nutrients.

Discussion Questions

1. Carrots are edible raw or cooked. List some vegetables that might be difficult to eat if they were not properly cooked. (Green beans, brussel sprouts, beets, collards.)

2. How would the experiment you just did be helpful in food preparation? (Can analyze recipes better; can make changes in recipes.)

3. What are the advantages and disadvantages of cutting vegetables into small pieces for cooking? (Advantage — they cook faster. Disadvantage — they overcook; lose nutrients.)

Experiment 4: Cooking Vegetables by Conventional and Microwave Cooking Methods

Purpose

To discover the effects of cooking fresh broccoli for two different time periods by conventional and microwave cooking methods.

Food for Today Reference

Ch. 20, "Vegetables" (pp. 306-308, "Cooking Vegetables")

This experiment can also be used with Ch. 16, "Microwave Cooking," to compare microwave and conventional cooking methods.

Procedure Hints

To save time, you may wish to assign each lab group to prepare either the two conventional or the two microwave variations, not all four. Adjust the supplies for each group accordingly. Have each group circle their assigned variations on the Observation Chart. After finishing the experiment procedures, each group should display their samples. The class as a whole can then observe and compare the microwave and conventional variations.

Expected Results

The shorter times for both cooking methods should produce properly cooked broccoli. The longer cooking times will result in overcooking the vegetable.

There should be little, if any, difference in either sample of properly cooked broccoli. However, there will be a big difference in the two overcooked samples. Microwaves cook so quickly that moisture evaporates rapidly and the food toughens when it is overcooked. When vegetables are overcooked by the conventional method, they turn mushy.

"Conclusions" Answer Key

1. A and C — the two properly cooked ones.
2. Probably A and C.
3. Overcooked broccoli is mushy in conventional method but tough in microwave.
4. Answers may vary. Overcooked broccoli may have a strong flavor.
5. Shouldn't be any difference between A and C.
6. Can judge recipes better; will watch cooking time on vegetables; can convert conventional vegetable recipes to microwave.

Discussion Questions

1. What can you do with the broccoli overcooked in the microwave? (Put through blender and make soup or a sauce; add to stews, casseroles.)
2. What are the advantages of cooking vegetables in the microwave? (Faster; in many cases more nutrients are retained, although this depends on the type of vegetable.)
3. If you had your choice, which method of cooking vegetables would you prefer? Why? (Answers will vary.)

Experiment 5: Recrisping Celery

Purpose

In this experiment, wilted celery is recrisped to demonstrate the process of osmosis.

Food for Today Reference

Ch. 21, "Salads and Salad Dressings" (p. 324, "Making a Salad")

This experiment can also be used in Ch. 20, "Vegetables" (p. 303, "Storing Fresh Vegetables") to emphasize the importance of storing vegetables properly.

This experiment can also be used in Ch. 5, "Food and Your Well-Being" (pp. 64-65, "Feeding the Cells"). See the Teacher's Wraparound Edition, bottom of pp. 64-65, "More About Feeding the Cells," which explains the process of osmosis.

Procedure Hints

Make certain the glass containers used in the experiment are tall enough to support the stalk of celery. Otherwise, they may tip over.

The day before the experiment, separate the celery stalks from the bunch and leave out at room temperature overnight, uncovered, so they wilt and the ends dry out. You may be able to buy wilted celery at a very low price. Even so, separate the stalks from the bunch the day before to allow the ends to dry out.

Expected Results

The celery with the cut end should have drawn more colored water into it. The ends of the uncut celery would have dried, so that it takes longer for the water to begin moving through the cell walls.

"Conclusions" Answer Key

1. Each dot represented a pathway by which the red water solution was drawn upward through the celery stalk.
2. The two in water should have been crisp.
3. All should have the same flavor. But color can sometimes affect taste. People associate colors with specific flavors, so the "red" celery may taste different to some people, even though the red color is flavorless.
4. Cut celery should have absorbed more water.
5. Moisture needed for proper storage of crisp vegetables; recrisping wilted vegetables.

Discussion Questions

1. What kinds of vegetables wilt and why? (Those with a high water content; those stored where moisture evaporates. Wilt due to evaporation from the cells.)
2. How would you relate this experiment to proper storage of vegetables? (Refrigerate crisp vegetables in covered container to retain moisture.)
3. How would you relate the information you learned in this experiment to a fresh flower arrangement? (Cut a slice off the bottom of the stem before immersing in water.)

Experiment 6: The Effect of Acid on Protein

Purpose

To demonstrate how protein molecules change when they come in contact with an acid.

Food for Today Reference

Ch. 22, "Dairy Foods" (p. 341, "Preparing Dairy Foods")

Procedure Hints

The shape of protein molecules can be changed (denatured) by many different methods. One method is to add acid to certain foods, like milk. The process begins by turning the milk thick. As denaturation continues, the milk turns grainy, then it curdles and finally coagulates into curds which separate from the liquid.

This experiment has practical value. If a recipe calls for sour milk, plain milk can be soured (denatured) by adding vinegar.

Heat speeds up the denaturation process. When milk is added to an acid mixture and heated, it can curdle easily.

Expected Results

In general, the two vinegar mixtures will have the following appearance:

- *5 mL (1 tsp.) vinegar:* immediately — no change; 5 min. — grainy; 10 min. — slightly curdled; 15 min. — slightly more curdled, translucent.
- *10 mL (2 tsp.) vinegar:* immediately — curdled; 5 min. — curdled; 10 min. — curdled; 15 min — curds separated, clear liquid.

"Conclusions" Answer Key

1. The control showed no reaction. B and C curdled — the reaction was faster in C.
2. It will get grainy and begin to curdle.
3. Should be C after 15 min.
4. Any recipe calling for sour milk such as quick bread; also any recipe that mixes milk and an acid, which would call for care in preparation to avoid curdling.

Discussion Questions

1. What happens when milk is mixed with an acid? (The protein changes, going through different steps from grainy until it curdles.)
2. Of what practical use is this information? (Be cautious when working with milk mixtures containing acid foods so they don't curdle.)
3. When would you want protein in milk to denature? (When making sour milk or cheese.)

Experiment 7: Separating Fat from Cream

Purpose

In this experiment, invisible fat is separated from cream by agitation and coalescence.

Food for Today Reference

Ch. 22, "Dairy Foods" (p. 332, "Buttermilk" and "Butter")

This experiment can also be used in Ch. 4, "The Nutrients You Need," or in Chapter 7, "Controlling Your Weight," to demonstrate the existence of invisible fats. Students may have difficulty understanding the concept of invisible fats in foods such as dairy products, meats, and grains. The concept becomes a reality as they observe cream turning into globules of fat (butter).

Procedure Hints

Make certain the cream is at room temperature. Have students take turns shaking the jar.

Compare the method in the experiment with the old-fashioned butter churn. The marble in the jar serves the same purpose as the paddles in the churn — to agitate the cream more vigorously and speed up coalescence.

If desired, provide samples of commercial buttermilk and skim milk (at room temperature) for students to taste. Ask which tastes most like the "homemade buttermilk" that was left after the butter separated from the cream in the jar. (Commercial buttermilk tastes different because it has been soured with lactic acid. The taste of the homemade buttermilk may be more similar to the commercial skim milk, except that flecks of butter may remain.) Students may also want to compare their homemade butter with commercial butter for color, texture, and flavor.

Expected Results

The cream should separate to form butter and buttermilk, as described in the answer key below.

"Conclusions" Answer Key

1. No, the fat that formed the butter was invisible.
2. The off-white cream became yellow butter and whitish buttermilk.
3. Went from thick to grainy to curds, then globules separated from liquid, which was thin and watery.
4. Agitation caused the invisible fat to coalesce, forming butter.
5. No, milk does not contain enough fat to coalesce when agitated.

Discussion Questions

1. List foods, in addition to cream, that contain hidden fat. (Milk; milk products such as cheese, ice cream, and yogurt; meat; grains.)
2. How does knowing about the presence of invisible fats in food help people who are trying to lose weight? (Since fat contains 9 calories per gram while carbohydrate and protein contain only 4 calories per gram, foods with invisible fat are calorie-rich and should be avoided on a reducing diet.)
3. What conclusions can you reach about cheese, which is made from milk? (Cheese is made by coalescing milk solids, so it contains all the fat in the milk.)

Experiment 8: The Effect of Gelatin on a Frozen Dessert

Purpose

This experiment demonstrates the use of gelatin as a stabilizing agent in a frozen dessert.

Food for Today Reference

Ch. 22, "Dairy Foods" (p. 342, "Making Frozen Dairy Desserts")

Procedure Hints

This experiment takes two days. On the first day, students prepare two versions of the dessert and freeze them. On the second day, they make their observations. The dessert must be allowed to freeze completely so accurate observations can be made.

Any frozen fruit can be used in place of the raspberries. Don't substitute whipped topping for the whipping cream. The topping contains stabilizers and would not give the same results as whipping cream.

Expected Results

In general, the version with the gelatin should have a better appearance, smoother texture, and slower melting rate. The flavor preference will be a matter of opinion.

"Conclusions" Answer Key

1. Gelatin, because of its stabilizing action.
2. Gelatin, because it has smaller ice crystals.
3. No gelatin, because it was not stabilized so the ice crystals melted quickly.
4. Will vary — personal preference.
5. A stabilizing agent helps to make a more acceptable frozen dessert.
6. Can make better frozen desserts.

Discussion Questions

1. What other methods could be used to make the mixture smooth? (Add more fat, beat mixture during freezing.)
2. Read labels on different brands of commercial ice cream, including "natural" varieties. What ingredients act as stabilizers? (Answers will vary, depending on label. Common stabilizers include guar gum, carrageenan, locust bean gum, alginate, agar, lecithin, sodium carboxymethylcellulose, and gelatin.)

Experiment 9: Tenderizing Meat

Purpose

This experiment demonstrates the effect of mechanical and chemical meat tenderizers by comparing tenderized samples with an untreated control.

Ch. 23, "Meat" (p. 358, on tenderizing meat)

Procedure Hints

Be sure the same muscle is used for all three samples in this experiment. For example, the samples should be all top round steak or bottom round.

Stress to students the importance of piercing the meat in the sample with the chemical tenderizer. This helps get the tenderizer into the meat. Some brands of chemical tenderizer call for a holding period to get more uniform distribution of the tenderizer throughout the interior of the meat. Adjust procedure as needed for the brand of tenderizer the students use.

All three samples should be cooked at one time in the same skillet for the same length of time.

Variation: Substitute two marinades for the mallet and enzyme methods. One marinade should contain an acid, which will tenderize the meat, and the other should not have an acid. Refrigerate overnight and panbroil the next day.

Expected Results

Sample "B — Chemical" would probably be most tender with "C — Mallet" a close second. "A — Control" would be least tender. Differences between B and C will vary considerably depending on how hard the meat was pounded with a mallet, how deeply it was pierced with a fork, and the original toughness or tenderness of the meat.

"Conclusions" Answer Key

1. B, maybe C, because they were tenderized.
2. A — it's not tenderized.
3. A — most; B, C — least. Will vary, but difference should be in whether or not it was tenderized.
4. Preferences will vary, but usually a tenderized sample.
5. They break down tough meat fibers and connective tissue to make meat more tender.
6. Can broil thin inexpensive cuts by making them tender; stretch food budget.

Discussion Questions

1. What other methods can be used to tenderize meat? (Grinding; scoring with a knife; using a marinade with acid such as vinegar, lemon juice, or tomato juice.)
2. When might you choose one tenderizing method over another? (Might not have time to use marinade; may not have grinder or mallet at home; enzyme is fast and easy.)
3. What could you use in place of the mallet if you didn't have one? (Anything non-breakable that is clean, washable, and could be used for pounding — wooden potato masher, edge of a small heavy pan, edge of small skillet.)

Experiment 10: Effects of Added Ingredients on Egg White Foams

Purpose

This experiment compares the beating time, volume, and stability of egg white foams which include sugar, salt, acid, and fat. A foam made from untreated egg white serves as a control.

Food for Today Reference

Ch. 26, "Eggs" (pp. 403-405, "Beating Egg Whites")

Procedure Hints

To conduct the complete experiment, at least five lab groups are needed. Assign each group the variation they are to prepare as specified on the experiment sheet. If it is not possible to have five lab groups working at one time, adapt the experiment accordingly. Each group may be able to complete more than one variation in the time allotted, or the experiment may be extended over more than one class period. You may also wish to eliminate one or more variations. If so, alter question 4 under "Conclusions" accordingly.

All of the egg whites should be at the same temperature for beating. Egg whites beat to a greater volume when they have been allowed to stand for about 30 minutes at room temperature. Therefore, you may want to remove the eggs from the refrigerator about 30 minutes before class is to begin, separate them, and let the whites stand.

If you have students separate the eggs, remind them to work carefully to avoid breaking the yolk. If any of the yolk gets into the white, use that egg white for sample "E — Egg Yolk." Be sure none of the other samples contain egg yolk.

Warn students to beat the foam only to stiff peaks. If they overbeat the egg whites, they will have to start over.

When students make their observations, all the samples of beaten egg whites must be in identical containers. If there is any difference in size and shape of the containers, students will not be able to compare the height measurement from one sample to another. If you do not have enough identical glass mixing bowls, use available bowls for beating, then have students transfer the foam into identical tall drinking glasses for observation. A glass container will allow students to observe the sides and bottom of the foam as well as the top.

For sanitation reasons, caution students not to insert the ruler into the egg whites to measure the height of the foam.

Variation: Have students compare foam that results from beating room-temperature egg whites and cold egg whites. (The cold egg whites will take longer to beat and will have less volume, but better stability.)

Expected Results

Each of the added ingredients should affect the egg white foam as described in #4 under " 'Conclusions' Answer Key" (below). The effect of egg yolk will be most noticeable, with sugar also having a significant effect. The effects of salt and cream of tartar may be less noticeable. Differences between the control, salt, and cream of tartar samples may be affected by uncontrolled variables such as size and freshness of the eggs.

"Conclusions" Answer Key

1. "A — Control" should have the greatest volume, but "D — Cream of Tartar" will be very close.
2. "B — Sugar."
3. Either "B — Sugar" or "D — Cream of Tartar."
4. *Sugar* — increases beating time; decreases volume somewhat; improves stability.
   Salt — may increase beating time, decrease volume, and reduce stability.
   Cream of tartar — increases beating time somewhat; may decrease volume slightly; improves stability.
   Egg yolk — keeps egg whites from going beyond foamy stage; results in little or no volume.
5. Evaluate recipes for foam volume and stability; add sugar or cream of tartar if needed; add salt to other recipe ingredients, not egg whites; understand importance of keeping whites fat-free when beating.

Discussion Questions

1. When deciding whether to add sugar to egg whites, what would be the most important consideration — beating time, volume, or stability? Why? What else should you consider? (The longer beating time would be important if you had to beat the eggs by hand. When using an electric mixer, stability would probably be the most important consideration because the improved stability would make up for the slight decrease in volume. The flavor of the sugar should also be considered.)
2. If you don't have cream of tartar and didn't want to add sweetness to the egg whites, what could you use to stabilize the foam? Why? (Lemon juice or vinegar because they are acids.)
3. Why should a plastic bowl not be used when beating egg whites? (The plastic may have fat clinging to it, which would prevent the egg white foam from forming.)

Experiment 11: The Effect of Gluten Development on Muffins

Purpose

The experiment demonstrates the effect of overmixing muffin batter, resulting in overdevelopment of gluten.

Food for Today Reference

Ch. 28, "The Basics of Baking" (p. 423, "Flour")
Ch. 29, "Quick and Yeast Breads" (p. 438, "Muffin Method")

Procedure Hints

You may wish to prepare correctly mixed muffins ahead of class so students have a standard to which they can compare their products. You may also wish to supply students with a copy of "Standards Scorecard — Muffins and Quick Breads" (HO-39).

When mixing muffins, the batter must be stirred only long enough to moisten the dry ingredients. If overstirred, gluten will overdevelop, resulting in tunnels and a coarse, tough texture.

Have students count strokes accurately. Remind students that the batter will be lumpy in some variations. Students often want to stir until the batter is smooth, like cake batter.

Expected Results

The muffins from batter that was stirred 18 strokes (B) and 30 strokes (C) will be overmixed. Overmixed muffins have peaks and tunnels, uneven shape, and tougher texture. The tops will be smooth rather than lumpy.

"Conclusions" Answer Key

1. The extra stirring overdeveloped the gluten, which made it difficult for the gases from the baking powder to escape, creating tunnels or holes inside the muffin.
2. Decreased quality. It created a product with a smooth but tough crust. The inside was coarse and tough, with tunnels and holes. The muffin was not evenly browned.
3. The one that was mixed the least (A) because the gluten was not overdeveloped.
4. To create a good muffin, don't stir the batter any more than absolutely necessary to moisten the flour. Scoop the batter gently into muffin cups.
5. Any baked product using the muffin method should be mixed the same way — with the least amount of stirring. Can evaluate mixing methods in recipes and solve own baking problems.

Discussion Questions

1. How did you feel baking a batter that was lumpy rather than smooth, like cake batter? (Probably wanted to stir more.)
2. What have you learned from this experiment? (Importance of following mixing directions.)
3. What personal characteristic must you use when working with mixtures involving gluten? (Judgment — the amount of gluten development varies with the kind of product desired. All batters and doughs cannot

be mixed the same way — it depends on the amount of gluten that must be developed. Must judge the correct amount of mixing to achieve desirable results.)

Experiment 12: Reaction Speed of Chemical Leavening Agents

Purpose

This experiment demonstrates how baking powder, baking soda, and cream of tartar react with various liquids to produce carbon dioxide.

Food for Today Reference

Ch. 28, "The Basics of Baking" (p. 426, "Leavening Agents")

Procedure Hints

The experiment involves seven different reactions. They must be conducted one at a time, with observations made on one test before beginning the next one. When the Observation Chart is filled, students can draw conclusions.

Timing is critical in this experiment because seconds are involved. A stopwatch would be an ideal way to keep time, but a watch or clock with a second hand can be used.

If custard cups and other equipment are to be reused, they must be carefully washed in warm, sudsy water rather than just quickly rinsed. Even the slightest trace of a residue from one part of the experiment can affect the reaction in the next part.

Expected Results

Cups A and B will not react. The other cups should "fizz up" for 10-30 seconds, then continue to produce tiny carbon dioxide bubbles for several minutes. For differences in the type and length of the reactions, see numbers 1-5 below.

"Conclusions" Answer Key

1. Cups A and B (baking soda and water)
2. Cup C (baking soda and vinegar)
3. Cups F and G (double-acting baking powder).
4. Cup C (baking soda and vinegar).
5. Probably Cup F (double-acting baking powder and cold water), although D, E, and G are other possible answers.
6. Carbon dioxide gas. (Students may or may not have noticed vapor.)
7. A chemical reaction between acid and base produces carbon dioxide gas. Baking soda and vinegar react quickly and powerfully, but stop fizzing sooner. Double-acting baking powder reacts more slowly. Heat speeds up the production of carbon dioxide.
8. Can evaluate recipes, solve baking problems, shop carefully for leavening agents, make successful substitutions in recipes.

Discussion Questions

1. If a quick bread recipe used milk and you wanted to use buttermilk to give it a different flavor, what adjustment would you have to make? Why? (Substitute baking soda for part of the baking powder. Baking soda provides the base to balance the acid in the buttermilk and produce carbon dioxide for leavening.) (Have students look up quick bread recipes using baking powder and baking soda and discuss the reasons for the leavenings used.)
2. What does this experiment tell you about storing chemical leavening agents? (Must be stored in tightly closed container in dry area; moisture begins chemical reaction.)
3. Why do you think double-acting baking powder is so popular? How does it differ from the homemade baking powder (baking soda and cream of tartar)? (Most of the leavening action of double-acting baking powder is released after the mixture starts to bake. Therefore it gives better results. When homemade baking powder is used, the mixture must be put in the oven quickly or it may not rise properly.)

Experiment 13: How Shortened Cakes Rise

Purpose

In this experiment, three variations of a simple cupcake recipe are prepared to determine how chemical leavening agents affect shortened cakes.

Food for Today Reference

Ch. 28, "The Basics of Baking" (pp. 426-427, "Chemical Leavenings")

Can also be used in Ch. 30, "Cookies, Cakes, and Frostings" (p. 458, "Shortened Cakes")

Procedure Hints

For optimum results, the three samples should be baked together in the same pan. If time permits, all three variations could be prepared by the same group and baked together. (Adjust supplies for each group accordingly.) If not, assign each group the variation they are to prepare as specified on the experiment sheet.

The version using baking soda and cream of tartar must be prepared last and the pan placed in the oven immediately. As soon as the baking soda and cream of tartar are mixed with liquid, the chemical reaction begins. If too much time elapses before the batter is placed in the oven, most of the carbon dioxide will have escaped before the heat can set the structure of the cupcakes. The cupcakes will not rise much.

Expected Results

Samples A (5 mL [1 tsp.] baking powder) and C (cream of tartar/baking soda) should produce similar products if C was placed in the oven immediately after mixing. If too long a time elapsed, C may not rise as much as the others. B (15 mL [3 tsp.] baking powder) may collapse slightly because it rises too fast, not giving the heat enough time to set the structure before the carbon dioxide dissipates. It will also have a coarser grain. Those with sensitive taste may also detect a slightly unpleasant metallic flavor in B.

"Conclusions" Answer Key

1. Probably A or C. Tender, fine texture; better flavor.
2. All should rise, but B may collapse slightly. C may not rise properly if it is not put in oven immediately.
3. Baking soda, to balance the acid in the buttermilk.
4. Accurate measurements give best results.
5. Normally should be no difference if other factors are the same and if baking soda mixture is baked immediately.

Discussion Questions

1. Under what conditions would you use baking soda/cream of tartar instead of baking powder? (If called for in recipe — many old recipes use it — or as a substitute if baking powder is not available. However, the substitution may affect product quality.)
2. Discuss the differences in texture in the three different samples. (B should be coarser and may contain tunnels. A and C should be tender with a fine grain.)
3. Which cupcakes had the best flavor? Why? (A and C should have best. Extra baking powder in B might give a slightly unpleasant metallic flavor.)

Experiment 14: Effects of Sugar and Salt on Yeast Growth

Purpose

In this experiment, sugar and salt are added to two yeast mixtures to determine their effect on leavening action. An untreated sample of yeast serves as a control.

Food for Today Reference

Ch. 28, "The Basics of Baking" (p. 427, "Yeast")

This experiment can also be used in Ch. 29, "Quick and Yeast Breads" (pp. 441-449, "Making Yeast Bread")

The experiment can also be used in Ch. 12, "Storing Food" (p. 179, "Yeasts") to demonstrate how yeast grows and can make some foods ferment.

Procedure Hints

To make it easier for students to time the reaction of the yeast mixtures, you may want to have each lab group prepare only one variation. Adjust the supplies for each group accordingly. Have students circle their assigned variation on the Observation Chart. Students should obtain information from the other lab groups to fill in the "Elapsed Time" blanks on the Observation Chart. Have all students observe the mixtures in all three cups after 20 minutes.

Timing is critical in this experiment. Use a stopwatch if it is available, but a clock or watch with a second hand can also be used.

When cleaning up, have students rinse custard cups with cold water before washing them in warm, sudsy water. Rinsing will prevent the yeast mixture from hardening on the cup edges.

Expected Results

Sample B, with extra sugar, should be the most active. Sample C, with salt, should be the least active. Sample A, the control, should be moderately active.

"Conclusions" Answer Key

1. B (with extra sugar).
2. C (with salt).
3. The additional sugar in B provided "food" for the yeast, making it more active and producing gas more rapidly. The salt in C inhibited the activity of the yeast, causing it to produce gas more slowly.
4. In a dough mixture for white bread, the ingredients work together. The sugar stimulates the production of gas and the salt keeps the production controlled to allow the bread to rise slowly and completely.
5. Can make recipe changes; can speed up rising process; can evaluate bread baking problems.
6. Vary temperature of water; use different yeast, such as fresh cake or rapid-rising.

Discussion Questions

1. What functions do sugar and salt serve in bread? (Sugar provides food for the yeast and stimulates production of carbon dioxide gas, producing more bubbles. The salt slows the rate of carbon dioxide production, producing smaller bubbles.)
2. If the salt were omitted from a bread recipe, how (other than flavor) would the finished product be different from normal bread? (The bread would have large holes where gas bubbles developed. The holes would not be evenly dispersed throughout the loaf. The loaf might have an irregular shape.)
3. How could the action of the yeast be increased? (Adding more sugar — up to a point — and less salt.)

Experiment 15: Gluten Development in Yeast Bread

Purpose

In this experiment, yeast dough is kneaded for two different time periods to determine the effect of kneading on gluten development.

Food for Today Reference

Ch. 29, "Quick and Yeast Breads" (p. 445, "Kneading Yeast Dough")

Also refer to p. 439, "Kneading the Dough," in the same chapter. Although this refers to kneading biscuit dough, the basic method is the same. However, the purpose of kneading differs in biscuits and yeast dough. In kneading biscuit dough, the goal is to mix the ingredients rather than develop a strong gluten. If biscuit dough is overkneaded and gluten overdeveloped, the biscuits will be tough. Yeast dough must be kneaded longer to develop a strong gluten.

Procedure Hints

This experiment takes two days. The first day, the dough is prepared, kneaded, and refrigerated. It is baked the next day and observations made. If the class period is too short, the experiment may have to be extended to a third day so the bread will have time to cool before being cut. Warm bread is difficult to cut, which could affect the grain and structure of the slice.

While it's virtually impossible to overknead yeast dough by hand, it can be done easily with a mixer or food processor. If you have a mixer with a dough hook or a food processor, you may want to add another version, using the appliance to overknead yeast dough so students can see what happens.

Expected Results

Sample B, kneaded 8-10 minutes, should have the best characteristics and flavor.

"Conclusions" Answer Key

1. B
2. Will vary.
3. B should be easier to chew because gluten developed, allowing bread to rise. A is compact and hard because not enough leavening action.
4. B, but answers may vary.
5. Personal preference.
6. Follow kneading instructions when making bread.

Discussion Questions

1. What shortcuts can be taken to cut down on kneading time? (None if kneaded by hand; can use mixer with dough hook or food processor.)
2. Describe a yeast dough that has been kneaded for the proper length of time. (It will be silky smooth, elastic, and will be easily formed into a ball; small gas bubbles will be visible on the surface.)
3. How does the time dough is kneaded relate to the kind of product desired? (If the purpose is just to mix ingredients, like biscuits, dough is kneaded only a brief time. If more gluten development is wanted, dough must be kneaded longer.)

Experiment 16: Moisture Absorption by Cookies

Purpose

This experiment demonstrates hygroscopicity, the ability of substances, in this case sugar and honey, to take up and retain moisture. It compares the effects of honey and sugar on the texture of cookies. It also compares the effects of two storage methods on honey and sugar cookies.

Food for Today Reference

Ch. 28, "The Basics of Baking" (p. 429, "Sweeteners")

This experiment can also be used in Chapter 12, "Storing Food" or in Ch. 30, "Cookies, Cakes, and Frostings" (p. 456, "Storing Cookies") to demonstrate how moisture in the air can affect the crispness of cookies.

You may want students to review the terms sucrose, fructose, and glucose from Ch. 4, "The Nutrients You Need" (p. 39, "Types of Sugar").

Procedure Hints

The experiment extends over several days. Honey and sugar cookies are baked and evaluated the first day. Then they are stored in containers and on plates left exposed to the air. A sample of each is tested the following day and then another sample of each is tested 3-4 days later.

Honey is sweeter than sugar and has a stronger flavor, so less is needed. In this experiment, only half as much honey as sugar is used.

It's important that both variations of the recipe bake on the same cookie sheet so that they bake for the same time. If any dough remains after filling half the cookie sheet, students should bake it on another sheet.

A small piece of foil or baking parchment placed under one of the sugar cookies will identify that version. Once the cookies are baked, the physical difference between the two will be apparent. However, students will need to remember which is which, so identification throughout the experiment is important.

Expected Results

The batter for honey cookies will be slightly darker than for sugar cookies. The honey cookies will be flatter with a dark brown edge. They will have a softer texture and characteristic honey flavor.

The honey cookies kept in the storage container should remain soft. The sugar cookies kept in the storage container may stay crisp or soften somewhat, depending on conditions. Humidity in the air will have a great influence on the outcome of the experiment. In high or moderate humidity, the cookies stored in the open air will absorb moisture and become softer, especially the honey ones. In low humidity, the cookies stored in the open air will dry out, but the honey ones will dry out less.

"Conclusions" Answer Key

1. Sugar cookie. Because honey is more hygroscopic, the honey cookies take up and retain moisture more readily and therefore are less crisp.
2. Answers may vary depending on personal taste. The sugar cookies will probably taste sweeter, whereas honey cookies should have a strong flavor characteristic of honey. (Although honey is naturally sweeter than granulated sugar, less honey was used.)
3. The answer will depend on humidity in the air during the experiment, as explained under "Expected Results." The difference is caused by moisture taken up from or lost to the air.
4. If room air was very dry, sugar cookies would probably be more affected because they would lose moisture more readily than the honey cookies. Otherwise, honey cookies would probably be more affected because they would take up more moisture than sugar cookies. (See "Expected Results.")
5. Evaluating recipes; storing cookies properly; buying cookies (can understand labels better).

Discussion Questions

1. What additional evidence can you provide that there is moisture in the air? (Moisture condenses on glasses of cold beverages; eyeglasses get foggy when entering warm area from cold; popcorn becomes soggy; bathroom mirror fogs up when shower is on.)
2. If moist cookies dried out, how might you possibly add moisture? (Place a piece of cut fruit, such as an apple slice, in the container with the cookies.)
3. Discuss different kinds of containers that might be suitable and not suitable for storing soft and crisp cookies. (Soft cookies: tightly closed metal, plastic, or foil are suitable. Crisp cookies: loosely covered containers, cardboard, paper, or wax paper are usually suitable because they allow moisture to evaporate, but should not be used in humid weather because they would allow moisture to enter.)

Experiment 17: How Mixing Methods Affect A Shortened Cake

Purpose

In this experiment, shortened cake batter is mixed by hand and beaten with an electric mixer for two different time periods to determine how the mixing method affects the finished products.

Food for Today Reference

Ch. 30, "Cookies, Cakes, and Frostings" (p. 458, "Shortened Cakes")

Procedure Hints

For optimum results, the three samples should be baked together in the same pan. If time permits, all three variations could be prepared by the same group and baked together. (Adjust supplies for each group accordingly.) If not, assign each group the variation they are to prepare as specified on the experiment sheet.

You may wish to give students a copy of "Standards Scorecard: Shortened Cakes" (HO-45) and "Problem Solvers: Shortened Cakes" (HO-47).

You may also want to prepare a sample of a properly mixed product before the class begins so students will have a standard for judging the experimental samples.

Expected Results

"A — Hand Mixed" will be undermixed. It might show uneven color, will have a coarse texture, and will not rise as much as B.

"B — 2 min." will be properly mixed and should have characteristics of a well-made shortened cake.

"C — 5 min." will be overmixed. Because more gluten has been developed than needed, it will be tough and compact with a coarse grain.

"Conclusions" Answer Key

1. A — coarse, possibly with tunnels; B — fine, even grain; C — coarse and compact.
2. B. The proper amount of gluten was developed to give a good structure and texture.
3. A and C. A is undermixed and C is overmixed.
4. Batter must be mixed enough to mix ingredients well and develop a small amount of gluten to provide structure.
5. Can evaluate recipe instructions; can solve baking problems; will be able to judge amount of mixing needed.

Discussion Questions

1. What purpose does mixing a batter serve? (It mixes the ingredients and develops just enough gluten.)
2. If you didn't want to eat the samples that didn't turn out properly, what could you do with them? (Run them through a blender to make crumbs and use for pie crust or as topping on desserts.)
3. Did the mixing method affect the flavor? Explain. (Yes. Flavor would not be well blended in undermixed cupcakes; might taste specific ingredients rather than a blend.)

Experiment 18: The Effects of Fats on Pastry

Purpose

This experiment tests the effects of four different fats on pastry.

Ch. 31, "Pies and Pastries" (p. 466, "Ingredients for the Crust" and pp. 466-467, "Preparing the Dough")

This experiment can also be used with Ch. 28, "The Basics of Baking" (p. 428, "Fats and Oils").

Procedure Hints

To conduct the complete experiment, at least four lab groups are needed. Assign each group the variation they are to prepare as specified on the experiment sheet. If it is not possible to have four lab groups working at one time, adapt the experiment accordingly. You may wish to extend the experiment over more than one class period or simply eliminate one or two of the variations.

Because all ingredients need to be at room temperature, they should be removed from the refrigerator before class begins.

Be sure to use leaf lard. Hydrogenated lard does not give the same results in pastry.

Expected Results

Sample A (Lard) should be notable for its flakiness, resulting in greater height when the wafers are stacked. Sample B (Butter) will be the least tender but should have a buttery flavor and a richer yellow-brown color than A or C. Sample C (Shortening) will be flaky and tall. Sample D (Oil) should be the most tender but the least flaky, and will resemble Sample B (Butter) in appearance.

"Conclusions" Answer Key

1. D — Oil, A — Lard, C — Shortening, and B — Butter.
2. The kind of fat used affects the tenderness of the product, with oil giving the most tender product and butter the least tender.
3. A — Lard, C — Shortening, B — Butter, and D — Oil.
4. The kind of fat used affects the flakiness of the product. Leaf lard and shortening produce the most flaky product and oil the least flaky.
5. Answers will vary. Butter usually gives the best flavor, with lard next. However, students may dislike the flavor of lard.
6. Flaky pastry tends to be a little higher (taller) than others. Wafers made with lard and shortening (A and C) should be higher. However, the thickness to which the pastry was originally rolled would also influence the height.
7. The kind of fat used would affect the characteristics of the pastry product.
8. Can vary pastry recipe, depending on results desired; can evaluate pastry recipes.

Discussion Questions

1. Were any of the pastry versions easier to mix and handle than others? (Answers will vary.)

2. Did the kind of fat used affect the color of the crust? (The butter crust might be a little deeper in color and darker because of the added yellow color.)
3. What else could be added to pastry for flavor? (Spices, ground nuts, poppy seeds, grated sharp cheese.)

Experiment 19: Creating a Smooth Sauce

Purpose

This experiment uses three different methods for making a sauce thickened with flour to determine which is most effective.

Food for Today Reference

Ch. 32, "Stocks, Soups, and Sauces" (pp. 484-485, "Making Sauces")

Procedure Hints

Allowing the samples to stand while the next variation is prepared may affect texture. For more consistent observations, you may want to have students complete their observations of one sample before preparing the next variation.

If time is short, you may want to have each lab group prepare only one variation. Adjust the supplies for each group accordingly. Have students circle their assigned variation on the Observation Chart. When the experiment procedures have been completed, have students share their observations on ease of mixing. Let each student observe all three samples for texture and flavor. *Caution:* Be sure a clean spoon is used each time a sample is tasted.

Expected Results

Sample "B — Hot Water" may be a little difficult for the students to mix. Lumps may form. Adding flour to cold water (A) or melted fat (C) should produce a smooth mixture.

"Conclusions" Answer Key

1. C, because the melted fat best separates the starch granules and prevents them from clumping together and forming lumps.
2. B. The flour formed lumps in the hot water and it was difficult to eliminate them. The stirring process was considerably longer.
3. C should be the smoothest.
4. The sauces should have the same flavor, but students may prefer C.
5. Answers will vary, depending on preference.
6. Can solve problems in using flour as a thickener; can evaluate recipes.

Discussion Questions

1. Where else would you use flour as a thickener besides making a sauce? (Soups, gravies, puddings.)

2. What could you do if the sauce was lumpy? (Try to beat the lumps out; strain out the lumps and add more flour, if necessary, to make it thicker.)

3. What could you add to the sauce to give it more flavor or a different flavor? (Seasonings, grated cheese.)

Experiment 20: Heat and Protein Coagulation

Purpose

This experiment demonstrates the effect of cooking time on the coagulation of protein (eggs).

Food for Today Reference

Ch. 32, "Stocks, Soups, and Sauces" (p. 486, "Eggs" and p. 487, "Custards")

This experiment can also be used with Ch. 26, "Eggs" (p. 399, "What Happens When an Egg Cooks?")

Procedure Hints

This experiment will take two days. The first day, students will prepare and bake the custard. They will probably have time to remove the first three samples. After class, at the end of 60 minutes, remove the final sample. Refrigerate all custard samples until the next day. Students can complete the experiment then, making observations, filling in the chart, and drawing conclusions.

There are many variables that can affect the outcome of the experiment. The timing in the experiment is based on using cold ingredients just removed from the refrigerator. If the ingredients are at room temperature, the mixture may cook more quickly. If too much sugar is used, the custard will have to bake longer. The water poured into the baking pan should be very hot but not boiling. Boiling water will overcoagulate the protein, resulting in a porous structure.

Expected Results

Samples A (20 min.) and B (35 min.) will be undercooked. Sample A may still be liquid, while B may be only slightly runny. Sample C (40 min.) should be properly cooked with good appearance, texture, and flavor. Sample D (60 min.) will be darker in color, dry porous, and perhaps tough around the edges.

"Conclusions" Answer Key

1. C — 40 min. It is coagulated and firm without being over- or undercooked.

2. C — 40 min. It is coagulated and firm without being over- or undercooked.

3. Answers will vary depending on personal preference.

4. Answers will vary depending on personal preference.

5. A — 20 min., which may not even have started to set, and possibly B — 35 min., which may be slightly runny.

6. A. It is undercooked.

7. Egg mixtures must be cooked carefully to avoid under- and overcooking; can evaluate recipes more easily; can solve problems when cooking egg mixtures.

Discussion Questions

1. If you were baking custard for a dessert and wanted to prepare the entire meal in the oven, what other foods would you serve? (Foods that could bake at the same temperature, like meat loaf and broccoli casserole.)

2. Discuss the relationship between cooking egg mixtures until done and the problem of salmonella bacteria in eggs. (Because of the presence of salmonella in some raw eggs, egg mixtures should be cooked thoroughly but not overcooked so the protein toughens.)

3. Where else is custard used besides in desserts? (Quiche, a custard base with different foods added, such as cooked meat, cheese, vegetables. Discuss different kinds of quiche.)

Experiment 21: Taste-Testing Fruit Juice

Purpose

In this experiment, students conduct a blindfold test to judge fruit juice by smell, taste, and touch.

Food for Today Reference

Ch. 33, "Beverages" (p. 491, "Beverage Facts")

This experiment may also be used in Ch. 1, "Your Food Choices," (p. 4, "Enjoyment") or in Ch. 19, "Fruits" (p. 290, "Buying and Storing Canned Fruits and Juices").

Procedure Hints

You may want to use this experiment as an introduction to food science. It will give the students experience in making sensory evaluations. As a result, students may find it easier to evaluate the products in subsequent experiments.

Use blindfolds the students feel comfortable with, such as cloth napkins or dish towels. Or students may be asked to bring their own blindfolds, such as large handkerchiefs or scarves.

Remind the Assistants to place cups securely into the Judges' hands since Judges will not be able to see them.

After each pair of students has completed three trials of the taste test, you may want to repeat the entire experiment. This time have students switch places, with the Assistants acting as Judges.

Results from all the judges can be tabulated, if desired, to determine what percentage preferred each juice.

Expected Results

Results will vary depending on personal preference.

"Conclusions" Answer Key

All answers call for personal opinion and will vary.

Discussion Questions

1. Why is it difficult to judge sensory characteristics objectively? (People have their own ideas and likes and dislikes. Also, sensory characteristics cannot be measured like height or weight can.)
2. Why does industry use taste-testing panels? (Product must appeal to largest possible number of consumers; taste-testing helps them to make improvements.)
3. What other foods would you like to taste-test in the same manner? Why? (Answers will vary.)

Experiment 22: The Role of Pectin in Jelly

Purpose

This experiment determines the effect of pectin and sugar in making jelly.

Food for Today Reference

Ch. 34, "Preserving Food at Home" (p. 508, "What Happens When You Make Jelly?" and p. 509, "Jams and Jellies")

Procedure Hints

To conduct the complete experiment, at least three lab groups are needed. Assign each group the variation they are to prepare as specified on the experiment sheet. If it is not possible to have three lab groups working at one time, adapt the experiment by extending it over more than one class period.

Use plain white bread to test spreadability and flavor of the jelly. Because it's so bland, it will not influence the flavor. Its softness will test the spreadability of the jelly.

Expected Results

Sample B should produce an acceptable jelly. A (no pectin) and C (extra sugar) should rate lower in consistency and spreadability because they will not gel properly. Flavor preferences may vary, but students may feel that C (with extra sugar) is too sweet.

"Conclusions" Answer Key

1. A (no pectin) did not gel; B (250 mL [1 cup] sugar) gelled properly; C (500 mL [2 cups] sugar) gelled but not as well as B.
2. Pectin needs the right amount of acid to gel. The amount of sugar must balance the amount of pectin and acid. Too much or too little sugar creates a weak gel or prevents the gel from forming.
3. Should be B (pectin + 250 mL [1 cup] sugar). It had the best gel.

Discussion Questions

1. What is the purpose of pectin? (Pectin, a natural substance present in many fruits, has gelling ability when cooked. It causes fruit juice or fruit mixtures to gel so they can be easily spread on bread.)
2. Why must jams and jellies be processed in hot water? (To destroy harmful microorganisms that might make it spoil.)
3. How did people make jams and jellies before the invention of commerical pectin? (Fruits high in pectin, such as apples, were added to the mixture. Jams were cooked until enough moisture evaporated to obtain correct sugar and pectin concentrations.)

Vocabulary for Sensory Evaluation

When you are making observations, be as specific as possible. Here are some examples of terms to help you accurately describe the quality you are evaluating.

AROMA

buttery	fruity	sour
fishy	sulphuric	herbal
spicy	nutty	yeasty
odorless	musty	lemony
acidic	flowery	rancid
burnt	smoky	sweet
Oriental	Italian	

FLAVOR

orangy	spicy	sweet
lemony	metallic	acidic
smoky	musky	moldy
sour	sweet	salty
fishy	fresh	stale
bitter	tangy	bland
buttery	tart	rancid
flat		

APPEARANCE

foamy	smooth	separated
layered	liquid	crystallized
peaked	stiff	watery
creamy	lopsided	curdled
coarse	clear	powdery
bubbly	lumpy	tunneled
specific colors	rounded	caved in
greasy	flat	

TEXTURE

pulpy	gooey	greasy
fluffy	paste-like	airy
foamy	stiff	watery
chunky	lumpy	runny
curdled	heavy	sticky
chewy	grainy	gritty
brittle	crisp	thick
tender	tough	creamy
smooth	rough	dense
light	rubbery	elastic
spongy	crumbly	fine
oily	moist	dry
coarse	slimy	slick
mushy	soft	hard
stringy	tunneled	flaky

Conducting Food Science Experiments

Food science laboratory experiments differ from food preparation laboratories. Rather than trying to produce a standard food product, you will be investigating ingredients and cooking methods. By observing what happens in each experiment, you will learn the effects of the various ingredients and methods used.

Most experiments involve several variations so you can make comparisons. These variations are achieved by substituting different ingredients (variable substances) or using different preparation or treatment methods. Many of the variations will not produce a standard food product. These "failures" will help you understand the scientific principles that underlie successful food preparation.

Many experiments include a control sample. A *control* is the standard in an experiment with which other samples are compared. For example, suppose an experiment calls for adding an acid to milk. An untreated sample of milk serves as the control to which the treated samples are compared.

The experiments are designed to follow scientific laboratory procedures as much as possible. As in any laboratory work, you will need to follow standard safety and sanitation procedures at all times.

THE EXPERIMENT WORKSHEET

Before beginning an experiment, read the experiment worksheet carefully. Make certain you understand what you are to do. Ask questions, if necessary.

The worksheet begins with a goal, "To help you to . . ." Next you will find scientific terms with their definitions. Under "See also . . ." you will find specific page numbers in *Food for Today* where you can find basic information that will help you understand the experiment. "Background Information" gives you additional explanation and an overview of the experiment. Next you will find a list of supplies. Use the check-off blanks to be sure you have everything you need for the experiment.

Procedure

Under "Procedure," the worksheet gives you step-by-step directions for conducting the experiment. Each step is numbered and has a check-off blank. Check off each one as you do it so you don't miss any steps.

Follow the directions carefully. Measure accurately. Mix each sample exactly the same way, unless the directions state differently. Otherwise, you won't get the proper results.

If the same equipment is used for several parts of the same experiment, wash it carefully before proceeding with the next part. For example, if you are doing two variations — one involving vinegar and the other baking soda — you must be sure that the measuring spoon is free of any baking soda before measuring the vinegar. Otherwise, the residue of baking soda, even if it is only a small amount, can affect the outcome of the vinegar variation. This is called cross-contamination — one substance is accidentally introduced into another part of the experiment.

Containers for the variations must be labeled carefully at each step so you don't get them mixed up. Follow instructions carefully for labeling. It will make your observations more accurate.

A pencil or nontoxic waterproof marker is recommended for labels that are placed on the edges of plates and that might accidentally be moistened. Ordinary pens usually smear when wet, making it difficult to read the label.

Observations

Experimental work is valuable only when a written record is kept of the data and observations. Your observations will be written on an Observation Chart, which is part of the experiment worksheet.

Most of the observations made in these experiments are sensory — using the senses such as seeing, smelling, feeling, and tasting. At times you will also be asked to make some simple objective observations, such as measuring the height of a sample. Science laboratories use scales, microscopes, and other special equipment to evaluate the characteristics of foods. Such observation methods are beyond the scope of these experiments.

When you are asked to measure height or length, use a ruler and record your measurements in metric units (centimeters) as well as standard units (inches). Metric measures are used by scientists.

Write your observations as single words or brief phrases in the correct row and column on the Observation Chart. If you change your mind as you begin to compare the variations, cross out or erase your first impression and write in the new one.

(Continued on next page)

In writing your observations, be as specific as possible. Avoid general descriptions such as "good," "bad," or "nice." Specific descriptive words or phrases such as "musty," "large tunnels," "flaky," or "curdled" will make it easier to compare the results of your experiment with your classmates. Your teacher will provide you with examples of words you can use in describing your observations.

Pay close attention to detail when you make your observations. Here are some guidelines to help you make specific kinds of sensory observations:

- **Aroma.** Smell the product and think about the aroma. If the aroma is faint, you can direct more of the aroma toward your nose. With one hand, fan the air in one direction from the product toward your nostrils.
- **Flavor.** Have the sample at an appropriate temperature. If food is too hot or too cold, you may not be able to taste it as well. When tasting, put a small amount of the product on your tongue. Then move the food around in your mouth so that it reaches all the parts of the tongue. Taste buds are located mainly on the sides and back of the tongue. To sense the flavor as fully as possible, make certain the food reaches the parts of the tongue with the most taste buds. Chew solids until they liquify. When you are tasting more than one sample, take a sip of water or rinse your mouth after tasting. This will remove the flavor of the sample before you taste the next sample.

- **Appearance.** Look at the product closely to note shape, texture, and color. Cut solid products so you can examine the inside. When cutting, use a sharp knife and a cutting board. Cut with a back-and-forth sawing motion. If the product is a liquid, put a small amount on a spoon or a small plate so that you can examine it more closely.
- **Texture.** You can determine texture by looking at the product and examining details, feeling it with the fingers, or sensing it in the mouth. How does it feel when you bite into it?

Conclusions

Once you have made your observations, you will make conclusions regarding the results of the experiment. Answer the questions listed in this section of your worksheet. Since all the conclusions are based on your personal observations, your answers may vary from those of your classmates. If the results of your experiment are not what you expect, the difference may be in the way the experiment was conducted.

You will be asked to explain the practical application of the experiment. How can you use the information in your daily life? Will it make you a better shopper? Will it help you prepare better meals or become a better manager? Will it improve your decision-making skills?

Finishing Up

This section of the experiment worksheet gives you suggestions for using the samples from the experiment. Remember that cleanup is also part of finishing the experiment.

Glossary of Selected Food Science Terms

Following is a list of terms and definitions that can be helpful in gaining an understanding of food science concepts. The terms listed here relate primarily to concepts discussed in the Food Science features and experiments that are part of the *Food for Today* program. You may also wish to refer to the glossary found on pages 581-587 of the *Food for Today* textbook for basic nutrition and food preparation terms.

acid. One of many compounds that have certain characteristics in common, including a sour taste, the ability to turn blue litmus paper red, and a value below 7 on the pH scale.

anthocyanin (an–thuh–SIGH–uh–nehn). A pigment (coloring agent) that gives red color to some plants, such as red cabbage.

antioxidant (an–tie–OX–ih–dent). A substance that prevents browning.

bacteria (back–TEER–ee–uh). One-celled living things so small they can be seen only with a microscope.

base. One of many compounds that have certain characteristics in common, including a bitter taste, the ability to turn red litmus paper blue, and a value above 7 on the pH scale. Also called "alkali."

calorie. *See* **kilocalorie.**

calorimeter (kal–uh–RIM–uh–ter). Scientific instrument used to measure calories.

carbon dioxide (KAR–bun die–OX–ide). A colorless gas made of carbon and oxygen. In baked products, it is produced by some leavening agents and helps the product to rise.

carotene (CARE–uh–teen). Pigment (coloring agent) that gives some plants, such as carrots, a yellow/orange color. Can be converted by the human body to vitamin A.

cell. A tiny unit of living matter. All plant and animal tissues are made up of cells.

cellulose (SELL–you–lohse). Fibers that are in the cell walls of plants and that cannot be digested by humans.

chemical leavening agent. A substance that uses a chemical reaction between acid and base ingredients to produce carbon dioxide, making baked products rise.

chemical reaction. A process in which substances are changed into new and different substances.

chlorophyll (KLOHR–oh–fill). Pigment (coloring agent) that gives green color to many plants.

coagulation (koh–ag–you–LAY–shun). A process in which a liquid changes into a semi-solid or solid mass.

coalesce (koh–uh–LESS). To come together, as when fat droplets come together to form globules.

collagen (KOLL–uh–jen). A white, fairly thin connective tissue in meat.

compound. Two or more elements chemically combined to form a pure substance.

concentration. The relative amount of one substance in a certain volume of another substance.

conduction. Heat transfer by direct contact.

control. The standard in an experiment with which other samples are compared.

convection. Heat transfer through the motion of molecules in air or liquid.

convection current. A cycle of movement that occurs when air or liquid is heated, rises, cools, sinks, is heated again, and so on.

dehydration (dee–hy–DRAY–shun). Water loss.

denaturation (dee–nay–chur–AY–shun). A change in the shape of protein molecules, resulting in a change in the product.

double-acting baking powder. A chemical leavening agent that produces carbon dioxide when liquid is added and again when heat is applied.

egg white foam. Beaten egg whites.

element. The simplest type of substance. All matter is made up of one or more elements.

enzyme (EN–ziym). A chemical (made up of complex proteins) that speeds up chemical reactions.

flavone (FLAY-vone). A pigment (coloring agent) that gives white color to some plants, such as cauliflower.

freezer burn. Condition in food that has been improperly frozen, resulting in a dry, discolored surface and off-flavor; caused by exposure of ice crystals to air.

gel. A semi-rigid, elastic mass consisting of liquid trapped in a network of solid particles.

gelatinization (jih–LAH–tihn–uh–ZAY–shun). The process that occurs when starch granules absorb liquid and swell.

germination (jur–muh–NAY–shun). The sprouting process of a seed.

gluten (GLOO–ten). The protein complex formed when wheat flour is mixed with liquid. Gives shape and structure to baked goods.

hydrogenated (high–DRAH–jih–nay–ted). Treated in a chemical process that adds hydrogen, turning oil into a solid fat.

hygroscopicity (HIGH–gruh–skop–IH–suh–tee). The ability of a substance to take up and retain moisture.

hypothesis (hy–PAH–thuh–sihs). An educated guess based on existing information.

invert sugar. A mixture of fructose and glucose (two types of sugar).

kilocalorie. The amount of heat energy needed to raise the temperature of 1 kilogram of water by 1°C; scientifically correct term for what most people call "calorie."

leavening agent. Any substance that helps a baked product to rise. *See also* **chemical leavening agent.**

litmus paper. Specially treated paper used as an indicator of whether a substance is an acid or a base.

microorganism (my–kro–OR–guh–niz–um). A tiny living thing of microscopic size.

microwaving. Using invisible waves of energy to cook food in a microwave oven.

mixture. Two or more substances that are physically, but not chemically, combined.

mold. A microscopic plant that grows as a fuzzy patch on plant or animal matter.

molecule. The smallest particle of an element or compound that retains all the properties of that element or compound.

osmosis (ahs–MOE–sihs). The movement of fluids through semipermeable membranes.

oxidation (ox–ih–DAY–shun). Chemical reaction in which oxygen is united with other substances.

pectin (PECK–tihn). A carbohydrate, found in many fruits, that has the ability to gel liquid under certain conditions.

pH scale. A range of numbers from 0 to 14 used to measure how acidic or basic a substance is. Acids have a pH of 0 (strong acid) to 6.9 (weak acid). Bases have a pH of 7.1 (weak base) to 14 (strong base). A pH of 7 indicates the substance is neutral — neither an acid nor a base.

photosynthesis (foh–toh–SIN–thuh–sihs). Process in which plants capture the energy in sunlight and use it to make carbohydrates.

radiation. A method of heat transfer in which waves of radiant energy strike and heat objects.

scientific method. A procedure used by scientists for the systematic pursuit of knowledge.

semipermeable (sem–ih–PUR–mee–uh–buhl). Allowing only certain substances to pass through.

sensory characteristics (SEN–sore–ee). Qualities of food identified by the five human senses of seeing, hearing, smelling, feeling, and tasting.

sol (SAWL). A substance consisting of small solid particles distributed throughout a liquid.

solute (SAWL–yoot). A dissolved substance.

solution. A mixture consisting of extremely small particles dissolved in a liquid.

solvent (SAWL–vunt). A liquid in which a substance is dissolved to form a solution.

stabilizer (STAY–buh–lie–zer). A substance that helps keep a mixture from changing chemically or physically. Also called a **stabilizing agent.**

sublime. To change directly from a solid to a vapor.

theory. A proposed explanation based on scientific experiments.

yeast. A microscopic, nongreen plant. When used as a leavening agent, produces carbon dioxide gas, making baked products rise.

Name _____   Class _____   Date _____

Experiment 1
Oxidation of Fruit

To help you to . . .
- compare the effects of various liquids on the browning of fresh fruit.

See also . . .
- *Food for Today* p. 292, "Serving Fruits" (Ch. 19)

Look for these terms . . .
- *oxidation* (ox–ih–DAY–shun): a chemical reaction in which oxygen is united with other substances.
- *antioxidant* (an–tie–OX–ih–dent): a substance that prevents browning.

BACKGROUND INFORMATION

Oxidation is the process by which a substance chemically reacts with oxygen. When some fruits are cut and exposed to oxygen in the air, they turn brown. An *antioxidant* prevents the oxidation process and keeps fruit from turning brown.

In this experiment, you will coat apple slices with water, ascorbic acid, and lemon juice. Untreated slices of apple will serve as a control. You will observe the effect of the liquids on the darkening of the fruit.

As you pare and cut the apple, work quickly but carefully. If you take too long to cut the fruit, it may start to brown. If any of the fruit has started to brown before you dip it into the mixture, cut the brown part off first.

SUPPLIES

- _____ 1 sweet eating apple (Delicious, MacIntosh)
- _____ 1 ascorbic acid tablet or 20 mL (4 tsp.) powdered ascorbic acid
- _____ 30 mL (2 Tbsp.) lemon juice
- _____ cold water
- _____ 4 medium bowls
- _____ 3 small bowls
- _____ 1 set of measuring spoons
- _____ 1 liquid measuring cup
- _____ 1 cutting board
- _____ 1 paring knife
- _____ 1 chef's knife
- _____ tongs
- _____ pen or pencil
- _____ 7 self-sticking labels
- _____ timer or clock

PROCEDURE

- _____ 1. Mark four labels as follows: "A — Control"; "B — Ascorbic Acid"; "C — Lemon Juice"; and "D — Water."
- _____ 2. Fasten each label to the outside of one of the four medium bowls.
- _____ 3. Mark three labels as follows: "Ascorbic Acid," "Lemon Juice," and "Water."
- _____ 4. Fasten each label to the outside of one of the three small bowls.
- _____ 5. Dissolve the ascorbic acid tablet in 125 mL (½ cup) of water in the small bowl labeled "Ascorbic Acid." (If you are using ascorbic acid powder, dissolve in 90 mL [6 Tbsp.] water.)
- _____ 6. Combine the lemon juice with 90 mL (6 Tbsp.) cold water in the small bowl labeled "Lemon Juice."
- _____ 7. Put 125 mL (½ cup) cold water in the small bowl labeled "Water."
- _____ 8. Quickly pare and slice ¼ of the apple.
- _____ 9. Use the tongs to dip the apple slices into the ascorbic acid solution.
- _____ 10. Remove the apple slices and put them into the medium bowl labeled "B — Ascorbic Acid." Wash tongs.
- _____ 11. Quickly pare and slice another ¼ of the apple and dip in the lemon juice mixture.
- _____ 12. Remove the slices and place them in the bowl marked "C — Lemon Juice." Wash tongs.
- _____ 13. Quickly pare and slice the other ¼ of the apple and dip in the water.
- _____ 14. Remove the slices and place them in the bowl labeled "D — Water."
- _____ 15. Pare and slice the final ¼ of the apple and place in the bowl marked "A — Control."
- _____ 16. Let the fruit stand at room temperature.

E-1 (continued)

OBSERVATIONS

_____ 1. After 10 minutes, observe the apple slices in the four bowls for color and amount of browning. Record your observations in the appropriate blanks in all four columns on the Observation Chart.

_____ 2. After 20 minutes, observe the apple slices for color and amount of browning. Record your observations in the appropriate blanks on the Observation Chart.

_____ 3. After 30 minutes, observe the apple slices for color and amount of browning. Record your observations in the appropriate blanks on the Observation Chart.

_____ 4. Observe the texture of the fruit by touching it and tasting it. Record your observations in the appropriate blanks in all four columns on the Observation Chart.

_____ 5. Taste the fruit for flavor. Record your observations in the appropriate blanks on the Observation Chart.

Observation Chart				
Characteristics	A Control	B Ascorbic Acid	C Lemon Juice	D Water
Browning: 10 Minutes				
20 Minutes				
30 Minutes				
Texture				
Flavor				

CONCLUSIONS

1. Which apple slices turned brown? Why? _____

_____

_____

2. Which apple slices did not turn brown? Why? _____

_____

_____

3. Which antioxidant was most effective? _____

_____

4. What conclusions can you draw about lemon juice? _____

_____

5. What other juices can you use to keep fresh fruit from turning brown? Why? _____

_____

6. Which apple slices did you prefer to eat? Why? _____

_____

_____

7. When would you use this information in food preparation? _____

_____

_____

_____

FINISHING UP

- After the experiment, serve all the fruit as a snack.

Experiment 2
Effects of Acids and Bases on Vegetables

To help you to . . .
- determine the effects of acids and bases when cooking vegetables.

See also . . .
- *Food for Today* pp. 307-308, "Cooking in Liquid" (Ch. 20)

Look for these terms . . .
- *chlorophyll* (KLOHR–oh–fill): pigment that gives green color to many plants.
- *anthocyanin* (an–thuh–SIGH–uh–nehn): a pigment that gives red color to some plants.
- *flavone* (FLAY–vone): pigment that gives white color to some plants.
- *carotene* (CARE–uh–teen): pigment that gives yellow or orange color to some plants.

BACKGROUND INFORMATION

For purposes of cooking, vegetables are classified according to color. Each group contains specific natural pigments, which give plants color. *Chlorophyll* gives vegetables their characteristic green color. *Anthocyanin* is responsible for the red, purple, and blue colors in some fruits and vegetables. *Carotene* gives vegetables a yellow or orange color and can be turned into vitamin A during the digestion process. *Flavone* contributes the white coloring to vegetables.

Acids or bases can be present in the water supply or added to cooking water. They can affect vegetables during cooking.

In this experiment, you will cook a vegetable in water (saucepan A), in acid (lemon juice or vinegar, saucepan B), and in a base (baking soda, saucepan C). The vegetables cooked in water will be the control with which you will compare the other two.

Note that the cooking method used for this experiment is not the one usually recommended for cooking vegetables. You will cover the vegetables with liquid to make certain they are completely immersed in the cooking solutions.

SUPPLIES

- _____ ONE of the following as directed by your teacher:
  - _____ 3 carrots
  - _____ 1 small head red cabbage
  - _____ 1 bunch broccoli or 375 mL (1½ c.) green beans
  - _____ 1 small head cauliflower or other white vegetable such as turnips, parsnips, or white onions (Frozen vegetables may be substituted if necessary but cooking time will be shorter.)
- _____ 3 small or medium saucepans with lids
- _____ water-soluble marking pen
- _____ 50 mL (¼ cup) vinegar or lemon juice
- _____ 15 mL (1 Tbsp.) baking soda
- _____ tap water
- _____ measuring spoons
- _____ tongs or slotted spoon, depending on vegetable used
- _____ liquid measuring cup
- _____ 3 small dishes
- _____ fork
- _____ 6 self-sticking labels
- _____ pencil or nontoxic waterproof marker
- _____ timer
- _____ 3 glass jars or containers
- _____ large storage container
- _____ cooling rack

PROCEDURE

- _____ 1. With the water-soluble marking pen, mark the saucepans on the sides: "A," "B," and "C."
- _____ 2. With a pencil or nontoxic waterproof marker, write each of the following on two self-sticking labels: "A — Water"; "B — Acid"; and "C — Base."
- _____ 3. Place one set of labels near the rims of the small dishes. Use the other set of labels on the glass jars or containers.
- _____ 4. If fresh vegetables are used, wash and clean them carefully and cut into pieces about 2.5 cm (1 in.) square. Put edible dis-

_____ carded pieces into storage container and save for soup. If frozen vegetables are used, be sure they are thawed enough so you can divide them.

_____ 5. Divide the vegetable you are working with into three equal portions.

_____ 6. Place each portion into a separate saucepan.

_____ 7. Add vinegar or lemon juice (acid) to saucepan B.

_____ 8. Add baking soda (base) to saucepan C.

_____ 9. Add cold tap water to each pan until the water just covers the vegetables.

_____ 10. Cover the three pans.

_____ 11. Cook on high heat, watching the pans carefully.

_____ 12. When steam begins to appear at the edges of the lid, turn the heat down to medium or medium-low so the water does not boil over.

_____ 13. Simmer the vegetables until those in pan "A" are fork-tender. Time will vary from 10-20 minutes, depending on the vegetable.

_____ 14. Remove the pans from the range. Place them on a cooling rack or a heatproof surface.

_____ 15. Carefully lift the lids from the pans so the steam flows away from you.

_____ 16. With tongs or a slotted spoon, lift the vegetables from saucepan A, let the liquid drain off, and place them on the dish labeled "A — Water." Pour the cooking liquid into the glass jar with the same label.

_____ 17. Using the same procedure, lift the vegetables from saucepan B and place them on the dish labeled "B — Acid." Pour the cooking liquid into the glass jar with the same label.

_____ 18. Lift the vegetables from saucepan C and place them on the dish labeled "C — Base." Pour the cooking liquid into the glass jar with the same label.

OBSERVATIONS

_____ 1. Examine the three samples and notice their color. Record your observations in the proper blanks on the Observation Chart.

_____ 2. Smell the vegetables and note differences in aromas, if any, in the three samples. Record your observations on the Observation Chart.

_____ 3. Cut the vegetables with a _fork_. Note the differences in texture and record your observations on the Observation Chart.

_____ 4. Carefully bite on a piece of each sample. Note differences in texture and record your observations on the Observation Chart.

_____ 5. Taste a small portion of each vegetable and record your observations on the Observation Chart.

_____ 6. Observe the color of the liquids in the glass jars. Write your observations on the Observation Chart.

_____ 7. Pour the cooking liquid from the three glass jars into the storage container.

Observation Chart			
Vegetable cooked: _____		Pigment: _____	
Characteristics	A — Water (Control)	B — Acid	C — Base
Color of Vegetables			
Aroma			
Texture			
Flavor			
Color of Liquid			

E–2 (continued)

CONCLUSIONS

1. Would all vegetables with the same type of color pigment as the one you cooked react the same in acids and bases? Why or why not? _____

_____

2. Compare the results of your experiment with those of your classmates who cooked different colored vegetables. What conclusions do you reach regarding the use of acids and bases in cooking vegetables? _____

_____

_____

3. What conclusions can you reach regarding the effect of acids and bases on the texture of vegetables?

_____

_____

_____

4. Which of the three methods produced the most acceptable vegetable? Why did you prefer it? _____

_____

_____

5. Of what practical use is the information you learned from this experiment? _____

_____

_____

6. When adding tomatoes to a casserole, what textures would you expect in the other vegetables in the following situations?

a. tomatoes added with raw vegetables _____

_____

b. vegetables precooked and then mixed with tomatoes _____

_____

7. How would the information you learned in this experiment help you if you lived in an area with hard water (high in minerals)? _____

_____

FINISHING UP

- Discard any vegetables you have tasted or touched with your fingers.
- Put any edible vegetables in the storage container, refrigerate, and use them to prepare soup.

382

Name _____ Class _____ Date _____

The Effect of Vegetable Piece Size on Cooking Time

To help you to . . .
- determine how the piece size of a vegetable affects cooking time.

See also . . .
- *Food for Today* pp. 306-308, "Cooking Vegetables" (Ch. 20)

Look for these terms . . .
- *cellulose* (SELL–you–lohse): fibers that are in the cell walls of plants and that cannot be digested by humans.
- *carotene* (CARE–uh–teen): pigment that gives plants a yellow/orange color. Can be converted by the human body to vitamin A.

BACKGROUND INFORMATION

Cellulose is the substance that gives plants their structure.

When vegetables are cooked, the cellular structure softens so that the vegetables can be eaten and digested. When vegetables are overcooked, the cellular structure breaks down.

Pigments give plants their color. *Carotene* gives a yellow/orange color. The human body can convert some forms of carotene into vitamin A. When the cellular structure of plants breaks down, pigments escape into the water.

In this experiment, you will prepare carrots which have been cut into three different sizes. You will cook the carrots for a total time of 20 minutes, testing them every five minutes for color, texture, and flavor.

You will have five minutes to make your observations on one set of samples before it's time to conduct the next set of observations. You will have to work quickly, but not carelessly. Be careful and specific in your observations.

SUPPLIES

- _____ 3 carrots, about 15 cm (6 in.) long
- _____ 375 mL (1½ cups) water
- _____ timer
- _____ three 0.9 L (1-qt.) saucepans with lids
- _____ paring knife
- _____ chef's knife
- _____ cutting board
- _____ liquid measuring cup
- _____ ruler
- _____ spoon
- _____ tongs
- _____ fork
- _____ 1 sheet of aluminum foil, about 45 cm (18 in.) long
- _____ 11 self-sticking labels
- _____ pencil or nontoxic waterproof marker

PROCEDURE

- _____ 1. Make a "container" for identifying the carrot samples. Start by placing the sheet of aluminum foil on your desk or work surface with the longer side running crosswise.
- _____ 2. Fold the foil in thirds by overlapping the top and bottom of the sheet. Press down on folds.
- _____ 3. Unfold foil. You should have two creases going across the sheet, dividing it into three equal sections.
- _____ 4. Now fold the sheet of foil in half by bringing the left and right edges together. Press down on folds.
- _____ 5. Fold the sheet in half once again in the same direction. Press down on folds.
- _____ 6. Unfold the sheet. The pattern created by the folds should resemble the drawing shown in step 9. There should be four columns across and three squares in each column for a total of 12 squares.
- _____ 7. Write your name on one of the labels and attach it to the bottom of the foil so that you don't get it mixed up with your classmates' foil.
- _____ 8. Mark seven labels as follows: "A — 3 mm (⅛ in.)"; "B — 12 mm (½ in.)"; "C — 2.5 cm (1 in.)"; "5 min."; "10 min."; "15 min."; and "20 min."
- _____ 9. Attach labels to foil as shown on the drawing on the next page.

E–3 (continued)

Labels for Foil	5 Min.	10 Min.	15 Min.	20 Min.
	A			
Your Name	**B**			
	C			

_____ 10. Mark the remaining three labels as follows: "A — 3 mm (¹/₈ in.)"; "B — 12 mm (¹/₂in.)" and "C — 2.5 cm (1 in.)."

_____ 11. Attach a label to the handle of each of the saucepans.

_____ 12. Clean and pare all three carrots.

_____ 13. Carefully cut one carrot into 3-mm (¹/₈-in.) slices.

_____ 14. Cut the second carrot into 12-mm (¹/₂-in.) slices.

_____ 15. Cut the third carrot into 2.5-cm (1-in.) slices. You should have at least four pieces.

_____ 16. Pour 125 mL (¹/₂) cup water into each saucepan, cover, and bring to a boil.

_____ 17. When the water comes to a boil, add the 3-mm (¹/₈-in.) slices to pan "A," the 12-mm (¹/₂-in.) slices to pan "B," and the 2.5-cm (1-in.) slices to pan "C."

_____ 18. Cover each saucepan with a tight-fitting lid.

_____ 19. Bring the liquid in all three samples to a boil.

_____ 20. Lower the heat and simmer. Set the timer for 5 minutes.

_____ 21. At the end of 5 minutes, use the tongs to remove several pieces of carrot from saucepans "A" and "B" and one piece of carrot from saucepan "C." Let the rest of the carrots continue cooking.

_____ 22. Place the carrots in the proper squares on the aluminum foil, in the first column marked "5 Min."

_____ 23. Reset the timer for 5 minutes.

OBSERVATIONS

_____ 1. Observe the color of the water in the three saucepans and the color of the carrots. Write your observations in the proper blanks on the Observation Chart.

_____ 2. Try to cut and mash each sample with a fork. Observe the texture of each sample. Record your observations in the proper blanks on the Observation Chart.

_____ 3. Taste each sample and note texture and flavor. Record your observations in the proper blanks on the Observation Chart.

_____ 4. When the timer rings, remove several pieces of carrot from saucepans "A" and "B" and one large piece from saucepan "C." Place them on the foil in the appropriate squares in the second column, labeled "10 Min." Let the remaining carrots continue cooking.

_____ 5. Reset the timer for another 5 minutes.

_____ 6. Make your observations on the samples in the second column on the foil, following steps 1-3.
  _____ Step 1
  _____ Step 2
  _____ Step 3

_____ 7. When the timer rings, remove several pieces of carrot from saucepans "A" and "B" and one large piece from saucepan "C." Place them on the foil in the appropriate squares in the third column, labeled "15 Min." Let the remaining carrots continue cooking. You should have at least one more piece of carrot left in saucepan "C."

_____ 8. Reset the timer for a final 5 minutes.

_____ 9. Make your observations on the samples in the third column on the foil, following steps 1-3.
  _____ Step 1
  _____ Step 2
  _____ Step 3

_____ When the timer rings, remove several carrots from saucepans "A" and "B" and the last piece from saucepan "C." Place them on the foil in the appropriate squares in the fourth column, labeled "20 Min."

_____ 11. Make your observations on the samples in the fourth column on the foil, following steps 1-3.
  _____ Step 1
  _____ Step 2
  _____ Step 3

(Continued on next page)

Observation Chart				
Sample	5 minutes	10 minutes	15 minutes	20 minutes
A — 3 mm (1/8 in.): Color of water				
Color of carrot				
Texture				
Flavor				
B — 12 mm (1/2 in.): Color of water				
Color of carrot				
Texture				
Flavor				
C — 2.5 mm (1 in.): Color of water				
Color of carrot				
Texture				
Flavor				

E–3 (continued)

CONCLUSIONS

1. What happened to the color of the water during cooking? Explain. _____

_____

_____

2. What happened to the color of the carrots? Explain. _____

_____

_____

3. Which piece of carrot softened first? Why? _____

_____

_____

4. Which pieces could not be cut with a fork? Why? _____

_____

_____

5. How does the size of the vegetable affect cooking results? _____

_____

_____

6. What conclusions do you reach about preparing vegetables for cooking? _____

_____

_____

7. Of what practical use is the information you learned in this experiment? _____

_____

_____

8. How would an orange color in the water affect the nutritional value of the carrots? _____

_____

_____

FINISHING UP

- The carrots may be eaten immediately or saved for later use. They may be added to a tossed salad or used in a spaghetti sauce.

FOOD FOR TODAY TEACHER'S RESOURCE BOOK
Protected by Copyright

Name _____ Class _____ Date _____

Cooking Vegetables by Conventional and Microwave Cooking Methods

To help you to . . .

- determine the effect of conventional and microwave cooking on fresh broccoli.

Look for this term . . .

- *microwaving:* using invisible waves of energy to cook food in a microwave oven.

See also . . .

- *Food for Today* pp. 306-308, "Cooking Vegetables" (Ch. 20)
- *Food for Today* p. 312, "Microwave Cooking" (Ch. 20)

BACKGROUND INFORMATION

Vegetables change in several ways when properly cooked. The fiber is broken down, making them easier to chew. When the starch is cooked, vegetables are easier to digest. The flavor becomes milder and smaller amounts of the nutrients are lost.

In this experiment, you will cook fresh broccoli four different ways: simmering for 12 minutes, simmering for 20 minutes, microwaving for 7 minutes, and microwaving for 14 minutes. You will observe the color, texture, and flavor of each sample.

Both parts of the experiment — simmering and microwaving — can be carried on at the same time. However, be sure your timing is accurate.

SUPPLIES

- _____ 1.4 L (1½ qt.) saucepan with lid
- _____ 1.4 L (1½ qt.) microwavable dish with cover
- _____ 4 small white paper plates
- _____ fork
- _____ 0.9 kg (2 lb.) fresh broccoli
- _____ water

- _____ liquid measuring cup
- _____ tongs
- _____ 2 timers
- _____ 4 self-sticking labels
- _____ pencil or nontoxic waterproof marker

PROCEDURE

- _____ 1. With the pencil, mark labels as follows: "A — Sim. 12 min."; "B — Sim. 20 min."; "C — Micro 7 min."; and "D — Micro 14 min."
- _____ 2. Attach each label to the rim of a paper plate, near the edge.
- _____ 3. Clean broccoli. Cut away tough parts of stalks. Split tender ends. Wash carefully.
- _____ 4. Pour 125 mL (½ cup) water into saucepan and bring to a boil.
- _____ 5. Add half the broccoli and cover the saucepan.
- _____ 6. Simmer for 12 minutes.
- _____ 7. Use the tongs to remove half of the broccoli and place it on the plate labeled "A — Sim. 12 min."
- _____ 8. Cover the pan and continue simmering the rest of the broccoli for an additional 8 minutes.

- _____ 9. Remove the broccoli and place it on the plate labeled "B — Sim. 20 min."
- _____ 10. Place the remaining uncooked broccoli in a microwavable dish.
- _____ 11. Add 125 mL (½ cup) water and cover.
- _____ 12. Cook for 7 minutes on High, turning the dish after 3½ minutes.
- _____ 13. Remove half of the broccoli and place it on the plate labeled "C — Micro 7 min."
- _____ 14. Continue to microwave the remaining broccoli for 7 more minutes, turning the dish after 3½ minutes.
- _____ 15. Remove the broccoli and place it on the plate labeled "D — Micro 14 min."

E–4 (continued)

OBSERVATIONS

_____ 1. Observe the color of the four samples. Record your description of the color in the proper blanks in the Observation Chart.

_____ 2. Cut the four samples with a fork and observe their texture.

_____ 3. Put one sample at a time in your mouth and chew it. Record your observations about texture in the proper blanks on the Observation Chart.

_____ 4. Taste each sample. Record your observations about flavor in the proper blanks on the Observation Chart.

Observation Chart				
Characteristics	**A** **Simmer** **12 min.**	**B** **Simmer** **20 min.**	**C** **Microwave** **7 min.**	**D** **Microwave** **14 min.**
Color				
Texture				
Flavor				

388   (Continued on next page)

(Continued on next page)

CONCLUSIONS

1. Which samples had the most acceptable color? _____
_____

2. Which samples had the most acceptable texture? _____
_____

3. How do you think texture relates to the cooking method used? _____
_____
_____

4. Which samples had the best flavor? Why did you prefer them? _____
_____
_____

5. Were there any differences between the simmered broccoli and microwaved broccoli? Explain. _____
_____
_____
_____

6. Of what practical use is the information you learned in this experiment? _____
_____
_____
_____

FINISHING UP

- The broccoli can be eaten. It can also be refrigerated and used in salads, casseroles, or soups.

Name _____ Class _____ Date _____

Experiment 5
Recrisping Celery

To help you to . . .
- demonstrate the effect of osmosis on wilted celery.

See also . . .
- *Food for Today* p. 303, "Storing Fresh Vegetables" (Ch. 20)
- *Food for Today* p. 324, "Making a Salad" (Ch. 21)

Look for these terms . . .
- *osmosis* (ahs–MOE–sihs): the movement of fluids through semipermeable membranes.
- *semipermeable* (sem–ih–PUR–mee–uh–buhl): allowing only certain substances to pass through.
- *solute* (SAWL–yoot): a dissolved substance.

BACKGROUND INFORMATION

In the process of *osmosis*, fluids pass through semipermeable membranes, such as the cell membranes in plants. (*Semipermeable* means that some, but not all, substances can pass through the membrane.) Osmosis occurs whenever there is a different concentration of *solutes* — substances dissolved in liquid — on each side of the membrane. The fluids pass from the area of lesser solute concentration to the area of greater solute concentration. This process equalizes the concentration on each side of the membrane.

One example of osmosis occurs when wilted celery is placed in water. Water passes through the cell membranes into the cells of the celery, and the celery turns crisp.

In this experiment, you will use three stalks of limp celery. One will serve as the control. The other two stalks will be placed in colored water so you can observe the osmosis process.

SUPPLIES

_____ 3 stalks limp celery, different lengths
_____ 30 mL (2 Tbsp.) red food coloring
_____ tap water
_____ 2 tall glasses or containers
_____ liquid measuring cup
_____ measuring spoons
_____ paring knife

_____ cutting board
_____ 3 small white paper plates
_____ 5 self-sticking labels
_____ pencil or nontoxic waterproof marker
_____ clock or timer
_____ ruler

PROCEDURE

_____ 1. Mark labels as follows: one with "A — Control"; two with "B — Uncut Celery"; and two with "C — Cut Celery."
_____ 2. Attach the label marked "A — Control" to the edge of one paper plate.
_____ 3. Attach one label marked "B — Uncut Celery" to the outside of a tall glass and the other to the edge of the second paper plate.
_____ 4. Label the other glass and plate with the two labels marked "C — Cut Celery."
_____ 5. Measure 15 mL (1 Tbsp.) red food coloring and 50 mL (¼ cup) cold tap water into each tall glass.

_____ 6. Compare the lengths of celery. Use the longest and shortest for variations "B" and "C" and set the other on plate "A" as the control.
_____ 7. Place the two stalks of celery for variations "B" and "C" on a cutting board so the tops are lined up evenly.
_____ 8. Using the paring knife, cut the longer stalk so it is even with the shorter one. Do not cut the shorter stalk.
_____ 9. Immediately place the stalk you just cut into the glass marked "C — Cut Celery."
_____ 10. Place the other stalk into the glass marked "B — Uncut Celery."
_____ 11. Wait 20 minutes.

OBSERVATIONS

_____ 1. Remove the celery from the glass container marked "B — Uncut Celery." Rinse gently in cold tap water.

_____ 2. Beginning at the top end of the celery, cut off 2.5-cm (1-in.) segments until you see red dots appearing on the lower section of the celery. Place the segments on the paper plate marked "B — Uncut Celery."

_____ 3. With a ruler, measure the length of the remaining piece of celery. Record the length in the appropriate blank in the second column on the Observation Chart.

_____ 4. Remove the celery from the glass marked "C — Cut Celery." Rinse gently in cold tap water.

_____ 5. Beginning at the top end of the celery, cut off 2.5-cm (1-in.) segments until you see red dots appearing on the lower section of the celery. Place the segments on the paper plate marked "C — Cut Celery."

_____ 6. With a ruler, measure the length of the remaining piece of celery. Record the length in the proper blank in the third column on the Observation Chart.

_____ 7. Compare the crispness of the celery on plates "B" and "C" with the control stalk of celery which was not placed in water. Record your observations in the proper blanks on the Observation Chart.

_____ 8. Cut a segment of the control sample and taste it. Record your observations in the proper blanks on the Observation Chart.

_____ 9. Taste a red segment from each of the other samples, B and C. Record your observations in the proper blanks on the Observation Chart.

_____ 10. Taste an uncolored segment from samples "B" and "C." Record your observations regarding flavor in the proper blanks on the Observation Chart.

Observation Chart			
Characteristics	**A** **Control**	**B** **Uncut Celery**	**C** **Cut Celery**
Length of piece with red color		cm in.	cm in.
Crispness			
Flavor		Colored: Uncolored:	Colored: Uncolored:

E–5 (continued)

CONCLUSIONS

1. Why did red dots appear when you began to cut the two stalks that had been put in water? _____
_____

_____

2. Of the three stalks, which did you prefer for crispness? Why? _____
_____

_____

3. Which did you prefer for flavor? Why? _____
_____

_____

4. Was there any difference between the amount of water absorbed by the cut and uncut celery? Why or why not?
_____

_____

5. Of what practical use is the information you gained from this experiment? _____
_____

_____

FINISHING UP

- You may want to discard the celery containing the food coloring.
- Eat the uncolored celery as a snack.

- The control sample can be recrisped by the same method or refrigerated and used later in salads or in cooking.

FOOD FOR TODAY TEACHER'S RESOURCE BOOK
Protected by Copyright

Name _____   Class _____   Date _____

Experiment 6
The Effect of Acid on Protein

To help you to . . .
- observe the effect of acid on liquid protein

See also . . .
- *Food for Today* p. 341, "Preparing Dairy Foods" (Ch. 22)

Look for these terms . . .
- *denaturation* (dee–nay–chur–AY–shun): change in the shape of protein molecules, resulting in a change in the product.
- *coagulate* (koh–AG–yoo–late): to become thicker, changing from a liquid to a semisolid or solid mass.

BACKGROUND INFORMATION

Denaturation means that the shape of protein molecules is changed. Denaturation can be caused by heat, freezing, pressure, irradiation, chemicals, or mechanical treatment such as beating or whipping. For example, denaturation occurs when a liquid protein, such as milk or egg white, is heated. If the heating and denaturation continue, the protein molecules will clump together. The liquid will *coagulate* to form a solid. Denaturation is the first step in the coagulation process.

In this experiment, you will add vinegar to two samples of milk and observe what happens. A sample of untreated milk will serve as a control.

SUPPLIES

_____ 150 mL (¾ cup) milk at room temperature
_____ 15 mL (3 tsp.) vinegar
_____ 3 glass custard cups
_____ glass measuring cup
_____ measuring spoons

_____ 3 self-sticking labels
_____ pencil or waterproof marker pen
_____ clock or timer
_____ 2 spoons

PROCEDURE AND OBSERVATIONS

_____ 1. Mark the labels as follows: "A — Control"; "B — 5 mL (1 tsp.) Vinegar"; and "C — 10 mL (2 tsp.) Vinegar."

_____ 2. Attach a label to the outside of each custard cup.

_____ 3. Measure 50 mL (¼ cup) milk into each custard cup.

_____ 4. Add 5 mL (1 tsp.) vinegar to the milk in custard cup B and stir.

_____ 5. Add 10 mL (2 tsp.) vinegar to the milk in custard cup C and stir with a clean spoon.

_____ 6. Observe the appearance of all three samples. Record your observations in the appropriate blanks on the Observation Chart.

_____ 7. Let samples stand 5 minutes at room temperature.

_____ 8. Observe the appearance of the samples. Record your observations in the appropriate blanks on the Observation Chart.

_____ 9. After five more minutes (a total of 10 minutes), observe the appearance of the samples. Record your observations in the appropriate blanks on the Observation Chart.

_____ 10. After five more minutes (a total of 15 minutes), observe the appearance of the samples. Record your observations in the appropriate blanks on the Observation Chart.

Observation Chart			
	Appearance		
Time	**A** **Control**	**B** **5 mL (1 tsp.) Vinegar**	**C** **10 mL (2 tsp.) Vinegar**
Immediately			
5 minutes			
10 minutes			
15 minutes			

CONCLUSIONS

1. What differences did you observe in the three samples? _____
_____

2. How can you tell if protein is denatured? _____
_____

3. Which sample coagulated the most? _____
_____

4. Find a recipe in which you could apply the knowledge you learned in this experiment. Write the recipe name
and where it can be found. _____
_____

FINISHING UP

- Mix the samples together and use them in a recipe
calling for sour milk, such as biscuits, breads, or
cakes.

Name _____ Class _____ Date _____

Separating Fat from Cream

To help you to . . .
- determine the effect of agitation on the fat in cream.

See also . . .
- *Food for Today* p. 332, "Buttermilk" and "Butter" (Ch. 22)

Look for this term . . .
- *coalesce* (koh–uh–LESS): to come together, as when fat droplets come together to form globules.

BACKGROUND INFORMATION

Invisible fat in cream can be turned into visible fat by agitating it. Through agitation, the fat droplets *coalesce*, or come together to form globules. As agitation continues, the globules get larger and larger until they separate from the liquid.

In this experiment, you will make butter from cream by shaking the cream in a jar with a marble. The marble helps to increase the agitation, speeding up the process.

SUPPLIES

- _____ 250 mL (1 cup) heavy whipping cream, at room temperature, plus enough extra for tasting
- _____ glass jar with a tight lid
- _____ glass or ceramic marble
- _____ drinking cups
- _____ bowl
- _____ wooden spoon
- _____ rubber scraper
- _____ airtight storage container
- _____ spoon

PROCEDURE

- _____ 1. Observe the condition of the cream, noting its color and texture. Pour a small sample of cream into a drinking cup and taste it, noting its texture and flavor. Record your observations in the proper blanks on the Observation Chart. Discard any leftover cream from the tasting sample.
- _____ 2. Place 250 mL (1 cup) cream and marble in glass jar.
- _____ 3. Screw the lid on the jar tightly.
- _____ 4. Shake jar vigorously.
- _____ 5. When the fat coalesces into a ball of butter, drain off the liquid, called buttermilk, into a glass.
- _____ 6. Remove the marble from the jar.
- _____ 7. Place butter in a bowl and run cold water over it to rinse off the buttermilk.
- _____ 8. Squeeze butter against the side of the bowl with a wooden spoon or rubber scraper to press out the water.
- _____ 9. Pack butter into an airtight container.

OBSERVATIONS

- _____ 1. Observe the color and texture of the butter you made. Record your observations in the proper blanks on the Observation Chart.
- _____ 2. Taste the butter. Record your observations regarding texture and flavor in the proper blanks on the Observation Chart.
- _____ 3. Observe the buttermilk you made. Record your observations regarding its color and texture on the Observation Chart.
- _____ 4. Taste the buttermilk. Record your observations regarding texture and flavor in the proper blanks on the Observation Chart.

	Observation Chart		
Characteristics	**Cream**	**Butter**	**Buttermilk**
Color			
Texture			
Flavor			

CONCLUSIONS

1. When you observed the cream at the beginning of the experiment, could you see the butter in it? Explain.

_____

_____

_____

2. Describe how the color of the cream changed during the process of agitation. _____

_____

3. Describe how the texture of the cream changed during the process of agitation. _____

_____

4. What conclusions do you draw about the effect of agitation on cream? _____

_____

5. Would the results of this experiment have been the same if you had agitated milk? Explain. _____

_____

FINISHING UP

- Refrigerate the butter in an airtight container and use as needed.

Name _____ Class _____ Date _____

Experiment 8
The Effect of Gelatin on a Frozen Dessert

To help you to . . .
- test how gelatin, a stabilizer, affects a frozen dessert.

See also . . .
- *Food for Today* p. 342, "Making Frozen Dairy Desserts" (Ch. 22)

Look for this term . . .
- *stabilizer* (STAY–buh–lie–zer): a substance that can help keep a mixture from changing chemically or physically.

BACKGROUND INFORMATION

Frozen desserts often include *stabilizers* such as gelatin. The gelatin soaks up water from the mixture and keeps large ice crystals from forming as the mixture freezes. This affects the characteristics of the finished product.

In this experiment, you will prepare two variations of a simple frozen raspberry dessert. One is made with gelatin and the other is not. You will compare the appearance, texture, flavor, and melting characteristics of the two samples to determine the effects of adding gelatin.

SUPPLIES

- _____ 500 mL (1 pt.) whipping cream
- _____ one 227-g (8-oz.) package frozen raspberries, thawed
- _____ 125 mL (½ cup) sugar
- _____ 10 mL (2 tsp.) lemon juice
- _____ one 35-g (¼-oz.) envelope unflavored gelatin
- _____ 90 mL (6 Tbsp.) cold water
- _____ 45 mL (3 Tbsp.) boiling water
- _____ small dish or cup
- _____ two 0.9-L (1-qt.) freezer-safe containers with lids
- _____ electric mixer with large mixing bowl

- _____ liquid measuring cup
- _____ dry measuring cup
- _____ measuring spoons
- _____ rubber scraper
- _____ spatula
- _____ large mixing bowl
- _____ ice
- _____ 4 self-sticking labels
- _____ pencil or marker
- _____ 2 medium mixing bowls
- _____ 2 custard cups
- _____ 2 spoons

PROCEDURE

- _____ 1. Mark two labels as follows: "A — Gelatin" and "B — No Gelatin."
- _____ 2. Fasten the labels to the outside of the two freezer-safe containers.
- _____ 3. With the electric mixer, whip cream and set aside. Be careful not to overbeat the cream — it will turn into butter.
- _____ 4. Place thawed raspberries in a medium mixing bowl.
- _____ 5. Add sugar and lemon juice to raspberries. Mix well.
- _____ 6. Place half the raspberry mixture into the second medium mixing bowl.
- _____ 7. Place the gelatin in a small dish or cup.
- _____ 8. Add 45 mL (3 Tbsp.) cold water to gelatin and let stand until softened.
- _____ 9. Add boiling water to softened gelatin and stir until gelatin dissolves.

- _____ 10. Add the gelatin mixture to *one* of the two bowls of raspberry mixture. Stir.
- _____ 11. Set the gelatin-raspberry mixture in a large mixing bowl filled with ice until the mixture thickens to the consistency of honey. (Do not let the mixture gel.)
- _____ 12. Fold in one-half of the whipped cream.
- _____ 13. Pour the mixture into the freezer container labeled "A — Gelatin." Place lid securely on container.
- _____ 14. Add 45 mL (3 Tbsp.) cold water to the other raspberry mixture.
- _____ 15. Fold the remaining whipped cream into the raspberry mixture.
- _____ 16. Pour the mixture into the freezer container labeled "B — No Gelatin." Place lid securely on container.
- _____ 17. Freeze both containers overnight.

_____ 18. The next day, mark two labels as follows: "A — Gelatin" and "B — No Gelatin."

_____ 19. Fasten the labels to the outside of two custard cups.

_____ 20. Remove the two freezer containers from the freezer.

_____ 21. Spoon a small amount of the dessert from the container labeled "A — Gelatin" into the custard cup labeled "A — Gelatin."

_____ 22. Using a clean spoon, place a small amount of the dessert from the other container into the other custard cup.

OBSERVATIONS

_____ 1. Observe the appearance of both desserts. Record your observations in the appropriate blanks on the Observation Chart.

_____ 2. Observe the texture of both desserts. Record your observations in the appropriate blanks on the Observation Chart.

_____ 3. Taste both desserts. Record your observations on the Observation Chart.

_____ 4. By this time, both desserts should have started to melt. Observe how they melt and how they look when melted. Record your observations in the appropriate blanks on the Observation Chart.

Observation Chart		
Characteristics	**A** **Gelatin**	**B** **No Gelatin**
Appearance		
Texture		
Flavor		
Melting characteristics		

(Continued on next page)

CONCLUSIONS

1. Which dessert has the best appearance? What is the reason for the difference? _____
_____
_____

2. Which recipe is smoother? Why? _____
_____
_____

3. Which dessert melted faster? Why? _____
_____
_____

4. Which dessert did you prefer? Why did you prefer it? _____
_____
_____

5. What conclusions do you draw from this experiment? _____
_____
_____

6. Of what practical use is the information you learned in this experiment? _____
_____
_____

FINISHING UP

■ Both desserts may be eaten as snacks.

Name _____ Class _____ Date _____

Tenderizing Meat

To help you to . . .
- compare the tenderizing effects of an enzyme and a mechanical tenderizer on meat.

See also . . .
- *Food for Today* p. 358 on tenderizing meat (Ch. 23)

Look for this term . . .
- *enzyme* (EN–ziym): a chemical that speeds up chemical reactions.

BACKGROUND INFORMATION

Less tender cuts of meat can be tenderized in a variety of ways. Tenderizing occurs when meat fibers and connective tissues are cut or broken by mechanical or chemical methods.

In this experiment, you will treat a less-tender cut of meat by two different methods — using a commercial meat tenderizer (chemical) and pounding with a mallet. You will then panbroil the meat to compare the effectiveness of the different methods with an untreated control.

Commercial tenderizers contain *enzymes* which speed up the changes meat undergoes as it ages. If left on the meat too long, they can result in loss of flavor, color, and texture. For this reason, it's important to follow instructions on the meat tenderizer container carefully.

SUPPLIES

_____ small piece of round steak, 2 cm (¾ in.) thick
_____ cutting board
_____ sharp knife
_____ mallet
_____ instant meat tenderizer (use amount suggested on container)
_____ fork

_____ skillet
_____ tongs
_____ 6 paper plates
_____ 6 self-sticking labels
_____ pencil or nontoxic marker
_____ 3 different colored toothpicks

PROCEDURE

_____ 1. Mark two labels with each of the following: "A — Control"; "B — Chemical"; "C — Mallet."

_____ 2. Attach labels to each of the 6 paper plates on the rim close to the edge.

_____ 3. Divide plates into two groups, with one of each label in each group. Use one set of labeled plates when preparing the meat for cooking. Use the other set after the meat has cooked.

_____ 4. Cut the meat into 3 equal parts.

_____ 5. Place one piece of meat on the cutting board.

_____ 6. Pound the meat with a mallet until it is 1 cm (³/₈ in.) thick, turning it over at least once.

_____ 7. Place the pounded meat on the paper plate labeled "C — Mallet."

_____ 8. Place another piece of meat on the plate labeled "B — Chemical."

_____ 9. Sprinkle the meat on the plate with the instant meat tenderizer and pierce several times with a fork.

_____ 10. Place the untreated meat on the paper plate labeled "A — Control."

_____ 11. Stick a different colored toothpick on each piece of meat. Record the color of the toothpick in the proper blank on the Observation Chart. This will help you identify the meat after it has cooked.

_____ 12. Place the three pieces of meat in a skillet, being careful not to remove the toothpicks.

_____ 13. Discard the three paper plates that held the raw meat.

_____ 14. Panbroil meat until done, turning once. (Remove the toothpick, use tongs to turn the piece of meat, and replace the toothpick.) Make certain the toothpick does not fall out of the meat. If it does, lay it on top of the meat so you can identify it.

_____ 15. When meat is done, place on the clean, labeled paper plates, matching the colored toothpick to the label on the appropriate plate.

OBSERVATIONS

_____ 1. Try cutting each sample with the side of a fork. Record your observations in the proper blanks on the Observation Chart.

_____ 2. Next, cut each sample with a knife. Record your observations in the proper blanks on the Observation Chart.

_____ 3. Put a piece of one sample in your mouth and count the number of times you have to chew until it completely dissolves. Repeat with a piece of the same size from the other two samples. Record the number of chews for each sample in the proper blanks on the Observation Chart.

_____ 4. Eat another small piece from each of the samples, observing texture and flavor. Record your observations in the proper blanks on the Observation Chart.

Observation Chart			
Observations	**A** Control	**B** Chemical	**C** Mallet
Color of toothpick			
Fork test			
Knife test			
Chew test			
Texture			
Flavor			

CONCLUSIONS

1. Which piece(s) could you cut with a fork? What caused the tenderness? _____

_____

_____

2. Which piece, if any, was difficult to cut with a knife? Why was it tougher? _____

_____

_____

3. Which piece took the most number of chews? Which piece took the least? Explain the reason for the

difference. _____

_____

_____

4. Which piece had the best texture and flavor? _____

_____

5. What conclusions do you draw about the effect of tenderizers on meat? _____

_____

_____

6. Of what practical use is the information you gained from this experiment? _____

_____

_____

FINISHING UP

- If any of the meat is too tough to eat, refrigerate it
  and use it for a stew.

Experiment 10

Effects of Added Ingredients on Egg White Foams

To help you to . . .
- determine the effects of sugar, salt, acid, and fat on an egg white foam.

See also . . .
- *Food for Today* pp. 403-405, "Beating Egg Whites" (Ch. 26)

Look for these terms . . .
- *egg white foam:* beaten egg whites.
- *denaturation* (dee–nay–chur–AY–shun): a change in the shape of protein molecules, resulting in a change in the product.
- *stabilizing agent:* a substance that helps keep a mixture from changing chemically or physically.

BACKGROUND INFORMATION

Egg white has the ability to form an *egg white foam* because of the proteins it contains. During beating, the proteins undergo *denaturation*. This means that the protein molecules change shape. The molecules unfold and form a protein mesh. Air bubbles are trapped in the mesh and expand it. The denatured protein provides a rigid structure for the foam, while the air adds volume.

Sometimes other ingredients are added to the egg whites — on purpose or accidentally — before beating. These added ingredients can affect the results. For example, some ingredients act as *stabilizing*

agents because they help the foam keep its shape. Other ingredients have the opposite effect — they decrease stability. Added ingredients can also affect how much beating time is needed and the final volume of the foam.

In this experiment, you will prepare one of five variations of beaten egg white: either with sugar, with salt, with cream of tartar (an acid), with a few drops of egg yolk (which contains fat), or an untreated control. By observing your sample and comparing the results from other samples, you can determine the effects of adding each ingredient.

SUPPLIES

_____ 2 egg whites, room temperature
_____ ONE of the following as directed by your teacher:
_____ 60 mL (4 Tbsp.) granulated sugar
_____ 2 mL (½ tsp.) salt
_____ 1 mL (¼ tsp.) cream of tartar
_____ 1 egg yolk
_____ no addition (control sample)
_____ glass mixing bowl (identical to those used by the other groups)

_____ electric mixer
_____ measuring spoons
_____ rubber scraper
_____ long metal or wooden skewer
_____ 3 self-sticking labels
_____ pencil, pen, or marker
_____ ruler
_____ clock with second hand

PROCEDURE

_____ 1. Mark one label according to the variation you have been assigned by your teacher: "A — Control"; "B — Sugar"; "C — Salt"; "D — Cream of Tartar"; or "E — Egg Yolk."
_____ 2. Attach the label to the outside of the glass mixing bowl.
_____ 3. Place egg whites in the bowl.
_____ 4. Note the starting time.
_____ 5. Use the electric mixer to beat the egg whites just until they are foamy.
_____ 6. Follow the variation you have been assigned by your teacher.

_____ Variation A: Continue beating; do not add any other ingredient.
_____ Variation B: Add sugar 15 mL (1 Tbsp.) at a time. Beat after each addition to dissolve sugar.
_____ Variation C: Add salt to the egg whites and continue beating.
_____ Variation D: Add cream of tartar to the egg whites and continue beating.
_____ Variation E: Add 2 drops of egg yolk to the whites and continue beating.
_____ 7. Beat until stiff peaks form. *Do not overbeat.*
_____ 8. Note the time you stopped beating.

OBSERVATIONS

_____ 1. Record the total beating time in the proper blank on the Observation Chart.

_____ 2. Gently spread the foam so it is level in the bowl.

_____ 3. Insert the skewer into the foam. Attach a self-sticking label to the skewer so the bottom edge marks the top of the foam. Remove the skewer.

_____ 4. Use the ruler to measure the part of the skewer that was immersed in the foam. Record the height in metric and standard measures in the proper blank on the Observation Chart.

_____ 5. Observe the appearance of the foam. Record your observations in the proper blank on the Observation Chart.

_____ 6. Let the foam stand for 15 minutes.

_____ 7. Level the foam again and measure its height as before. Record the height in the proper blank on the Observation Chart.

_____ 8. Observe the appearance of the foam. Record your observations in the proper blank on the Observation Chart.

_____ 9. Fill in the rest of the Observation Chart with the results obtained by your classmates.

_____ 10. Circle the letter of the variation you prepared.

Observation Chart					
Characteristics	A Control	B Sugar	C Salt	D Cream of Tartar	E Egg Yolk
Beating time					
Height just after beating	cm in.	cm in.	cm in.	cm in.	cm in.
Appearance just after beating					
Height after 15 min.	cm in.	cm in.	cm in.	cm in.	cm in.
Appearance after 15 min.					

(Continued on next page)

CONCLUSIONS

1. Which variation reached the greatest height? _____

2. Which took the longest to reach the stiff peak stage? _____

3. Which sample retained its height and appearance the longest? _____

4. Summarize the effects each of the following ingredients had on the egg white foam:

sugar _____

_____

salt _____

_____

cream of tartar (acid) _____

_____

egg yolk (fat) _____

_____

5. Of what practical value is the information you learned in this experiment? _____

_____

_____

FINISHING UP

- Combine Sample E with the remaining egg yolk. Store for use in a recipe calling for a whole egg.

- Combine the egg white foams and use for meringue, cookies, or cake.

Name _____ Class _____ Date _____

The Effect of Gluten Development on Muffins

To help you to . . .

- determine the effect of gluten, developed by stirring muffin batter, on the finished muffins.

Look for this term . . .

- *gluten* (GLOO–ten): the protein complex formed when wheat flour is mixed with liquid.

See also . . .

- *Food for Today* p. 423, "Flour" (Ch. 28)
- *Food for Today* p. 438, "Muffin Method" (Ch. 29)

BACKGROUND INFORMATION

Gluten is made up of the proteins in flour. As batter is mixed, the gluten develops into an elastic mesh. Air or gas becomes trapped in the gluten, forming tiny cells that expand as the product is heated. The more gluten is mixed, the stronger it becomes. The stronger it is, the more easily it expands.

In this experiment, you will make a muffin recipe which yields six muffins. The batter will be mixed three different ways, giving you an opportunity to compare the effects of mixing method on the finished muffins.

SUPPLIES

_____ 250 mL (1 cup) all-purpose flour
_____ 8 mL (1½ tsp.) double-acting baking powder
_____ 1 mL (¼ tsp.) salt
_____ 15 mL (1 Tbsp.) granulated sugar
_____ 30 mL (2 Tbsp.) vegetable oil
_____ 125 mL (½ cup) milk
_____ 1 egg
_____ 6 paper muffin cup liners (2 each of 3 colors)
_____ muffin pan with 6 cups
_____ measuring spoons
_____ dry measuring cups
_____ liquid measuring cup

_____ sifter
_____ spatula
_____ medium mixing bowl
_____ small mixing bowl
_____ fork
_____ wooden spoon
_____ rubber scraper
_____ cooling rack
_____ knife
_____ cutting board
_____ ruler

PROCEDURE

_____ 1. Preheat oven to 200°C (400°F).
_____ 2. Place muffin cup liners in pan so that two of the same color are next to each other.
_____ 3. Measure flour, baking powder, salt, and sugar into a sifter.
_____ 4. Sift dry ingredients together into medium mixing bowl.
_____ 5. Break egg into small mixing bowl and beat lightly with a fork.
_____ 6. Add vegetable oil and milk to beaten egg. Mix with a fork.
_____ 7. Add mixed liquid ingredients to dry ingredients in medium mixing bowl.
_____ 8. Stir batter 12 strokes with a wooden spoon. Count strokes carefully. Batter will be barely moistened.

_____ 9. Spoon out enough batter into the muffin pan to fill two paper liners of the *same color* two-thirds full. On the Observation Chart, write the color of the paper liners you just filled in the appropriate blank under "A — Stirred 12 Strokes."
_____ 10. Stir the remaining batter 6 more strokes.
_____ 11. Spoon out enough batter to fill two muffin liners of a second color two-thirds full. On the Observation Chart, write the color of the liners you just filled in the appropriate blank under "B — Stirred 18 Strokes."
_____ 12. Stir the remaining batter 12 more strokes.
_____ 13. Fill the remaining two muffin liners of the same color two-thirds full. On the Observation Chart, write the color of the liners you just filled in the appropriate blank under "C — Stirred 30 Strokes."

_____ 14. Place the muffin pan in the preheated oven at 200°C (400°F) and bake for 15-18 minutes or until golden brown.

_____ 15. Remove the muffin pan from the oven.

_____ 16. Gently remove the muffins from the pan and place on a cooling rack. Keep the muffins in matching colored liners together, so you have three pairs of muffins.

_____ 17. Remove the paper liner from one muffin of each pair. Set each muffin on its removed liner so you can identify it.

_____ 18. Using a sharp knife and a cutting board, carefully cut one of the muffins without the liner in half from top to bottom.

_____ 19. Place the two halves on the correct liner next to the whole muffin with the same color liner.

_____ 20. Repeat the process by cutting one muffin from each of the remaining pairs in half. Place the cut halves on the correct color liner, next to the matching whole muffin.

OBSERVATIONS

_____ 1. Observe the shape of each sample. Record your observations in the proper blanks on the Observation Chart.

_____ 2. Observe the crust of each sample. Notice characteristics such as color and smoothness. Record your observations in the proper columns on the Observation Chart.

_____ 3. Measure the height of each sample with a ruler. Do this by measuring one of the cut halves. Record the height of each sample in both metric and standard measures on the Observation Chart.

_____ 4. Examine a cut half of each sample and note the texture and color. Do you see any tunnels or holes? Record your observations on the Observation Chart.

_____ 5. Break off a small piece of one of the halves and chew it. Judge it for texture and tenderness. Record your observations on the Observation Chart.

	Observation Chart		
Characteristics	**A** **Stirred** **12 Strokes**	**B** **Stirred** **18 Strokes**	**C** **Stirred** **30 Strokes**
Color of paper liner			
Outside: Shape			
Crust			
Height	cm in.	cm in.	cm in.
Inside: Texture			
Color			
Tenderness			

CONCLUSIONS

1. What was the effect of increased stirring on the development of gluten in the batter? _____

_____

_____

2. How did the increase in the number of times the batter was stirred affect the quality of the muffins? Explain.

_____

_____

_____

3. Which muffin sample was the best example of a quality product? What is the reason for the difference?

_____

_____

4. What conclusions can you draw from this experiment? _____

_____

_____

5. Of what practical use is this information? _____

_____

FINISHING UP

▪ Serve the muffins as a snack or with a meal.

Name _____ Class _____ Date _____

Reaction Speed of Chemical Leavening Agents

To help you to . . .
- compare the reaction speed when combining various chemical leavening agents with various liquids.

See also . . .
- *Food for Today* p. 426, "Leavening Agents" (Ch. 28)

Look for these terms . . .
- *chemical leavening agent:* a substance that uses a chemical reaction between acid and base ingredients to produce carbon dioxide gas, making baked products rise.
- *double-acting baking powder:* a chemical leavening agent that produces carbon dioxide when liquid is added and again when heat is applied.

BACKGROUND INFORMATION

One way to cause a baked product to rise is by using a *chemical leavening agent.* There are several different kinds of chemical leavening agents, but they all work on the same principle. The combination of an acid and a base, when mixed with a liquid, creates carbon dioxide gas. Bubbles of gas add volume to the baked product.

A commonly used base is sodium bicarbonate, or baking soda. It can be used with various acid ingredients, depending on the recipe. Liquids such as vinegar, sour milk, or buttermilk are acids. Cream of tartar is a powdered acid.

Baking powder is a combination of acid and base in one product. One type of baking powder can be made at home by mixing baking soda with cream of tartar. A different formula is used for *double-acting baking powder,* the type that is commonly sold in this country today.

Different chemical leavening agents release carbon dioxide at different rates. The speed with which car-

bon dioxide is released affects the finished baked product.

In this experiment, you will conduct seven different procedures using baking soda, commercial baking powder, and a homemade baking powder. Each of these chemicals will be combined with hot and cold water. The baking soda will also be combined with vinegar. You will compare the type of reaction and how long each reaction lasts.

When conducting the experiment, do one version at a time so that you can make the necessary observations. Follow directions carefully.

Note that the dry ingredients are placed in the cup *first* and then the liquid is added. If you reverse the process, the results may not be accurate. Be sure the cups are dry before placing the chemicals in them. Even the slightest trace of moisture will begin a chemical reaction. After each use, wash and dry the measuring spoons so they are clean and dry for the next variation.

SUPPLIES

- _____ 17 mL (3½ tsp.) baking soda
- _____ 5 mL (1 tsp.) cream of tartar
- _____ 10 mL (2 tsp.) double-acting baking powder
- _____ 45 mL (3 Tbsp.) cold tap water
- _____ 45 mL (3 Tbsp.) hot tap water
- _____ 15 mL (1 Tbsp.) vinegar (any type)
- _____ measuring spoons
- _____ 7 glass custard cups
- _____ 7 drinking straws for stirring
- _____ 7 self-sticking labels
- _____ waterproof marker or pencil
- _____ clock with a second hand (or stopwatch)

PROCEDURE AND OBSERVATIONS

- _____ 1. Refer to the list of leavening agents in the Observation Chart. Write the cup letter and name of each leavening agent on a self-sticking label, using waterproof marker or pencil.
- _____ 2. Attach one label to each of seven custard cups.
- _____ 3. Line up the seven custard cups in the same order in which they are listed on the Observation Chart, but do not place them too close to each other.
- _____ 4. Place a straw, which will be used for mixing, next to each cup.

E–12 (continued)

_____ 5. Place each leavening agent, described in the Observation Chart, in the properly labeled cup. Be sure to wash and dry the measuring spoon before using it for a different substance so you do not cross-contaminate the mixtures.

_____ 6. Beginning with cup A, add the liquid indicated on the Observation Chart and stir with the straw next to the cup.

_____ 7. Time the length of the reaction and observe what happens. On the Observation Chart, record the length and a description of the reaction. Discard the straw you used for stirring.

_____ 8. Repeat steps 6-7 for cup B.
_____ Step 6
_____ Step 7

_____ 9. Repeat steps 6-7 for cup C.
_____ Step 6
_____ Step 7

_____ 10. Repeat steps 6-7 for cup D.
_____ Step 6
_____ Step 7

_____ 11. Repeat steps 6-7 for cup E.
_____ Step 6
_____ Step 7

_____ 12. Repeat steps 6-7 for cup F.
_____ Step 6
_____ Step 7

_____ 13. Repeat steps 6-7 for cup G.
_____ Step 6
_____ Step 7

Observation Chart			
Leavening Agent	Add Liquid	Length of Reaction	Description of Reaction
Cup A: 5 mL (1 tsp.) baking soda	+ 15 mL (1 Tbsp.) cold water		
Cup B: 5 mL (1 tsp.) baking soda	+ 15 mL (1 Tbsp.) hot water		
Cup C: 5 mL (1 tsp.) baking soda	+ 15 mL (1 Tbsp.) vinegar		
Cup D: 1 mL (¼ tsp.) baking soda + 2 mL (½ tsp.) cream of tartar	+15 mL (1 Tbsp.) cold water		
Cup E: 1 mL (¼ tsp.) baking soda + 2 mL (½ tsp.) cream of tartar	+ 15 mL (1 Tbsp.) hot water		
Cup F: 5 mL (1 tsp.) double-acting baking powder	+ 15 mL (1 Tbsp.) cold water		
Cup G: 5 mL (1 tsp.) double-acting baking powder	+ 15 mL (1 Tbsp.) hot water		

410

(Continued on next page)

CONCLUSIONS

1. Which mixture(s) produced little or no reaction? _____

_____

2. Which produced the most immediate and powerful reaction? _____

_____

3. Which mixture(s) were slowest in starting to react? _____

_____

4. Which reaction lasted the shortest time? _____

_____

5. Which reaction lasted the longest time? _____

_____

6. Did you observe any vapor during the reactions? How would you explain the presence of vapor? _____

_____

_____

7. What conclusions do you draw from this experiment? _____

_____

_____

8. Of what practical use is this information? _____

_____

_____

FINISHING UP

- The mixtures are not usable and should be discarded after the experiment.

Name _____ Class _____ Date _____

Experiment 13

How Shortened Cakes Rise

To help you to . . .
- observe how different amounts and types of chemical leavening agents affect shortened cakes.

See also . . .
- *Food for Today* pp. 426-427, "Chemical Leavenings" (Ch. 28)

Look for these terms . . .
- *chemical leavening agent:* a substance that uses a chemical reaction between acid and base ingredients to produce carbon dioxide gas, making baked products rise.
- *double-acting baking powder:* a chemical leavening agent that produces carbon dioxide when liquid is added and again when heat is applied.

BACKGROUND INFORMATION

Two commonly used *chemical leavening agents* are baking soda and baking powder. Baking soda must be used with an acid ingredient, such as sour milk. The soda is a base and combines with the acid in the milk to form carbon dioxide. Carbon dioxide expands when it is heated, causing baked products to rise.

When an acidic liquid is added to a batter containing baking soda, the soda and acid react immediately. Therefore the batter should be placed in the oven as soon as possible. Otherwise, the carbon dioxide escapes before the baking process starts and the product does not rise properly.

Baking powder is a combination of a dry base and a dry acid. When liquid is added, the base and acid react, giving off carbon dioxide. *Double-acting baking powder* reacts a second time in the heat of the oven.

In this experiment, your class will prepare three variations of a simple cupcake recipe. One version uses 5 mL (1 tsp.) baking powder, another uses 15 mL (3 tsp.) baking powder, and the third uses baking soda and cream of tartar (a dry acid). You will observe how each of these variations affects the appearance, texture, and flavor of the finished product.

SUPPLIES

- _____ 250 mL (1 cup) cake flour
- _____ 125 mL (½ cup) granulated sugar
- _____ 1 egg
- _____ 50 mL (¼ cup) butter or margarine
- _____ 50 mL (¼ cup) milk
- _____ 5 mL (1 tsp.) vanilla
- _____ ONE of the following as directed by your teacher:
  - _____ 5 mL (1 tsp.) double-acting baking powder
  - _____ 15 mL (3 tsp.) double-acting baking powder
  - _____ 1 mL (¼ tsp.) baking soda and 2 mL (½ tsp.) cream of tartar
- _____ muffin tin for 4 cupcakes
- _____ 4 muffin tin liners of the same color (but of a different color than the other groups are using)

- _____ 2 mixing bowls
- _____ wooden spoon
- _____ rubber scraper
- _____ liquid measuring cup
- _____ sifter
- _____ dry measuring cups
- _____ measuring spoons
- _____ spatula
- _____ large spoon
- _____ cooling rack
- _____ 2 small paper plates
- _____ 2 self-sticking labels
- _____ pen, pencil, or marker
- _____ sharp knife
- _____ cutting board
- _____ ruler

PROCEDURE

- _____ 1. Preheat oven to 180°C (350°F).
- _____ 2. Line muffin tin with the paper liners. (If you do not have colored liners, use a nontoxic marker to mark plain muffin liners).
- _____ 3. In a mixing bowl, sift together flour, sugar, and ONE of the following as instructed

by your teacher:
- _____ **A:** 5 mL (1 tsp.) double-acting baking powder.
- _____ **B:** 15 mL (3 tsp.) double-acting baking powder.
- _____ **C:** 1 mL (¼ tsp.) baking soda and 2 mL (½ tsp.) cream of tartar.

_____ 4. Set dry mixture aside.

_____ 5. Use the wooden spoon to cream butter or margarine in the second bowl.

_____ 6. Beat the egg, milk, and vanilla into the creamed butter.

_____ 7. Add liquid ingredients to dry ingredients all at once.

_____ 8. Beat with a wooden spoon only until the batter is smooth.

_____ 9. Spoon batter into the four paper liners in the muffin tin. Fill the liners no more than ⅔ full. If you have more batter, use extra liners and make more cupcakes.

_____ 10. Write the name of the liner color in the appropriate blank on the Observation Chart. Write the liner colors used by the other groups in the appropriate spaces. Circle the letter of the variation you prepared.

_____ 11. Bake in the preheated oven at 180°C (350°F) for 15 minutes.

_____ 12. Mark the two labels according to the variation you made: "A — 5 mL (1 tsp.) Baking Powder"; "B — 15 mL (3 tsp.) Baking Powder"; or "C — Baking Soda/Cream of Tartar."

_____ 13. Fasten the labels to the paper plates, as close to the edge as possible.

_____ 14. When the cupcakes are done, remove them from the oven.

_____ 15. Remove cupcakes from pan and cool on cooling rack.

_____ 16. Place one whole uncut cupcake on the first paper plate. Using a sharp knife and a cutting board, cut another cupcake in half. Place halves on the paper plate with the whole cupcake.

_____ 17. Cut remaining two cupcakes in small pieces for class members to sample. Place these pieces on the second paper plate.

_____ 18. Place paper plates so class members can observe and sample your cupcakes.

OBSERVATIONS

_____ 1. With a ruler, measure the height of a cupcake in each sample. Record your observations in both metric and standard measure in the appropriate blanks on the Observation Chart.

_____ 2. Observe the outside texture and color of a cupcake in each sample. Record your observations in the appropriate blanks on the Observation Chart.

_____ 3. Examine the texture and color of the inside of the cut cupcakes. Record your observations in the appropriate blanks on the Observation Chart.

_____ 4. Taste each of the three samples, noting texture and flavor. Record your observations in the appropriate blanks on the Observation Chart.

	Observation Chart		
Characteristics	**A** **5 mL (1 tsp.)** **Baking Powder**	**B** **15 mL (3 tsp.)** **Baking Powder**	**C** **Baking Soda/** **Cream of Tartar**
Color of liner			
Height	cm in.	cm in.	cm in.
Outside: Color			
Texture			
Inside: Color			
Texture			
Flavor			

(Continued on next page)

CONCLUSIONS

1. Based on your observations, which leavening agent produced the best quality cupcake? Explain.

_____

_____

2. Which cupcakes did not rise properly? Explain. _____

_____

_____

3. If you were making a bread or cake recipe using buttermilk, what kind of leavening would you use? Why?

_____

_____

4. Based on your observations, what conclusion do you reach about measuring ingredients? _____

_____

_____

5. Did you notice any difference in the cupcakes made with baking powder and those made with baking soda?
Explain. _____

_____

_____

FINISHING UP

- Cupcakes may be eaten as snacks.

- Slice cupcakes and use as a base for desserts such as shortcake.

Name _____   Class _____   Date _____

Experiment 14

Effects of Sugar and Salt on Yeast Growth

To help you to . . .

- test the effects of sugar and salt on the leavening action of yeast.

Look for this term . . .

- *yeast:* a microscopic, nongreen plant that can produce carbon dioxide gas, making baked goods rise.

See also . . .

- *Food for Today* p. 427, "Yeast" (Ch. 28)
- *Food for Today* pp. 441-449, "Making Yeast Bread" (Ch. 29)

BACKGROUND INFORMATION

Yeast is a microscopic plant. It grows and reproduces rapidly if it has moisture, warmth, and the proper amount of food such as sugar and flour. As it grows, it gives off carbon dioxide, which forms bubbles and makes dough rise. Yeast also gives baked products a distinct flavor and aroma.

In this experiment, you will prepare a standard mixture of yeast, water, flour, and sugar in three custard cups. Cup A is the control mixture. One extra ingredient will be added to each of the other two cups. You will observe the effect of the added ingredient on the growth of the yeast.

SUPPLIES

- _____ 3 pkgs. active dry yeast
- _____ 90 mL (6 Tbsp.) tap water at room temperature
- _____ 45 mL (3 Tbsp.) all-purpose flour
- _____ 33 mL (2 Tbsp. + ¾ tsp.) granulated sugar
- _____ 5 mL (1 tsp.) salt
- _____ three 175-mL (6-oz.) glass custard cups

- _____ measuring spoons
- _____ 3 spoons
- _____ clock with second hand (or stopwatch)
- _____ timer (or use clock)
- _____ 3 self-sticking labels
- _____ waterproof marker

PROCEDURE

- _____ 1. Mark the self-sticking labels as follows: "A — Control"; "B — Sugar"; "C — Salt."
- _____ 2. Fasten one label to the side of each custard cup.
- _____ 3. Measure the following ingredients into each of the three custard cups:
  - _____ 1 pkg. active dry yeast
  - _____ 15 mL (1 Tbsp.) all-purpose flour
  - _____ 1 mL (¼ tsp.) granulated sugar
- _____ 4. Add 30 mL (2 Tbsp.) water to "A — Control." Stir the mixture in with a spoon and place the spoon next to the cup.
- _____ 5. Check the time, including seconds, and record it on the Observation Chart as "Start Time" for "A — Control."

- _____ 6. Add 30 mL (2 Tbsp.) granulated sugar and 30 mL (2 Tbsp.) water to "B — Sugar." Stir with a clean spoon to combine and place the spoon next to the cup.
- _____ 7. Check the time, including seconds. Write down the "Start Time" for "B — Sugar" on the Observation Chart.
- _____ 8. Add 5 mL (1 tsp.) salt and 30 mL (2 Tbsp.) water to "C — Salt." Stir with a clean spoon to combine. Place the spoon next to the cup.
- _____ 9. Check the time, including seconds. Write down the "Start Time" for "C — Salt" on the Observation Chart.

OBSERVATIONS

_____ 1. Note the time, including seconds, at which each mixture first forms a carbon dioxide bubble. Record the time on the Observation Chart in "Time of First Bubble."

_____ 2. Subtract the "Start Time" from the "Time of the First Bubble" to determine how long it took for the first bubble to form. Record the time in "Elapsed Time."

_____ 3. Set timer for 20 minutes (or use clock).

_____ 4. After 20 minutes, observe the appearance of the mixture in each cup. Write a description of each in the appropriate blanks on the Observation Chart.

Observation Chart			
Observations	A Control	B Sugar	C Salt
Start time			
Time of first bubble			
Elapsed Time			
Description at 20 minutes			

(Continued on next page)

CONCLUSIONS

1. Which mixture produced gas most rapidly? _____

_____

2. Which mixture produced gas least rapidly? _____

_____

3. What conclusions can you draw from the differences in appearance of the three mixtures after 20 minutes?

_____

_____

4. What conclusions can you draw about the effects of sugar and salt on the leavening action of yeast in dough?

_____

_____

_____

5. Of what practical use is this information? _____

_____

_____

6. List at least two other ways you can vary this experiment to find out more about yeast. _____

_____

_____

_____

FINISHING UP

- Use the yeast to make bread. Since the yeast in "C — Salt," contains salt, reduce the salt in the recipe by 5 mL (1 tsp.).

Name _____ Class _____ Date _____

Experiment 15
Gluten Development in Yeast Bread

To help you to . . .
- determine the effect of kneading on the development of gluten in yeast dough.

Look for this term . . .
- *gluten* (GLOO–ten): the protein complex formed when wheat flour is mixed with liquid; gives shape and structure to baked goods.

See also . . .
- *Food for Today* p. 439, "Kneading the Dough" (Ch. 29)
- *Food for Today* p. 445, "Kneading Yeast Dough" (Ch. 29)

BACKGROUND INFORMATION

Gluten is made up of the proteins in flour. As dough is kneaded, gluten develops, and the dough becomes smooth and elastic. Because it is elastic, the dough can expand easily, giving bread a coarser texture than baked products that are not kneaded, such as cakes.

In this experiment you will make two loaves of bread, kneading each one for a different amount of time. The dough will be prepared one day and baked the next.

SUPPLIES

_____ $2^7/8$ to $3^1/8$ cup all-purpose flour
_____ 5 mL (1 tsp.) active dry yeast
_____ 275 mL ($1^1/8$ cup) warm water — 43°C (110°F).
_____ 5 mL (1 tsp.) salt
_____ 15 mL (1 Tbsp.) sugar
_____ 8 mL ($^1/2$ Tbsp.) + 5 mL (1 tsp.) shortening
_____ large mixing bowl
_____ measuring spoons
_____ wooden spoon
_____ rubber scraper
_____ sharp knife

_____ dry measuring cup
_____ 2 small loaf pans, 7.5 × 17 × 5 cm (3" × $6^3/4$" × 2")
_____ strip of baking parchment or aluminum foil, 3 cm × 15 cm (1" × 6")
_____ plastic wrap
_____ 2 cooling racks
_____ spatula
_____ 2 self-sticking labels
_____ pencil or marker
_____ ruler

PROCEDURE

_____ 1. Use 5 mL (1 tsp.) shortening to grease the two loaf pans. Place the parchment or foil strip in one pan so that it extends over the edge of the pan.
_____ 2. Soften yeast in the warm water in a large mixing bowl.
_____ 3. Add 8 mL ($^1/2$ Tbsp.) shortening and sugar.
_____ 4. Stir to dissolve.
_____ 5. Add salt and one-half of flour.
_____ 6. Mix.
_____ 7. Continue adding flour to form a soft dough.
_____ 8. Turn out on a lightly floured surface and knead for 15 seconds.
_____ 9. Divide dough in half.
_____ 10. Place half of dough in the greased loaf pan with the parchment or foil strip. This will identify it as "A — 15 Sec."

_____ 11. Knead remaining dough 8-10 minutes or until smooth and elastic.
_____ 12. Place dough in second greased pan. This loaf will be "B — 10 Min."
_____ 13. Let both loaves rise until double, approximately 1 to $1^1/2$ hours.
_____ 14. After rising is completed, cover both loaf pans with a greased piece of plastic wrap.
_____ 15. Refrigerate.
_____ 16. The following day, preheat the oven to 180°C (350°F).
_____ 17. Bake both loaves for 20 minutes at 180°C (350°F).
_____ 18. Mark two labels as follows: "A — 15 Sec." and "B — 10 Min."
_____ 19. Attach one label to each cooling rack, near the edge.

_____ 20. When bread is done, remove the pans from the oven.

_____ 21. Remove the loaf from the pan with the parchment or foil strip and place on cooling rack labeled "A — 15 Sec."

_____ 22. Remove the loaf from the other pan and place on cooling rack labeled "B — 10 Min."

_____ 23. Let loaves cool.

OBSERVATIONS

_____ 1. Cut loaves in half.

_____ 2. With a ruler, measure the height of each loaf where it was cut. Record the height in both metric and standard measures in the proper blanks on the Observation Chart.

_____ 3. Observe the appearance of each loaf, both outside and inside. Record your observations in the proper blanks on the Observation Chart.

_____ 4. Cut a slice from each loaf. Keep each slice on the cooling rack so you do not mix them up.

_____ 5. Tear each slice apart and note the texture of the crust and interior. Record your observations in the proper blanks on the Observation Chart.

_____ 6. Put a small portion of the crust from sample "A" in your mouth and chew it. Do the same with sample "B." Note the texture. Record your observations in the proper blanks on the Observation Chart.

_____ 7. Put a small portion of the bread without crust from sample "A" in your mouth and chew it. Do the same with sample "B." Record your observations in the proper blanks on the Observation Chart.

_____ 8. Taste a small portion of sample "A" for flavor. Do the same with sample "B." Record your observations in the proper blanks on the Observation Chart.

Observation Chart		
Characteristics	**A** **15 Seconds** **(With Parchment/Foil)**	**B** **10 Minutes**
Height	cm in.	cm in.
Appearance: Outside		
Inside		
Texture: Crust		
Inside		
Flavor		

(Continued on next page)

E–15 (continued)

CONCLUSIONS

1. Which crust has the preferable appearance? _____

_____

2. Describe the differences in the two loaves, both inside and outside. _____

_____

_____

3. Which loaf was easier to chew? What do you think is the reason for the difference? ____

_____

_____

4. Which loaf had a better flavor? _____

_____

5. In general, which loaf did you prefer? Why? _____

_____

6. Of what practical use is the information you gained in this experiment?. _____

_____

_____

FINISHING UP

- Store the bread and use whenever needed.

- Make bread crumbs: slice bread and let dry at room temperature. Use blender to make crumbs. Store in a tightly covered container and use as needed.

Experiment 16
Moisture Absorption by Cookies

To help you to . . .
- observe the effect of two different sweeteners and two different storage methods on moisture absorption by cookies.

See also . . .
- *Food for Today* p. 429, "Sweeteners" (Ch. 28)
- *Food for Today* p. 456, "Storing Cookies" (Ch. 30)
- *Food for Today* p. 39, "Types of Sugar" chart (Ch. 4)

Look for these terms . . .
- *hygroscopicity* (HIGH–gruh–skop–IH–suh–tee): the ability of a substance to take up and retain moisture.
- *invert sugar:* a mixture of fructose and glucose (two types of sugar).

BACKGROUND INFORMATION

Hygroscopicity is the ability to take up and retain moisture. Air contains water vapor, which changes form and reacts with other chemicals.

Granulated sugar, also known as sucrose, attracts water. *Invert sugar,* which is a combination of fructose and glucose, attracts and retains more water than granulated sugar does. In other words, it has greater hygroscopicity.

Honey contains invert sugars. Because it is a liquid, honey tends to make baked products moist. It also absorbs and holds more moisture from the air than granulated sugar does. This can affect the characteristics of the product during storage.

In this experiment, you will prepare two versions of a simple sugar cookie. One is made with granulated sugar and the other with honey. Each version will be placed on one half of a cookie sheet so that both versions bake under the same conditions. If you have any dough left after filling half of the cookie sheet, use another cookie sheet.

Samples will be stored in different ways. You will observe the samples after baking, the next day, and several days later to determine the effects of the sweetener and storage method.

SUPPLIES

- _____ 150 mL (⅔ cup) + 5-10 mL (1-2 tsp.) shortening
- _____ 90 mL (6 Tbsp.) granulated sugar
- _____ 45 mL (3 Tbsp.) honey
- _____ 6 mL (1 tsp.) vanilla
- _____ 1 egg, beaten and divided in half
- _____ 20 mL (4 tsp.) milk
- _____ 375 mL (1½ cup) all-purpose flour
- _____ 8 mL (1½ tsp.) baking powder
- _____ electric mixer and bowl
- _____ dry measuring cups
- _____ measuring spoons
- _____ spatula
- _____ rubber scraper
- _____ teaspoon (flatware)
- _____ sifter
- _____ large cookie sheet
- _____ 1 narrow strip of baking parchment or aluminum foil, 1 cm × 8 cm (½" × 3")
- _____ 2 cooling racks
- _____ small bowl
- _____ custard cup
- _____ wire whisk or fork
- _____ 2 storage containers with lids
- _____ 4 small paper plates
- _____ 8 self-sticking labels
- _____ pen or nontoxic marker

PROCEDURE

_____ 1. Mark the labels as follows: four with "A — Sugar" and four with "B — Honey."

_____ 2. Stick the four labels marked "A — Sugar" to the side of one storage container, to the edge of one cooling rack, and to two paper plates close to the rim.

_____ 3. Repeat the process with the four labels marked "B — Honey," using the remaining storage container, cooling rack, and paper plates.

_____ 4. Preheat oven to 190°C (375°F).

_____ 5. Grease cookie sheet with 5-10 mL (1-2 tsp.) shortening. With your finger, make a line in the shortening, dividing the cookie sheet in half.

_____ 6. Sift 175 mL (¾ cup) flour and 4 mL (¾ tsp.) baking powder together in small bowl. Set aside.

_____ 7. With the electric mixer, cream 75 mL (⅓ cup) shortening, sugar, and 3 mL (½ tsp.) vanilla in bowl.

_____ 8. Add ½ beaten egg and 10 mL (2 tsp.) milk and beat well.

_____ 9. Add dry ingredients and blend well.

_____ 10. Observe the color of the batter. Record your observation in the proper blank on the Observation Chart.

_____ 11. Drop by teaspoonfuls onto one half of the greased cookie sheet. Under one of the cookies place the strip of baking parchment or aluminum foil, which will mark the cookies on that half as "A — Sugar." If any cookie dough is left over, use another greased cookie sheet.

_____ 12. Wash equipment carefully. (You will use it again to prepare the second batch of cookies.)

_____ 13. Sift 75 mL (¾ cup) flour and 4 mL (¾ tsp.) baking powder together. Set aside.

_____ 14. Cream 75 mL (⅓ cup) shortening, honey, and 3 mL (½ tsp.) vanilla in a bowl.

_____ 15. Add ½ beaten egg and 10 mL (2 tsp.) milk and beat well.

_____ 16. Add dry ingredients and blend well.

_____ 17. Observe the color of the batter. Record your observations in the proper blank on the Observation Chart.

_____ 18. Drop by teaspoonfuls onto the remaining half of the cookie sheet.

_____ 19. Bake at 190°C (375°F) for 8-10 minutes or until nicely browned.

_____ 20. Remove cookies from the half of the cookie sheet with the strip of parchment or foil and place on the cooling rack labeled "A — Sugar."

_____ 21. Remove cookies from the other half of the cookie sheet and place on the cooling rack labeled "B — Honey."

_____ 22. When the cookies are cool, remove three cookies from the cooling rack labeled "A" and put them on one paper plate labeled "A — Sugar."

_____ 23. Remove three cookies from the cooling rack labeled "B" and put them on one paper plate labeled "B — Honey."

_____ 24. Place the remaining cookies from the cooling rack labeled "A" in the storage container labeled "A — Sugar."

_____ 25. Place the remaining cookies from the cooling rack labeled "B" in the storage container labeled "B — Honey."

_____ 26. Cover the two storage containers with tight-fitting lids.

OBSERVATIONS

_____ 1. Examine the outside appearance of the cookies on each paper plate. Record your observations in the appropriate blanks on the Observation Chart.

_____ 2. Break one cookie from each plate in half and observe crispness and inside appearance. Record your observations in the proper blanks on the Observation Chart.

_____ 3. Taste each of the broken cookies for flavor and crispness. Record your observations in the proper blanks on the Observation Chart.

_____ 4. Leave the remaining two cookies on the paper plates overnight. They should be exposed to the air at room temperature. (Keep the other cookies in the storage container.)

_____ 5. The next day, remove one cookie from each of the storage containers. Place each cookie on the appropriate empty paper plate.

_____ 6. Observe the crispness of the cookies you just removed by breaking and tasting. Record your observations in the appropriate blanks on the Observation Chart. Make sure you use the columns marked "Container."

_____ 7. Save the paper plates for another test in 3-4 days.

_____ 8. Observe the crispness of one of the cookies stored on each of the paper plates by breaking and tasting. Record your observations in the appropriate blanks on the Observation Chart. Make sure you use the columns marked, "Air."

(Continued on next page)

_____ 9. Store the cookies for an additional 3-4 days.

_____ 10. Remove a cookie from each of the storage containers and place on the appropriate empty paper plate.

_____ 11. Observe the crispness of the cookies you just removed by breaking and tasting. Record your observations in the appropriate blanks on the Observation Chart, in the columns marked "Container."

_____ 12. Observe the crispness of the remaining cookies stored on each of the paper plates. Record your observations in the appropriate blanks on the Observation Chart in the columns marked, "Air."

Observation Chart				
Characteristics	**A** **Sugar Cookies** **(Foil or Parchment)**		**B** **Honey Cookies**	
Color of batter				
Right after baking, when cool: Appearance Outside				
Appearance Inside				
Crispness				
Flavor				
Crispness after storage:	**Container**	**Air**	**Container**	**Air**
Next day				
3-4 days later				

(Continued on next page)

CONCLUSIONS

1. Which cookie was crisper right after baking, sugar or honey? Why? _____
_____
_____

2. Which cookie is sweeter, sugar or honey? Why? _____
_____
_____

3. In general, how did the cookies left in the open air for 3-4 days compare to the ones stored in the containers for the same length of time? What caused the difference? _____
_____
_____

4. Which cookie, sugar or honey, was more affected by being left in the open air for 3-4 days? Why? _____
_____
_____

5. Of what practical use is the information you learned in this experiment? _____
_____
_____

FINISHING UP

- Cookies may be eaten as snacks.

Name _____ **Class** _____ **Date** _____

How Mixing Methods Affect a Shortened Cake

To help you to . . .
- observe how different mixing times and methods can affect a shortened cake.

See also . . .
- *Food for Today* p. 458, "Shortened Cakes" (Ch. 30)

Look for this term . . .
- *gluten* (GLOO–ten): protein complex formed when wheat flour is mixed with liquid; forms the structure of cake.

BACKGROUND INFORMATION

Cake batter needs to be beaten enough to properly develop *gluten*, which forms the structure of the cake. If the cake is not mixed enough, the structure will not be strong enough to hold up and the cake will not rise properly. However, if the batter is overmixed, gases escape during mixing. The batter also becomes too thick, so that remaining gas cells can't expand during baking. The cake is tough and compact.

In this experiment, your class will prepare three batches of cupcakes. Each batch will be mixed differently: one by hand, and the other two by mixer but for different times. Be sure you mix the batter for the exact time for your variation.

SUPPLIES

- _____ 250 mL (1 cup) all-purpose flour
- _____ 125 mL (½ cup) sugar
- _____ 1 egg
- _____ 50 mL (¼ cup) milk
- _____ 5 mL (1 tsp.) vanilla
- _____ 5 mL (1 tsp.) baking powder
- _____ 4 muffin pan liners of the same color (but of a different color than the other groups are using)
- _____ muffin tin for 4 cupcakes
- _____ 2 mixing bowls
- _____ electric mixer
- _____ wooden spoon
- _____ rubber scraper
- _____ liquid measuring cup
- _____ sifter
- _____ dry measuring cups
- _____ measuring spoons
- _____ spatula
- _____ large spoon
- _____ cooling rack
- _____ 2 small paper plates
- _____ 2 self-sticking labels
- _____ pen, pencil, or marker
- _____ sharp knife
- _____ cutting board

PROCEDURE

- _____ 1. Preheat oven to 180°C (350°F).
- _____ 2. Line muffin tin with the paper liners. If you do not have colored liners, use a nontoxic marker to mark plain muffin liners.
- _____ 3. Sift together flour, sugar, and baking powder into a mixing bowl.
- _____ 4. Set dry mixture aside.
- _____ 5. Use the wooden spoon to cream butter or margarine in the second bowl.
- _____ 6. Beat the egg, milk, and vanilla into the creamed butter.
- _____ 7. Add liquid ingredients to dry ingredients all at once.
- _____ 8. Do ONE of the following as instructed by your teacher:
- _____ **A:** Beat by hand only until the dry ingredients are barely moistened.
- _____ **B:** Beat with an electric mixer for 2 minutes.
- _____ **C:** Beat with an electric mixer for 5 minutes.
- _____ 9. Spoon batter into the four paper liners in the muffin tin.
- _____ 10. Write the liner color used by each group in the appropriate blanks on the Observation Chart. Circle the letter of the variation you prepared.
- _____ 11. Bake in preheated oven at 180°C (350°F) for 15 minutes.

E–17 (continued)

_____ 12. Mark the two labels according to the variation you made: "A — Hand-Mixed"; "B — 2 Minutes"; or "C — 5 Minutes."

_____ 13. Attach the labels to the rim of the paper plates near the edge.

_____ 14. When the cupcakes are done, remove them from the oven.

_____ 15. Remove the cupcakes from the pan and cool on cooling rack.

_____ 16. Place one whole uncut cupcake on the first paper plate. Using a sharp knife and a cutting board, cut another cupcake in half. Place halves on the paper plate with the whole cupcake.

_____ 17. Cut remaining two cupcakes in small pieces for class members to sample. Place these pieces on second paper plate.

_____ 18. Place paper plates so class members can observe and sample your cupcakes.

OBSERVATIONS

_____ 1. With a ruler, measure the height of a cupcake from each sample. Record the height in both metric and standard measures in the appropriate blanks on the Observation Chart.

_____ 2. Observe the outside texture and color of a cupcake in each sample. Record your observations in the appropriate blanks on the Observation Chart.

_____ 3. Examine the texture and color of the inside of the cut cupcakes. Record your observations in the appropriate blanks on the Observation Chart.

_____ 4. Taste each of the three samples. Record your observations in the appropriate blanks on the Observation Chart.

Observation Chart			
Characteristics	A Hand-Mixed	B 2 Minutes (mixer)	C 5 Minutes (mixer)
Color of liner			
Height	cm in.	cm in.	cm in.
Outside: Texture			
Color			
Inside: Texture			
Color			
Flavor			

(Continued on next page)

CONCLUSIONS

1. How did the texture vary among the three samples? _____

_____

_____

2. Based on the above observations, which mixing method produced the best quality cupcake? Why was that method more successful? _____

_____

_____

3. Which cupcakes did not rise sufficiently? What caused the problem? _____

_____

_____

4. Based on your observations, what conclusions do you reach regarding the mixing of shortened cakes?

_____

_____

5. Of what practical use is the information you gained from this experiment? _____

_____

_____

FINISHING UP

- The cupcakes may be eaten as snacks.

Name _____ Class _____ Date _____

Experiment 18

The Effects of Fats on Pastry

To help you to . . .

- test the effects of four different fats on pastry.

See also . . .

- *Food for Today* pp. 466-467, "Ingredients for the Crust" and "Preparing the Dough" (Ch. 31)
- *Food for Today* p. 428, "Fats and Oils" (Ch. 28)

Look for these terms . . .

- *gluten* (GLOO–ten): protein complex formed when wheat flour is mixed with liquid.
- *hydrogenated* (high–DRAH–jih–nay–ted): treated in a chemical process that adds hydrogen, turning oil into a solid fat.

BACKGROUND INFORMATION

Fats make pastry tender by shortening the strands of *gluten* in the dough. They also add color, flavor, and texture to baked goods. The type of fat used affects the characteristics of the finished product.

In this experiment, four pie crusts, each using a different fat, are made. One is made with leaf lard (fat from pigs). Another is made with butter. The third is made with vegetable shortening, which is oil that has been *hydrogenated* to make it solid. The final pie crust is made with vegetable oil. Each crust is shaped into wafers and baked on a cookie sheet. You will observe the wafers after baking to determine the effects of using each type of fat.

SUPPLIES

All ingredients should be at room temperature.

_____ 500 mL (2 cups) all-purpose flour
_____ 5 mL (1 tsp.) salt
_____ 40 mL (4 tsp.) tap water
_____ ONE of the following as directed by your teacher:
_____ 38 mL (2½ Tbsp.) leaf lard
_____ 38 mL (2½ Tbsp.) butter
_____ 38 mL (2½ Tbsp.) vegetable shortening (unflavored)
_____ 38 mL (2½ Tbsp.) vegetable oil
_____ cookie sheet
_____ mixing bowl

_____ pastry blender
_____ dry measuring cups
_____ measuring spoons
_____ spatula
_____ fork
_____ rolling pin
_____ pizza cutter
_____ waxed paper
_____ cooling rack
_____ self-sticking label
_____ pen or marker
_____ ruler

PROCEDURE

_____ 1. Mark your label in one of the following ways as assigned by your teacher: "A — Lard"; "B — Butter"; "C — Shortening"; or "D — Oil."

_____ 2. Attach the label to the cooling rack, near the edge of the rack.

_____ 3. Preheat oven to 220°C (425°F).

_____ 4. Put flour, salt, and the fat assigned by your teacher in mixing bowl.

_____ 5. With a pastry blender, cut fat into pea-sized particles.

_____ 6. Sprinkle water over blended ingredients.

_____ 7. Toss mixture with a fork until it begins to form a ball.

_____ 8. Shape into a ball with the hands. Do not knead. Work quickly so the heat from your hands doesn't begin to melt the solid fat.

_____ 9. Place ball of dough on a sheet of waxed paper.

_____ 10. Flatten the dough into a rectangular shape with your hands.

_____ 11. Place another sheet of waxed paper on top of the dough.

_____ 12. With the rolling pin, roll the dough into a rectangular shape between the waxed paper until 3 mm (¹/₈ in.) thick.

_____ 13. Peel off the upper waxed paper.

_____ 14. Pick up the dough with the sheet of waxed paper, turn it upside down, and place dough down on an ungreased cookie sheet.

_____ 15. Peel off the waxed paper.

_____ 16. With the pizza cutter, score into 5-cm (2-in.) squares. Do not separate the pastry as you cut.

_____ 17. Prick each wafer four times with a fork.

_____ 18. Bake in the preheated oven at 220°C (425°F) for about 8-10 minutes or until the edges are a light brown.

_____ 19. Use a spatula to remove wafers from cookie sheet to the cooling rack.

_____ 20. Place cooling rack where all students can observe and taste your product.

_____ 21. On the Observation Chart, circle the letter of the variation you prepared.

OBSERVATIONS

_____ 1. Stack 4 wafers from each group.

_____ 2. Measure each stack and record the height in metric and standard measures in the proper blanks on the Observation Chart.

_____ 3. Examine the appearance (including color) of one wafer from each group. Record your observations in the proper blanks on the Observation Chart.

_____ 4. Break one wafer from each group and note the texture. Record your observations in the proper blanks on the Observation Chart.

_____ 5. Taste a wafer from each group. Record your observations about flavor in the proper blanks on the Observation Chart.

Observation Chart				
Characteristics	A Lard	B Butter	C Shortening	D Oil
Height of 4 wafers	cm in.	cm in.	cm in.	cm in.
Appearance/Color				
Texture				
Flavor				

(Continued on next page)

CONCLUSIONS

1. List the samples in order of tenderness, beginning with the most tender. _____

_____

2. What conclusions do you draw about the effect of fat on tenderness? _____

_____

_____

3. List the samples in order of flakiness, beginning with the most flaky. _____

_____

4. What conclusions do you draw about the effect of fat on flakiness? _____

_____

_____

5. Which sample had the best flavor? _____

_____

6. Which stack of wafers was the tallest? The shortest? Why? _____

_____

_____

_____

7. What conclusions do you draw about using fat in pastry? _____

_____

_____

8. Of what practical use is the information you gained from this experiment? _____

_____

_____

FINISHING UP

- The pastry wafers can be eaten as snacks or served
  with salads and soups.

Name _____ Class _____ Date _____

Experiment 19
Creating a Smooth Sauce

To help you to . . .

- determine which preparation method is best for producing a smooth sauce when flour is used as a thickener.

See also . . .

- *Food for Today* pp. 484-485, "Making Sauces" (Ch. 32)

Look for this term . . .

- *gelatinization* (jih–LAY–tihn–uh–ZAY–shun): the process that occurs when starch granules absorb liquid and swell.

BACKGROUND INFORMATION

When starch granules such as flour are mixed with liquid and heated, they undergo *gelatinization*. The granules absorb liquid and swell. As heating continues, the starch mixture thickens into a paste. This process is the basis for many sauces.

One of the most important steps in this process is the mixing of starch and liquid before heating begins. In this experiment, you will prepare a simple sauce using three different mixing methods. You will then compare the samples to determine how the mixing method affected the finished products.

When making your observations, observe the texture of the sauce by spooning a small amount on a colored plate. The colored background will make it easier to see variations in thickness. Test texture by rubbing some of the sauce between your fingers. You can also observe texture by tasting the sauce and determining how it "feels" in your mouth.

SUPPLIES

_____ 750 mL (3 cups) cold tap water
_____ 135 mL (9 Tbsp.) all-purpose flour
_____ 45 mL (3 Tbsp.) butter or margarine
_____ 3 chicken bouillon cubes
_____ teakettle or saucepan
_____ small saucepan
_____ 250 mL (1 cup) liquid measure
_____ measuring spoons
_____ spatula

_____ fork or wire whisk
_____ 3 small bowls
_____ wooden spoon
_____ rubber scraper
_____ 6 small self-sticking labels
_____ pencil or nontoxic waterproof marker
_____ 6 spoons
_____ 3 small colored paper plates
_____ timer

PROCEDURE

_____ 1. Heat 250 mL (1 cup) cold tap water in a teakettle or saucepan.

_____ 2. Mark two labels "A — Flour + Cold Water." Mark another two labels "B — Flour + Hot Water" and the remaining two, "C — Melted Butter + Flour."

_____ 3. Arrange 3 small bowls in a row. Place a small colored paper plate in front of each bowl.

_____ 4. Stick one label "A" on the side of the first bowl and one on the rim of the paper plate in front of the bowl.

_____ 5. Label the second bowl and paper plate with the labels marked "B."

_____ 6. Label the third bowl and paper plate with the labels marked "C."

_____ 7. Measure 250 mL (1 cup) cold water and pour into a small saucepan.

_____ 8. Measure 45 mL (3 Tbsp.) all-purpose flour and add to the water in the saucepan.

_____ 9. Use a fork or wire whisk to completely mix the flour and the cold water.

_____ 10. Add 15 mL (1 Tbsp.) butter or margarine and 1 chicken bouillon cube to the mixture.

_____ 11. Heat the mixture on low heat, stirring gently with whisk or wooden spoon until bubbly.

_____ 12. Allow to bubble for one minute while stirring constantly.

_____ 13. Remove from the heat and pour the sauce into the small bowl labeled "A — Flour + Cold Water."

_____ 14. Recall how easily and quickly the sauce mixed, from the time you combined the first two ingredients to the finished product. Record your observations in the proper blank on the Observation Chart.

_____ 15. Wash all equipment carefully.

_____ 16. Measure 250 mL (1 cup) very hot water from the teakettle and pour into the clean saucepan.

_____ 17. Measure 45 mL (3 Tbsp.) all-purpose flour and add to the hot water in the saucepan.

_____ 18. Use a fork or wire whisk to completely mix the flour and the hot water.

_____ 19. Add 15 mL (1 Tbsp.) butter or margarine and 1 chicken bouillon cube to the mixture.

_____ 20. Heat the mixture on low heat, stirring gently with a whisk or wooden spoon until bubbly.

_____ 21. Allow to bubble for one minute while stirring constantly.

_____ 22. Remove from the heat and pour the sauce into the small bowl labeled "B — Flour + Hot Water."

_____ 23. Recall how easily and quickly the sauce mixed. Record your observations in the proper blank on the Observation Chart.

_____ 24. Wash all equipment carefully.

_____ 25. Measure 15 mL (1 Tbsp.) butter or margarine and place into the clean saucepan.

_____ 26. Melt butter or margarine, using low heat.

_____ 27. Add 45 mL (3 Tbsp.) all-purpose flour to the melted butter. Mix thoroughly, using a wooden spoon or wire whisk.

_____ 28. Add 250 mL (1 cup) cold tap water and 1 bouillon cube to the butter-flour mixture.

_____ 29. Heat slowly over low heat, stirring with a wooden spoon or wire whisk, until mixture bubbles.

_____ 30. Continue to stir and cook for 1 minute.

_____ 31. Remove from heat.

_____ 32. Pour sauce into the small bowl labeled "C — Melted Butter + Flour."

_____ 33. Recall how easily and quickly the sauce mixed. Record your observations in the proper blank on the Observation Chart.

OBSERVATIONS

_____ 1. Spoon a little sauce from bowl "A" onto the paper plate marked "A." Place the spoon on the paper plate beside the sample.

_____ 2. Examine the texture, feeling it with your fingers if necessary. Put a small amount on your tongue to "feel" the texture in your mouth. Record your observations in the appropriate blank in column "A" on the Observation Chart.

_____ 3. Using a clean spoon, transfer a little sauce from bowl "B" onto the paper plate marked "B." Place the spoon on the paper plate beside the sample.

_____ 4. Examine the texture as you did with sample A. Record your observations in the appropriate blank in column "B" on the Observation Chart.

_____ 5. Using a clean spoon, transfer a little sauce from bowl "C" onto the paper plate marked "C." Place the spoon on the paper plate beside the sample.

_____ 6. Examine the texture as you did with the two previous samples. Record your observations in the appropriate blank in column "C" on the Observation Chart.

_____ 7. Using a clean spoon, taste a small amount of sauce from bowl "A." Record your observations in the appropriate blank in column "A" on the Observation Chart.

_____ 8. Using a clean spoon, taste a small amount of sauce from bowl "B." Record your observations in the proper blank in column "B" on the Observation Chart.

_____ 9. Using a clean spoon, taste a small amount of sauce from bowl "C." Record your observations in column "C" on the Observation Chart.

Characteristics	A Flour + Cold Water	B Flour + Hot Water	C Melted Butter + Flour
Observation Chart			
Ease of mixing			
Texture			
Flavor			

CONCLUSIONS

1. Which sauce mixed most easily? Why? _____
_____
_____

2. Which sauce was most difficult to mix? Why? _____
_____
_____

3. Which sauce did you prefer for texture? Why? _____
_____

4. What differences did you note in the flavor of the three sauces? _____
_____

5. If you were handed a list of ingredients for preparing a similar sauce but no mixing directions, which method would you use? Why? _____
_____

6. Of what practical use is the information you learned in this experiment? _____
_____

FINISHING UP

- Discard the paper plates. Use the sauces left in the bowls to prepare creamed vegetables, cream soup, or a casserole.

- If any sauce is unpleasantly lumpy, put it through a strainer before using it.

Name _____ Class _____ Date _____

Experiment 20
Heat and Protein Coagulation

To help you to . . .
- test the effect of cooking time on the coagulation of protein.

See also . . .
- *Food for Today* pp. 486-487, "Eggs" and "Custards" (Ch. 32)

Look for these terms . . .
- *coagulation* (koh–ag–you–LAY–shun): a process in which a liquid changes into a semi-solid or solid mass.
- *denaturation* (dee–nay–chur–AY–shun): a change in the shape of protein molecules, resulting in a change in the product.

BACKGROUND INFORMATION

Coagulation is the process by which liquid protein changes into a semi-solid or solid. The process begins when protein molecules undergo *denaturation* or a change in their shape. The molecules unfold, collide with other protein molecules, and then clump together to form a solid. Adding heat is one way to coagulate protein.

In this experiment, you will prepare a simple baked custard. The custard is baked in four custard cups which are placed in a pan of hot water. The hot water protects the custard from the oven heat and makes it easier for you to control the coagulation process. You will not overcook the custard as easily.

At specific intervals, you will remove a custard sample from the oven. You will observe the effect of baking custards for different lengths of time.

SUPPLIES

_____ 1 egg, well beaten
_____ 150 mL (⅔ cup) milk
_____ 25 mL (5 tsp.) sugar
_____ 1 mL (¼ tsp.) vanilla
_____ water
_____ 4 custard cups
_____ 25 cm (9 in.) square pan
_____ mixing bowl
_____ fork or wire whisk
_____ liquid measuring cup

_____ measuring spoons
_____ spatula
_____ wooden spoon
_____ rubber scraper
_____ teakettle
_____ cooling rack
_____ 4 small paper plates
_____ 4 self-sticking labels
_____ pencil or marker
_____ 4 spoons

PROCEDURE

_____ 1. Heat water in teakettle but do not boil.
_____ 2. Preheat oven to 160°C (325°F).
_____ 3. Combine beaten egg, milk, sugar, and vanilla in bowl and mix well.
_____ 4. Divide mixture evenly into four custard cups.
_____ 5. Place custard cups in square baking pan. Be careful that cups do not touch each other or sides of the pan.
_____ 6. Using a pot holder, pull the oven rack out just enough so you can set the pan on it. Pour hot water into pan up to the level of the custard in the cups.
_____ 7. Gently push the oven rack back into the oven.

_____ 8. Bake the custard at 160°C (325°F).
_____ 9. Mark the four self-sticking labels as follows: "A — 20 Min."; "B — 35 Min."; "C — 40 Min."; and "D — 60 Min."
_____ 10. Place four small paper plates on a cooling rack.
_____ 11. Stick a label on the rim of each of the plates close to the edge.
_____ 12. Remove one custard cup from the oven at the end of the following baking times:
_____ 20 minutes
_____ 35 minutes
_____ 40 minutes
_____ 60 minutes
_____ 13. Place each custard cup on the proper paper plate on the cooling rack.

OBSERVATIONS

_____ 1. Observe the outside appearance of each sample in the cups. Record your observations in the appropriate blanks on the Observation Chart.

_____ 2. Spoon a little custard from each cup onto the plate on which the cups rests.

_____ 3. Examine the appearance and texture of the inside of the custard. Record your observations in the appropriate blanks on the Observation Chart.

_____ 4. Taste each of the samples, using a clean spoon for each. Record your observations in the appropriate blanks on the Observation Chart.

Observation Chart				
Characteristics	A 20 Minutes	B 35 Minutes	C 40 Minutes	D 60 Minutes
Appearance: Outside				
Inside				
Texture				
Flavor				

CONCLUSIONS

1. Which custard has the best appearance? Explain. _____
_____
_____

2. Which custard has the best texture? Explain. _____
_____
_____

3. Which has the best flavor? Explain. _____
_____
_____

4. Overall, which of the samples would you prefer? _____
_____
_____

5. Which of the samples would you prefer the least? Why? _____
_____
_____

6. Were any of the samples inedible? If so, what made them inedible? _____
_____
_____

7. Of what practical use is the information you learned in this experiment? _____
_____
_____
_____

FINISHING UP

- The custard may be eaten as a snack.

- If any of the samples have not cooked completely, put them back in the oven after you have made your observations and bake until done.

Name _____   Class _____   Date _____

Experiment 21
Taste-Testing Fruit Juice

To help you to . . .
- use the senses of smell, taste, and touch in a blind-fold rating of fruit juice.

Look for this term . . .
- *sensory characteristics* (SEN–sore–ee): qualities of food identified by the five human senses of seeing, hearing, smelling, feeling, and tasting.

See also . . .
- *Food for Today* p. 491, "Beverage Facts" (Ch. 33)
- *Food for Today* p. 290, "Buying and Storing Canned Fruit and Juices"

BACKGROUND INFORMATION

Food science experiments often require observation of *sensory characteristics* — how food looks, tastes, smells, feels, and even sounds. These qualities are difficult to evaluate because they are based on human judgment, which is individual and not always consistent.

Sensory evaluation methods are used by taste-testing panels, which are one of many testing methods common in the food industry. Several people make up the panel of judges. They can be blind-folded or not, depending on the type of evaluation desired.

As a rule, people tend to score the first portion they sample higher than others. To avoid this problem, judges have a "pre-tasting" session in which they taste a sample but do not give it a score.

In this experiment, you will be judging four different kinds of orange juice: frozen, fresh, canned, and powdered. Each cup will have 45 mL (3 Tbsp.) juice. During the experiment, you will work with a classmate. One of you will be the Judge, who taste-tests the fruit juice. The other will be the Assistant.

The Judge will be blindfolded, so the fruit juices will be evaluated by taste, aroma, and touch — the "feel" of the juice in the mouth. When taste-testing, do not drink all the juice in the cup. Just sip a small mouthful and swish it around in your mouth so you get the full flavor and "feel" of the juice before swallowing it. Smell the aroma of the juice in the cup. You will score the juice on the rating scale described on the Score Chart.

Rely on your first impressions. But if you cannot make up your mind, take another sip. Once you have completed testing one sample and have started another one, you will not be allowed to re-taste a previous one.

The Assistant serves the juice to the Judge and should be careful to place the cup firmly in the Judge's hand. Remember, the Judge is blindfolded and cannot see where the cup is. When the Judge has given a score, the Assistant will mark it on the Judge's Score Chart. The Assistant should be careful to mark the score in the proper blank. The Assistant will then remove the cup from the Judge's hand and place it on another tray. Between each sample, the Assistant should hand the Judge a glass of water to clear the tastebuds. After the Judge has sipped water, the Assistant will hand the Judge the next cup.

The taste test will be repeated three times, with the order of the samples changed each time. Repeating the taste test makes it easier to reach consistent, valid conclusions. The Assistant should keep a list of the order in which the samples are served to make sure that all three taste tests are conducted in a different order.

Samples of juice should be the same temperature — chilled but no ice. They should all be served in the same kind of drinking container.

SUPPLIES

_____ blindfold
_____ 13 3-oz. paper cups
_____ 2 trays
_____ markers
_____ pen
_____ 175 mL (¾ cup) frozen orange juice, reconstituted
_____ 175 mL (¾ cup) fresh orange juice

_____ 175 mL (¾ cup) canned orange juice
_____ 175 mL (¾ cup) powdered orange juice, mixed according to package directions
_____ glass of water
_____ pencil or nontoxic waterproof marker
_____ 4 self-sticking labels
_____ paper towels

PROCEDURE

_____ 1. Mark the four labels as follows: "A — Fresh"; "B — Frozen"; "C — Canned"; and "D — Powdered." Attach each label to side of the appropriate juice container.

_____ 2. Use the pen to mark the sides of each set of 3 paper cups as follows: "A — Fresh"; "B — Frozen"; "C — Canned"; "D — Powdered." You should have four groups of cups, three with the same label in each group.

_____ 3. Arrange the juice containers and cups on a tray in groups, beginning with "A" and ending with "D."

_____ 4. Mark the remaining cup "X" and place on the tray. That cup will be used for the pre-judging sample.

_____ 5. Fill each cup half full with the juice from the container labeled the same as the cup. Use any juice for cup "X."

_____ 6. Place a glass of water on the tray and an empty tray next to the one holding the samples.

_____ 7. The Judge should sit across the table from the Assistant.

_____ 8. The Assistant should have the Judge's Score Chart, a pen, and a supply of paper towels to wipe up spills.

_____ 9. The Assistant should also have a sheet of paper to keep track of the order in which the beverages are served. Each time the experiment is repeated, the order of the beverages should be changed.

_____ 10. Blindfold the Judge.

OBSERVATIONS

_____ 1. Give cup "X" to the Judge. Then give the Judge the glass of water.

_____ 2. Trial 1: Assistant place a sample in the Judge's hand.

_____ 3. Judge smells and tastes the juice and gives it a rating from 1 (poor) to 4 (excellent).

_____ 4. Assistant writes down Judge's rating in proper blank on Score Chart.

_____ 5. Assistant removes cup from Judge's hand and places it on empty tray.

_____ 6. Assistant places glass of water in Judge's hand and removes it when Judge has taken a sip.

_____ 7. Assistant places second cup in Judge's hand, noting on list the order in which the juices are tasted.

_____ 8. Judge smells and tastes the juice from the second cup and gives it a rating from (1) poor to 4 (excellent).

_____ 9. Assistant writes down Judge's rating in proper blank on Score Chart and removes cup from Judge's hand.

_____ 10. The process is repeated with the two remaining samples, completing Trial 1. Assistant should remember to give Judge a sip of water after each sample.

_____ 11. For Trial 2, the process is repeated. However, the order in which the juices are served is changed by the Assistant.

_____ 12. The process is repeated once more for Trial 3, with the order in which the juices are served changed again.

_____ 13. When the three trials are completed, there should be a number in each blank on the Score Chart.

Score Chart				
Judge's name: _____	A Fresh	B Frozen	C Canned	D Powdered
Trial 1				
Trial 2				
Trial 3				
Totals				

Rating scale: 4 = Excellent: "I love it."
3 = Good: "I like it."
2 = Fair: "It's OK but I wouldn't buy it."
1 = Poor: "I don't like it."

CONCLUSIONS

1. Add the numbers in each column. Which juice was the "favorite" (i.e., had the highest number)? _____

_____

2. Which juice was the least "favorite" (i.e., had the lowest score)? _____

_____

3. How did the results of the test compare with the way you normally feel about the four products tested?

_____

_____

_____

4. Were you surprised at the results? Why? _____

_____

_____

5. How do you think using the blindfold affected the outcome of the test? _____

_____

_____

FINISHING UP

▪ Any remaining juice can be used for a snack.

Name _____ **Class** _____ **Date** _____

The Role of Pectin in Jelly

To help you to . . .
- determine the effect of pectin and sugar when making jelly.

See also . . .
- *Food for Today* pp. 508-509, "What Happens When You Make Jelly" and "Jams and Jellies" (Ch. 34)

Look for these terms . . .
- *gel:* a semi-rigid, elastic mass consisting of liquid trapped in a network of solid particles.
- *pectin:* a carbohydrate found in many fruits that has the ability to gel liquid under certain conditions.

BACKGROUND INFORMATION

Jelly is an example of a gel. A *gel* is a semi-rigid, elastic mass. It is a special combination of solid and liquid. The solid particles are linked together into a network, and the liquid is trapped in the spaces between.

Pectin is a carbohydrate that occurs naturally in the cell walls of most plants, but especially in fruit. When pectin is cooked with sugar and acid, it forms a network that traps water, making a spreadable jelly.

The right amounts of acid and sugar are needed to help pectin do its work. The correct level of acid changes the nature of the pectin so it will gel. Sugar molecules attach themselves to the water that is present, freeing the pectin molecules so they can bind with each other.

In this experiment, your class will prepare three variations of a basic jelly. One version is made without pectin but with 250 mL (1 cup) sugar. Another is made with pectin and 250 mL (1 cup) sugar, and the third with pectin and 500 mL (2 cups) sugar. You will observe how these differences in ingredients affect the finished products.

SUPPLIES

_____ 40 mL (2½ Tbsp.) powdered pectin, if needed for your variation
_____ 50 mL (¼ cup) + 30 mL (2 Tbsp.) OR 85 g (3 oz.) frozen apple juice concentrate, thawed
_____ ONE of the following as directed by your teacher:
_____ 250 mL (1 cup) sugar
_____ 500 mL (2 cups) sugar
_____ 250 mL (1 cup) cold water
_____ 1 heavy 2-3 L (2-3 qt.) saucepan
_____ 1 slice plain white bread
_____ 1 0.5-L (1-pt.) glass jelly jar or other heat-resistant glass

_____ large metal cooking spoon
_____ 5 self-sticking labels
_____ 3 small paper plates
_____ pen or marker
_____ liquid measuring cup
_____ dry measuring cups
_____ measuring spoons
_____ rubber scraper
_____ spatula
_____ 3 small spoons
_____ 3 knives

PROCEDURE

_____ 1. Mark three labels as follows: "A — No Pectin"; "B — Pectin + 250 mL (1 cup) Sugar"; and "C — Pectin + 500 mL (2 cups) Sugar."
_____ 2. Fasten to the rims of the three small paper plates.
_____ 3. Mark two labels with the name of the variation assigned to you by your teacher.
_____ 4. Fasten one label to the handle of the saucepan.
_____ 5. Fasten one label to the jelly jar or glass.

_____ 6. Put thawed apple juice concentrate in the saucepan.
_____ 7. Add ONE of the following as instructed by your teacher:
_____ cold water (A).
_____ cold water and powdered pectin (B and C).
_____ 8. Stir until completely mixed.
_____ 9. Cook over high heat, stirring constantly, until bubbles form around the edge.

_____ 10. Add ONE of the following as instructed by your teacher:

     _____ 250 mL (1 cup) sugar (A and B).

     _____ 500 mL (2 cups) sugar (C).

_____ 11. Boil for 1 minute, stirring constantly.

_____ 12. Skim off any foam with a large metal cooking spoon.

_____ 13. Remove from heat and pour into your jelly jar.

_____ 14. Cool. (If necessary, jelly can be cooled in the refrigerator.)

_____ 15. Place your jelly where it can be observed and tasted by all class members.

OBSERVATIONS

_____ 1. Spoon a small portion of each sample of jelly onto the appropriate paper plate, using a separate spoon for each sample.

_____ 2. Observe the consistency of each sample. Record your observations in the appropriate blanks on the Observation Chart. Circle the letter of the variation you prepared.

_____ 3. Break the slice of bread into 3 pieces.

_____ 4. Spread one piece with sample "A — No Pectin" and note how well the jelly spreads on the bread. Record your observations in the proper blank on the Observation Chart.

_____ 5. Taste sample "A" with the bread and then taste a small amount directly from the spoon. Record your observations in the proper blank on the Observation Chart.

_____ 6. Spread another piece of bread with sample "B — Pectin + 250 mL (1 cup) Sugar." Record your observations in the proper blank on the Observation Chart.

_____ 7. Taste sample "B" with the bread and then taste a small amount directly from the spoon. Record your observations in the proper blank on the Observation Chart.

_____ 8. Spread another piece of bread with sample "C — Pectin + 500 mL (2 cups) Sugar." Record your observations in the proper blank on the Observation Chart.

_____ 9. Taste sample "C" with the bread and then taste a small amount directly from the spoon. Record your observations in the proper blank on the Observation Chart.

Observation Chart			
Characteristics	**A** **No Pectin** **250 mL (1 cup) Sugar**	**B** **Pectin and** **250 mL (1 cup) Sugar**	**C** **Pectin and** **500 mL (2 cups) Sugar**
Consistency			
Spreadability			
Flavor			

CONCLUSIONS

1. What was the main difference between the three jellies? _____

_____

_____

2. Explain the differences in quality in relation to the amount of pectin and sugar used. _____

_____

_____

3. Which jelly did you prefer? Why? _____

_____

_____

FINISHING UP

- After you have completed the experiment, you can make a jelly from version "A": add 40 mL (2½ Tbsp.) powdered pectin to the mixture and follow Steps 8-14.

- The jelly has not been processed, so it must be refrigerated. Do not store at room temperature. Use as soon as possible.

Testing Program

TABLE OF CONTENTS

Testing Program

Name _____

Date _____

Chapter 1 Test

I. True-False. Read the following statements carefully. In the space at the left of each statement, write TRUE if the statement is true. Write FALSE if the statement is incorrect.

_____ 1. People eat to meet physical and psychological needs.

_____ 2. People who are hungry may have trouble learning.

_____ 3. Physical health means your mental and emotional well-being.

_____ 4. When people leave their native countries, they usually forget about their customs and food traditions.

_____ 5. People tend to feel uneasy and insecure when they find it difficult to obtain food.

_____ 6. In some cultures a food may be unacceptable for eating, while in other cultures the same food may be treated as a delicacy.

_____ 7. Most of the thousands of food choices in a nearby supermarket are possible because of modern food processing, transportation, and storage methods.

_____ 8. Resources can help you meet needs and goals.

_____ 9. Television commercials have little effect on food choices.

_____ 10. Personal food choices are seldom influenced by other people.

_____ 11. Trends can affect the food supply.

_____ 12. Hilly regions are the best for growing crops.

_____ 13. Ethnic and regional foods are limited to certain areas or groups of people in the United States.

II. Multiple Choice. In the space at the left, write the letter of the choice that BEST completes each statement.

_____ 14. Money, skills, and imagination are examples of:
A. physical needs
B. emotional needs and desires
C. resources
D. social and cultural influences

_____ 15. Security, enjoyment, self-esteem, and belonging are examples of:
A. physical needs
B. emotional needs and desires
C. resources
D. social and cultural influences

_____ 16. Family traditions, advertising, current trends, and religious customs are examples of:
A. physical needs
B. emotional needs and desires
C. resources
D. social and cultural influences

_____ 17. To weigh your wants and needs and set goals, you use your:
A. values
B. self-esteem
C. resources
D. instinct

_____ 18. The body's need for food is called:
A. appetite
B. starvation
C. nutrition
D. hunger

III. Completion. In the space at the left, write the word that BEST completes each statement. As a clue, the total number of letters in the word is given.

_____ (7)

19. A group of characteristics including types of dress, language, and customs is known as ___?___.

_____ (7)

20. Regional foods are a blending of the foods that are plentiful in any area and the food ___?___ of the people who settled there.

_____ (11)

21. People can often use resources that they have as ___?___ for resources that are in short supply.

_____ (10)

22. Extreme, life-threatening hunger is called ___?___.

_____ (9)

23. Chemicals called ___?___ give energy and help the body to grow and repair itself.

_____ (10)

24. Using resources wisely to meet goals is called ___?___.

_____ (6)

25. ___?___ have to do with the relative importance of things in a person's life.

_____ (6)

26. Foods that come from other cultures are called ___?___ foods.

_____ (8)

27. Food specialties that have developed in particular areas of the United States are called ___?___ foods.

_____ (9)

28. The way you live and the things you do make up your ___?___.

IV. Matching. Find the management step in the right column that BEST corresponds to each description in the left column. Write the letter of the answer in the blank space provided. Do not use any letter more than once. Some letters will not be used.

Descriptions

_____ 29. The first of five steps that can help you manage wisely.

_____ 30. The second of five steps that can help you manage wisely.

_____ 31. The third of five steps that can help you manage wisely.

_____ 32. The fourth of five steps that can help you manage wisely.

_____ 33. The fifth of five steps that can help you manage wisely.

Terms

A. carry out and monitor your plan
B. consider your resources
C. delegate the problem
D. set your goals
E. evaluate the results
F. revise your values
G. make a plan

Name _____

Date _____

Chapter 2 Test

I. True-False. Read the following statements carefully. In the space at the left of each statement, write TRUE if the statement is true. Write FALSE if the statement is incorrect.

_____ 1. Additives are used to preserve foods, add nutrients, or give color or flavor to foods.

_____ 2. Additives not on the GRAS list are known as fortified.

_____ 3. Without additives, our food supply would be seriously limited.

_____ 4. Additives, such as salt, sugar, and spices, can be used by manufacturers without getting permission from the FDA.

_____ 5. The government has the legal authority to request a food manufacturer to remove a product from the market.

_____ 6. Brown and white eggs have the same nutritive value.

_____ 7. Organic foods and natural foods are exactly the same.

_____ 8. Replacing nutrients lost in processing is known as restoration.

_____ 9. Food processors cannot use the word "natural" when foods are highly processed.

_____ 10. Natural foods are less expensive than foods not labeled "natural."

_____ 11. Enriched and fortified usually mean the same thing — that nutrients have been added.

_____ 12. The nutritional quality of organic and nonorganic food is the same.

_____ 13. Brown sugar and honey are more nutritious sweeteners than ordinary table sugar.

_____ 14. People may believe a food fad claim for which there is no scientific evidence because they want it to be true.

_____ 15. Foods grown in poor, deficient soil have fewer and poorer quality nutrients.

_____ 16. Some vitamins found in foods such as grapefruit can help break down body fat and cause weight loss.

_____ 17. Organic farming methods do not pollute water supplies.

_____ 18. Food quacks are not allowed to advertise in newspapers or on radio and television.

_____ 19. All nutrients can be poisonous if eaten in large enough amounts.

_____ 20. Each food product has a manufacturing lot number stamped on the container in case it has to be recalled.

II. Matching.
Find the term in the right column that BEST corresponds to each description in the left column. Write the letter of the term in the blank space provided. Do not use any term more than once. Some terms will not be used.

Descriptions

_____ 21. A request or order to remove a product from the market.

_____ 22. A safe limit for chemicals, such as contaminants, in the human body.

_____ 23. Keeps oil mixtures in salad dressings well blended so they do not separate.

_____ 24. A substance added to a food product for a specific purpose.

_____ 25. Includes substances which are found acceptable by the Food and Drug Administration and may be used by manufacturers without getting special permission.

_____ 26. Drugs used to fight off infections.

_____ 27. Regulates the proper disposal of wastes.

Terms

A. additive
B. emulsifier
C. vitamin A
D. FDA (Food and Drug Administration)
E. antibiotics
F. GRAS list
G. tolerance level
H. USDA (U.S. Dept. of Agriculture)
I. EPA (Environmental Protection Agency)
J. recall
K. contaminants
L. ascorbic acid
M. pesticide ban

III. Completion.
In the space at the left, write the word that BEST completes each statement. As a clue, the total number of letters in the word is given.

_____
(4)

28. Food ___?___ are mistaken beliefs about foods based on myths, misinformation, or exaggerated claims.

_____
(6)

29. Food ___?___ pretend to be trained food experts for their own profit.

_____
(7)

30. Foods grown without the use of added chemical fertilizers or sprays are known as ___?___ foods.

_____
(5)

31. The length of time food holds its original flavor and quality is called ___?___ life.

_____
(12)

32. Substances that get into food by accident as it is grown, processed, stored, or packaged are known as ___?___.

_____
(5)

33. You have ___?___ days to change your mind and cancel a contract from a door-to-door salesperson.

448

Part One Test

I. Matching. Find the term in the right column that BEST corresponds to each description in the left column. Write the letter of the term in the blank space provided. Do not use any term more than once. Some terms will not be used.

Descriptions

				Terms
Ch. 1	_____	1.	The body's need for food.	A. tolerance level
Ch. 1	_____	2.	The things that can help a person meet needs or goals.	B. organic foods
				C. culture
Ch. 1	_____	3.	A group of characteristics that includes beliefs, particular types of dress, language, and customs.	D. pesticides
				E. resources
Ch. 1	_____	4.	The way a person lives and the things he/she does.	F. starvation
				G. shelf life
Ch. 2	_____	5.	Sometimes called "natural" or "health" foods.	H. lifestyle
Ch. 2	_____	6.	The length of time in which food holds its original flavor and quality.	I. additive
				J. hunger
Ch. 2	_____	7.	Substances that get into food by accident as it is grown, processed, stored, or packaged.	K. food fads
				L. contaminants
Ch. 2	_____	8.	Mistaken beliefs about foods that are based on myths, misinformation, or exaggerated claims.	
Ch. 2	_____	9.	The safe limits of chemicals that the body can adapt to and withstand.	
Ch. 2	_____	10.	Chemicals used to prevent insects and disease from damaging or destroying crops.	

II. True-False. Read the following statements carefully. In the space at the left of each statement, write the word TRUE if the statement is true. Write FALSE if the statement is incorrect.

Ch. 1	_____	11.	Starvation, in its extreme form, is known as hunger.
Ch. 1	_____	12.	In poorly developed countries, the variety, quality, and amount of food available is usually severely limited.
Ch. 1	_____	13.	The food habits of many cultures have been influenced by religion.
Ch. 1	_____	14.	Emotions do not usually play an important part in making food choices.
Ch. 1	_____	15.	Resources for getting food include time, energy, knowledge, and skills.
Ch. 1	_____	16.	Management means using your goals to acquire resources.
Ch. 1	_____	17.	It is impossible to substitute one resource for another.
Ch. 2	_____	18.	Using additives in products is a recent food practice.
Ch. 2	_____	19.	Federal laws control foods sold across state lines.
Ch. 2	_____	20.	Vitamins and minerals found naturally in foods are superior to those that are manufactured in laboratories.
Ch. 2	_____	21.	Food quacks often use scare tactics to get people to buy their products.
Ch. 2	_____	22.	The government can request a manufacturer to remove a food product from the market.

(Continued on next page)

III. Completion. In the space at the left, write the word that BEST completes each statement. As a clue, the total number of letters in the word is given.

Ch. 1 _____ (8)

23. As part of good management, after carrying out a plan you should ___?___ the results.

Ch. 1 _____ (9)

24. ___?___ are the chemicals in food that the body needs in order to function.

Ch. 1 _____ (13)

25. The body's physical condition is closely related to a person's mental and emotional well-being, or ___?___ health.

Ch. 1 _____ (6)

26. ___?___ refer to the relative importance of things in a person's life.

Ch. 1 _____ (8)

27. Food specialties that developed in a particular area of the U.S. are known as ___?___ foods.

Ch. 2 _____ (9)

28. ___?___ in food are used to preserve freshness and add nutrients, flavor, and color.

Ch. 2 _____ (11)

29. Replacing nutrients lost in processing is known as ___?___.

Ch. 2 _____ (7)

30. Many food processors use the word "___?___" to describe food products, even though artificial ingredients are used or the foods are highly processed.

Ch. 2 _____ (11)

31. Studies show that ___?___, or drugs, in meat may be linked to human health problems.

Ch. 2 _____ (9)

32. Enriched and ___?___ usually mean the same thing — that nutrients have been added.

Ch. 1 _____ (10)

33. ___?___ is an individual's feeling that he/she is a worthwhile, capable person.

Name _____

Date _____

Chapter 3 Test

I. True-False. Read the following statements carefully. In the space at the left of each statement, write TRUE if the statement is true. Write FALSE if the statement is incorrect.

_____ 1. The more vitamins you get, the healthier you'll be.

_____ 2. Poor nutrition can lead to poor health.

_____ 3. Nutrients include carbohydrates, fats, proteins, vitamins, minerals, and water.

_____ 4. Milk by itself has all the nutrients needed for good health.

_____ 5. A large dose of vitamin C may cause diarrhea.

_____ 6. Your body can use only a certain amount of each nutrient.

_____ 7. The amount and kinds of nutrients that you need will remain the same throughout your life.

_____ 8. Every nutrient has definite functions in your body.

_____ 9. All vitamins can be stored by the body for future use.

_____ 10. Vitamins and minerals are needed in large amounts.

_____ 11. A person who eats too much can be malnourished.

_____ 12. Deficiency and malnutrition mean the same thing.

_____ 13. Getting too much of one vitamin may create unexpected health problems.

_____ 14. Scientific experiments have shown that vitamin D helps prevent scurvy.

_____ 15. People need the exact amounts of nutrients shown in RDA or U.S. RDA charts.

_____ 16. Poor nutrition can make it difficult to study or concentrate.

_____ 17. A hypothesis is a statement of fact.

_____ 18. Nutrients needed by the human body fall into four categories.

_____ 19. Your body must have an adequate supply of all the nutrients.

_____ 20. Researchers still have much to learn about nutrients and how they function in the body.

_____ 21. Poor nutrition can cause people to become tired and depressed.

II. Matching.
Find the term in the right column that BEST corresponds to each description in the left column. Write the letter of the term in the blank space provided. Do not use any term more than once. Some terms will not be used.

Descriptions

_____ 22. A technical chart that gives nutrient and calorie recommendations for specific ages, weights, and heights.

_____ 23. Caused by poor nutrition over a long period of time.

_____ 24. Nutrients working together in the human body.

_____ 25. An easy-to-understand nutrient chart developed for consumers.

_____ 26. Nutrients needed in very small amounts each day.

_____ 27. Blood disorder caused by too little iron in the diet.

_____ 28. A severe shortage of a nutrient.

Terms

A. vitamins
B. anemia
C. U.S. RDA
D. teamwork
E. deficiency
F. carbohydrates
G. starvation
H. calories
I. RDA
J. malnutrition
K. FDA

III. Completion.
In the space at the left, write the word that BEST completes each statement. As a clue, the total number of letters in the word is given.

_____
(7)

29. To be sure you get the essential nutrients, eat a(n) ___?___ of foods every day.

_____
(9)

30. The term ___?___ can be defined as the food you eat and how your body uses the nutrients in that food.

_____
(6)

31. Researchers follow a five-step process called the scientific ___?___.

_____
(5)

32. The human body needs about ___?___ different nutrients found in food.

_____
(10)

33. Eating small amounts of different foods each day is called eating in ___?___.

Chapter 4 Test

I. Matching. Find the term in the right column that BEST corresponds to each description in the left column. Write the letter of the term in the blank space provided. Do not use any term more than once. Some terms will not be used.

Descriptions

Terms

_____ 1. The "building blocks" of protein.

_____ 2. A condition, found especially in older people, caused by a deficiency of calcium.

_____ 3. Help speed chemical reactions that constantly take place in the body.

_____ 4. Another name for sugars.

_____ 5. Bulk or roughage necessary for the digestion process.

_____ 6. May help lower the level of harmful cholesterol in the blood.

_____ 7. Minerals needed by the body in very small amounts.

_____ 8. Illness caused by shortage of proteins over time, resulting in stunted growth and mental retardation.

A. unsaturated fats
B. vitamins
C. complete proteins
D. fiber
E. kwashiorkor
F. osteoporosis
G. trace elements
H. starches
I. fatty acids
J. simple carbohydrates
K. amino acids
L. saturated fats
M. pellagra

II. True-False. Read the following statements carefully. In the space at the left of each statement, write TRUE if the statement is true. Write FALSE if the statement is incorrect.

_____ 9. Starches are complex carbohydrates.

_____ 10. The fiber in whole grains, fruits, and vegetables is easily digested.

_____ 11. A deep yellow, orange, or green color is a clue to the presence of vitamin **A**.

_____ 12. Pound for pound, fats supply half as much energy as proteins and carbohydrates.

_____ 13. Cholesterol occurs in foods of animal origin.

_____ 14. Pregnant women and nursing mothers need extra proteins to build new cells.

_____ 15. Vitamins supply energy.

_____ 16. Most animal foods, such as fish, poultry, meat, dairy products, and eggs, provide complete proteins.

_____ 17. A person with rickets has poorly developed bones.

_____ 18. There may be a relationship between sodium in the body and high blood pressure.

_____ 19. Scurvy can be prevented by eating enough meat.

_____ 20. If you want to lose weight, you should avoid eating carbohydrates.

_____ 21. According to health experts, the average American diet is too high in fats.

III. Multiple Choice. In the space at the left, write the letter of the choice that BEST completes each statement.

_____ 22. All of the following are types of sugar EXCEPT:
A. maltose
B. laxtrose
C. sucrose
D. fructose

_____ 23. An excellent example of nutrient teamwork is:
A. calcium and iron
B. thiamin
C. calcium and phosphorus
D. folic acid

_____ 24. Nutritionists believe that the percentage of your daily caloric intake that should come from carbohydrates is about:
A. 15 percent
B. 35 percent
C. 55 percent
D. 75 percent

_____ 25. All of the following are high in fats EXCEPT:
A. margarine
B. whole milk
C. chocolate
D. fruits

_____ 26. Health experts recommend that of the calories you take in, fats should supply:
A. 30 percent or less
B. 30 to 35 percent
C. 40 to 45 percent
D. 50 percent or more

_____ 27. An example of a water-soluble vitamin is:
A. vitamin A
B. vitamin K
C. vitamin C
D. vitamin D

_____ 28. The best food sources of calcium are:
A. meat, eggs, and beans
B. milk, cheese, and yogurt
C. oranges, grapefruit, and strawberries
D. whole grains

_____ 29. Carbohydrates that have been removed from their natural sources are called:
A. simple carbohydrates
B. complex carbohydrates
C. hidden carbohydrates
D. processed carbohydrates

IV. Completion. In the space at the left, write the word that BEST completes each statement. As a clue, the total number of letters in the word is given.

_____ 30. A(n) __?__ is a substance that the body can turn into a vitamin.
(10)

_____ 31. Seeds that grow in a pod, such as beans and peas, are called __?__ .
(7)

_____ 32. Combining different plant proteins over the course of a day is called protein __?__ .
(15)

_____ 33. Fats and oils can be made more solid, and more saturated, through a process called __?__ .
(13)

Name _____

Date _____

Chapter 5 Test

I. Matching. Find the term in the right column that BEST corresponds to each description in the left column. Write the letter of the term in the blank space provided. Do not use any term more than once. Some terms will not be used.

Descriptions

_____ 1. The body uses this to burn food in order to produce energy.

_____ 2. Inactive.

_____ 3. The smallest blood vessels in the body.

_____ 4. An inability to go to sleep.

_____ 5. Absorb the nutrients as the food is digested.

_____ 6. Muscle action that churns food and pushes it along.

_____ 7. A substance that speeds up a chemical reaction in the body.

_____ 8. A thin, mushy mixture of partly digested food.

_____ 9. Produces bile; acts on fats that have been broken down by digestion.

Terms
A. sedentary
B. capillaries
C. chyme
D. stomach
E. digestion
F. enzyme
G. stress
H. insomnia
I. peristaltic waves
J. villi
K. oxygen
L. liver
M. adipose

II. True-False. Read the following statements carefully. In the space at the left of each statement, write TRUE if the statement is true. Write FALSE if the statement is incorrect.

_____ 10. No diet can guarantee health or well-being.

_____ 11. The average body temperature is 98.6°F.

_____ 12. Digestion begins when food enters the stomach.

_____ 13. Fats and high-protein foods pass through the stomach quickly.

_____ 14. Your health depends on your heredity, lifestyle, and environment, as well as your diet.

_____ 15. Ulcers are usually caused by eating the wrong foods.

_____ 16. The body's need for food is greater than its need for water.

_____ 17. Adults continue to grow new cells to replace those that are worn out.

_____ 18. The human body must be exercised or it loses its ability to move and becomes weak.

_____ 19. Body cells are replaced more rapidly when you are awake than when you sleep.

III. Multiple Choice. In the space at the left, write the letter of the choice that BEST completes each statement.

_____ 20. The percent of your body weight that is composed of water is about:
A. 10 percent   C. 65 percent
B. 25 percent   D. 90 percent

_____ 21. Chemical digestion begins in the:
A. stomach   C. small intestine
B. pancreas   D. mouth

_____ 22. An average meal containing carbohydrates, proteins, and fats leaves the stomach in about:
A. two hours   C. one hour
B. four hours   D. 24 hours

_____ 23. The energy the body needs to maintain basic processes is called:
A. reproduction   C. basal metabolism
B. competition   D. excretion

_____ 24. According to the Dietary Guidelines for Americans, you should do all of the following EXCEPT:
A. avoid food with fiber   C. avoid too much sugar
B. avoid excessive amounts of fat   D. avoid too much sodium

_____ 25. The use of alcohol and other drugs is linked with all of the following problems EXCEPT:
A. such medical problems as liver disease, cancer, and brain damage   C. poor judgement and reactions
B. loss of nutrients in the body   D. tendency to overeat

_____ 26. All of the following are true of exercise EXCEPT:
A. has emotional and physical benefits   C. improves flexibility
B. needs to be done a minimum of 7 hours per week   D. conditions muscles

IV. Completion. In the space at the left, write the word that BEST completes each statement. As a clue, the total number of letters in the word is given.

_____ (6) 27. The strain put on your body by the way you react to a situation is called ___?___ .

_____ (8) 28. The heat energy of foods is measured in ___?___ .

_____ (7) 29. ___?___ increases the risk of cancer, heart disease, lung disease, and osteoporosis.

_____ (5) 30. The stomach's function is to break down food so the nutrients can be absorbed by the ___?___ intestine.

_____ (7) 31. The heart and lungs can be strengthened with ___?___ exercise, such as jogging or brisk walking, which makes the body use more oxygen than it normally does.

_____ (8) 32. A person's total health — physical, mental, and emotional — is called ___?___ .

_____ (5) 33. Your body must have ___?___ to perform all the chemical processes that take place.

Name _____

Date _____

Chapter 6 Test

I. Matching. Find the term in the right column that BEST corresponds to each description in the left column. Write the letter of the term in the blank space provided. Do not use any term more than once. Some terms will not be used.

Descriptions

_____ 1. Should supply you with about one-third of your daily food needs.

_____ 2. Plant protein plus eggs.

_____ 3. A main dish.

_____ 4. A bowl of cereal with milk.

_____ 5. Ordering food items individually.

_____ 6. More nutrients with fewer calories.

_____ 7. Salad dressing and margarine.

Terms

A. a complete protein
B. salad
C. high nutrient density
D. a la carte
E. entree
F. Fats-Sweets Group
G. snack
H. a good food mixture
I. balanced meal
J. Milk-Cheese Group
K. breakfast
L. Meat-Poultry-Fish-Beans Group

II. True-False. Read the following statements carefully. In the space at the left of each statement, write TRUE if the statement is true. Write FALSE if the statement is incorrect.

_____ 8. A balanced meal has foods from two or three main food groups in the Daily Food Guide.

_____ 9. Studies show that about one out of every three meals is eaten away from home.

_____ 10. Snacks should be eliminated from your daily food pattern.

_____ 11. A food is put into a particular group because it contains the nutrients that group provides.

_____ 12. Many health professionals suggest that lunch should be the largest meal of the day.

_____ 13. The more nutrients a food has in relation to the number of calories, the lower the nutrient density.

_____ 14. Making nutritious food choices can be more difficult when you eat out.

_____ 15. Animals eat up to 10 pounds of grain for each pound of meat they yield.

_____ 16. Studies show that people who skip breakfast do less work, have problems concentrating in school or on the job, and feel tired and nervous.

_____ 17. Orange juice, pizza, and milk for breakfast is not a nutritious morning meal.

_____ 18. Because potato chips are high in nutrients but low in calories, they are a good choice for snacks.

_____ 19. Jam and jelly are classified in the Fruit-Vegetable Group.

III. Multiple Choice. In the space at the left, write the letter of the choice that BEST completes each statement.

_____ 20. The number of slices of bread from the Bread-Cereal Group that equal one serving is:
A. one slice
B. two slices
C. three slices
D. four slices

_____ 21. The chief sources of proteins in the vegan diet are:
A. fruits and vegetables
B. milk and eggs
C. legumes and grains
D. chicken and turkey

_____ 22. The lunch that is the most balanced is:
A. plain hamburger and milk
B. tomato soup, turkey sandwich, and milk
C. macaroni and cheese, apple slices, and milk
D. grilled chicken, green beans, peaches, and ice water

_____ 23. The number of servings daily from the Milk-Cheese Group that teenagers need is:
A. 1 to 2 servings
B. 3 servings
C. 4 or more servings
D. as many servings as possible

_____ 24. The number of servings daily from the Fruit-Vegetable Group that teenagers need is:
A. 1 serving
B. 2 servings
C. 6 servings or more
D. 4 servings

_____ 25. The number of servings daily of the Meat-Poultry-Fish-Beans Group that teenagers need is:
A. 1 serving
B. 2 servings
C. 3 servings
D. 5 servings

_____ 26. The number of servings daily of the Bread-Cereal Group that teenagers need is:
A. 1 serving
B. 2 servings
C. 4 servings
D. 5 or more servings

IV. Completion. In the space at the left, write the word that BEST completes each statement. As a clue, the total number of letters in the word is given.

_____ (4) 27. The Daily Food Guide has ___?___ main food groups.

_____ (4) 28. The number and ___?___ of servings needed daily from each food group is listed in the Daily Food Guide.

_____ (9) 29. The Fats-Sweets Group of the Daily Food Guide is low in ___?___.

_____ (5) 30. Each day it is best to eat ___?___ amounts of a variety of foods.

_____ (6) 31. A combination of legumes plus ___?___ provides a complete protein.

_____ (6) 32. A snack dip made with ___?___ is lower in calories than one made with sour cream.

_____ (6, 3) 33. Some restaurants have a(n) ___?___, where you can serve yourself nutritious foods. (two words)

458

Chapter 7 Test

I. True-False. Read the following statements carefully. In the space at the left of each statement, write TRUE if the statement is true. Write FALSE if the statement is incorrect.

_____ 1. If you cut your calorie intake by 100 calories a day, you could lose one pound of weight per week.

_____ 2. Height-weight tables show weights based on small, medium, and large body frames.

_____ 3. People who are 10 percent above their normal weight according to height-weight charts, are considered overweight.

_____ 4. Health experts recommend that you should not lose more than 1½ to 2 pounds a week.

_____ 5. When you diet, your body thinks it is starving and begins to use more calories for all of its processes.

_____ 6. The body takes about a week to accept new behavior.

_____ 7. A physician should be consulted before a person begins dieting or taking any medication to lose weight.

_____ 8. Frustration and tension can affect a person's appetite.

_____ 9. The best clue to your appropriate weight is your appearance.

_____ 10. Your basic body type is acquired not inherited.

_____ 11. People who are extremely underweight can have as many health problems as overweight people.

_____ 12. Your weight should remain the same if you eat the same number of calories as you use.

_____ 13. It is difficult to tell the difference between high-calorie foods and low-calorie foods because the textures are similar.

_____ 14. Having patience is an important part of gaining or losing weight.

_____ 15. Fasting — going completely without food for several days or longer — is a very dangerous diet practice.

II. Multiple Choice. In the space at the left, write the letter of the choice that BEST completes each statement.

_____ 16. Bread, potatoes, and macaroni are:
A. fatty foods
B. starchy foods
C. high in calories
D. diet foods

_____ 17. The activity that uses more calories than the others is:
A. walking
B. bowling
C. dancing
D. scrubbing

_____ 18. Calories measure:
A. body weight
B. fatness
C. food energy
D. basal metabolism

19. Your daily caloric intake that should come from complex carbohydrates is about:
    A. 50 percent
    C. 25 percent
    B. 15 percent
    D. 70 percent

20. Keeping your weight the same is known as a:
    A. seesaw diet
    C. bulimia
    B. maintenance program
    D. fast

21. People who are underweight can gain weight by:
    A. choosing higher-calorie foods from the Daily Food Guide
    C. taking vitamin supplements
    B. drinking a large soft drink before meals
    D. exercising less and sleeping more

22. Overweight people are subject to all of the following problems EXCEPT:
    A. such diseases as cancer and heart trouble
    C. extra effort needed for breathing
    B. strain on bones and muscles
    D. inability to perspire

23. A small amount of exercise added to your activities can help speed up your metabolic rate and thereby decrease your:
    A. nervousness
    C. sleeplessness
    B. energy
    D. setpoint

24. When you diet, your first weight loss will consist of:
    A. water
    C. sugars
    B. protein
    D. fat

III. Matching. Find the term in the right column that BEST corresponds to each description in the left column. Write the letter of the term in the blank space provided. Do not use any term more than once. Some terms will not be used.

Descriptions

25. A method used to measure the amount of fat stored under the skin.

26. Losing and regaining weight repeatedly.

27. Tend to be juicy, watery-crisp, and have fiber.

28. Methods and substances promoted for quick weight loss.

29. Medication that causes the body to lose water but not fat.

30. Tend to be oily, thick, sticky, or concentrated.

31. The weight your body tries to maintain.

32. A group of people who support each other in their dieting efforts.

33. Serious illness resulting from overeating and self-induced vomiting.

Terms

A. diuretics
B. setpoint
C. endomorphs
D. overweight
E. diet clubs
F. anorexia nervosa
G. high-calorie foods
H. low-calorie foods
I. "miracle" diets
J. bulimia
K. pinch test
L. seesaw dieting
M. height-weight charts

Chapter 8 Test

I. True-False. Read the following statements carefully. In the space at the left of each statement, write TRUE if the statement is true. Write FALSE if the statement is incorrect.

_____ 1. Teenage athletes need the same amount of food as other average teenagers.

_____ 2. Generally, single people will find it to their advantage to buy food in small quantities for food variety.

_____ 3. Research shows that many health problems during pregnancy are related to poor nutrition.

_____ 4. Infants should be given sugar water to improve their appetite.

_____ 5. Your need for good nutrition begins the moment you are born.

_____ 6. Since athletes lose sodium and potassium through perspiration, both must be replaced by using mineral tablets.

_____ 7. A pregnant woman should eat twice as much food as usual to provide extra nutrients for the unborn baby.

_____ 8. Some research evidence suggests that soft drinks, coffee, and tea should be avoided during pregnancy because they may be harmful.

_____ 9. When the mother has used drugs, such as cocaine or heroin, during her pregnancy, her newborn baby can be a drug addict.

_____ 10. A mother who is breast-feeding needs extra nutrients, just as she did when she was pregnant.

_____ 11. Extra vitamins help give an athlete more energy.

_____ 12. Some foods can cause medications to lose their effectiveness.

II. Multiple Choice. In the space at the left, write the letter of the choice that BEST completes each statement.

_____ 13. A pregnant woman's bones and teeth may be affected if her diet does not contain enough:
    A. potassium   C. calcium
    B. iron   D. magnesium

_____ 14. Pregnancy during adolescence presents special risks for:
    A. the baby   C. the mother
    B. both the mother and baby   D. the pediatrician

_____ 15. Large, strong muscles are built by:
    A. exercise   C. extra amounts of water
    B. extra amounts of protein   D. heredity

_____ 16. If adults do not eat less than they ate as adolescents:
    A. their weight will stay the same   C. they will lose weight
    B. they will gain weight   D. their weight will depend on body type

_____ 17. As people progress through their life cycle, their nutrient requirements:
    A. increase   C. change
    B. remain the same   D. decrease

_____ 18. People with heart disease may have to decrease their consumption of:
    A. complex carbohydrates   C. vitamins
    B. sodium and foods high in saturated fats   D. proteins

III. Matching. Find the term in the right column that BEST corresponds to each description in the left column. Write the letter of the term in the blank space provided. Do not use any term more than once. Some terms will not be used.

Descriptions

_____ 19. A physician who specializes in caring for babies and young children.

_____ 20. A creamy, yellow, nutritious fluid secreted from the breast during the first few days of nursing.

_____ 21. The various stages of life from birth to old age.

_____ 22. An eating plan requiring the avoidance of table salt and salted food.

_____ 23. An eating plan that limits foods high in saturated fats.

_____ 24. A problem or illness that is long-lasting or recurring.

_____ 25. Abnormal loss of body fluids.

_____ 26. A physician who specializes in caring for pregnant women.

_____ 27. A disease in which the body does not manufacture enough insulin or when the insulin doesn't work efficiently.

_____ 28. An unpleasant or dangerous varying reaction to certain foods.

Terms

A. low-carbohydrate diet
B. colostrum
C. diabetes
D. fetus
E. dehydration
F. low-cholesterol diet
G. low-sodium diet
H. obstetrician
I. allergy
J. pediatrician
K. life cycle
L. chronic
M. low birth weight

IV. Completion. In the space at the left, write the word that BEST completes each statement. As a clue, the total number of letters in the word is given.

_____ (8) 29. Some pregnant women develop ___?___ for certain foods.

_____ (5) 30. The problems caused by ___?___ alcohol syndrome include low birth weight and distorted facial features.

_____ (7) 31. Another word for germ-free is ___?___.

_____ (7) 32. Another name for breast-feeding a baby is ___?___.

_____ (5) 33. Popcorn, hot dogs, nuts, and raisins can easily cause babies to ___?___.

Part Two

Nutrition for Good Health

Name _____

Date _____

Part Two Test

I. Matching. Find the term in the right column that BEST corresponds to each description in the left column. Write the letter of the term in the blank space provided. Do not use any term more than once. Some terms will not be used.

Descriptions

Ch. 3 _____ 1. A shortage of a nutrient or nutrients necessary to health.

Ch. 3 _____ 2. The foods a person eats and how the body uses the nutrients in that food.

Ch. 4 _____ 3. Minerals needed by the body in tiny quantities.

Ch. 4 _____ 4. The "building blocks" of protein that must be supplied by food because they cannot be made by the body in sufficient amounts.

Ch. 4 _____ 5. A fat-like substance found in foods of animal origin.

Ch. 4 _____ 6. A bone disease caused by a calcium deficiency.

Ch. 5 _____ 7. The health of the total person.

Ch. 5 _____ 8. The amount of energy needed by the body to maintain basic processes.

Ch. 5 _____ 9. Strain put on the body by the way a person reacts to a situation.

Ch. 6 _____ 10. A scientific aid to help a person select the right kinds and recommended servings of food each day.

Ch. 6 _____ 11. The amount of nutrients a food gives in relation to the number of calories.

Ch. 7 _____ 12. Keeping your body weight at the weight you want it to be.

Ch. 7 _____ 13. An eating disorder characterized by weight loss from starvation.

Ch. 8 _____ 14. An unborn, developing baby.

Ch. 8 _____ 15. A group of problems including low birth weight, mental retardation, and distorted facial features.

Terms

A. fetal alcohol syndrome
B. bulimia
C. wellness
D. provitamin
E. essential amino acids
F. nutrient density
G. malnutrition
H. fiber
I. Daily Food Guide
J. calories
K. setpoint
L. stress
M. maintenance program
N. fetus
O. deficiency
P. anorexia nervosa
Q. basal metabolism
R. cholesterol
S. RDA
T. trace elements
U. osteoporosis
V. sterile
W. nutrition

II. True-False. Read the following statements carefully. In the space at the left of each statement, write the word TRUE if the statement is true. Write FALSE if the statement is incorrect.

Ch. 3 _____ 16. Your body must have an adequate supply of all the nutrients, so they can work together as teams.

Ch. 3 _____ 17. The larger the amounts of vitamins and minerals you get every day, the healthier you will be.

Ch. 4, 7 _____ 18. A good diet includes avoiding carbohydrates.

Ch. 4 _____ 19. Health experts recommend that only about 30% or less of the calories you take in should be from fat.

Ch. 4 _____ 20. Fat-soluble vitamins cannot be stored by the body, so excess amounts are removed with waste products.

Ch. 5 _____ 21. The digestive system breaks food down into tiny particles and releases nutrients for the body to use.

Ch. 5 _____ 22. The body's need for water is greater than it is for food.

Ch. 5 _____ 23. Nutrients are used by the body to create energy, build and repair cells, and regulate body processes.

Ch. 6 _____ 24. A combination of legumes and dairy products provides a complete protein.

Ch. 6 _____ 25. Although skipping breakfast is not recommended, the nutrients can be made up later in the day and performance at school or on the job is not affected.

Ch. 6 _____ 26. Breakfast foods should be limited to the traditional ones, such as cereal, juice, and milk.

Ch. 7 _____ 27. Health experts recommend that you should lose no more than 1½ to 2 pounds per week.

Ch. 7 _____ 28. Many "miracle" diets can do serious damage to the body because they lack nutrients needed every day.

Ch. 8 _____ 29. Athletes should eat plenty of protein foods to build large muscles.

Ch. 8 _____ 30. It is best to eat a meal at least one hour before competing in any athletic event.

Ch. 8 _____ 31. Teen mothers are more likely than adult mothers to have babies who are stillborn, premature, or have a low birth weight.

Ch. 8 _____ 32. Elderly people do not need to eat food from all four main food groups every day because their energy needs are less.

III. Multiple Choice. In the space at the left, write the letter of the choice that BEST answers each question.

Ch. 3 _____ 33. Which nutrients are essential for the human body to function well?
A. carbohydrates
B. proteins and fats
C. vitamins and minerals
D. all of the above

Ch. 3 _____ 34. What may result from poor nutrition?
A. overweight or underweight problems
B. skin problems
C. tooth decay
D. all of the above

Ch. 3 _____ 35. What best describes the U.S. RDA?
A. a technical nutrient chart used mainly by health professionals
B. a simplified nutrient chart developed by the Food and Drug Administration (FDA)
C. a nutrient chart designed for persons under the age of 18
D. a nutrient chart designed primarily for adults and the elderly

Ch. 4 _____ 36. Which of the following contains NO cholesterol?
A. foods of animal origin
B. cells of the body
C. vegetable oil
D. all of the above

Ch. 4 _____ 37. Which of the following is not a fat-soluble vitamin?
A. vitamin B
B. vitamin A
C. vitamin D
D. vitamin E

Ch. 5 _____ 38. When does digestion begin?
A. when food enters the stomach
B. as soon as a bite of food is taken into the mouth
C. when food enters the small intestine
D. when food enters the large bowel

Ch. 5 _____ 39. What must the body have in order to carry on all the life processes?
A. oxygen and water
B. variety of nutritious food
C. exercise and sleep
D. all of the above

Ch. 6 _____ 40. Which of the following meals should be the largest meal of the day according to many health professionals?
A. breakfast meal
B. noon meal
C. evening meal
D. midmorning meal

Ch. 6 _____ 41. How many servings of milk do teenagers need each day?
A. 1 to 2 servings
B. 2 to 3 servings
C. 3 or more servings
D. 4 or more servings

Ch. 6 _____ 42. Why are fruit juices better for you than carbonated drinks?
A. because they are high in sugar
B. because they contain vitamins
C. because they contain protein
D. because they are higher in calories

Ch. 6 _____ 43. How are foods divided into groups in the Daily Food Guide?
A. by the nutrients they contain
B. by the number of servings recommended each day
C. by the amount of calories in each food
D. by the similarity in color

Ch. 7 _____ 44. How long does the human body take to accept new behavior or eating habits?
A. at least a week
B. at least three weeks
C. a minimum of two months
D. one year or more

Ch. 7 _____ 45. In order to gain weight, a person should do which of the following?
   A. choose higher-calorie foods from   C. exercise regularly
      the food groups
   B. eat smaller meals five or six   D. all of the above
      times a day

Ch. 7 _____ 46. What is the name of the eating disorder that includes overeating and self-induced vomiting?
   A. anorexia nervosa   C. bulimia
   B. peristalsis   D. diabetes

Ch. 7 _____ 47. How many calories does a person need to cut in order to lose about half a kilogram (a pound) of weight a week?
   A. 300 calories a day   C. 700 calories a day
   B. 500 calories a day   D. 1000 calories a day

Ch. 5, 7 _____ 48. What is a calorie?
   A. a way of measuring body fat by   C. a unit that measures the heat
      pinching the skin   energy of foods
   B. a fatty substance in foods that   D. a substance similar to an
      causes weight gain   amino acid

Ch. 8 _____ 49. Since athletes lose sodium and potassium through perspiration, what do they need to do?
   A. take salt tablets and potassium   C. avoid drinking water to slow
      supplements   down perspiration
   B. eat foods high in potassium   D. not make any adjustments since
                                            salt and potassium are present
                                            in most foods

Ch. 8 _____ 50. What may occur when a pregnant woman does not get enough calcium in her daily diet?
   A. delivery of a blue-baby   C. the taking of calcium from the
                                            mother's bones and teeth to
                                            supply the unborn baby

   B. development of anemia   D. the placement of the baby on a
                                            calcium formula immediately
                                            after birth

Chapter 9 Test

I. True-False. Read the following statements carefully. In the space at the left of each statement, write TRUE if the statement is true. Write FALSE if the statement is incorrect.

_____ 1. Ideally, the kitchen should not contain more than three work centers.

_____ 2. The one-wall kitchen is generally used in very spacious rooms.

_____ 3. A corridor kitchen should have a door at each end for good traffic flow.

_____ 4. If possible, traffic through the kitchen should not go through the work triangle.

_____ 5. A wall outlet with three holes ensures you that there is a grounding wire.

_____ 6. Food, heat, and moisture in kitchens attract insects and other pests.

_____ 7. Inadequate wiring may cause appliances, such as toasters and grills, to take a long time to heat.

_____ 8. A basic safety rule for all kitchen appliances is that they should be grounded to prevent electrical shock.

_____ 9. Electricity follows the path of most resistance to the ground.

_____ 10. Fluorescent lighting requires more wattage than incandescent lighting.

_____ 11. The problem of fuses blowing frequently can be solved by installing a larger fuse.

_____ 12. Spice racks should be placed near the range center for easy use.

_____ 13. Some plants are poisonous and should not be placed near food preparation areas.

_____ 14. A mirror can be installed over a cooktop to allow a cook in a wheelchair to see what's in the pots and pans.

II. Multiple Choice. In the space at the left, write the letter of the choice that BEST completes each statement.

_____ 15. A kitchen arrangement where appliances, storage cabinets, and counter space are in a continuous line is:
A. corridor
B. U-shaped
C. L-shaped
D. one-wall

_____ 16. A type of paint finish applied to kitchen walls because it washes more easily is:
A. semigloss finish
B. flat finish
C. metallic finish
D. varnish finish

_____ 17. A device that keeps too much electricity from flowing through the wires in an electric circuit is a(n):
A. fuse
B. conduit
C. neutral core
D. adapter

_____ 18. Flour, sugar, and a blender should be stored in the:
A. refrigerator-freezer center
B. range center
C. mixing center
D. sink center

_____ 19. Cooking tools should be stored in the:
A. sink center
B. range center
C. mixing center
D. none of these

_____ 20. A trash compactor would best be located at the:
  A. refrigerator-freezer center   C. near kitchen exit
  B. range center   D. sink center

_____ 21. A floor surface that is uncomfortable to stand on for a long period of time is:
  A. vinyl tile   C. ceramic tile
  B. carpeting   D. sheet vinyl

_____ 22. It is a safer and more efficient choice for a person confined to a wheelchair to have a:
  A. freestanding range   C. gas range
  B. built-in oven and separate cooktop   D. none of these

_____ 23. The kitchen environment must be all of the following EXCEPT:
  A. sanitary   C. moisture-proof
  B. spacious   D. heat proof

III. Matching. Find the term in the right column that BEST corresponds to each description in the left column. Write the letter of the term in the blank space provided. Do not use any term more than once. Some terms will not be used.

Descriptions

_____ 24. Provides a path for the electricity to travel if something happens to the wiring.

_____ 25. A pattern or system of work.

_____ 26. A kitchen counter extension.

_____ 27. Areas into which kitchens are divided.

_____ 28. The range, refrigerator-freezer, and sink arranged in a three-point pattern.

_____ 29. A separate counter in what might otherwise be unused space.

_____ 30. The appliances, cabinets, and counter space are arranged on two facing walls.

_____ 31. Has appliances, cabinets, and counter space on two adjacent walls.

_____ 32. The least efficient kitchen plan.

_____ 33. The most efficient kitchen plan.

Terms
A. island
B. conduit
C. corridor kitchen
D. grounding
E. L-shaped kitchen
F. peninsula
G. fuse
H. one-wall kitchen
I. U-shaped kitchen
J. work centers
K. work flow
L. work triangle
M. traffic

Name _____

Date _____

Chapter 10 Test

I. Matching. Find the term in the right column that BEST corresponds to each description in the left column. Write the letter of the term in the blank space provided. Do not use any term more than once. Some terms will not be used.

Descriptions

_____ 1. Defrosting a refrigerator by turning it off to allow the ice to melt.

_____ 2. Small appliances that can be moved from place to place.

_____ 3. Oven with a special cleaning cycle.

_____ 4. A conventional oven with fans which circulate the heated air quickly and speed up the cooking process.

_____ 5. A used appliance which is checked, repaired, and is in working condition.

_____ 6. Type of refrigerator-freezer in which refrigerator section only is automatically defrosted.

Terms

A. convection oven
B. induction oven
C. frostless
D. manual defrost
E. self-cleaning oven
F. portable
G. rebuilt
H. cycle defrost
I. continuous cleaning oven
J. reconditioned
K. nonelectrical

II. Multiple Choice. In the space at the left, write the letter of the choice that BEST completes each statement.

_____ 7. When buying an appliance on the installment plan, the fee you pay for borrowing money is known as the:
A. contract
B. purchase price
C. interest
D. down payment

_____ 8. An EnergyGuide label on a manual defrost refrigerator-freezer gives:
A. a description of the appliance and estimated yearly energy cost
B. the number of times per year the unit must be defrosted
C. the average temperatures of the refrigerator and the freezer
D. a description of the warranty and manufacturer's guarantee

_____ 9. If a warranty is called "limited":
A. its guarantee is for a shorter period of time than a full warranty
B. it has restrictions in addition to the time limit
C. it has not been UL approved
D. it covers only labor costs to the repair of the appliance

_____ 10. A convection oven does NOT:
A. brown meats evenly
B. cook food faster than a microwave
C. maintain an even cooking temperature
D. cook food faster than a conventional oven

_____ 11. In a microwave oven, foods cook by:
A. radon
B. magnetic attraction
C. friction
D. induction

_____ 12. Aluminum cookware:
A. conducts heat rapidly and evenly
B. does not darken or stain
C. can be put in a dishwasher
D. should not be scoured

_____ 13. When buying a gas range, you should look for the:
A. UL seal
B. FTC seal
C. EnergyGuide label
D. AGA seal

_____ 14. When buying pans, look for:
    A. riveted handles   C. tight-fitting lids
    B. a matching set   D. curved bottom

_____ 15. Stainless steel cookware:
    A. may darken if overheated   C. may rust
    B. heats quickly and evenly   D. should not be scoured

_____ 16. When buying small appliances, look for all of the following EXCEPT:
    A. good balance   C. UL seal on appliance, not just the cord
    B. metal handles on heat-generating D. easy cleaning ability
       appliances

_____ 17. Heat that is transferred by direct contact is an example of:
    A. radiation   C. convection
    B. transaction   D. conduction

III. True-False. Read the following statements carefully. In the space at the left of each statement, write TRUE if the statement is true. Write FALSE if the statement is incorrect.

_____ 18. Delivery and installation costs of appliances are always included in the quoted selling price.

_____ 19. The annual percentage rate is the same wherever you shop.

_____ 20. If a product under warranty fails to perform during a specified time, it will be repaired or replaced by the dealer or manufacturer.

_____ 21. The Underwriter's Laboratories, Inc., seal indicates that the appliance has been approved as safe to use.

_____ 22. Reading consumer magazines is a good way to get an idea of which brands and models are considered to be better built.

_____ 23. It is usually best to buy a major appliance, such as a range or refrigerator-freezer, with as many special features as possible.

_____ 24. When you cannot pay cash, it may be cheaper to arrange a loan through a bank or other loan center than to sign an installment contract with the store.

_____ 25. A refrigerator-freezer with a single outer door can be used to freeze fresh foods.

_____ 26. There is no time limit with a full warranty.

_____ 27. Using small electric appliances can save time and energy.

_____ 28. When making a purchase, high prices guarantee the best quality.

_____ 29. A frost-free refrigerator-freezer costs more to buy and operate than a cycle defrost model.

_____ 30. Any type of detergent can be used in an automatic dishwasher.

_____ 31. A large food processor may not be a good buy for a person who cooks just for himself/ herself.

_____ 32. An induction cooktop uses a magnetic attraction between a pan and a heating element.

_____ 33. When an appliance does not work, the first step is to report the problem to the Better Business Bureau.

Chapter 11 Test

I. True-False. Read the following statements carefully. In the space at the left of each statement, write TRUE if the statement is true. Write FALSE if the statement is incorrect.

_____ 1. Studies show that as much as 40 percent of the food dollar can be saved if a shopping list is followed.

_____ 2. Shoplifting and careless handling of food by consumers add to the price of food.

_____ 3. Do not buy damaged, leaking, rusty, or bulging cans of food at any price.

_____ 4. In figuring meat costs, the price per serving is more important than the price per pound.

_____ 5. Food stores in the United States are required by law to have unit pricing.

_____ 6. Understanding sales techniques used by stores can help you shop for food and save money.

_____ 7. The standard of identity specifies the ingredients that can be used in a common product, such as ketchup or jelly.

_____ 8. When you try to cut down on food costs, you must also learn to settle for lower quality.

_____ 9. Larger sizes are not necessarily more economical.

_____ 10. Coupons don't automatically mean savings.

_____ 11. The first ingredient listed on a food label is the one present in the smallest amount.

_____ 12. Dairy products in aseptic packages can be stored safely without refrigeration.

_____ 13. It can be cheaper to prepare a food from scratch.

_____ 14. You can get good value and prices by choosing one good grocery store and shopping there.

_____ 15. If the label reads "noodles with beef," it means the product has more beef than noodles.

II. Multiple Choice. In the space at the left, write the letter of the choice that BEST completes each statement.

_____ 16. A buyer of goods and services is a:
A. supplier
B. manufacturer
C. consumer
D. manager

_____ 17. Foods that spoil easily are known as:
A. imitation foods
B. perishable foods
C. fresh foods
D. processed foods

_____ 18. The costliest items of the amount spent on marketing food are:
A. corporate profits
B. business taxes
C. advertising
D. labor and packaging

_____ 19. The most expensive foods usually are:
A. dairy products
B. produce
C. grains and breads
D. meats

_____ 20. The best way to choose the most reasonably priced food is to:
  A. buy generic products   C. check nutrient value
  B. compare unit pricing   D. use coupons

_____ 21. The nutrition label must list all these items EXCEPT:
  A. cholesterol per serving   C. number of servings
  B. serving size   D. calories per serving

_____ 22. When the demand for food is greater than the supply, prices tend to be:
  A. lower   C. similar
  B. higher   D. fluctuating

_____ 23. A system that allows computerized checkout counters to total the cost of a purchase is the:
  A. standard of identity   C. unit pricing
  B. universal product code   D. none of these

III. Matching. Find the term in the right column that BEST corresponds to each description in the left column. Write the letter of the term in the blank space provided. Do not use any term more than once. Some terms will not be used.

Descriptions

_____ 24. A date appearing on packaged food to help you judge the freshness of the food.

_____ 25. The package is made of layers of plastic paperboard, aluminum foil, and adhesive formed into a single sheet.

_____ 26. A store in which ready-to-eat food products are sold.

_____ 27. The package is made of aluminum foil sandwiched between layers of plastic.

_____ 28. The last date a product should be used.

_____ 29. Gives helpful information about the nutrients in a food product.

_____ 30. A product is not likely to be at peak quality after this date.

_____ 31. One thing this may indicate is the price per ounce.

_____ 32. A store brand.

_____ 33. Foods that have been processed to make them easier to prepare.

Terms

A. private label
B. convenience foods
C. freshness date
D. delicatessen
E. nutrition label
F. interest
G. open dating
H. retort pouch
I. aseptic package
J. UPC code
K. unit pricing
L. expiration date
M. convenience stores

Chapter 12 Test

I. Matching. Find the term in the right column that BEST corresponds to each description in the left column. Write the letter of the term in the blank space provided. Do not use any term more than once. Some terms will not be used.

Descriptions

_____ 1. Recommended temperature for freezing and storing foods in freezer.

_____ 2. Tiny one-celled, disease-causing organisms that prefer protein foods such as milk, eggs, poultry, and fish.

_____ 3. Small plants that can cause some foods to ferment.

_____ 4. Chemical substances that speed up chemical changes, resulting in loss of flavor, color, and texture.

_____ 5. Best range of refrigerator temperature to provide cold storage for perishable foods.

_____ 6. Recommended dry storage temperature.

_____ 7. Unpleasant taste and smell caused by breakdown of fats in food.

Terms

A. bacteria
B. dehydration
C. enzymes
D. microorganisms
E. rancidity
F. 13°C to 21°C
   (55°F to 70°F)
G. yeast
H. 15°C to 52°C
   (60°F to 125°F)
I. 2°C to 4°C
   (36°F to 40°F)
J. −18°C (0°F) or lower
K. mold
L. toxins

II. True-False. Read the following statements carefully. In the space at the left of each statement, write TRUE if the statement is true. Write FALSE if the statement is incorrect.

_____ 8. The waste products of bacteria can be poisonous, capable of causing illness and even death.

_____ 9. Cold temperatures help to prevent bacteria from multiplying.

_____ 10. Most perishable foods can be stored safely for three to four weeks in the refrigerator.

_____ 11. Prompt storage of food at home helps to preserve the quality of the food.

_____ 12. Most microorganisms live best in cold temperatures.

_____ 13. Milk and cream should be stored in the coldest part of the refrigerator.

_____ 14. Freezer burn is caused by improper packaging of food.

_____ 15. Freezing temperatures will kill microorganisms.

_____ 16. Mold will grow even on refrigerated food.

_____ 17. The refrigerator door shelves are usually warmer than the interior of the refrigerator.

_____ 18. Frozen food should be thawed at room temperature.

_____ 19. The area under the kitchen sink is a good place to store food.

_____ 20. Fruits and vegetables should be stored in the coldest part of the refrigerator.

_____ 21. You can safely refreeze a food if there are still ice crystals in it.

_____ 22. Refrigerator shelves should be lined with foil or waxed paper to keep them clean.

_____ 23. Never taste a thawed uncooked food to see if it is still good because even a small taste could make you sick.

_____ 24. Frozen foods lose quality if they are stored too long.

_____ 25. In wrapping food for freezing, the food should be tightly wrapped and as much air as possible squeezed out.

_____ 26. All microorganisms are harmful to humans.

III. Completion. In the space at the left, write the word or words that BEST complete each statement. As a clue, the total number of letters in the word is given.

_____ 27. When using plastic containers for freezing, allow about 2.5 cm (1 in.)
(4, 5)   of ___?___ at the top between the food and the lid so the food can expand when it freezes. (two words)

_____ 28. An itemized list of food on hand is called a(n) ___?___.
(9)

_____ 29. Bacteria, yeasts, and molds are all different types of ___?___.
(14)

_____ 30. Poisonous waste products from bacteria are called ___?___.
(6)

_____ 31. Fuzzy microscopic plants are ___?___.
(5)

_____ 32. Foods that easily spoil or decay are ___?___.
(10)

_____ 33. Food must be stored at the right ___?___ and in the proper conditions to prevent spoilage.
(11)

Name _____

Date _____

Part Three Test

I. True-False. Read the following statements carefully. In the space at the left of each statement, write the word TRUE if the statement is true. Write FALSE if the statement is incorrect.

Ch. 9   _____   1. When possible, food and utensils should be stored in the locations where they are first and most often used.

Ch. 9   _____   2. It is desirable to have all traffic through the kitchen inside the work triangle.

Ch. 9   _____   3. Kitchen planners suggest having no more than three work centers in a kitchen.

Ch. 9   _____   4. The L-shaped kitchen usually has the shortest walking distance between appliances and has the best traffic and work pattern.

Ch. 9   _____   5. When a fuse "blows," it means that more electricity is flowing through the circuit than the wiring is designed to handle.

Ch. 9   _____   6. Faulty wiring may cause lights to dim when appliances are used.

Ch. 9   _____   7. If a home has three-hole wall outlets, it is proof that there is a grounding wire for appliances.

Ch. 10   _____   8. When shopping for an appliance, the best buy is usually the least expensive.

Ch. 10   _____   9. Different microwave ovens vary in the amount of power they use, so you should check the wattage when purchasing one.

Ch. 10   _____   10. The frost-free type refrigerator costs less to buy and operate.

Ch. 10   _____   11. When an appliance doesn't work, one of the first things to do is check to see whether or not it is plugged in.

Ch. 10   _____   12. EnergyGuide labels provide estimated costs for installing an appliance.

Ch. 10   _____   13. A full warranty covers all parts, labor, and shipping costs involved in the repair of defects without a time limit.

Ch. 10   _____   14. Detachable cords should first be plugged into the wall outlet and then connected to the appliance.

Ch. 11   _____   15. Discount food stores offer more customer services and lower prices than supermarkets.

Ch. 11   _____   16. How quickly food gets to the marketplace depends on how much processing it needs.

Ch. 11   _____   17. By law, a picture of the product must appear on the food label.

Ch. 11   _____   18. Ingredients on a food label are listed by weight in increasing order.

Ch. 11   _____   19. Nutrition information on labels is given for the total quantity of food in the container.

Ch. 11   _____   20. Open dating is usually found only on bakery products.

Ch. 11   _____   21. Buying damaged, leaking, rusty, or bulging cans of food is a good way to save money.

Ch. 11 _____ 22. Studies show that coupons increase the price of food.

Ch. 11 _____ 23. The pack date is the day the product was packaged, manufactured, or processed.

Ch. 11 _____ 24. By law, nutrition labels are required for all packaged foods.

Ch. 12 _____ 25. The way food is stored determines how long it keeps its nutrients and quality.

Ch. 12 _____ 26. Not all microorganisms are harmful to the human body.

Ch. 12 _____ 27. Plastic containers for freezing should be filled to the top to eliminate air.

Ch. 12 _____ 28. Leftovers should be allowed to cool at room temperature before storing in the refrigerator or freezer.

Ch. 12 _____ 29. Freezing temperatures kill microorganisms.

II. Matching. Find the term in the right column that BEST corresponds to each description in the left column. Write the letter of the term in the blank space provided. Do not use any term more than once. Some terms will not be used.

Descriptions

Ch. 9 _____ 30. A continuous line of appliances and cabinets on two adjoining walls.

Ch. 9 _____ 31. A continuous arrangement of appliances and cabinets on three adjoining walls.

Ch. 10 _____ 32. A guarantee to the purchaser by the manufacturer for repair or replacement of the item within a certain time period.

Ch. 10 _____ 33. An appliance which has been cleaned, perhaps painted, and is in working condition.

Ch. 10 _____ 34. A type of oven that makes food molecules vibrate against each other.

Ch. 11 _____ 35. Specifies the ingredients a common food must contain.

Ch. 11 _____ 36. The cost per ounce, item, or other convenient measure displayed on a tag attached to the shelf.

Ch. 11 _____ 37. Indicates the time limit of a product's peak quality.

Ch. 12 _____ 38. Fuzzy microscopic plants that live on food.

Ch. 12 _____ 39. Poisonous waste products which come from bacteria and are capable of causing illness and even death.

Ch. 12 _____ 40. Indicates that refrigeration is necessary.

Terms

A. standard of identity
B. perishable
C. rebuilt
D. universal product code
E. warranty
F. L-shaped kitchen
G. molds
H. freshness date
I. toxins
J. convection oven
K. one-wall kitchen
L. reconditioned
M. unit pricing
N. microwave oven
O. U-shaped kitchen
P. inventory
Q. induction oven
R. pull or sell date

476

(Continued on next page)

III. Multiple Choice. In the space at the left, write the letter of the choice that BEST completes each statement.

Ch. 9 _____ 41. A plan that makes use of space that might otherwise go unused in a large kitchen is the:
  A. island kitchen
  B. one-wall kitchen
  C. basic kitchen
  D. L-shaped kitchen

Ch. 10 _____ 42. When buying kitchen equipment, you should do all of the following EXCEPT:
  A. visit several stores to compare prices, quality, warranties, and special features
  B. inquire about delivery and installation cost
  C. analyze your family's needs as well as available space
  D. choose the appliance that has the most special features

Ch. 11 _____ 43. In order to assist you when shopping, a shopping list should:
  A. be arranged according to the layout of the store
  B. be alphabetical for easy use
  C. have your family's favorite foods listed first
  D. be limited in the number of items listed

Ch. 11 _____ 44. Generic foods are:
  A. quality foods with brand names
  B. quality foods without brand names
  C. private labels for a specific store
  D. unlabeled substandard products sold by manufacturers

Ch. 11 _____ 45. Foods that are canned, packaged, or frozen are best known as:
  A. enriched foods
  B. processed foods
  C. irradiated foods
  D. fortified foods

Ch. 11 _____ 46. All of the following statements relating to buying food are true EXCEPT:
  A. most convenience foods cost less than those made from scratch
  B. unit pricing makes it easier to compare prices
  C. price per serving is more important than price per pound
  D. shoplifting increases the prices all consumers pay for products

Ch. 12 _____ 47. For dry storage, food should be stored:
  A. under the sink to save space
  B. above the refrigerator or range
  C. in the lower drawer of a range
  D. in cool, dark areas away from moisture, light, and heat

Ch. 12 _____ 48. After shopping, the first foods to be stored at home should be:
  A. meat and poultry
  B. dairy products
  C. frozen foods
  D. produce

Ch. 12 _____ 49. The inside temperature of a manual-defrost refrigerator:
  A. remains the same throughout the refrigerator
  B. has the warmest area at the bottom and door shelves
  C. has the coldest temperature in the middle shelf area
  D. has the warmest area on the top shelf

Ch. 12 _____ 50. Foods that freeze well include:
  A. potatoes and fresh fruit
  B. mayonnaise and custards
  C. poultry and bread
  D. lettuce and celery

Chapter 13 Test

I. True-False. Read the following statements carefully. In the space at the left of each statement, write TRUE if the statement is true. Write FALSE if the statement is incorrect.

_____ 1. Careful handling of food helps to prevent bacteria from multiplying.

_____ 2. Bacteria must have food, moisture, and the right temperature in order to grow.

_____ 3. Sanitation means taking necessary precautions to destroy all bacteria.

_____ 4. Sharp knives are safer than dull ones.

_____ 5. Never use a metal object to remove food from an electrical appliance while it is still connected to an outlet.

_____ 6. In the kitchen, you need separate towels for wiping hands and wiping dishes.

_____ 7. Mixing two or more household cleaning products together may release poisonous gases.

_____ 8. To rescue a person who is in contact with electricity, use your hands to drag him/her from the source.

_____ 9. When cutting, always slant the blade of the knife away from you.

_____ 10. Food poisoning symptoms usually begin from 1 to 2 hours after eating.

_____ 11. If you get a burn, use cold water instead of an ointment.

_____ 12. If grease catches fire when you are frying, throw cold water on it.

_____ 13. A damp oven mitt on a hot pan can create enough steam to cause a serious burn.

_____ 14. More accidents occur in the kitchen than in any other room of the house.

_____ 15. Partially cooking food will stop the growth of bacteria.

_____ 16. Use your bare fingers to pick up broken glass so you can easily grasp the glass.

_____ 17. Household cleansers should be stored under the kitchen sink.

II. Matching. Find the term in the right column that BEST corresponds to each description in the left column. Write the letter of the term in the blank space provided. Do not use any term more than once. Some terms will not be used.

Descriptions

_____ 18. Any poison produced by bacteria in food.

_____ 19. Bacteria often found in improperly home-canned foods that cause severe illness or death.

_____ 20. Known as food poisoning.

_____ 21. Seedlike, single cells from which bacteria grow.

_____ 22. Can be caused by a person sneezing or coughing while preparing food.

_____ 23. An odorless, deadly gas.

Terms

A. childproofing
B. botulism
C. carbon monoxide
D. food-borne illness
E. perfringen poisoning
F. flammable
G. sulfur dioxide
H. salmonella
I. shock
J. spores
K. staphylococcal poisoning
L. toxin

III. Multiple Choice. In the space at the left, write the letter of the choice that BEST completes each statement.

_____ 24. Freezing temperatures cause most bacteria to:
A. increase in number
B. decrease in number
C. stop multiplying
D. die off and disappear

_____ 25. The food most likely to be contaminated with salmonella bacteria is:
A. cooked spaghetti
B. fresh poultry
C. bread
D. salad dressing

_____ 26. The single most important cause of kitchen accidents is:
A. human carelessness
B. heavily trafficked areas
C. faulty equipment
D. improper clothing

_____ 27. The Heimlich maneuver is used to help someone who:
A. is choking
B. has a burn
C. has swallowed poison
D. has a severe cut

_____ 28. The illness that is not a type of food-borne illness is:
A. perfringen poisoning
B. appendicitis
C. salmonellosis
D. staphylococcal poisoning

_____ 29. All of the following are true statements about kitchen safety and sanitation EXCEPT:
A. wear short sleeves or roll up long ones
B. wear disposable plastic gloves if you have an open cut on your hands
C. keep countertops, cookware, and floors clean
D. brush your hair back from your face with your hands while working with food

IV. Completion. In the space at the left, write the word or words that BEST complete each statement. As a clue, the total number of letters in the word is given.

_____ 30. Keeping yourself clean to avoid transferring harmful bacteria to food is personal ___?___.
(7)

_____ 31. Cleaning fluids and aerosol sprays are ___?___ and should not be used or stored near a source of heat.
(9)

_____ 32. Rescue ___?___ may be needed to save someone who has suffered an electric shock.
(9)

_____ 33. Smoke from a fire is thinner near the ___?___.
(5)

Name _____

Date _____

Chapter 14 Test

I. Matching. Find the term in the right column that BEST corresponds to each description in the left column. Write the letter of the term in the blank space provided. Do not use any term more than once. Some terms will not be used.

Descriptions

_____ 1. Usually has a serrated edge.

_____ 2. Used to spread frosting on a cake.

_____ 3. A long, narrow knife.

_____ 4. Squeezing the ball end draws liquid into the tube.

_____ 5. Removes food from sides of bowl.

_____ 6. Used to help retain nutrients in vegetables.

_____ 7. Used for baking angel food and chiffon cakes.

_____ 8. A short-bladed knife for cleaning and peeling foods.

_____ 9. Has a blade that swivels.

Terms

A. paring knife
B. steamer
C. peeler
D. slicing knife
E. straight-edge spatula
F. strainer
G. rubber scraper
H. baster
I. Dutch oven
J. pastry brush
K. bread knife
L. tube pan
M. chef's knife
N. wire whisk

II. True-False. Read the following statements carefully. In the space at the left of each statement, write TRUE if the statement is true. Write FALSE if the statement is incorrect.

_____ 10. It pays to buy good quality cookware.

_____ 11. The same type of measuring tool is used for measuring small amounts of both dry and liquid ingredients.

_____ 12. Knowing how to use a tool properly is not important as long as the job gets done.

_____ 13. Vegetable brushes can substitute for pastry brushes.

_____ 14. Many nonelectrical tools and utensils can substitute for expensive electrical appliances.

_____ 15. A strainer removes unwanted parts, such as seeds, from food.

_____ 16. Special plastic cookware is now made for use in a conventional oven.

_____ 17. It is a good idea to limit your purchase of kitchen tools to those that can be stored in easily reached places.

_____ 18. A utility knife has a long, heavy blade.

_____ 19. A butcher knife is a heavy-duty knife that is widest near the point.

III. Matching. Find the tool in the right column that BEST corresponds to each use in the left column. Write the letter of the tool in the blank space provided. Do not use any term more than once. Some tool choices will not be used.

Uses

_____ 20. Beat, stir, and mix hot foods.

_____ 21. Bake foods and food combinations.

_____ 22. Bake bar cookies and sheet cakes.

_____ 23. Dip liquids such as soup from a pan to a bowl.

_____ 24. Shred vegetables and cheese.

_____ 25. Drain liquid from food.

_____ 26. Lift or turn food without piercing it.

_____ 27. Renew the sharp edge on a knife.

_____ 28. Beat and blend; especially good for egg white mixtures.

_____ 29. Heat foods that would burn easily over direct heat.

_____ 30. Fry, sauté, or panbroil.

_____ 31. Cut shortening into dry ingredients.

_____ 32. Cut pastry, dried fruits, and vegetables.

_____ 33. Help fill bottles with liquid.

Tools

A. sharpening steel
B. flour sifter
C. paring knife
D. pastry blender
E. ladle
F. vegetable brush
G. wire whisk
H. kitchen shears
I. dry measuring cups
J. tube pan
K. tongs
L. wooden spoon
M. double boiler
N. skillet
O. casserole
P. colander
Q. funnel
R. grater
S. jelly-roll pan

Name _____

Date _____

Chapter 15 Test

I. True-False. Read the following statements carefully. In the space at the left of each statement, write TRUE if the statement is true. Write FALSE if the statement is incorrect.

_____ 1. One quart equals 2 pints.

_____ 2. Foods cooked in liquid, such as vegetables and eggs, cook faster at high altitudes.

_____ 3. In the metric system liters measure weight and grams measure volume.

_____ 4. When a liquid simmers, the bubbles rise slowly but don't break the surface.

_____ 5. It is easy to decrease a recipe for baked products, such as cakes, because generally they do not depend on exact amounts of ingredients.

_____ 6. A recipe in the narrative form is easier to follow than one in the action form.

_____ 7. One cup equals 8 fluid ounces.

_____ 8. The standard recipe form is the one most widely used in cookbooks.

II. Completion. In the space at the left, write the word or words that BEST complete each statement. As a clue, the total number of letters in the word is given.

_____ (8) 9. Cooking in liquid includes boiling, simmering, stewing, and ___?___.

_____ (8) 10. Dry-heat cooking methods include baking, roasting, and ___?___.

_____ (10) 11. ___?___ is a cooking method that involves cooking food quickly in a small amount of oil until just tender.

_____ (8) 12. Moist-heat cooking includes steaming and ___?___.

_____ (6) 13. To accurately measure brown sugar, it must be ___?___ into the measuring cup.

_____ (6) 14. The ___?___ system is a system of measurement based on the number 10.

III. Matching. Find the term in the right column that BEST corresponds to each description in the left column. Write the letter of the term in the blank space provided. Do not use any term more than once. Some terms will not be used.

Descriptions

		Terms
_____	15. Number of servings or pieces that will result from a recipe.	A. wok
_____	16. A method of measuring solid fat.	B. sauté
_____	17. Panfry.	C. baste
_____	18. Temperature at which fats begin to break down, causing them to discolor and develop an off-flavor and odor.	D. smoking point
		E. simmer
		F. 160°C (320°F)
		G. score
_____	19. To cover a food with water and simmer until tender.	H. yield
_____	20. A pan with a rounded bottom that is generally used for stir-frying.	I. water displacement method
		J. stew
_____	21. To brush or pour liquid over food as it cooks.	K. plastic cooking bag
		L. steamer
		M. skimming

IV. Matching. Find the term in the right column that BEST corresponds to each description in the left column. Write the letter of the term in the blank space provided. Do not use any term more than once. Some terms will not be used.

Food Preparation Descriptions

		Terms
_____	22. To use high heat to brown meat.	A. mince
_____	23. To work dough by pressing and folding until it becomes smooth and elastic.	B. blanch
		C. flake
_____	24. To cook a liquid until it becomes more concentrated.	D. reduce
_____	25. To cut food into the smallest possible pieces.	E. knead
_____	26. To break into small pieces with a fork.	F. cube
		G. toss
_____	27. To heat a liquid such as milk to the simmering point.	H. score
_____	28. To soak in an acid-oil mixture.	I. shred
_____	29. To cut into small squares.	J. marinate
_____	30. To add water to a concentrated food to return it to its natural state.	K. coat
		L. reconstitute
_____	31. To cover food evenly with flour.	M. scald
_____	32. To make very thin, straight cuts in the surface of a food.	N. cream
		O. fold in
_____	33. To beat until soft and smooth.	P. sear
		Q. skim
		R. dredge

Name _____

Date _____

Chapter 16 Test

I. True-False. Read the following statements carefully. In the space at the left of each statement, write TRUE if the statement is true. Write FALSE if the statement is incorrect.

_____ 1. All food should be covered during microwave cooking.

_____ 2. Microwave ovens use less energy than conventional ovens.

_____ 3. Sealing food in aluminum foil speeds microwave cooking.

_____ 4. Other appliances can be plugged into the same circuit as a microwave oven.

_____ 5. One advantage of microwave cooking is that more nutrients are retained because foods do not need to be cooked in additional water.

_____ 6. Never turn the microwave oven on when it is empty.

_____ 7. Dry foods cook faster than moist foods in a microwave oven.

_____ 8. As a rule, foods cook fastest in the center of the microwave oven.

_____ 9. The more fat and sugar a food contains, the slower it cooks.

_____ 10. Small, even pieces cook more quickly than one large piece of the same food.

_____ 11. Square chunks of food cook more quickly than long, thin ones in the microwave.

_____ 12. Foods in square or rectangular pans may overcook in the corners.

_____ 13. Plastic wrap can be used as a lid in the microwave oven.

_____ 14. The microwave oven is a handy place to dry clothes quickly.

_____ 15. In a microwave oven, food must be turned or stirred to help it cook evenly.

II. Multiple Choice. In the space at the left, write the letter of the BEST choice that completes each statement.

_____ 16. Microwave energy is expressed in:
   A. watts of electricity   C. power setting
   B. amperes of electricity   D. thermal units

_____ 17. Foods that take less time to cook in the microwave oven are:
   A. rice   C. vegetables
   B. macaroni   D. pasta

_____ 18. A low-power setting should be used for:
   A. heating   C. cooking
   B. defrosting   D. browning

_____ 19. Cooking time in a microwave oven is affected by the:
   A. amount of food   C. original temperature of the food
   B. shape of food   D. all of these

_____ 20. All of the following cookware materials are recommended for use in a microwave oven EXCEPT:
   A. metal   C. plastics
   B. paper   D. ceramic

_____ 21. A food that can generally be cooked in a microwave is:
        A. an egg in the shell   C. a tuna casserole
        B. french fries   D. all of these

_____ 22. To prepare a conventional recipe in the microwave oven, you will need to reduce the cooking time for most recipes by about:
        A. ½   C. 5 minutes
        B. ¼   D. 10 minutes

_____ 23. If foods in a microwave oven overcook, the:
        A. power needs to be reduced   c. food should be stirred
        B. food should be covered tightly   D. food should be turned

III. Completion. In the space at the left, write the word that BEST completes each statement. As a clue, the total number of letters in the word is given.

_____ 24. Arrange food in the oven or in a cooking dish in a(n) __?__ .
(6)

_____ 25. To keep food from __?__ in the microwave oven, pierce the food's skin in several places.
(9)

_____ 26. An important step in microwave cooking is __?__, during which the food continues to cook although the microwave power is turned off. (two words)
(8, 4)

_____ 27. __?__ should not be used on the surface of foods because it draws out moisture during microwaving.
(4)

_____ 28. The more solid and compact the food, the __?__ it cooks.
(6)

IV. Matching. Find the term in the right column that BEST corresponds to each description in the left column. Write the letter of the term in the blank space provided. Do not use any term more than once. Some terms will not be used.

Descriptions

_____ 29. The amount of energy the microwave oven uses to generate microwaves.

_____ 30. Caused by vibration of food particles in a microwave oven.

_____ 31. The order in which foods for a meal are cooked.

_____ 32. The actual time food cooks with microwave energy.

_____ 33. Certain areas of microwave ovens that get more power than others.

Terms
A. friction
B. cooking power
C. microwave time
D. arcing
E. hot spots
F. waiting time
G. sequence
H. energy field
I. center
J. magnetism

Name _____

Date _____

Chapter 17 Test

I. True-False. Read the following statements carefully. In the space at the left of each statement, write TRUE if the statement is true. Write FALSE if the statement is incorrect.

_____ 1. One good way to conserve energy is to cool leftovers at room temperature before refrigerating.

_____ 2. An example of an appealing meal is one with all strong-flavored foods.

_____ 3. Pre-preparation and assembling needed items before you begin to work are basic principles in working efficiently.

_____ 4. Meal planning helps to ensure that meals are nutritious.

_____ 5. There is an unlimited supply of pure water.

_____ 6. There is little that can be done to make leftovers interesting.

_____ 7. Preheating the oven is recommended for all foods.

_____ 8. A dripping faucet wastes very little water.

_____ 9. Foods that contrast in color and texture are called "complements."

_____ 10. The foods at each meal should have a variety of shapes and sizes.

_____ 11. To conserve energy, use small appliances instead of large ones whenever possible.

_____ 12. Metal pans and bakeware absorb and hold more heat than those made of glass and glass-ceramic.

_____ 13. Experts agree that the world's growing population is not a major cause of the worldwide food shortage.

_____ 14. To time a meal, plan backwards from the time the meal should be ready.

_____ 15. In hot weather, people generally enjoy eating cold foods, such as salads.

_____ 16. A beginner should prepare complicated recipes in order to master cooking skills quickly.

_____ 17. The easiest way to handle cleanup is to save it all until the end.

_____ 18. Always throw out the water in which vegetables and other foods have been cooked.

_____ 19. Only put drinking water on the table if people will drink it.

_____ 20. Getting food to the people who need it is part of the world food problem.

II. Matching.
Find the term in the right column that BEST corresponds to each description in the left column. Write the letter of the term in the blank space provided. Do not use any term more than once. Some terms will not be used.

Descriptions

_____ 21. Avoiding waste of nutrients.

_____ 22. Using resources wisely to achieve specific goals.

_____ 23. Any food that is no longer suitable for eating.

_____ 24. The process of getting things ready for use ahead of time.

_____ 25. Time, skills, money, and equipment.

_____ 26. Aid to nutrition planning.

_____ 27. Determining cooking time is part of this.

Terms

A. reserves
B. planning
C. timetable
D. management
E. food waste
F. Daily Food Guide
G. pre-preparation
H. technology
I. recipe
J. food conservation
K. resources
L. goals

III. Completion.
In the space at the left, write the word or words that BEST complete each statement. As a clue, the total number of letters in the word is given.

_____ (7)   28. To reprocess used products so that they can be used again is to ___?___ them.

_____ (12)   29. The preservation and wise use of resources is ___?___.

_____ (7)   30. The world food supply is a(n) ___?___ resource.

_____ (9)   31. ___?___ are often used in kitchens today for everything from weight control to budgeting to making appliances work.

_____ (14)   32. Measuring dry ingredients before measuring shortening is an example of work ___?___.

_____ (11)   33. Fitting various tasks together for best use of time is called ___?___.

Chapter 18 Test

I. Matching. Find the term in the right column that BEST corresponds to each description in the left column. Write the letter of the term in the blank space provided. Do not use any term more than once. Some terms will not be used.

Descriptions

_____ 1. Usually includes a number of courses, each served separately on clean plates.

_____ 2. Serving dishes are brought to the table, and plates are stacked in front of the host or hostess.

_____ 3. Food is served in dishes that are passed from one person to another at the table.

_____ 4. Term for meals served to people seated at a table.

_____ 5. Combination of formal and modified English styles of table service.

_____ 6. A food arrangement in which people serve themselves from an assortment of food.

_____ 7. Food is placed on plates in the kitchen and then brought to the table.

Terms

A. formal service
B. compromise service
C. simple service
D. buffet service
E. modified English service
F. special service
G. family style
H. table service
I. plate service
J. French system

II. True-False. Read the following statements carefully. In the space at the left of each statement, write TRUE if the statement is true. Write FALSE if the statement is incorrect.

_____ 8. Earthenware, ironstone, and stoneware are all types of dinnerware.

_____ 9. Tumblers and stemware are different types of glassware.

_____ 10. Avoid serving foods that have to be cut before they are eaten at a buffet.

_____ 11. In passing food, it is best to avoid confusion by passing it in the same direction, generally to the left.

_____ 12. Most countries follow the same set of table manner rules that is used in the United States.

_____ 13. Don't cut up a large piece of food all at once; cut off each bite or two just before you eat it.

_____ 14. Chicken may be eaten with the fingers in an informal restaurant.

_____ 15. You need not wait until everyone at your table is served before you start eating.

_____ 16. Your napkin should be tucked into your collar before starting to eat.

_____ 17. Napkins should be placed to the right of the plate when setting the table.

III. Matching. Find the term in the right column that BEST corresponds to each description in the left column. Write the letter of the term in the blank space provided. Do not use any term more than once. Some terms will not be used.

Descriptions

_____ 18. Has only a coating of silver over a base of metal.

_____ 19. Short, wooden tools used to pick up food and transfer it to the mouth.

_____ 20. A glass-like protective finish on dinnerware.

_____ 21. Consists of dinnerware, glassware, and flatware.

_____ 22. This means please reply to an invitation.

_____ 23. Made of silver with copper added to harden it.

_____ 24. Tableware that can be purchased separately.

_____ 25. Long, narrow cloths that cover the center of the table.

_____ 26. Highly resistant to breakage, chipping, and cracking; can go right from freezer to oven.

_____ 27. The tableware needed for one person at a meal.

_____ 28. Consists of an arrangement of dishes, flatware, glasses, and linens for one person.

Terms

A. runners
B. place setting
C. tableware
D. cover
E. silverplate
F. glaze
G. sterling silver
H. ironstone
I. open stock
J. R.S.V.P.
K. glass-ceramic
L. tumbler
M. flatware
N. chopsticks

IV. Multiple Choice. In the space at the left, write the letter of the choice that BEST completes each statement.

_____ 29. By law, sterling silver must contain:
A. 25.5 percent silver   C. 70.5 percent silver
B. 50.5 percent silver   D. 92.5 percent silver

_____ 30. The most expensive and formal dinnerware is:
A. earthenware   C. melamine
B. china   D. stoneware

_____ 31. When buying tableware, you should first select:
A. tablecloth and napkins   C. flatware
B. glassware   D. dinnerware

_____ 32. A practice that is considered essential to good table manners is:
A. watching the actions of your   C. tucking your napkin under your chin
   host or hostess
B. blowing on hot food to cool it   D. breaking up food all at one time

_____ 33. The fork to be used first is placed:
A. to the right of the spoon   C. farthest from the plate
B. to the right of the knife   D. closest to the plate

Part Four Test

I. True-False. Read the following statements carefully. In the space at the left of each statement, write the word TRUE if the statement is true. Write FALSE if the statement is incorrect.

Ch. 13 _____ 1. Food contaminated with harmful bacteria always has an odor or an off-flavor.

Ch. 13 _____ 2. The proper way to treat a burn is to apply grease to the injured area.

Ch. 13 _____ 3. Warming up leftover food at low temperatures is sufficient since it has been previously cooked.

Ch. 13 _____ 4. Utensils used for raw food should be washed and rinsed before using them for cooked food.

Ch. 14 _____ 5. One set of measuring cups is used for measuring both dry and liquid ingredients.

Ch. 14 _____ 6. Dull knives cause more accidents than sharp ones.

Ch. 14 _____ 7. A whisk is used to cut shortening into dry pastry ingredients.

Ch. 14 _____ 8. A pressure cooker can reduce cooking times.

Ch. 15 _____ 9. Rapid boiling cooks food faster than a slow, rolling boil.

Ch. 15 _____ 10. As the altitude increases, water boils at a lower temperature, so foods cooked in liquid take longer to cook.

Ch. 15 _____ 11. To check a liquid measurement, hold the measuring cup in your hand at eye level.

Ch. 15 _____ 12. Fat can be heated to higher temperatures than water.

Ch. 15 _____ 13. Salt should be used before broiling to bring out flavor.

Ch. 16 _____ 14. In a microwave oven, friction produced by food molecules vibrating against each other creates heat and cooks the food.

Ch. 16 _____ 15. Dry foods cook more quickly than moist foods in a microwave oven.

Ch. 17 _____ 16. Pre-preparation means assembling all ingredients and utensils after beginning to put the recipe together.

Ch. 17 _____ 17. Conservation means using resources wisely.

Ch. 18 _____ 18. Flatware refers to the utensils used in cooking foods.

Ch. 18 _____ 19. The easiest serving style for a large group is compromise service.

Ch. 18 _____ 20. Table manners are similar from country to country.

II. Matching. Find the term in the right column that BEST corresponds to each description in the left column. Write the letter of the term in the blank space provided. Do not use any term more than once. Some terms will not be used.

	Descriptions	**Terms**
Ch. 13 _____	21. Taking necessary precautions to keep bacteria down to as small a number as possible.	A. stir-fry
Ch. 13 _____	22. Bacteria often carried by pets, insects, or rodents.	B. colander
		C. sauté
Ch. 14 _____	23. Used to lift and turn hot foods without piercing them.	D. arcing
Ch. 14 _____	24. A large, perforated bowl for draining liquid from food such as spaghetti.	E. sanitation
		F. cover
Ch. 15 _____	25. Cook food quickly in a small amount of oil until just tender.	G. ladle
		H. recycle
Ch. 15 _____	26. Cook food in liquid at a temperature just below boiling.	I. hot spots
		J. conservation
Ch. 15 _____	27. Cook uncovered food in a small amount of fat in a frying pan.	K. compromise service
		L. standing time
Ch. 15 _____	28. Simmer in small amounts of liquid so the food retains its shape.	M. family style
		N. work simplification
Ch. 16 _____	29. Certain areas of microwave ovens that get more power than other areas.	O. salmonella
		P. tongs
Ch. 16 _____	30. The period that food continues to cook after the microwave power is turned off.	Q. simmer
		R. formal service
Ch. 17 _____	31. Fitting various tasks together for the best use of time.	S. power setting
Ch. 17 _____	32. To reprocess used products so they can be used again.	T. dovetailing
		U. personal hygiene
Ch. 17 _____	33. Food is placed in serving dishes in the kitchen and then passed from one person to another at the table.	V. restoration
		W. poach
Ch. 18 _____	34. An elaborate method of serving food; also known as Continental or Russian.	X. staphylococcus
		Y. center
Ch. 18 _____	35. Items of table service consisting of dishes, flatware, glasses, and linen for one person.	Z. wok

(Continued on next page)

III. Multiple Choice. In the space at the left, write the letter of the choice that BEST completes each statement.

Ch. 13 _____ 36. It is important to scrub your hands immediately after all of the following EXCEPT:
A. handling raw meat, poultry, fish, or eggs
B. coughing, sneezing, or touching your hair or face
C. playing with pets
D. chopping vegetables

Ch. 14 _____ 37. To remove food from liquid, you should use a:
A. basting spoon
B. wooden spoon
C. slotted spoon
D. ladle

Ch. 14 _____ 38. A knife most suitable for dividing cuts of meat is a:
A. butcher knife
B. boning knife
C. utility knife
D. chef's knife

Ch. 15 _____ 39. Brown sugar is measured by:
A. sifting it to remove any lumps
B. packing it into a cup until the sugar holds the cup's shape when inverted
C. spooning it into a cup and shaking the cup firmly
D. spooning it loosely into a measuring cup

Ch. 15 _____ 40. The cooking method you choose depends on all of the following EXCEPT:
A. your personal preference
B. the food you are preparing
C. the equipment and time available
D. how many work centers are available

Ch. 15 _____ 41. The yield in a recipe refers to the:
A. unit cost per serving
B. caloric weight of ingredients
C. number of servings
D. number of courses

Ch. 15 _____ 42. When you cut food into very small pieces, you are:
A. paring
B. mincing
C. scoring
D. dredging

Ch. 16 _____ 43. All of the following are true statements about the microwave oven EXCEPT:
A. it defrosts, reheats, and cooks foods rapidly
B. it cooks all foods in less time
C. foods do not need to be cooked in additional water
D. it needs to be connected to a separate, grounded, 110-volt circuit

Ch. 16 _____ 44. Suitable containers for microwaving include:
A. metal cookware and aluminum foil
B. all plastic and glass-ceramic types
C. paper containers
D. containers that are not heat-resistant

Ch. 16 _____ 45. Food cooks more evenly in the microwave oven when it is placed in:
A. round pans
B. square pans
C. rectangular pans
D. plastic containers

Ch. 17 _____ 46. The clues to managing meals successfully include:
A. planning and making decisions
B. using the Daily Food Guide
C. using available resources
D. all of the above

Ch. 17 _____ 47. Experts estimate that people in the United States waste at least:
  A. one percent of the edible food
  B. five percent of the edible food
  C. ten percent of the edible food
  D. up to twenty percent of the edible food

Ch. 18 _____ 48. Buying open stock tableware means that:
  A. items are sold together as a set
  B. items are usually less expensive than those sold differently
  C. pieces can be added or replaced readily
  D. it is of inferior quality

Ch. 18 _____ 49. When setting a table, the flatware should be arranged so the:
  A. knife is to the left of the plate
  B. forks are to the right of the plate
  C. piece you use first is farthest from the plate
  D. piece you use first is closest to the plate

Ch. 18 _____ 50. An important practice in exhibiting good table manners is to:
  A. cool hot food by blowing on it
  B. avoid talking with food in your mouth
  C. tuck the napkin under your chin when eating
  D. cut up large pieces of food all at one time

Name ____________________

Date ____________________

Chapter 19 Test

I. True-False. Read the following statements carefully. In the space at the left of each statement, write TRUE if the statement is true. Write FALSE if the statement is incorrect.

_______ 1. Most fruits are picked underripe.

_______ 2. Some fruits must be cooked to make them edible.

_______ 3. Tender fruits that hold their shape may be broiled.

_______ 4. Avoid buying fresh fruit that is heavy for its size because it has thick skin and little juice.

_______ 5. Wash berries, cherries, and grapes before storing them.

_______ 6. Products labeled "fruit juice" may contain a small amount of other liquid, such as water.

_______ 7. An ice coating on a package of frozen fruit means that it has thawed and refrozen.

_______ 8. For cooking, buy firm and slightly underripe fruits.

_______ 9. Overcooked, microwaved fruits become tough, hard, and dry.

_______ 10. Citrus fruits spoil very quickly unless they are refrigerated.

II. Completion. In the space at the left, write the word that BEST completes each statement. As a clue, the total number of letters in the word is given.

_______ (7) 11. Fresh fruits and vegetables are called __?__.

_______ (5) 12. Fruits can be cooked in liquid, broiled, fried, or __?__.

_______ (9) 13. Dried fruits cook faster if they are __?__ in hot water.

_______ (11) 14. Fruits are a natural __?__ food because they can be served with a minimum of preparation.

_______ (8) 15. While many fruits can be purchased year-round, some fruits are __?__ and can be purchased only during certain months.

_______ (5) 16. Cooking fruit breaks down the __?__ and makes the fruit easier to digest.

_______ (8) 17. Fruit sold in __?__ form has several pieces held together with flexible plastic tape or a rubber band.

_______ (10) 18. __?__ occurs when warm weather causes the chlorophyll to return to the skins of ripe oranges.

_______ (6) 19. Lemon, grapefruit, or __?__ juice can be used to keep cut fruit from turning brown.

_______ (9) 20. Cooking fruits for long periods of time affects flavor, color, and __?__.

_______ (5) 21. __?__ fruit includes raisins, dates, and apricots.

(Continued on next page)

_____ 22. ___?___ are fruit coated with batter and deep-fat fried.
(8)

_____ 23. As a rule, ___?___ fruit is not as nutritious as fresh fruit.
(6)

_____ 24. Bananas are a good source of ___?___.
(9)

_____ 25. Fruits cooked in sugar syrup should be cut into ___?___ pieces.
(5)

_____ 26. Dried fruits have a high concentration of ___?___.
(5)

III. Matching. Find the term in the right column that BEST corresponds to each description in the left column. Write the letter of the term in the blank space provided. Do not use any term more than once. Some terms will not be used.

Descriptions

_____ 27. Fruit that can never ripen after it is picked.

_____ 28. Fruit that has not yet reached top eating quality.

_____ 29. Fruit that has reached its full size.

_____ 30. Fruit that cannot be picked until it is fully mature, ripe, and full-flavored.

_____ 31. Fresh fruit that must be cooked to make it edible.

_____ 32. Fruit that is ready to eat.

_____ 33. Fruit that needs to be refrigerated in an airtight container.

Terms

A. mature fruit
B. ripe fruit
C. canned fruit
D. rhubarb
E. cut fruit
F. underripe fruit
G. dried fruit
H. citrus fruit
I. kumquat
J. immature fruit

Chapter 20 Test

I. Matching. Find the term in the right column that BEST corresponds to each description in the left column. Write the letter of the term in the blank space provided. Do not use any term more than once. Some terms will not be used.

Descriptions

_____ 1. A chemical that gives color to yellow and orange vegetables.

_____ 2. A bitter, poisonous chemical found in green potatoes.

_____ 3. Pigments which are soluble in water and cause white vegetables to darken when cooked.

_____ 4. Seeds which grow in a pod.

_____ 5. A green coloring matter found in some vegetables.

Terms

A. chlorophyll
B. solanine
C. cellulose
D. legumes
E. flavones
F. celeriac
G. carotene

II. Matching. Find the vegetable in the right column that BEST corresponds to each description in the left column. Write the letter of the answer in the blank space provided. Do not use any letters more than once. Not all letters will be used.

Descriptions

_____ 6. A vegetable that is a seed.

_____ 7. A vegetable that is a flower.

_____ 8. A vegetable that is the leaves of a plant.

_____ 9. A vegetable that is a root.

_____ 10. A vegetable that is a tuber.

_____ 11. A vegetable that is stem.

Vegetables

A. potato
B. asparagus
C. tomato
D. broccoli
E. cucumber
F. celeriac
G. carrot
H. spinach

III. True-False. Read the following statements carefully. In the space at the left of each statement, write TRUE if the statement is true. Write FALSE if the statement is incorrect.

_____ 12. Some vegetables are really fruits because they are the fleshy parts surrounding the seeds.

_____ 13. Canned whole vegetables usually cost less than canned pieces.

_____ 14. When combined with grain products such as rice or with animal foods, legumes provide high-quality proteins.

_____ 15. If stored properly, dried vegetables will keep their quality for months.

_____ 16. A small amount of acid in cooking water will help red vegetables retain their color.

_____ 17. Lentils must be soaked before cooking.

_____ 18. A pressure cooker is best used for vegetables that require a short cooking time.

_____ 19. Baked potatoes can explode in a microwave oven.

_____ 20. You should never purchase root vegetables that are sprouting.

_____ 21. Large amounts of water should not be used in cooking most vegetables.

_____ 22. Vegetables, especially fresh ones, are among the best sources of protein.

(Continued on next page)

_____ 23. In hot weather, potatoes and sweet potatoes should be refrigerated for longer storage.

_____ 24. Onions and potatoes should not be stored together.

_____ 25. Home-canned vegetables can be heated in the microwave oven.

IV. Multiple Choice. In the space at the left, write the letter of the choice that BEST completes each statement.

_____ 26. Of the following, the vegetable that is LOWEST in calories is:
   A. celery   C. peas
   B. corn   D. potatoes

_____ 27. Green peppers, tomatoes, and raw cabbage are among the best sources of:
   A. vitamin A   C. vitamin C
   B. thiamin   D. vitamin D

_____ 28. When buying vegetables, choose ones that are:
   A. small   C. extra large
   B. medium size   D. any size

_____ 29. Most fresh vegetables should be used within:
   A. 1 day   C. 5 to 7 days
   B. 2 to 5 days   D. 7 to 10 days

_____ 30. When strong-flavored vegetables such as onions and cabbage are overcooked, the flavor becomes:
   A. bitter   C. milder
   B. sweet   D. stronger

_____ 31. When cooking fresh vegetables, the first step is always to:
   A. boil water   C. cut them up
   B. wash the vegetables   D. peel off skins

_____ 32. Vegetables cooked with butter, brown sugar, and water are called:
   A. glazed   C. herbed
   B. creamed   D. scalloped

_____ 33. When stir-frying vegetables, all of the following rules should be followed EXCEPT:
   A. cut vegetables into small,   C. begin cooking with most
       uniform pieces   tender vegetables
   B. use a small amount of oil   D. cover pan near end of cooking time

Chapter 21 Test

I. True-False. Read the following statements carefully. In the space at the left of each statement, write TRUE if the statement is true. Write FALSE if the statement is incorrect.

_____ 1. Regardless of the other ingredients, a salad usually contains salad greens.

_____ 2. There are three basic kinds of salad dressings.

_____ 3. Fresh pineapple added to gelatin salads helps gelatin to thicken.

_____ 4. A molded salad can be made of rice or potatoes as well as gelatin.

_____ 5. A sharp knife is used to remove the core from head lettuce.

_____ 6. A chef's salad contains greens, strips of meat and cheese, and slices of hard-cooked eggs.

_____ 7. Yogurt can be used as a base for salad dressings.

_____ 8. French dressing contains egg yolks.

_____ 9. Most regular salad dressings are low in calories.

_____ 10. Tart fruits are usually served with a sweet or creamy dressing.

_____ 11. If greens are the main ingredient in a salad, add the dressing just before serving.

_____ 12. Protein salads are usually served as an accompaniment to a main dish.

_____ 13. A gelatin mold must be well oiled before pouring the mixture in so that it can be easily removed later.

_____ 14. Salads can be used as appetizers to stimulate the appetite.

_____ 15. Salads provide only a few nutrients because they do not contain foods from all the food groups.

II. Multiple Choice. In the space at the left, write the letter of the choice that BEST completes each statement.

_____ 16. A type of salad green that has dark green, broad curly leaves and a mild to bitter flavor is:
A. romaine lettuce   C. Chinese cabbage
B. escarole   D. leaf lettuce

_____ 17. Salad dressings made with yogurt:
A. should not contain lemon or lime juice   C. are less nutritious than other dressings
B. do not keep as well as other types   D. are lower in calories than other types

_____ 18. Salad ingredients should be drained to avoid:
A. bruising   C. diluting the salad dressing
B. wilting   D. spreading germs

_____ 19. Purchased salad dressings and mixes:
A. are a poor substitute for home-prepared dressings   C. are less expensive than home-prepared
B. can save you many hours of preparation time   D. have a shorter shelf life

_____ 20. To prevent the edges from turning brown, salad greens need to be:
    A. shredded   C. diced
    B. cut   D. torn

_____ 21. When buying iceberg lettuce, buy heads:
    A. that are tightly packed   C. that have a large core
    B. that "give" slightly when   D. that are slightly overmature
       squeezed gently   for milder flavor

_____ 22. Salad greens should be:
    A. washed before they are stored   C. stored without washing them first
    B. washed and drained for several   D. washed both before storing and
       hours before they are stored   before preparing

_____ 23. A salad green with tender, deep green leaves and a sharp flavor is:
    A. leaf lettuce   C. butterhead lettuce
    B. fresh spinach   D. Chinese cabbage

III. Matching. Find the term in the right column that BEST corresponds to each description in the left column. Write the letter of the term in the blank space provided. Do not use any term more than once. Some terms will not be used.

Descriptions	Terms
_____ 24. The main part of a salad.	A. base
_____ 25. A salad made with cheese, eggs, meat, poultry, fish, or shellfish.	B. salad bar
	C. cooked dressing
	D. layered salad
_____ 26. A hearty salad, usually without greens, using potatoes, rice, or pasta.	E. frozen salad
	F. tossed salad
_____ 27. A salad that is usually a mixture of greens.	G. protein salad
	H. French dressing
_____ 28. A combination of oil, vinegar, and seasonings.	I. main-dish salad
_____ 29. A rich dressing containing salad oil, egg yolk, vinegar or lemon juice, sugar, and seasonings.	J. body
	K. mixed salad
	L. mayonnaise
_____ 30. A dressing containing eggs, milk or water, and seasonings, thickened with flour.	M. arranged
_____ 31. The foundation of a salad on which the other ingredients are placed.	
_____ 32. A salad that usually combines fruit with whipped cream or cream cheese and mayonnaise.	
_____ 33. The ingredients in this type of salad are separate and form an attractive pattern.	

Name _____

Date _____

Chapter 22 Test

I. True-False. Read the following statements carefully. In the space at the left of each statement, write TRUE if the statement is true. Write FALSE if the statement is incorrect.

_____ 1. You can prevent a skin from forming on the surface of heated milk by stirring it constantly as it cooks.

_____ 2. Dry milk is a convenient form of milk that is economical for cooking.

_____ 3. If yogurt or sour cream separates, it should be discarded.

_____ 4. Fresh cheese is highly perishable.

_____ 5. Cheddar cheese tastes best when served directly from the refrigerator.

_____ 6. Milk reacts more quickly than cream to heat and acid.

_____ 7. Cheese comes in three forms: unripened, fresh, and natural.

_____ 8. To scald milk is to heat it just below boiling temperature until bubbles appear around the sides of the pan.

_____ 9. Milk and cream mixtures scorch quickly in a microwave oven.

_____ 10. The milkfat is the part of milk that contains most of the proteins, vitamins, minerals, and lactose.

_____ 11. Overcooked cheese becomes tough and stringy or rubbery.

II. Matching. Find the term in the right column that BEST corresponds to each description in the left column. Write the letter of the term in the blank space provided. Do not use any term more than once. Some terms will not be used.

Descriptions

_____ 12. A concentrated form of milk.

_____ 13. Milk that has separated into liquid and small lumps.

_____ 14. Must contain at least 3.25 percent milkfat.

_____ 15. Milk treated so the cream won't separate.

_____ 16. Skim milk to which lactic acid has been added to produce a tangy flavor and smooth, thick texture.

_____ 17. Milk that has not been pasteurized.

_____ 18. Milk to which vitamin D has been added.

_____ 19. Milk that has been heat-treated to kill all disease-producing bacteria.

Terms

A. pasteurized milk
B. goat's milk
C. homogenized milk
D. curdled milk
E. fortified milk
F. cheese
G. whole milk
H. milkfat
I. buttermilk
J. raw milk
K. cream
L. evaporated milk
M. sour cream
N. skim milk

III. Matching. Find the term in the right column that BEST corresponds to each description in the left column. Write the letter of the term in the blank space provided. Do not use any term more than once. Some terms will not be used.

Descriptions

_____ 20. A creamy, white, semisoft cheese known as pizza cheese.

_____ 21. The fatty part of whole milk.

_____ 22. A soft yellow cheese, usually foil-wrapped, used for dessert crackers or fruit.

_____ 23. A hard yellow cheese that is grated after being cured for a year.

_____ 24. A thick, smooth cream with a mild acid flavor.

_____ 25. Cheese that has not been allowed to age or ripen.

_____ 26. A custard-like product made by fermenting milk with a special bacteria culture.

_____ 27. A frozen whipped cream or whipped topping that has been sweetened and flavored.

_____ 28. Made from milk, fruit or juice, stabilizers, and sugar.

Terms

A. yogurt
B. cream
C. sour cream
D. Swiss cheese
E. sherbet
F. Parmesan cheese
G. frozen custard
H. whipping cream
I. fresh cheese
J. brie
K. mousse
L. mozzarella cheese
M. brick cheese
N. bombe
O. half-and-half

IV. Multiple Choice. In the space at the left, write the letter of the choice that BEST completes each statement.

_____ 29. Cream with 18 to 30 percent milkfat is:
A. heavy cream   C. whipping cream
B. half-and-half   D. light, or coffee, cream

_____ 30. Milk is low in:
A. vitamin D   C. iron
B. calcium   D. phosphorous

_____ 31. Skim milk has the following ingredient(s) removed:
A. fat   C. protein
B. calcium   D. carbohydrates

_____ 32. To avoid curdling, milk should be:
A. cooked rapidly   C. mixed with an acid
B. stirred constantly as it cooks   D. thickened with starch

_____ 33. Pasteurizing milk:
A. improves the keeping quality   C. allows the whey to be drained away
B. changes the flavor   D. decreases the amount of milkfat

Name _____

Date _____

Chapter 23 Test

I. True-False. Read the following statements carefully. In the space at the left of each statement, write TRUE if the statement is true. Write FALSE if the statement is incorrect.

_____ 1. Meat is mainly made up of the muscle portion of the animal.

_____ 2. Overcooking destroys protein.

_____ 3. Low temperatures cause greater shrinkage in meat than high temperatures.

_____ 4. Acids, such as lemon juice and tomatoes, help to make meat more tender.

_____ 5. To serve meat au jus, you must make a gravy with the drippings.

_____ 6. Tender cuts of meat are usually best cooked in dry heat.

_____ 7. Salt should be added to meat before it is broiled or pan-broiled.

_____ 8. Pork is not graded as beef is.

_____ 9. All meat shipped across state lines is inspected by the federal government for wholesomeness.

_____ 10. A round purple stamp on meat products indicates that it has passed state inspection.

_____ 11. Collagen softens when it is cooked slowly in moist heat or liquid.

_____ 12. When you open a package of hamburger that is red on the outside but slightly bluish on the inside, you know the meat is spoiled.

_____ 13. Veal comes from immature cattle.

_____ 14. Although it is cooked and crisp on the outside, a rare steak is just heated and perhaps slightly cooked on the inside.

_____ 15. Frozen meat should be thawed at room temperature.

_____ 16. Pork must be cooked to well done to prevent possible intestinal illness.

_____ 17. Microwaved meat has the characteristic flavor of that prepared in dry heat.

_____ 18. Cuts of meat can be identified by the shape of the bones.

_____ 19. Tofu, with its strong taste, is used to add flavor to sauces and casseroles.

II. Multiple Choice. In the space at the left, write the letter of the choice that BEST completes each statement.

_____ 20. Overcooked meat is:
   A. hard to digest
   B. low in calories
   C. very moist
   D. tender

_____ 21. Meats that have had some handling other than just cutting are called:
   A. variety meats
   B. prime meats
   C. select meats
   D. processed meats

_____ 22. Mutton is from:
   A. older sheep
   B. young sheep
   C. young cattle
   D. older pigs

_____ 23. Liver, kidney, and heart are examples of:
      A. choice meats   C. select meats
      B. variety meats   D. prime meats

_____ 24. Doneness of roasted meat is judged by:
      A. oven temperature   C. texture
      B. cooking method   D. internal temperature

_____ 25. Braising is a popular way of cooking:
      A. tender cuts of meat   C. less tender cuts of meat
      B. all cuts of meat   D. rib roast

_____ 26. The most tender cuts of meat come from the area of the animal that:
      A. gets the most movement   C. is closest to the neck
      B. has well-developed muscles   D. is along the backbone

_____ 27. Ground meats should be stored in the coldest part of the refrigerator and used:
      A. within a week   C. within a day or two
      B. within 3 or 4 days   D. within 8 to 10 days

III. Matching. Find the term in the right column that BEST corresponds to each description in the left column. Write the letter of the term in the blank space provided. Do not use any term more than once. Some terms will not be used.

Descriptions

_____ 28. Intestinal illness caused by a parasite in pork.

_____ 29. Fat flecks throughout meat.

_____ 30. A white, fairly thin tissue between layers of muscle.

_____ 31. The most common grade of meat sold in supermarkets.

_____ 32. Treated with ingredients such as salt, nitrates, and others that retard spoiling and give a special flavor and pink color.

_____ 33. The top grade of beef containing the most marbling, and sold mostly to restaurants.

Terms

A. collagen
B. select
C. elastin
D. choice
E. cured
F. tenderized
G. marbling
H. trichinosis
I. salmonella
J. prime
K. processed

Chapter 24 Test

I. True-False. Read the following statements carefully. In the space at the left of each statement, write TRUE if the statement is true. Write FALSE if the statement is incorrect.

_____ 1. Turkey and chicken are relatively low in fat.

_____ 2. Duck and goose have white as well as dark meat.

_____ 3. When microwaving poultry, piercing the skin keeps air bubbles from forming and breaking.

_____ 4. The wholesomeness of poultry is indicated by the grade.

_____ 5. Pan-fried poultry should be cooked quickly.

_____ 6. Less tender birds may be braised or cooked in liquid.

_____ 7. "Roasting" poultry in aluminum foil or in a special plastic cooking bag shortens the cooking time.

_____ 8. Liquid should not be added to stuffing that is prepared and refrigerated for use the next day.

_____ 9. The flavor of poultry is changed in birds whose bones have turned dark.

_____ 10. Salt the surface of poultry to be cooked in the microwave oven.

_____ 11. Never stuff a bird and refrigerate it for roasting the next day.

_____ 12. Grade AA is the highest grade for poultry.

_____ 13. Allow about ½ lb. per serving when buying whole chicken or turkey.

_____ 14. Cut-up chickens are usually more expensive than whole chickens.

_____ 15. To prepare a bird for microwave cooking, tie the legs and wings close to the body.

_____ 16. You will get about the same number of servings per pound from a large turkey as from a small turkey.

_____ 17. When starting to broil chicken or turkey pieces, place them skin side down in the pan.

_____ 18. Boned poultry means that the bones have been removed.

_____ 19. A duck has less meat than a chicken or turkey of the same weight.

II. Completion. In the space at the left, write the word that BEST completes each statement. As a clue, the total number of letters in the word is given.

_____ 20. When buying poultry look for ___?___ as a sign of quality.
(5)

_____ 21. ___?___ poultry has butter or oil added by the packer.
(11)

_____ 22. Poultry organs, including the heart, liver, and gizzard, are called ___?___.
(7)

_____ 23. A stewing chicken may be stewed, simmered, or ___?___.
(7)

(Continued on next page)

_____ 24. Before roasting, ___?___ the bird to make it compact, easier to
(5)   handle and cook, and more attractive to serve.

_____ 25. A young, tender, meaty chicken about 1.8 to 3.6 kg (4 to 8 lbs.) is
(5)   a(n) ___?___.

III. Multiple Choice. In the space at the left, write the letter of the choice that BEST completes each statement.

_____ 26. Properly wrapped poultry can be kept in the freezer for:
       A. several months   C. up to 1 month
       B. several weeks   D. about one year

_____ 27. Frozen poultry should be kept in its freezer wrapping and:
       A. thawed on the counter   C. thawed in warm water
       B. thawed in hot water   D. thawed in the refrigerator

_____ 28. An UNRELIABLE way to test the doneness of poultry is to:
       A. pierce with a fork   C. read the meat thermometer
       B. move the drumsticks gently   D. check the color of the skin

_____ 29. Purchased, prestuffed poultry should be:
       A. thawed in the refrigerator   C. thawed in cold water
       B. cooked while still frozen   D. thawed in warm water

_____ 30. A dry-heat method for cooking poultry is:
       A. braising   C. broiling
       B. stewing   D. simmering

_____ 31. A less tender class of poultry is a:
       A. roaster   C. capon
       B. stewing chicken   D. broiler

_____ 32. A roasted bird is easier to carve if, after cooking, it stands for:
       A. no additional time   C. about 15 minutes
       B. about 5 minutes   D. about 30 minutes

_____ 33. As a rule, fat in poultry:
       A. is distributed throughout the meat   C. is very low
       B. is found just under the skin   D. is fleshy

Chapter 25 Test

I. True-False. Read the following statements carefully. In the space at the left of each statement, write TRUE if the statement is true. Write FALSE if the statement is incorrect.

_____ 1. Grade standards have been established for all fish products.

_____ 2. Because each type of fish has a distinctive flavor, you cannot substitute one lean fish for another lean fish.

_____ 3. The shells of live clams and oysters should be tightly closed.

_____ 4. A shellfish has no spine or bones.

_____ 5. A dressed fish is cleaned and scaled, and usually has the head, tail, and fins removed.

_____ 6. Most shellfish are relatively low in calories and are good sources of protein and unsaturated fats.

_____ 7. Panfrying is an excellent cooking method for small whole fish.

_____ 8. When fully cooked, white-colored fish turns an opaque, milky white.

_____ 9. The less lean fish have about the same amount of fat as most meats.

_____ 10. Fish must be thawed before baking.

_____ 11. To keep fish from drying out while baking, it can be covered with buttered crumbs.

_____ 12. A microwave oven can be used to steam fish by covering the fish with waxed paper.

_____ 13. A fish fillet is a slice cut down through the backbone.

_____ 14. Acidic foods help get rid of fish odors.

_____ 15. Fish are ideal for microwaving.

_____ 16. Shellfish is naturally tender and needs to be cooked for only a short time at moderate temperatures.

II. Multiple Choice. In the space at the left, write the letter of the choice that BEST completes each statement.

_____ 17. Uncooked, fresh, white fish should be:
A. opaque, milky white
B. opaque with soft flesh
C. translucent with firm flesh
D. pinkish in color

_____ 18. Fish is usually cooked at:
A. medium to high temperatures
B. low to medium temperatures
C. very low temperatures
D. very high temperatures

_____ 19. One pound of fish steaks will provide:
A. one serving
B. two servings
C. three servings
D. four servings

_____ 20. Whole fish is fish:
A. cut into large steaks
B. just as it is caught
C. cleaned and scaled with the head retained
D. cleaned and scaled with the head removed

_____ 21. When fish is overcooked, the protein:
   A. is destroyed   C. becomes odorless
   B. becomes flaky   D. toughens

_____ 22. Unused portions of cooked or canned fish should be:
   A. used within 3 to 4 days   C. discarded right away
   B. used within 24 hours   D. used within a week

_____ 23. The form of fish with the least waste is:
   A. steaks   C. dressed fish
   B. whole fish   D. fillets

_____ 24. Crustaceans include:
   A. shrimp and crab   C. carp and flounder
   B. oysters and clams   D. shad and trout

III. Matching. Find the term in the right column that BEST corresponds to each description in the left column. Write the letter of the term in the blank space provided. Do not use any term more than once. Some terms will not be used.

Descriptions

_____ 25. Fish belonging to the group of less lean fish.

_____ 26. Fish belonging to the group of lean fish.

_____ 27. Shellfish that has a black or green vein running along its back.

_____ 28. A kind of mollusk.

_____ 29. Usually boneless sides of a fish cut away from the backbone.

_____ 30. Shellfish with a very rigid outer shell.

_____ 31. Shellfish with a segmented outer covering.

_____ 32. Clams and oysters purchased without shells.

_____ 33. Crustacean that has shed its old shell and is growing a new one.

Terms
A. fillet
B. mollusk
C. crustacean
D. scallop
E. shucked
F. soft-shell crab
G. rock lobster
H. shrimp
I. mackerel and salmon
J. white-colored fish
K. tuna and halibut
L. steak

Name _____

Date _____

Chapter 26 Test

I. Matching. Find the term in the right column that BEST corresponds to each description in the left column. Write the letter of the term in the blank space provided. Do not use any term more than once. Some terms will not be used.

Descriptions

_____ 1. A puffy, baked mixture of beaten egg whites, yolks, and cream sauce.

_____ 2. Prevents egg whites from being beaten to a fluffy consistency.

_____ 3. Egg whites beaten with sugar and flavoring and then baked.

_____ 4. Baked eggs.

_____ 5. Eggs cooked without shells in water.

_____ 6. Used to promote rising in some baked products.

_____ 7. A combination of egg whites and ingredients that replace yolks.

_____ 8. When a layer of liquid forms between meringue and filling.

_____ 9. Keeps ingredients from separating.

Terms

A. hard-cooked eggs
B. egg substitutes
C. shirred eggs
D. egg yolk
E. beaten egg whites
F. French omelet
G. soufflé
H. meringue
I. poached eggs
J. emulsifying agent
K. weep
L. bleed

II. True-False. Read the following statements carefully. In the space at the left of each statement, write TRUE if the statement is true. Write FALSE if the statement is incorrect.

_____ 10. Eggs are low-protein foods.

_____ 11. Egg size is determined not by how large an egg appears but by how much it weighs.

_____ 12. The highest grade of eggs is grade A.

_____ 13. Eggs absorb odors and must be kept covered.

_____ 14. Adding liquid to eggs that are to be scrambled makes them lighter and fluffier.

_____ 15. Eggs with white shells are less nutritious than eggs with brown shells.

_____ 16. The gray-green discoloration on the yolks of some hard-cooked eggs is due to overcooking.

_____ 17. Eggs separate more easily when they are cold.

_____ 18. When an egg white is beaten or whipped, it becomes thick and turns colorless and transparent.

_____ 19. Egg yolks must be pierced before being cooked in the microwave.

_____ 20. When you bring eggs home from the store, you should rinse them and place them in a covered plastic container.

_____ 21. Eggs should be cooked at medium to high temperatures.

_____ 22. The yolk of the egg is the part that is high in cholesterol.

_____ 23. A soft meringue will weep if it is placed on a hot filling.

_____ 24. Eggs in the shell can be cooked in a microwave oven if you make a tiny hole in the large end of the egg.

III. Multiple Choice. In the space at the left, write the letter of the choice that BEST completes each statement.

_____ 25. Recipes for baked goods such as cakes usually assume that the eggs used are:
A. large
B. medium
C. extra large
D. small

_____ 26. Cooling hard-cooked eggs in cold water:
A. will make them easier to peel
B. will cause them to crack
C. will darken egg yolks
D. will retain nutrients

_____ 27. Raw eggs will keep in the refrigerator:
A. approximately 2 weeks
B. up to 4 weeks
C. up to 1 week
D. up to 6 weeks

_____ 28. Egg whites will darken if you use:
A. a glass bowl
B. a plastic bowl
C. an aluminum bowl
D. a ceramic bowl

_____ 29. When it is cooked, egg protein:
A. becomes thinner
B. thickens
C. evaporates
D. breaks down

_____ 30. Hard-cooked eggs should be refrigerated and eaten:
A. within 1 to 2 days
B. within 2 to 3 days
C. within a week
D. within two weeks

_____ 31. Eggs are graded by:
A. size
B. yolk and white firmness
C. weight
D. shell color

_____ 32. A grade B egg can be used to prepare:
A. fried eggs
B. eggs poached in water
C. scrambled eggs
D. eggs poached in milk

_____ 33. To prepare hard-cooked eggs, place them in a pan, cover with cold water, heat to the boiling point, and:
A. simmer for 15 minutes
B. continue to boil for 10 minutes
C. remove from heat and immediately place eggs in cold water
D. remove from heat and let stand in hot water for 15 minutes

Chapter 27 Test

I. True-False. Read the following statements carefully. In the space at the left of each statement, write TRUE if the statement is true. Write FALSE if the statement is incorrect.

_____ 1. Grain products are complex carbohydrates and an excellent source of energy and fiber.

_____ 2. Brown rice takes longer to cook than white rice.

_____ 3. The germ of a grain kernel contains fiber.

_____ 4. The microwave oven is ideal for cooking pasta and rice.

_____ 5. When combined with legumes, grain products provide high-quality proteins.

_____ 6. In processing, the bran and the endosperm are removed from the grain kernel, leaving only the germ.

_____ 7. Whole-grain products are made of the entire kernel and contain most of the original nutrients.

_____ 8. Cereals advertised as "natural" are always high in nutrients.

_____ 9. Pasta includes macaroni but not noodle products.

_____ 10. Rice grains broken into tiny particles are as nutritious as unbroken ones.

II. Matching. Find the term in the right column that BEST corresponds to each description in the left column. Write the letter of the term in the blank space provided. Do not use any term more than once. Some terms will not be used.

Descriptions

_____ 11. The outer covering of grain, which contains fiber and the B vitamins.

_____ 12. Rice with a nutlike flavor and chewy texture.

_____ 13. The sprouting section of grain inside the kernel from which a new plant can grow.

_____ 14. Grain products in which nutrients lost in processing are replaced.

_____ 15. Technically not a rice, but a grain of water grass.

_____ 16. A grain which is used mainly in soups.

_____ 17. Seed of the grain plant.

_____ 18. The part of the grain that is made up primarily of starch and protein.

Terms

A. whole-grain products
B. enriched products
C. grits
D. barley
E. kernel
F. endosperm
G. hominy
H. brown rice
I. germ
J. converted rice
K. wild rice
L. bran

III. Multiple Choice. In the space at the left, write the letter of the choice that BEST completes each statement.

_____ 19. In comparison to white rice, brown rice has:
   A. the same amount of nutrients   C. less nutrients
   B. more nutrients   D. less minerals

_____ 20. All of the following are true about cooking pasta EXCEPT:
   A. cook to "al dente" if serving immediately   C. rinse after cooking
   B. set cooked pasta over simmering water to keep hot   D. add a little cooking oil to prevent sticking

_____ 21. A type of Polish pasta consisting of dumplings stuffed with mashed potatoes or cottage cheese filling is:
   A. strudel   C. won tons
   B. ravioli   D. pierogi

_____ 22. A grain product that is a cross between rye and wheat, and is more nutritious than wheat is:
   A. bulgur   C. kasha
   B. grits   D. triticale

_____ 23. To avoid rancidity of the natural oils, whole-grain products kept longer than several weeks should be:
   A. stored in the refrigerator   C. kept in a dark, cool place
   B. kept in dry storage   D. stored at room temperature

_____ 24. Most grains when overcooked become:
   A. discolored   C. sticky
   B. hard   D. chewy

_____ 25. Pasta should be added to boiling water:
   A. slowly   C. in three stages
   B. all at one time   D. in different ways according to the type of pasta

IV. Completion. In the space at the left, write the word that BEST completes each statement. As a clue, the total number of letters in the word is given.

_____ (6)   26. Precooked, dried, cracked wheat is called ___?___.

_____ (7)   27. Whole wheat kernels are called wheat ___?___.

_____ (9)   28. ___?___ rice is cooked and then dehydrated.

_____ (5)   29. ___?___, which are sometimes used in place of rice or potatoes, are made from ground, hulled white corn.

_____ (5)   30. ___?___ wheat is used to make the special flour for pasta.

_____ (6)   31. Grains are the dried seeds or ___?___ of cereal grasses.

_____ (9)   32. ___?___ rice is dry and fluffy when cooked.

_____ (4)   33. Parboiled or ___?___ rice is partly cooked before it is milled.

Chapter 28 Test

I. Matching. Find the term in the right column that BEST corresponds to each description in the left column. Write the letter of the term in the blank space provided. Do not use any term more than once. Some terms will not be used.

Descriptions

_____ 1. Helps the baked product rise by providing air or gas that is trapped in the mixture.

_____ 2. A combination of baking soda and a dry acid.

_____ 3. Gives the structure to a baked product.

_____ 4. Fat from cream.

_____ 5. A microscopic plant that reproduces rapidly and makes dough rise.

_____ 6. Hydrogenated fat made from vegetable oil.

_____ 7. A leavening agent that must be used with an acidic food such as buttermilk.

_____ 8. The protein in flour that develops during mixing and kneading to give dough its elasticity.

Terms

A. shortening
B. eggs
C. cooking oil
D. leavening agent
E. yeast
F. baking soda
G. carbon dioxide
H. butter
I. flour
J. baking powder
K. gluten

II. True-False. Read the following statements carefully. In the space at the left of each statement, write TRUE if the statement is true. Write FALSE if the statement is incorrect.

_____ 9. Unless the recipe calls for it, you should not use whipped or diet margarine for baking.

_____ 10. Cake flour is used for most baked products.

_____ 11. Always flour baking pans when baking in a microwave oven.

_____ 12. Cakes and breads cooked in the microwave oven have greater volume than those cooked in a conventional oven.

_____ 13. Cakes without shortening, such as angel food cakes, should be baked in greased pans.

_____ 14. Powdered sugar that has caked should be discarded.

_____ 15. If a recipe is not specific, any type of baking powder may be used.

_____ 16. Although dry yeast can be substituted for compressed yeast, compressed yeast cannot be substituted for dry yeast.

_____ 17. Do not use salted butter or margarine to grease a baking pan.

_____ 18. Oil may be substituted for a solid fat and a solid fat for oil in baking.

_____ 19. The different textures of baked products are a result of varying oven temperatures and baking times.

III. Multiple Choice. In the space at the left, write the letter of the choice that BEST completes each statement.

_____ 20. Before baking most breads, pies, cakes, or pastries, the oven should be preheated for at least:
    A. 1 to 2 minutes   C. 10 minutes
    B. 5 minutes   D. 20 minutes

_____ 21. Cakes without shortening are:
    A. removed from the pans to cool   C. refrigerated immediately after baking
    B. cooled in the pans   D. often cracked on the surface

_____ 22. Dull metal pans retain more heat:
    A. than bright, shiny pans   C. when they are greased
    B. than glass and ceramic pans   D. when they are greased and floured

_____ 23. When using glass baking pans, set the oven temperature:
    A. 14°C (25°F) lower   C. 6°C (10°F) lower
    B. 14°C (25°F) higher   D. 6°C (10°F) higher

_____ 24. Whole-grain flour should be stored in:
    A. a warm, dry place   C. a loosely covered container
    B. the refrigerator   D. a dark cabinet

_____ 25. When adapting a conventional recipe for baking in the microwave:
    A. reduce the liquid slightly   C. decrease the amount of flour
    B. increase the leavening by one-third   D. increase the mixing time

_____ 26. When a leavened product is baked at too high a temperature:
    A. the product expands more than   C. the crust forms too fast
        it should
    B. the inside bakes before the   D. the dough dries out and the
        crust browns   product falls

IV. Completion. In the space at the left, write the word that BEST completes each statement. As a clue, the total number of letters in the word is given.

_____ 27. ___?___ causes cream puffs to rise.
        (5)

_____ 28. ___?___ flour is whole-grain flour ground to a heavy, coarse texture.
        (11)

_____ 29. ___?___ give flavor, add tenderness, and help crusts to brown.
        (10)

_____ 30. Among the purposes of ___?___ in baking is to trap air for leavening
        (4)   and help keep batters from separating.

_____ 31. ___?___ is a sweetener that should not be used for cooking or baking.
        (9)

_____ 32. ___?___ oil is not usually used for baking.
        (5)

_____ 33. A fat from pork is ___?___.
        (4)

514

Chapter 29 Test

I. True-False. Read the following statements carefully. In the space at the left of each statement, write TRUE if the statement is true. Write FALSE if the statement is incorrect.

_____ 1. A batter is a flour mixture thin enough to be poured or dropped from the mixing bowl.

_____ 2. Drop biscuits have the same flaky texture as rolled biscuits.

_____ 3. In the muffin method, liquid is poured all at once into the flour mixture and stirred only until the dry ingredients are moistened.

_____ 4. Yeast bread dough should be allowed to rise twice — once after it is kneaded and once after it is shaped.

_____ 5. No liquid other than water should be used to dissolve yeast.

_____ 6. Loaves of quick bread should be sliced before they cool.

_____ 7. Only yeast doughs require kneading.

_____ 8. Flours vary in the amount of liquid they can absorb.

_____ 9. To cut biscuits, press the cutter down firmly, then twist gently to be sure the dough is cut all the way around.

_____ 10. Batter breads are punched down to make them easier to shape.

_____ 11. Microwave ovens are better suited for reheating breads than for baking them.

_____ 12. Yeast bread is removed from the pans after it has cooled.

_____ 13. When making yeast breads, add enough flour to the mixture to make it cling together and leave the side of the bowl.

_____ 14. Quick breads are generally leavened with yeast.

_____ 15. Yeast doughs can be soft or stiff depending on the amount of flour used.

II. Multiple Choice. In the space at the left, write the letter of the choice that BEST completes each statement.

_____ 16. A type of quick bread made from a soft dough is:
    A. muffins   C. biscuits
    B. popovers   D. pancakes

_____ 17. A pour batter is used to make:
    A. muffins   C. doughnuts
    B. pancakes   D. biscuits

_____ 18. Kneaded dough for yeast bread is:
    A. sticky and rough   C. smooth and heavy
    B. sticky and smooth   D. smooth and elastic

_____ 19. The chief ingredient of yeast breads is:
    A. flour   C. milk
    B. shortening   D. sugar

_____ 20. Large tunnels are formed when muffins are:
   A. overmixed   C. overbaked
   B. undermixed   D. underbaked

_____ 21. Yeast breads do not get stale as quickly if they are:
   A. kept in a brown paper wrapper   C. kept in the refrigerator
   B. kept in a warm place   D. kept in a breadbox at room temperature

_____ 22. An acceptable method of letting yeast dough rise is:
   A. placing the bowl over a large bowl   C. placing the bowl on a low setting in
      of warm water   the microwave oven
   B. placing the bowl on or near   D. placing the bowl in a deep pan
      a furnace outlet   of hot water

_____ 23. If your rolled biscuits are NOT tender and flaky, you may have:
   A. kneaded the dough   C. used the biscuit method
   B. overmixed the liquid and dough   D. baked them on a cookie sheet

III. Matching. Find the term in the right column that BEST corresponds to each description in the left column. Write the letter of the term in the blank space provided. Do not use any term more than once. Some terms will not be used.

Descriptions

_____ 24. A way of cutting preparation time when making yeast bread.

_____ 25. An example of a quick bread made from a drop batter.

_____ 26. A flour mixture thick enough to be shaped by hand.

_____ 27. A yeast bread that uses more liquid.

_____ 28. A mixture thick enough to fall from a spoon and still hold its shape.

_____ 29. Has a fine texture and a smooth, often crispy crust.

_____ 30. Develops the gluten that will form the structure of the bread.

_____ 31. Lets excess gases escape, making it easier to shape dough.

_____ 32. Method of making yeast bread in which the yeast is first dissolved in warm water.

_____ 33. A mixture of yeast, water, and flour that is allowed to stand for two or more days until fermented.

Terms

A. sourdough starter
B. batter
C. yeast bread
D. batter bread
E. biscuits
F. punching down
G. conventional method
H. muffin method
I. quick breads
J. dough
K. muffins
L. drop batter
M. mixer method
N. kneading
O. sourdough bread
P. rolling

Chapter 30 Test

I. True-False. Read the following statements carefully. In the space at the left of each statement, write TRUE if the statement is true. Write FALSE if the statement is incorrect.

_____ 1. There are only three basic types of cakes.

_____ 2. Rolled cookie dough may be placed on a hot baking sheet.

_____ 3. When done, a cake should be starting to pull away from the sides of the pan.

_____ 4. Shortened cakes cannot be prepared by the quick-mix method.

_____ 5. When making angel food cakes, fold the dry ingredients into stiffly beaten egg whites.

_____ 6. Changing the size of a cake pan will not change the baking time.

_____ 7. Foam cakes contain no fat.

_____ 8. Tapping the top of a cake to test for doneness is not recommended.

_____ 9. Angel food and other foam cakes bake satisfactorily in a microwave oven.

_____ 10. Foam cake batter rises by clinging to the sides of a pan as the batter expands.

_____ 11. When done, microwaved cookies will look dry.

_____ 12. To test drop bar cookies for doneness, lightly press with one finger and the cooked dough will spring back.

_____ 13. Butter cakes are often made with margarine.

_____ 14. Cooked frostings should not be beaten once they have been cooked to a certain temperature.

_____ 15. Microwaved cookies should be allowed to cool on the baking tray.

_____ 16. In the quick-mix method of mixing a cake, the first step is to combine the flour, sugar, shortening, and part of the milk.

II. Multiple Choice. In the space at the left, write the letter of the choice that BEST completes each statement.

_____ 17. Unless a recipe states otherwise, the ingredients for a cake:
A. should be well chilled
B. should be at room temperature
C. should be cooled
D. are not affected by temperature

_____ 18. When adding dry and liquid ingredients to the creamed mixture using the conventional method for mixing cakes, begin and end with:
A. the dry ingredients
B. the liquid ingredients
C. either ingredient
D. dry and liquid ingredients together

_____ 19. Cakes baked in a microwave oven are usually:
A. drier
B. less flavorful
C. more fragile
D. lighter and fluffier

_____ 20. Frequently opening the oven as a cake bakes:
A. can cause the cake to overbake
B. can affect the way a cake rises
C. can cause a tough crust to form on the cake
D. has little effect on the cake

_____ 21. When time is limited, a good choice of homemade cookies to prepare would be:
    A. molded type   C. bar type
    B. refrigerator type   D. pressed type

_____ 22. In dry weather, crisp cookies should be stored in a container:
    A. with a loose-fitting lid   C. with soft cookies
    B. that is air-tight   D. with no lid

_____ 23. All of the following are true about frosting a cake EXCEPT:
    A. use frosting to hold layers together   C. brush away crumbs before frosting
    B. keep frosting covered as you work   D. frost the top of the cake first

_____ 24. When a whitish color, or bloom, appears on the surface of chocolate:
    A. it is harmful and the chocolate   C. it is harmless and the chocolate
       should be discarded   is still edible
    B. the chocolate should be refrigerated   D. the chocolate should be melted
                                        and used immediately

III. Matching. Find the term in the right column that BEST corresponds to each description in the left column. Write the letter of the term in the blank space provided. Do not use any term more than once. Some terms will not be used.

Descriptions

_____ 25. Cookies placed onto a cookie sheet with a teaspoon.

_____ 26. Cookies usually baked in a square or rectangular pan.

_____ 27. Cookies made from a stiff dough spread out and cut with cookie cutters.

_____ 28. Cookies shaped by hand into balls or other shapes.

_____ 29. Cookies made from chilled rolls of dough cut into slices and baked.

_____ 30. Cakes that contain a fat, flour, salt, sugar, eggs, and a liquid and are leavened with baking powder or baking soda.

_____ 31. Cakes that rely on steam and egg white for leavening.

_____ 32. Cakes in which the sifted dry ingredients, egg yolks, and liquids are beaten together until smooth, then folded into the beaten egg whites.

_____ 33. Cakes in which the beaten egg yolks are blended into the liquid and dry ingredients, then folded into the beaten egg whites.

Terms
A. sponge cakes
B. chiffon cakes
C. shortened cakes
D. bar cookies
E. pressed cookies
F. butter cakes
G. refrigerator cookies
H. drop cookies
I. foam cakes
J. molded cookies
K. rolled cookies
L. batter cookies

518

Chapter 31 Test

I. True-False. Read the following statements carefully. In the space at the left of each statement, write TRUE if the statement is true. Write FALSE if the statement is incorrect.

_____ 1. A shallow pan may be placed on the same rack as the pie pan to catch any filling that might boil over.

_____ 2. Pie dough should be mixed vigorously.

_____ 3. Piecrust can be used for making desserts, appetizers, and main dishes.

_____ 4. Crumb crusts are best for two-crust pies.

_____ 5. It is not necessary to grease a glass pie pan for microwaving a pie crust.

_____ 6. Pastry can be made with oil instead of solid fat.

_____ 7. Pastry dough should be stretched to fit into the pie pan.

_____ 8. Too much mixing and handling of pastry prevents the development of gluten in the flour.

_____ 9. Crumb crusts may be either chilled or baked before filling.

_____ 10. Baked piecrusts should have a slightly blistered appearance.

_____ 11. One way to keep an empty pie shell from puffing up during baking is to pierce holes in it with a fork.

_____ 12. The crusts in a two-crust pie should not be sealed together before baking so that steam can escape.

_____ 13. As a rule, color is the best indication of doneness when baking pies and shells.

_____ 14. Slits are cut in the top crust near the center of a two-crust pie.

_____ 15. Piecrust should be rolled until it is an even thickness of ¼ inch.

_____ 16. Cream puffs use air as leavening.

_____ 17. Two-crust pies can be successfully baked in a microwave oven.

II. Multiple Choice. In the space at the left, write the letter of the choice that BEST completes each statement.

_____ 18. The water most often used in making piecrust must be:
A. room temperature   C. hot
B. slightly chilled   D. cold

_____ 19. If too much water is used, pastry will be:
A. sticky   C. soft
B. crumbly   D. hard

_____ 20. All of the following are true of making a fruit pie EXCEPT:
A. bake before freezing, if you plan to store pie   C. use fresh, frozen, or canned fruit
B. use flour, cornstarch, or tapioca as a thickener   D. thicken the pie so it will hold its shape

_____ 21. When rolling pie dough, you should:
  A. place the rolling pin at the edge of the dough closest to you and roll away from yourself
  B. roll the dough from the center outward in all directions
  C. move the rolling pin back and forth quickly
  D. chill the dough first

_____ 22. For a two-crust pie, the bottom crust is:
  A. trimmed ½ inch smaller than the pan
  B. left ½ inch larger than the pan
  C. trimmed even with the edge of the pan
  D. trimmed to the same size as the top crust

_____ 23. If dough cracks when it is being rolled:
  A. it should be rolled again
  B. it should be moistened with warm water
  C. it should be discarded
  D. the cracks should be patched with a piece of extra dough

_____ 24. Good quality pastry is:
  A. smooth and shiny
  B. tender and flaky
  C. fragile and crumbly
  D. dry and flaky

III. Matching. Find the term in the right column that BEST corresponds to each description in the left column. Write the letter of the term in the blank space provided. Do not use any term more than once. Some terms will not be used.

Descriptions

_____ 25. A small, one-serving pie with no top crust.

_____ 26. Pastry with a crispy outer shell and a hollow interior filled with custard or other filling.

_____ 27. A bottom piecrust baked before filling.

_____ 28. A mixture of eggs, cream, cheese, and other ingredients baked in a piecrust.

_____ 29. A pie with a fluffy filling made from gelatin and fruit.

_____ 30. A pie filled with custard, usually topped with a meringue.

_____ 31. Pastry made by rolling dough out in layers with butter in between.

_____ 32. A top crust consisting of woven strips.

_____ 33. A piecrust edge made by using the finger of one hand to press dough between a finger and thumb of the other hand to make a V-shape.

Terms
A. lattice crust
B. pie shell
C. cream pie
D. fluted edge
E. tart
F. chiffon pie
G. meringue pie
H. convenience crust
I. cream puff
J. puff pastry
K. rope edge
L. quiche

Chapter 32 Test

I. True-False. Read the following statements carefully. In the space at the left of each statement, write TRUE if the statement is true. Write FALSE if the statement is incorrect.

_____ 1. There are two basic kinds of stock — brown and white.

_____ 2. White stock is generally mild in flavor.

_____ 3. A cream soup can be made with yogurt.

_____ 4. Ham is an excellent ingredient to use in making stock.

_____ 5. To make stock, cut meat into large pieces to extract as much flavor as possible during cooking.

_____ 6. All sauces may be frozen successfully.

_____ 7. When you make stocks, soups, and sauces, you are making good use of your resources.

_____ 8. The ingredients used in stock should be mature and have well-developed flavors.

_____ 9. You can use ingredients that might otherwise be discarded to make stocks.

_____ 10. To prevent a skin from forming on a cooked sauce mixture, put a lid on the saucepan.

_____ 11. Eggs are often used as thickeners because the protein thickens as the eggs cook.

_____ 12. Only all-purpose flour should be used as a flour thickener.

_____ 13. Most thickeners will lose their thickening powers if they are overcooked.

_____ 14. Cornstarch, which is often used for thickening desserts, has less thickening power than flour.

_____ 15. Leftover soup should be refrigerated and used within three days.

II. Completion. In the space at the left, write the word that BEST completes each statement. As a clue, the total number of letters in the word is given.

_____
(10)

16. Liquid thickened with ___?___ remains as clear as it was originally.

_____
(6)

17. Meat bones containing ___?___ add a delicious flavor to stock.

_____
(5)

18. ___?___ stock is made from chicken, chicken bones, and vegetables for use in soups and sauces.

_____
(7)

19. ___?___ forms a jelly-like bead as it thickens.

III. Multiple Choice. In the space at the left, write the letter of the choice that BEST completes each statement.

_____ 20. When a scum forms on stock as it is cooking:
A. boil the stock for 30 minutes
B. refrigerate the stock and then remove the scum
C. skim it off during the first 30 minutes
D. discard the stock

_____ 21. Consommé, one of the clear stocks:
A. is a vegetable stock
B. is a concentrated, seasoned, clarified meat stock
C. has a milder flavor than both broth and bouillon
D. contains diced bacon

_____ 22. When preparing a tapioca mixture:
A. stir it vigorously as it cooks
B. stir it occasionally as it cools
C. do not stir it until it has cooled completely
D. do not stir it as it cools

_____ 23. If a mixture thickened with eggs starts to curdle:
A. beat it vigorously
B. raise the temperature of the mixture
C. discard it
D. add warm water

_____ 24. Adding more sugar to a custard:
A. decreases the cooking time
B. makes the custard more firm
C. requires a lower cooking temperature
D. makes the custard less firm

IV. Matching. Find the term in the right column that BEST corresponds to each description in the left column. Write the letter of the term in the blank space provided. Do not use any term more than once. Some terms will not be used.

Descriptions

_____ 25. Seasoned, rich-colored liquid made from beef and bones along with vegetables.

_____ 26. Thickener made from equal amounts of butter and flour blended into a thick paste and rolled into small balls or a long roll.

_____ 27. Another name for broth.

_____ 28. To boil weak-flavored stock so that liquid evaporates, concentrating the flavor.

_____ 29. To simmer egg whites and crushed eggshell in stock until the egg white rises to the surface as foam.

_____ 30. A cream soup made with shellfish.

_____ 31. A mixture of fat and flour cooked and stirred until the mixture bubbles.

_____ 32. Flavorful liquid that has been thickened.

_____ 33. Sweetened milk thickened with eggs.

Terms
A. sauce
B. clarify
C. buerre manie
D. brown stock
E. bouillon
F. custard
G. bisque
H. degrease
I. roux
J. tapioca
K. reduce
L. consommé

Chapter 33 Test

I. True-False. Read the following statements carefully. In the space at the left of each statement, write TRUE if the statement is true. Write FALSE if the statement is incorrect.

_____ 1. Some people become addicted to the caffeine in the beverages they drink.

_____ 2. Cocoa contains more cocoa butter than chocolate.

_____ 3. Chocolate and cocoa both scorch easily.

_____ 4. Coffee is made by blending different varieties of beans, so the taste will vary from brand to brand.

_____ 5. If weaker coffee is desired, dilute full-strength coffee with hot water.

_____ 6. Flavored tea is the same as herb tea.

_____ 7. Ice cream, sherbet, or even small pieces of fruit can be added to a punch.

_____ 8. Boiling, overcooking, and even reheating can make coffee bitter.

_____ 9. Unlike coffee, tea does not contain caffeine.

_____ 10. Soft drinks contain a small amount of natural vitamins.

_____ 11. The strength of tea can be judged by its color.

_____ 12. Herb teas have a strong flavor and aroma.

_____ 13. When making coffee and tea, always start with fresh cold water.

_____ 14. Tea contains special oils that give a characteristic flavor, so it must be stored in an airtight container.

_____ 15. To brew tea means to boil tea leaves or bags in water until the flavor develops.

_____ 16. Beverages such as coffee, tea, and soft drinks are nutritious as well as refreshing.

_____ 17. Brewed tea should not be chilled in the refrigerator.

_____ 18. The base for a punch can consist of fruit juices, tea, milk, carbonated beverages, or a combination of beverages.

_____ 19. Tea should never be brewed in a metal container.

_____ 20. Chocolate is a better buy than cocoa because it keeps better in warm weather.

II. Matching. Find the term in the right column that BEST corresponds to each description in the left column. Write the letter of the term in the blank space provided. Do not use any term more than once. Some terms will not be used.

Descriptions	Terms
_____ 21. A cross between green and black tea.	A. flavored tea
_____ 22. Usually does not contain caffeine.	B. coffee
	C. herb tea
_____ 23. Undergoes very little processing and tastes like fresh leaves.	D. Souchong
_____ 24. The largest black tea leaves.	E. diet soda
	F. green tea
_____ 25. More highly processed, the leaves are fermented and graded according to size.	G. oolong tea
	H. Orange Pekoe
_____ 26. The smallest black tea leaves.	I. black tea

III. Multiple Choice. In the space at the left, write the letter of the choice that BEST completes each statement.

_____ 27. Decaffeinated coffee from which caffeine has been removed by a chemical process:
A. stays fresh longer than regular coffee
B. requires a special coffee maker
C. is available in the same forms as regular coffee
D. should be stored in the freezer

_____ 28. If substituting cocoa for chocolate in a recipe, add:
A. sugar
B. salt
C. water
D. fat

_____ 29. If stored in an airtight container in the refrigerator, opened coffee will hold its flavor:
A. about 2 weeks
B. about 4 weeks
C. up to 2 months
D. indefinitely

_____ 30. When preparing cocoa or chocolate, use:
A. only whole milk
B. low heat
C. high heat
D. no sugar

_____ 31. The difference among varieties of teas is determined by:
A. the leaf size
B. the type of plant
C. when the leaves are dried
D. how the leaves are processed

_____ 32. When preparing or reheating beverages in the microwave:
A. cover them with waxed paper
B. stir them just before placing in the microwave
C. warm them first at a low power setting
D. use high power to avoid the formation of a film or skin

_____ 33. To make iced coffee:
A. chill regular-strength coffee
B. chill strong coffee
C. pour strong coffee over ice cubes
D. use only freeze-dried coffee

Chapter 34 Test

I. True-False. Read the following statements carefully. In the space at the left of each statement, write TRUE if the statement is true. Write FALSE if the statement is incorrect.

_____ 1. You can always save money by preserving food at home.

_____ 2. Home-canned food can look and smell perfectly normal yet still contain dangerous toxins.

_____ 3. When preserving food, it is best to work with small amounts.

_____ 4. The use of sugar, sugar syrup, or ascorbic acid helps stop enzyme action in fruits before they are frozen.

_____ 5. The open kettle method of canning is safe for high-acid foods.

_____ 6. Microwave ovens can be used for canning.

_____ 7. When jars are sealed properly, a partial vacuum forms on the inside.

_____ 8. Drying is not considered an acceptable method of preserving vegetables at home.

_____ 9. Freezing preserves food at temperatures of 32°F or below.

_____ 10. Most fruits and vegetables are high-acid foods.

_____ 11. Some pickled products are soaked in a brine, a solution of water and salt.

_____ 12. Enzyme action in fruits to be frozen is stopped by blanching.

_____ 13. Precooking food before packing kills all the dangerous microorganisms.

_____ 14. Blanched vegetables are more likely to lose nutrients than vegetables that have not been blanched.

_____ 15. Jars and lids for canning must be sterilized before use.

_____ 16. A microwave oven is a good choice for drying herbs.

_____ 17. Signs of spoilage in home-canned foods include bubbling, cloudiness, mold, spurting liquid, unusually soft texture, and strange color.

II. Multiple Choice. In the space at the left, write the letter of the choice that BEST completes each statement.

_____ 18. Foods with freezer burn have:
  A. a dry, discolored surface   C. more moisture
  B. a strange odor   D. a burnt flavor

_____ 19. Foods should NOT be frozen in:
  A. heavy-duty plastic bags   C. rigid plastic containers
  B. large containers   D. glass containers

_____ 20. Before being eaten, home-canned vegetables and other low-acid foods must be boiled:
  A. 1 to 5 minutes   C. 10 to 15 minutes
  B. 15 to 20 minutes   D. at least 30 minutes

_____ 21. Large ice crystals on frozen foods are a sign that the food was:
  A. wrapped too tightly   C. frozen too quickly
  B. of inferior quality   D. frozen too slowly

_____ 22. Accurate information on preserving food is available from:
   A. a USDA Cooperative Extension office   C. the U.S. RDA
   B. the Food and Drug Administration   D. the U.S. Department of Commerce

_____ 23. The easiest and fastest method of preserving food is:
   A. the raw pack method   C. drying
   B. freezing   D. the pressure canning method

_____ 24. Oven canning is:
   A. acceptable for high-acid foods   C. no longer considered safe for any
                                           type of food
   B. acceptable for vegetables only   D. used only with the hot pack method

_____ 25. Whole fruits or large pieces cooked with sugar are:
   A. preserves   C. marmalades
   B. jams   D. conserves

III. Matching. Find the term in the right column that BEST corresponds to each description in the left column. Write the letter of the term in the blank space provided. Do not use any term more than once. Some terms will not be used.

Descriptions

_____ 26. Can or freeze food for future use.

_____ 27. Scald foods for a short time in boiling water to stop enzyme action.

_____ 28. Food is cooked on top of the range in an uncovered pan, then placed in hot, sterilized jars and sealed.

_____ 29. Dangerous type of bacteria that multiply in tightly sealed jars of low-acid foods.

_____ 30. Process for canning high-acid foods.

_____ 31. A canning method used for all low-acid foods.

_____ 32. Food is precooked for a short time, then packed into jars for processing.

_____ 33. An important carbohydrate found in fruit that helps jams and jellies jell.

Terms

A. blanch
B. botulism
C. brine
D. preserve
E. salmonella
F. raw pack method
G. boiling water bath method
H. open kettle method
I. pressure canning
J. hot pack method
K. pectin
L. ascorbic acid

526

Part Five

Food Preparation

Name _____

Date _____

Part Five Test

I. True-False. Read the following statements carefully. In the space at the left of each statement, write the word TRUE if the statement is true. Write FALSE if the statement is incorrect.

Ch. 19 _____ 1. Edible fruit skins and seeds are good sources of fiber.

Ch. 20 _____ 2. Vegetables are among the best sources of vitamins and minerals.

Ch. 21 _____ 3. It is best to cut rather than tear salad greens to prevent edges from turning brown.

Ch. 22 _____ 4. To prevent scum from forming when heating milk, cover the pan or stir the milk constantly as it cooks.

Ch. 22 _____ 5. Cheese becomes tough and rubbery if cooked at too low a temperature.

Ch. 23 _____ 6. When a meat thermometer cannot be used, doneness is best judged by cooking time.

Ch. 24 _____ 7. Whether cooking pieces of poultry or a whole bird in the microwave oven, pierce the skin to keep air bubbles from forming and bursting.

Ch. 25 _____ 8. Fish and shellfish have connective tissue that makes them tender.

Ch. 26 _____ 9. Eggs should not be washed before being stored.

Ch. 27 _____ 10. Stirring scrapes the starch off rice grains and makes the rice sticky.

Ch. 28 _____ 11. Fats and oils make baked products tender by coating gluten and keeping it from overdeveloping.

Ch. 29 _____ 12. The differences in texture and appearance between yeast and quick breads come mostly from the type of mixing method used.

Ch. 30 _____ 13. When mixing a shortened cake using the conventional method, all the dry ingredients are added to the creamed mixture at one time.

Ch. 31 _____ 14. It is safer to mix the dough for flaky pastry too much rather than too little.

Ch. 32 _____ 15. To clarify stock means to remove the excess fat when it solidifies.

Ch. 32 _____ 16. Mixing a thickener with a small amount of sugar or a cold liquid will help prevent the thickener from cooking into lumps when added to hot food.

Ch. 33 _____ 17. Flavored teas have no caffeine.

Ch. 34 _____ 18. Food that has been home-canned may look and smell normal but still contain dangerous toxins.

II. Completion. In the space at the left, write the word that BEST completes each statement. As a clue, the total number of letters in the word is given.

Ch. 19 _____ (6)

19. Fruit that has reached its full size is said to be __?__.

Ch. 20 _____ (7)

20. Vegetable seeds that grow in a pod and are dried before eating are called __?__.

Ch. 21 _____ (8)

21. The __?__ should complement and blend with the other flavors in salads.

Ch. 22 _____ (11)

22. According to federal law, all milk and milk products must be __?__ to kill disease-producing bacteria.

Ch. 23 _____ (10)

23. A commercial meat __?__, which contains a protein-digesting enzyme from plants, can be used on inexpensive cuts of meat.

Ch. 24 _____ (7)

24. Only very young, tender chickens or turkeys should be __?__.

Ch. 25 _____ (7)

25. __?__ cooking methods are a good choice for cooking fish because they bring out the natural flavor.

Ch. 26 _____ (9)

26. __?__ eggs are prepared by mixing eggs with milk or water and then cooking until the mixture has thickened.

Ch. 27 _____ (6)

27. Both rice and pasta must absorb __?__ in order to soften.

Ch. 28 _____ (6)

28. The amount of __?__ developed in dough depends on the length of time the dough is mixed or kneaded and on the type of flour.

Ch. 29 _____ (10)

29. When pressed for time in making yeast bread, use __?__ yeast.

Ch. 30 _____ (9)

30. In general, cookies and cakes have more calories and fewer __?__ than other foods.

Ch. 31 _____ (4)

31. Recipes for pastry often call for allowing the dough to __?__ before it is rolled.

Ch. 32 _____ (8)

32. To __?__ a stock means to remove the excess fat.

Ch. 33 _____ (10)

33. Soft drinks contain __?__, which may erode tooth enamel and deplete the body's calcium supply.

Ch. 34 _____ (6)

34. __?__ fruits do not freeze well.

III. Multiple Choice. In the space at the left, write the letter of the choice that BEST completes each statement.

Ch. 19 _____ 35. Most fresh fruits should be used:
A. within a week
B. within 2 weeks
C. within a few days
D. within a month

Ch. 20 _____ 36. When cooking vegetables, do all of the following EXCEPT:
A. use small amounts of water
B. pierce the skin of a baked potato before baking
C. wash fresh vegetables before cooking
D. heat home-canned vegetables in the microwave

Ch. 21 _____ 37. Head lettuce should be stored:
A. without being rinsed
B. after being rinsed and drained
C. with the core intact
D. with all leaves separated from the core

Ch. 22 _____ 38. Milk should be kept away from light because light destroys:
A. riboflavin
B. calcium
C. vitamin A
D. vitamin D

Ch. 23 _____ 39. To roast meat:
A. add a small amount of water to the pan
B. use a covered pan
C. use an open, shallow pan
D. do not use a rack

Ch. 24 _____ 40. Fresh poultry to be frozen should be:
A. wrapped tightly in aluminum foil or plastic-coated paper
B. wrapped loosely in aluminum foil or plastic-coated paper
C. wrapped loosely in waxed paper
D. wrapped tightly in waxed paper

Ch. 25 _____ 41. For more even microwave cooking of fish:
A. rinse the pieces in cool water, but do not dry them
B. place the larger, thicker pieces toward the middle of the baking dish
C. cover the dish for half the baking time
D. place the larger, thicker pieces near the edge of the baking dish

Ch. 26 _____ 42. Eggs can be frozen:
A. in the shell
B. by storing whites and yolks separately
C. by adding salt or sugar to the whites
D. if the whites and yolks are mixed together

Ch. 27 _____ 43. If a recipe calls for 1 cup of cooked pasta, the amount of dry pasta to use would be:
A. 1 cup
B. 2 cups
C. ½ cup
D. 1½ cups

Ch. 28 _____ 44. When a leavened product is baked at too low a temperature:
A. the crust browns before the inside is completely baked
B. the product often falls
C. the dough becomes too moist
D. the leavening gas builds up in the dough

Ch. 29 _____ 45. When making yeast bread, use:
  A. the exact amount of flour specified in the recipe
  B. only all-purpose white flour
  C. only self-rising flour
  D. just enough flour so that the dough clings together, leaving the sides of the bowl

Ch. 30 _____ 46. The quick-mix method of mixing cakes can be used:
  A. only for foam cakes
  B. for any shortened cake
  C. only when specified in a recipe
  D. to save time with any cake recipe

Ch. 31 _____ 47. Microwave baking is not recommended for:
  A. two-crust pies
  B. pie shells
  C. one-crust pies
  D. crumb crust pies

Ch. 32 _____ 48. Cooling strained stock in the refrigerator:
  A. helps concentrate the flavor
  B. helps retain nutrients
  C. allows the fat to solidify
  D. weakens the flavor

Ch. 33 _____ 49. All of the following are true about coffee and tea EXCEPT:
  A. both can be served iced
  B. both are nutritious
  C. both have caffeine
  D. both should be made with fresh, cold water

Ch. 34 _____ 50. The fastest and easiest method for preserving food is:
  A. the pressure canning method
  B. drying
  C. the raw pack method
  D. freezing

Name _____

Date _____

Chapter 35 Test

I. True-False. Read the following statements carefully. In the space at the left of each statement, write TRUE if the statement is true. Write FALSE if the statement is incorrect.

_____ 1. The climate of a country and lifestyles of its people influence what the people eat.

_____ 2. If you order "cafe au lait," you are ordering coffee with a scoop of ice cream.

_____ 3. One of the staple foods of North Africa is couscous, finely ground wheat mixed with salt and water and steamed.

_____ 4. Some African foods and styles of cooking were introduced by foreign colonists.

_____ 5. Tamales are a round, flat bread made of masa dough.

_____ 6. The Chinese typically serve sweet desserts with their meals.

_____ 7. Most of the foods eaten in developing countries are imported.

_____ 8. Soybeans play an important role in Oriental food dishes.

_____ 9. Little meat is eaten in East Africa because cattle, sheep, and goats are considered wealth, not food.

_____ 10. Russians typically eat thin slices of white bread with a meal.

II. Matching. Find the term in the right column that BEST corresponds to each description in the left column. Write the letter of the term in the blank space provided. Do not use any term more than once. Some terms will not be used.

Descriptions	Terms
_____ 11. Assorted appetizers served before the meal.	A. tofu
_____ 12. A spice mixture.	B. bubble and squeak
_____ 13. Basic foods and preparation methods.	C. borsch
_____ 14. An English favorite of chopped cooked beef, mashed potatoes, and leftover vegetables mashed together and fried until all pieces are brown and crisp.	D. bouillabaisse E. masa F. antipasto
_____ 15. Sweets made of dried fruits and nuts in a paper-thin pastry.	G. cuisine H. gourmet cooking
_____ 16. A Japanese meat and vegetable combination cooked in a wok.	I. sukiyaki J. curry K. schnitzel
_____ 17. Ground dried corn.	L. phyllo
_____ 18. Bean curd that tastes like a mild cheese.	M. sushi N. tortilla
_____ 19. A Russian beet soup.	O. mousse P. kippers Q. wurst

III. Multiple Choice. In the space at the left, write the letter of the choice that BEST completes each statement.

_____ 20. Because of religious beliefs, the type of meat seldom used in the Near and Middle East is:
 A. pork   C. poultry
 B. beef   D. lamb

_____ 21. Dal, a food eaten at a typical Indian meal, is a:
 A. lentil dish   C. rice dish
 B. curd dish   D. type of unleavened bread

_____ 22. Many of the foreign terms appearing in American menus are:
 A. Scandinavian   C. French
 B. Spanish   D. Chinese

_____ 23. Scandinavia refers to Finland, Norway, Denmark, and:
 A. Austria   C. the Netherlands
 B. Sweden   D. Greece

_____ 24. Fish and chips is a:
 A. Scandinavian favorite   C. German food
 B. British favorite   D. French food

_____ 25. A phrase that means foods are listed and priced individually on a menu is:
 A. table d'hôte   C. en croute
 B. a la king   D. a la carte

_____ 26. The Oriental diet is:
 A. high in calories   C. low in calories
 B. low in fiber   D. deficient in vitamin A

_____ 27. Because fuel supplies in the Orient have historically been limited, food is:
 A. cooked in solar ovens   C. cut into small pieces so it
                 cooks quickly
 B. usually eaten raw   D. served cold

IV. Completion. In the space at the left, write the word that BEST completes each statement. As a clue, the total number of letters in the word is given.

_____ 28. A popular method of serving food in Scandinavia is the ___?___
(11)

_____ 29. In small countries surrounded by water a common protein source is ___?___.
(4)

_____ 30. Thin French pancakes rolled around a filling are called ___?___.
(6)

_____ 31. If you wanted to find the price of pie with ice cream on a menu, the French term you would look for is ___?___.
(7)

_____ 32. The bread of Mexico is called a(n) ___?___.
(8)

_____ 33. Cubes of meat cooked on skewers over an open fire are called ___?___.
(11)

Chapter 36 Test

I. Matching. Find the term in the right column that BEST corresponds to each description in the left column. Write the letter of the term in the blank space provided. Do not use any term more than once. Some terms will not be used.

Descriptions

_____ 1. A hearty, regional soup thickened with okra.

_____ 2. A buffet feast in Hawaii.

_____ 3. A cornmeal mush baked into a cake.

_____ 4. Small pieces of cooked intestines served with a spicy sauce or dipped in batter and deep-fried.

_____ 5. Corn and beans cooked together.

_____ 6. A cooking style that developed from the food customs of Africa and the Amerindians.

_____ 7. A fish soup traditionally cooked in an iron pot.

_____ 8. A dish made from the tongue, liver, heart, and thymus gland of slaughtered cattle.

_____ 9. A cooking style that combines the food habits of four cultures — French, Spanish, Amerindian, and African.

Terms

A. chili con carne
B. cowboy stew
C. soul food
D. Creole cooking
E. poi
F. hush puppies
G. johnny cakes
H. Hopping John
I. luau
J. gumbo
K. clam chowder
L. succotash
M. kaffeeklatsch
N. chitterlings
O. sweetbreads
P. clambake
Q. sourdough

II. True-False. Read the following statements carefully. In the space at the left of each statement, write TRUE if the statement is true. Write FALSE if the statement is incorrect.

_____ 10. The early settlers in America survived by learning to grow and eat the crops of the native Americans.

_____ 11. As the pioneers moved westward, rye was the crop that sustained them.

_____ 12. The early German settlers in the Northeast showed the Amerindians how to fix succotash.

_____ 13. The kaffeeklatsch is a Pennsylvania Dutch custom of gathering with neighbors for mid-morning coffee and baked goods.

_____ 14. Lifestyles, like that of the cowboys of the Southwest, help shape regional cooking styles.

_____ 15. The immigrants from each country tended to cluster together and continue their food customs and culture.

_____ 16. Food customs along the Atlantic coast reflect a prominent Oriental influence.

_____ 17. The staple Amerindian food of the Northwest was buffalo.

III. Multiple Choice. In the space at the left, write the letter of the choice that BEST completes each statement.

_____ 18. Cornmeal batter dropped by the spoonful into deep, hot fat is called:
    A. johnny cake   C. gumbo
    B. hush puppies   D. spoon bread

_____ 19. The hearty foods that were the basis of the Pennsylvania Dutch diet were from:
    A. Holland   C. Virginia
    B. Poland   D. Germany

_____ 20. Foods of the Pacific Coast and the Northwest have traditionally been:
    A. mostly imported   C. hot and spicy
    B. elaborately prepared   D. prepared simply

_____ 21. Early settlers in the Midwest brought with them the food customs of:
    A. the southern states   C. the Old World and the eastern states
    B. the cowboys   D. Canada

_____ 22. Indian, Mexican, and Spanish cultures helped shape the cuisine of:
    A. the Midwest   C. the Southwest
    B. New England   D. the South

_____ 23. The Amerindians showed the early colonists how to plant:
    A. wild rice   C. pumpkins
    B. oats   D. cassava

_____ 24. Communications, technology, and travel have made regional foods:
    A. familiar throughout the country   C. disappear
    B. more distinctive than ever   D. become novelties

_____ 25. Creole and soul cooking developed in the:
    A. West   C. South
    B. Northeast   D. Pacific states

_____ 26. Prospectors in search of gold in California and Alaska depended on:
    A. cowboy stew   C. johnny cakes
    B. succotash   D. sourdough

_____ 27. Hawaiian cooking has been influenced by:
    A. Oriental cooking   C. Pacific coast cooking
    B. New Guinea cooking   D. French cooking

IV. Completion. In the space at the left, write the word that BEST completes each statement. As a clue, the total number of letters in the word is given.

_____ 28. The ___?___ is the region of the U.S. known for serving cooked
        (5)   greens, grits, and corn bread.

_____ 29. ___?___ was such a valuable food to many Amerindian tribes that
        (4)   they considered it a gift from the gods to be treasured and honored
                             in ceremony.

_____ 30. ___?___ cooking, like Creole cooking, is a Louisiana style renowned
        (5)   for its spicy foods.

_____ 31. When the ___?___ settled in the Southwest, they introduced new
        (7)   meat animals — sheep, goats, and cattle.

_____ 32. Hawaiians, like other island people, rely on ___?___ as their main
        (4)   protein source.

_____ 33. Early settlers of the Northeast learned to use the food sources and
       (11)   cooking methods of the ___?___.

Name _____

Date _____

Chapter 37 Test

I. True-False. Read the following statements carefully. In the space at the left of each statement, write TRUE if the statement is true. Write FALSE if the statement is incorrect.

_____ 1. When grilling, you can cause a flareup by starting the grill with gasoline.

_____ 2. Herbs, unlike spices, do not lose their flavor with age.

_____ 3. When using fresh herbs, use three to four times as much as dried herbs.

_____ 4. As long as the garage doors are kept wide open, grilling food in a garage is safe.

_____ 5. Cooking increases the strength of herb and spice flavors.

_____ 6. Veal is an inexpensive substitute for pork in recipes.

_____ 7. There is one correct seasoning for each specific food.

_____ 8. Recipes for puddings are less exacting than those for stews.

_____ 9. Casseroles are an ideal way to use leftover foods.

_____ 10. Chili powder is a spice made from pepper roots.

_____ 11. Since grilling is a dry-heat method of cooking, tender cuts of meat are best.

_____ 12. Windy days are best for outdoor cooking because the fire burns more quickly.

II. Matching. Find the term in the right column that BEST corresponds to each description in the left column. Write the letter of the term in the blank space provided. Do not use any term more than once. Some terms will not be used.

Descriptions	Terms
_____ 13. An individual tart with straight fluted sides.	A. seasoning blend
_____ 14. Carrot curls, radish roses, and a sprig of mint.	B. relishes
	C. yogurt
_____ 15. Chives, basil, and oregano.	D. buttermilk
_____ 16. Greens, dressing, croutons, and Parmesan cheese tossed in front of guests.	E. mustards
	F. cottage cheese
	G. vinegars
_____ 17. Cinnamon, pepper, and cloves.	H. herbs
_____ 18. A substitute for sour cream.	I. spices
	J. flan
_____ 19. Made from soured or fermented alcohol or wine.	K. phyllo
	L. chef's salad
_____ 20. Curry.	M. garnishes
	N. Caesar salad
	O. crepe

III. Multiple Choice. In the space at the left, write the letter of the choice that BEST completes each statement.

_____ 21. Many cheeses can replace one another as long as:
    A. their fat contents are the same   C. they are the same color
    B. their consistencies are the same   D. they taste the same

_____ 22. Spices are made from:
  A. plant leaves
  B. rare tropical trees
  C. roots, stems, and seeds of plants
  D. seasoning blends

_____ 23. Creative cooking means using:
  A. your artistic ability to create appealing meals
  B. money to purchase expensive gourmet foods
  C. prescribed ways of cooking foods
  D. traditional cooking methods

_____ 24. When you double the recipe for a casserole to be cooked in a microwave oven:
  A. use a deeper container and double the cooking time
  B. use a wider container and increase the cooking time by ⅓ to ½
  C. use two containers and double the power
  D. add more liquid and use a deeper container

_____ 25. The leaves of plants that are used as fresh or dried seasonings are:
  A. mustards
  B. teas
  C. herbs
  D. spices

_____ 26. When using a recipe that specifies an expensive cut of meat, you can often achieve the same effect by substituting:
  A. economical cuts of fish
  B. using extra seasoning and eliminating the meat
  C. economical cuts of meat
  D. pieces of rich-flavored cheese

_____ 27. When selecting an outdoor grill, make sure:
  A. the legs are sturdy
  B. the legs are flexible
  C. it can be used indoors
  D. the metal grid won't get stuck in the fire bowl

_____ 28. When food is cooked for a long time, such as stew, it is best to add seasonings:
  A. at the beginning of cooking
  B. during the last hour of cooking
  C. during the last five minutes of cooking
  D. a little at a time

_____ 29. The main purpose of having toppings on casseroles is:
  A. to add flavor
  B. to add texture
  C. to add decoration
  D. to keep the mixture from drying out

_____ 30. When choosing a garnish to add the finishing touch to a special meal, make sure:
  A. the flavor is compatible
  B. the flavor is tart
  C. it is elaborate
  D. it covers the top of the main course

_____ 31. A decorating tube is:
  A. used only by professional chefs
  B. used to make citrus garnishes
  C. used to make graceful borders and designs
  D. used to hold birthday candles

_____ 32. Distilled white vinegar is the:
  A. spiciest vinegar
  B. only one chef's use
  C. strongest vinegar
  D. mildest vinegar

_____ 33. Think about color when planning a special meal so that:
  A. all food colors match
  B. the color of the plate is the same as the main dish
  C. the color of the garnish complements the food
  D. the four primary colors are represented

536

Name _____

Date _____

Part Six Test

I. Matching. Find the term in the right column that BEST corresponds to each description in the left column. Write the letter of the term in the blank space provided. Do not use any term more than once. Some terms will not be used.

Descriptions

Ch. 35 _____ 1. A round, flat bread made of corn flour.

Ch. 35 _____ 2. A German pot roast marinated in an acid-oil mixture and cooked in a spicy sweet-sour sauce.

Ch. 35 _____ 3. A modern low-calorie version of haute cuisine.

Ch. 35 _____ 4. An ice cream from Italy containing fruits, nuts, or candies.

Ch. 35 _____ 5. Assorted appetizers served before the meal in Italy.

Ch. 35 _____ 6. An urn with a spigot that is used to serve tea in the Soviet Union.

Ch. 35 _____ 7. Meat cut into cubes, placed on skewers, and roasted over an open fire. A common dish in the Middle East.

Ch. 35 _____ 8. A North African mixture of finely ground wheat, salt, and water.

Ch. 36 _____ 9. Cornmeal batter dropped by the spoonful into deep hot fat.

Ch. 36 _____ 10. A hearty creole soup thickened with okra.

Ch. 36 _____ 11. An Amerindian dish of beans and corn.

Ch. 36 _____ 12. A Hawaiian word for a feast.

Ch. 36 _____ 13. Small cooked pieces of intestine served with a spicy sauce or deep-fat fried.

Ch. 36 _____ 14. A baked cornmeal mush that was a favorite food of early travelers.

Ch. 36 _____ 15. A main dish common to the cowboys of the Southwest.

Ch. 37 _____ 16. Decorative arrangements of edible food used to improve the appearance of a dish.

Ch. 37 _____ 17. An American dish that makes use of leftover foods.

Ch. 37 _____ 18. The leaves of plants that are used as fresh or dried seasonings.

Ch. 37 _____ 19. An acidic food that adds a distinctive flavor to food.

Ch. 37 _____ 20. Dried roots, stems, and seeds of plants grown mainly in the Tropics.

Terms

A. spumoni
B. shish kebobs
C. minestrone
D. hush puppies
E. casserole
F. vinegar
G. sauerbraten
H. crêpes
I. Hopping John
J. spices
K. blends
L. ragout
M. succotash
N. herbs
O. luau
P. garnishes
Q. tortilla
R. chitterlings
S. cowboy stew
T. antipasto
U. gumbo
V. samovar
W. johnny cake
X. couscous
Y. schnitzel
Z. nouvelle cuisine

II. True-False.
Read the following statements carefully. In the space at the left of each statement, write TRUE if the statement is true. Write FALSE if the statement is incorrect.

Ch. 35 _____ 21. The English dish of bubble and squeak is made of fish and shellfish.

Ch. 35 _____ 22. We can thank the French for introducing Neapolitan and spumoni ice creams.

Ch. 35 _____ 23. A great variety of food practices exist in Africa due to the diversity in the land and climate.

Ch. 35 _____ 24. In the Orient, preparing to cook takes longer than the actual cooking.

Ch. 35 _____ 25. Because of religious beliefs, pork is the meat most often used for cooking in the Near and Middle East.

Ch. 36 _____ 26. In Mexico, chocolate is used to flavor a meat sauce called mole poblano.

Ch. 36 _____ 27. The Amerindians introduced barbecued meat, roast turkey, corn, and maple sugar to the early immigrants.

Ch. 36 _____ 28. Due to their limited food supply, the people on the Pacific Coast and Northwest have to import much of their food.

Ch. 36 _____ 29. Soul food is a combination of the native food customs of African settlers, locally grown food, and Amerindian cooking.

Ch. 37 _____ 30. It is difficult to cook creatively on a low or limited budget since most of the foods needed are expensive.

Ch. 37 _____ 31. Fresh herbs are more concentrated than dried ones; therefore, less should be used in a recipe.

Ch. 37 _____ 32. Most spices can be classified as "hot" seasonings.

Ch. 37 _____ 33. When food is cooked for hours, such as stew or pot roast, it is best to add seasonings during the last hour.

Ch. 37 _____ 34. Less expensive cuts of meat can often be substituted for expensive cuts in gourmet recipes.

Ch. 37 _____ 35. A plastic apron provides the best protection for outdoor grilling.

III. Multiple Choice.
In the space at the left, write the letter of the choice that BEST completes each statement.

Ch. 35 _____ 36. A basic seasoning in East Africa is:
A. dal
B. curry
C. masala
D. ginger

Ch. 35 _____ 37. The use of fruits with meat and vegetables to create sweet-sour flavors is characteristic of the cooking in:
A. Scandinavia
B. Spain
C. Germany
D. Great Britain

Ch. 35 _____ 38. The type of cooking which can be considered the gourmet cooking of China is:
A. Shanghai
B. Cantonese
C. Peking
D. Szechuan

Ch. 35 _____ 39. In Japan, a meat and vegetable combination cooked in a wok is called:
A. sushi
B. tempura
C. hunan
D. sukiyaki

Ch. 35	_____	40. The smorgasbord, similar to a buffet, is a popular method of serving food in:

40. The smorgasbord, similar to a buffet, is a popular method of serving food in:
   A. Russia
   B. Scandinavia
   C. Germany
   D. Italy

Ch. 35 _____ 41. Paella is a national food dish in:
   A. Spain
   B. India
   C. North Africa
   D. Germany

Ch. 35 _____ 42. Provincial cooking in France is:
   A. complicated and difficult to copy
   B. hot and spicy
   C. relatively simple
   D. high in sugar and fat

Ch. 35 _____ 43. Borsch is a Russian soup made from:
   A. potatoes
   B. lentils
   C. chicken broth
   D. beets

Ch. 36 _____ 44. Creole cooking developed in the:
   A. West
   B. South
   C. Southwest
   D. North

Ch. 36 _____ 45. Steamed shellfish were introduced to American cooking by the:
   A. English
   B. Scandinavians
   C. Amerindians
   D. Pennsylvania Dutch

Ch. 36 _____ 46. The staple Amerindian food of the Northwest was:
   A. seafood
   B. small game animals
   C. buffalo
   D. beans

Ch. 36 _____ 47. The kaffeeklatsch, a gathering of people for coffee and baked goods, dates back to the customs of the:
   A. Irish
   B. Germans
   C. Scandinavians
   D. Spanish

Ch. 36 _____ 48. The staple food of the prospectors in search of gold in California and Alaska was:
   A. fish
   B. sourdough
   C. corn
   D. beef

Ch. 37 _____ 49. Choose an outdoor grill that has all of the following features EXCEPT:
   A. sturdy legs
   B. evenly balanced
   C. large enough grid for your needs
   D. rotating fire bowl

Ch. 37 _____ 50. Substitutions and innovative changes are easiest to make in:
   A. puddings
   B. baked goods
   C. casseroles
   D. candies

Chapter 38 Test

I. True-False. Read the following statements carefully. In the space at the left of each statement, write TRUE if the statement is true. Write FALSE if the statement is incorrect.

_____ 1. A person who wants a career must have a college degree.

_____ 2. A pastry chef is an entry-level position in the food service field.

_____ 3. Most people stay in their chosen careers throughout their work years.

_____ 4. Management careers in food service do not generally require education beyond high school.

_____ 5. Studies predict that today's average teenager may work from 35 to 45 years.

_____ 6. A good background in food services prepares you for a variety of jobs in hospitals, cafeterias, and other institutions.

_____ 7. If you are making a good income in your career, but no longer find satisfaction with your work, you should rethink your personal and career goals.

_____ 8. Nutritionists and dietitians are the same.

_____ 9. Nutritionists most often are involved in the supervision of food preparation.

_____ 10. Home economists can work as researchers creating new products or improving existing products.

II. Multiple Choice. In the space at the left, write the letter of the choice that BEST completes each statement.

_____ 11. To advance in food service industries, a college education is:
   A. helpful
   B. not necessary
   C. required
   D. dependent upon where you live

_____ 12. The employment outlook for careers in food and nutrition is:
   A. limited
   B. promising
   C. unpredictable
   D. unknown

_____ 13. The number of careers the average person who starts to work now will have during his/her lifetime is:
   A. only one
   B. at least five
   C. about three
   D. more than twelve

_____ 14. If you want a career in food and nutrition, the LEAST helpful of the following courses would be:
   A. English
   B. math
   C. communications
   D. history

_____ 15. The percentage of new business ventures that fail during the first five years is about:
   A. 20 percent
   B. 40 percent
   C. 55 percent
   D. 70 percent

III. Matching.
Find the term in the right column that BEST corresponds to each description in the left column. Write the letter of the term in the blank space provided. Do not use any term more than once. Some terms will not be used.

Descriptions

_____ 16. An advantage of working in food service.

_____ 17. Using science and engineering to develop new products.

_____ 18. Learning while at work.

_____ 19. Schools that teach you about baking or cooking in the food service industry.

_____ 20. A partnership plan between a school and local businesses for hiring and training qualified students.

_____ 21. A way to diagram job progress.

_____ 22. Work you do for a long period in your life.

_____ 23. A promotion to a higher rank or position.

_____ 24. To become skilled in one particular type of work.

_____ 25. An area dealing with consumer complaints and unfair marketing practices.

Terms

A. dietetics
B. communications
C. career ladder
D. FHA
E. high salaries
F. availability of jobs
G. food technology
H. job scale
I. Small Business Institute
J. home economics
K. advancement
L. on-the-job training
M. specialize
N. career
O. consumer affairs
P. vocational
Q. technological
R. HERO

IV. Matching.
Find the job in the right column that BEST corresponds to each description in the left column. Write the letter in the blank space provided. Do not use any job more than once. Some jobs will not be used.

Descriptions

_____ 26. Area in which home economists conduct programs and classes on home management, consumer education, and nutrition for adults and youths.

_____ 27. Administers federal food programs.

_____ 28. Own and run their own businesses.

_____ 29. Tries to help people improve their eating habits by holding classes and counseling individuals on nutrition.

_____ 30. Cleans the kitchen.

_____ 31. A career area in which home economists work for newspapers, magazines, and book publishers.

_____ 32. Serving food or doing related jobs.

_____ 33. Specializes in applying the principles of nutrition to feeding; some plan menus for people with certain medical problems.

Jobs

A. caterers
B. dietitians
C. customer service
D. food stylists
E. communications
F. nutritionists
G. sanitation worker
H. entrepreneurs
I. assistant chef
J. Cooperative Extension Service
K. Food and Nutrition Service

Chapter 39 Test

I. True-False. Read the following statements carefully. In the space at the left of each statement, write TRUE if the statement is true. Write FALSE if the statement is incorrect.

_____ 1. It is a wise practice to share personal problems with co-workers on the job.

_____ 2. Sometimes employers pay a fee to a private agency to find them qualified employees.

_____ 3. Never sign an employment contract before thoroughly understanding the terms explained on the form.

_____ 4. Relatives and friends can be excellent sources in finding out about job openings.

_____ 5. Part-time jobs are not "stepping stones" toward moving ahead in the world of work.

_____ 6. It is a waste of time to find out as much as you can about a business before a job interview.

_____ 7. Appearance is not significant in getting a job, unless it is a job in which you will have to work directly with the customer.

_____ 8. Volunteer work is helpful in gaining valuable work experience.

_____ 9. If you were not offered a job during an interview, it is a good idea to call the interviewer a few days later to express interest in the job.

_____ 10. A Social Security number is not essential when you apply for a part-time job.

_____ 11. States that require a work permit do so only for students who leave school and work full-time.

_____ 12. It is not necessary to answer every question on a job application.

_____ 13. Punctuality is an important trait in holding a job.

_____ 14. One of the most common causes of losing a job is not knowing how to get along with people.

_____ 15. Without experience, it is easier to get a part-time job than a full-time job.

_____ 16. Relatives are often accepted as references by employers.

II. Multiple Choice. In the space at the left, write the letter of the choice that BEST completes each statement.

_____ 17. Balancing your job and your personal life is achieved through:
   A. being responsible   C. leadership skills
   B. time management   D. keeping busy

_____ 18. The Social Security number assigned when you first begin to work:
   A. remains the same throughout life   C. cannot be replaced
   B. changes when you choose a new career D. changes if you move to another state

_____ 19. The Social Security fund receives contributions from:
   A. employee   C. Internal Revenue Service
   B. employer   D. employee and employer

_____ 20. If you have complaints about your job, you should discuss them with:
   A. your co-workers   C. your immediate supervisor
   B. your friends   D. your counselor

_____ 21. Newspaper want ads are grouped together by:
   A. job similarity   C. required work hours
   B. salary range   D. age and skills

_____ 22. Effective leaders do all of the following EXCEPT:
   A. make difficult decisions   C. are good listeners
   B. communicate ideas clearly D. do most of the work themselves

_____ 23. When you get a job through a Cooperative Education Program, you receive:
   A. school credit but no wages C. wages but no school credit
   B. both wages and school credit D. volunteer credit

_____ 24. Organizations that help people find a job for a fee are:
   A. job placement services   C. school placement offices
   B. private employment agencies D. cooperative education programs

III. Completion. In the space at the left, write the word that BEST completes each statement. As a clue, the total number of letters in the word is given.

_____ 25. Regulations about what you should wear on the job are called the
      (5, 4)   ___?___.

_____ 26. Customers, indirectly, pay an employee's ___?___.
      (5)

_____ 27. Money deducted from a paycheck under the heading ___?___ goes
      (4)   to a fund to support your retirement.

_____ 28. A form that asks for information about you for a job is a(n) ___?___.
      (11)

_____ 29. People an employer can ask about your ability or character are
      (10)   ___?___.

_____ 30. A(n) ___?___ tells the employer you are in good health and free from
      (6, 11)   communicable diseases.

_____ 31. A meeting between a person seeking a job and an employer is a(n)
      (9)   ___?___.

_____ 32. A(n) ___?___ is a trained person in your school who can guide you
      (9)   in your search for a job.

_____ 33. A summary information sheet listing your personal qualifications
      (6)   is a(n) ___?___.

Name _____

Date _____

Part Seven Test

I. Matching. Find the term in the right column that BEST corresponds to each description in the left column. Write the letter of the term in the blank space provided. Do not use any term more than once. Some terms will not be used.

Descriptions

Ch. 38 _____ 1. Employment with a company done regularly for pay.

Ch. 38 _____ 2. Promotion to a higher rank or position.

Ch. 38 _____ 3. To do one type of job and become skilled in it.

Ch. 38 _____ 4. Process of learning while you earn.

Ch. 38 _____ 5. Professionals who work to improve products, services, and practices that affect people's health, comfort, and well-being.

Ch. 38 _____ 6. Those whose jobs include supervising others and making decisions.

Ch. 38 _____ 7. A career field for those concerned with trying to help people improve their eating habits.

Ch. 38 _____ 8. Type of employment selected for a long period of time or in a certain field.

Ch. 38 _____ 9. Specialists in applying the principles of nutrition to feeding. Such a person might plan a special menu for a person with a medical problem.

Ch. 39 _____ 10. A meeting between the person seeking a job and the prospective employer.

Ch. 39 _____ 11. Organizations that specialize in helping people find jobs and in helping employers find workers.

Ch. 39 _____ 12. A summary information sheet listing a person's education, work experience, and personal qualifications.

Ch. 39 _____ 13. People an employer can ask about a job applicant's ability or character.

Ch. 39 _____ 14. A trained person in a school who can guide a job search.

Ch. 39 _____ 15. A federal insurance program which provides money for retirement.

Ch. 39 _____ 16. Rules and procedures employees are required to follow on the job.

Ch. 39 _____ 17. Questionnaire a prospective employer will ask you to fill out with information about yourself.

Terms

A. management
B. Social Security
C. home economists
D. dietitians
E. advancement
F. qualifications
G. job
H. résumé
I. career ladder
J. interview
K. work regulations
L. career
M. counselor
N. specialize
O. employment agencies
P. work permit
Q. on-the-job training
R. nutrition
S. references
T. opportunities
U. application form
V. HERO

II. True-False. Read the following statements carefully. In the space at the left of each statement, write the word TRUE if the statement is true. Write FALSE if the statement is incorrect.

Ch. 38 _____ 18. Entry-level jobs in food service are usually easy to get.

Ch. 38 _____ 19. A college education is helpful in climbing a career ladder of advancement in food service.

Ch. 38 _____ 20. Computer and math courses can be helpful in preparing for a job in food or nutrition.

Ch. 38 _____ 21. One advantage of food service jobs is that they rarely require hard physical labor.

Ch. 38 _____ 22. Job opportunities in the food service industry appear brighter than many other fields.

Ch. 38 _____ 23. Home economists are employed by the government to look for unfair marketing practices.

Ch. 39 _____ 24. Volunteer work is usually not considered work experience in applying for a job.

Ch. 39 _____ 25. The Social Security number assigned to you remains the same through life.

Ch. 39 _____ 26. The employer is the only one who contributes toward the Social Security fund.

Ch. 39 _____ 27. Knowing how to get along with people is an important part of keeping a job.

III. Multiple Choice. In the space at the left, write the letter of the choice that BEST completes each statement.

Ch. 38 _____ 28. Which of the following is LEAST likely to cause a person to make a career change?
A. old job eliminated by new technology
B. change in values and goals
C. job no longer gives satisfaction
D. a job promotion

Ch. 38 _____ 29. Which of the following is NOT a job in the food service industry?
A. sanitation
B. food preparation
C. dietetics
D. customer service

Ch. 38 _____ 30. Which of the following would probably be the best source of training to become a chef?
A. management training program
B. on-the-job training
C. vocational school
D. four-year college

Ch. 38 _____ 31. Which of the following is required of a registered dietitian?
A. a bachelor's degree and passing a state exam
B. a master's degree
C. a college degree, hospital internship, and passing a national exam
D. a degree and certification from a four-year college of nursing

Ch. 39 _____ 32. Which of the following would be the LEAST helpful resource when searching for a job?
A. family and friends
B. "Help Wanted" ads in the newspaper
C. private employment agencies
D. the Better Business Bureau

Ch. 39 _____ 33. Which of the following is NOT appropriate when being interviewed by a prospective employer?
A. ask questions about what the job involves
B. talk at length about your interests
C. be yourself
D. tell what makes you think you are qualified for the job

Teacher's Resource Book
Answer Key

Note: Answer keys for food science experiments are found in the Food Science Materials section (pages 357-370).

HO-15: How Would You Make This Kitchen Safe?

1. Too many appliances on one outlet.
2. Hot pad hanging over burner.
3. Bottle of cooking oil spilled on floor.
4. Pan containing hot food has handle sticking out.
5. Mixer cord across range.
6. Hot pad on burner.
7. Person standing on chair.
8. Electrical appliances placed close to sink.
9. Sharp knife left in sink.
10. Cord to iron extended across sink.
11. Cord to iron dangling over edge of counter.
12. Cabinet door left open.
13. Food stored in cabinet under sink.
14. Cleansers and other hazardous substances stored on low shelf.
15. Cleansers and other hazardous substances stored with food.
16. Throw rug could cause falls.
17. Broken glass on floor.
18. Cat eating in kitchen.

RECIPE WORKSHEET ANSWERS

R-1: Jogger's Snack Pak

1. a. 53%   b. 44%   c. 11%
2. Butter or margarine; sunflower seeds; nuts.
3. Some microwave ovens have an even cooking pattern. Therefore food must be turned or stirred to cook evenly.
4. Any three: measuring; chopping; tossing; stirring; toasting; cooling.
5. Use a microwave-safe dish. (See p. 250 of text for other possible answers.)
6. Some of the ingredients would brown.
7. Possible answers: fruit juices or fruit drinks; non-fat yogurt; skim milk.

R-2: Nachos — Pronto!

1. a. 44%   b. 39%   c. 13%
2. Cheese; tortilla chips.
3. Any three: use a microwave-safe dish; be careful of sharp edges on can and top after can is opened; avoid scraping fingers or knuckles when grating cheese; handle chilies carefully. (Other answers are possible.)
4. Any one: shredding; slicing; chopping; sprinkling; measuring.
5. Possible answers: chili powder; cumin; garlic salt; cayenne pepper; Italian seasoning mix; sesame seeds; bacon bits; ketchup; pizza sauce; chopped chives.
6. Possible answers: chili; bean dip and/or avocado dip with tortilla chips; salad; assorted fresh fruit; fruit drinks.
7. Answers will vary.

R-3: Snack-A-Pizza

1. a. 45%   b. 33%   c. 22%
2. Cheese; pepperoni.
3. Omit pepperoni; use part-skim mozzarella or other low-fat cheese.
4. Omit pepperoni; make homemade pizza sauce without salt.
5. Buy pre-shredded mozzarella cheese and pre-sliced pepperoni.
6. Conventional cooking takes roughly four times as long as microwave cooking.
7. Possible answers: tossed salad or fresh fruit; skim milk.

R-4: Lemony Poached Pears

1. a. 5%   b. 98%   c. 3%
2. The sugar and the pudding and pie filling mix are both relatively high in calories.
3. Baking in a plastic cooking bag.
4. Any two: slit cooking bag properly so it will not explode; open bag carefully to avoid steam burns; use bags specifically made for cooking; follow directions on the package; use a pan that is large enough to hold the food.
5. Use a non-metallic tie for the cooking bag; use a microwavable baking dish. (See p. 250 of text for other possible answers.)
6. Any three: paring; coring; mixing; beating; measuring; combining; cutting; rolling; chilling; sprinkling; baking.

R-5: Sautéed Apple Rings

1. a. 61%   b. 38%   c. 1%
2. Butter or margarine.
3. Sautéing.
4. Possible answers: use sharp knife that won't slip; use cutting board; don't cut toward self.
5. Any two: use a microwavable dish; lift cover so steam flows away from you; use potholders to remove dish from oven. (See p. 250 of text for other possible answers.)
6. Any two: apples are put in dish with cooked onions and covered for cooking; slices are rearranged halfway during cooking time; apples must be allowed to stand after cooking.
7. Answers will vary.

R-6: Broccoli-Onion Casserole

1. a. 44%   b. 35%   c. 20%
2. Possible answers: use skim milk; use a sauce that doesn't contain cheese; use plain sliced onions instead of french-fried and top with bread crumbs.
3. Any two: follow instructions for using opener so lid is properly cut away from can; handle sharp lid of opened can carefully; dispose of sharp lid immediately; use care in handling sharp edges of can opener.
4. Any two: wipe top of can with a clean damp cloth before opening to remove any dirt that might fall into food; rinse can and lid before throwing out to prevent attracting pests; clean can opener regularly to avoid accumulation of food.
5. Any three: simmering; draining; measuring; stirring; sprinkling; assembling casserole; baking.
6. Broccoli is rearranged halfway through cooking time; sauce is prepared in a glass measuring cup; baking dish is rotated halfway through cooking time.

R-7: Sautéed Collard Greens
1. a. 61%   b. 38%   c. 16%
2. Bacon.
3. Possible answers: do not wash before refrigerating; store in a plastic bag, airtight container, or the refrigerator's crisper compartment.
4. Any three: do not let fat overheat or burn; drain bacon carefully to avoid burns from hot fat; add collards carefully to avoid hot grease spatters; wipe up any grease spatters on the floor immediately. (Other answers are possible.)
5. Any four: frying; draining; crumbling; washing; cutting; stirring; turning; sautéing; tossing.
6. Any two: it doesn't produce grease spatters; it's quicker; more of the collard vitamins may be retained; in warm weather microwave cooking does not heat up your kitchen. (Other answers are possible.)

R-8: Tofuburgers
1. a. 49%   b. 27%   c. 27%
2. Sautéing; baking.
3. Any two: chop onion carefully on a cutting board with a sharp knife; sauté on medium heat so fat does not spatter or burn; pull oven racks in and out when placing pan in and removing it from the oven. (Other answers are possible.)
4. Any two: wash hands before mixing and shaping burgers; don't touch other parts of the body or other objects while handling the food; don't use hands to mix if you have an open sore or cut. (Other answers are possible.)
5. Any three: measuring; draining; squeezing; mincing; chopping; sautéing; crumbling; mixing; forming patties; brushing; turning; baking.
6. Yes. Tofu is made from soybeans, which are legumes. With the grain in the breadcrumbs, the combination supplies all essential amino acids.
7. Answers will vary but should include a grain like bread or roll; vegetables, fruit, and/or salad; and possibly a dairy product.

R-9: Vegetarian Pizza
1. a. 50%   b. 29%   c. 21%
2. Cheese; olive oil.
3. Any four: measuring; pressing and forming crust; mincing; combining; simmering; spreading; topping; sprinkling; brushing; baking.
4. Any four: make two small pizzas instead of one large; crust is partially baked on wax paper, flipped onto a plate, and then baked completely; sauce is not precooked; pizza is rotated during baking; cooking time is shorter.
5. Answers will vary.
6. Possible answers: fresh mushrooms sautéed in butter; green pepper slices or rings; tomato slices; pineapple chunks; tofu — thin slices, cubes, or crumbles; black or green olive slices or halves; thin zucchini slices; thin slices of cooked vegetables, such as carrots or broccoli.

R-10: At-Home Salad Bar
1. a. 52%   b. 19%   c. 30%
2. Ham; cheese; avocado.
3. Yes. Beans are legumes and the croutons are a grain product. The two eaten together would supply complete protein.
4. Possible answers: make sure hands, tools, and work areas are clean before cutting and combining food; keep cold foods refrigerated until ready to serve; provide a separate serving tool for each food; set out only enough food to serve everyone once and bring out more food later as needed.
5. Answers will vary but could include: bread or rolls; fresh fruit or a fruit salad; soup; beverage; possibly dessert.
6. Answers will vary but could include: other fresh vegetables; chilled cooked vegetables; fruit; pickled foods; prepared salads, such as potato, macaroni, cole slaw, and gelatin; nuts; seeds; smoked fish.
7. Answers will vary but could include soup and hot rolls or bread.

R-11: Dilled Cottage Cheese Dressing
1. a. 41%   b. 22%   c. 36%
2. Any three: handle blender blades carefully to avoid cuts or, if using an electric mixer, keep fingers away from beater blades when mixer is on; hold cucumber on cutting board when cutting; use a sharp knife; grate carefully to avoid scraping fingers or knuckles. (Other answers are possible.)
3. Any three: measuring; peeling; seeding; shredding; draining; blending; mixing; folding.
4. To remove excess moisture so dressing is not watery.
5. To give the dressing a smooth texture.
6. You could mix the remainder of the cottage cheese with any of the following: yogurt; sour cream; mayonnaise and milk.

R-12: Green Goddess Dressing
1. a. 72%   b. 11%   c. 8%
2. Use low-fat yogurt instead of sour cream.
3. Any four: measuring; chopping; mincing; combining; folding.
4. Because it adds a tangy flavor to salads that might otherwise lack distinct flavor.
5. Answers will vary. Many herbs and spices are used in flavored vinegars.

R-13: Chicken and Rice Salad
1. a. 50%   b. 33%   c. 17%
2. Mayonnaise; chicken.
3. Tomato; green peas.
4. Possible answers: handle sharp can lids carefully after opening; cut food on cutting board; be sure knives are sharp.
5. Possible answers: rinse out cans before discarding to prevent attracting pests; make sure work surface, hands, and tools are clean before preparing and assembling salad; keep salad chilled until ready to serve.
6. Any leftover cooked or canned meat.
7. Possible answers: whole grain rolls or crackers; beverage; fruit.

R-14: Avocado Dressing
1. a. 87%   b. 6%   c. 3%
2. Substitute low-fat yogurt for the sour cream and part of the mayonnaise.
3. Possible answers: if using a blender, handle blades carefully; use cutting board and sharp knife to cut avocado.
4. Any three: measuring; peeling; seeding; mashing; combining; blending; chilling.
5. Possible answer: as a dip with corn chips or crackers.

R-15: Fresh Spinach Salad
1. a. 63%   b. 31%   c. 11%
2. Avocado; mayonnaise; yogurt.
3. Any one: replace avocado with another fruit or vegetable; use nonfat yogurt; use a low-calorie bottled dressing.
4. Possible answers: clean spinach thoroughly and drain well; make sure work surface, cutting board, and hands are clean before preparing the salad; keep salad chilled until ready to serve.
5. Any four: measuring; washing; draining; peeling; slicing; mixing; mincing; pouring; assembling salad.
6. Possible answers: add protein, such as cooked meat or poultry, hard-cooked egg, cheese, or cooked beans with sunflower seeds or croutons.

R-16: Gelatin Squares
1. a. 15%   b. 67%   c. 20%
2. Any two: pour hot juice carefully to avoid burns; use a potholder when placing pan filled with hot mixture in the refrigerator; use a sharp knife to cut squares. (Other answers are possible.)
3. So the gelatin has a smooth, even texture and thickens properly.
4. Any two: apple, cranberry, canned pineapple, grapefruit, lime. (Other answers are possible.)
5. Vinegar or lemon juice.
6. Answers will vary.

R-17: Taco Salad Toss
1. a. 57%   b. 25%   c. 18%
2. Any three: measuring; coring; rinsing; slicing; stirring; draining; sautéing; browning; chopping; mincing; shredding; spreading; topping; tossing; simmering.
3. Sautéing; simmering.
4. Any three: handle sharp can lid carefully after opening can; fry carefully to avoid spattering fat; drain hot fat carefully; use sharp knife with a sawing motion when cutting. (Other answers are possible.)
5. Possible answers: keep raw beef away from food that will be served raw (vegetables, sour cream, and cheese); avoid cross-contamination by making sure that hands, work surface, and tools are clean before working with foods that will be served raw; serve salad immediately.
6. Answers will vary.

R-18: Crepes
1. a. 50%   b. 33%   c. 14%
2. Any two: keep burnable items away from the range; handle skillet carefully to avoid burns; do not let pan overheat to avoid grease spatters and fires. (Other answers are possible.)
3. Any three: measuring; sifting; mixing; combining; beating; melting; pouring; turning; browning; cooking crepes.
4. Any two: jam or jelly; canned pie fillings, such as apple or cherry; chopped cooked meat, poultry, or fish in a sauce; creamed vegetables. (Other answers are possible.)
5. Crepe batter uses little or no leavening agent and more eggs and liquid in relation to the flour content.
6. Possible answers: a large strawberry; thin, curled orange slices; whipped cream with chocolate shavings.

R-19: Cheese Filling for Crepes
1. a. 30%   b. 40%   c. 30%
2. Strawberries; orange juice.
3. Baking; boiling.
4. Any two: pull oven racks in and out when placing and removing pan; hold pan handle with potholder when stirring sauce; do not let potholder get close to the flame or heating element. (Other answers are possible.)
5. Answers will vary.
6. Answers will vary.

R-20: Hearty Chowder with Toast
1. a. 61%   b. 27%   c. 14%
2. a. Peas and carrots.
   b. Milk and cheese.
3. Any four: handle sharp can lid carefully after opening can; use sharp knife and cutting board to chop onions; use caution to avoid scraping fingers or knuckles when grating; do not overheat fat when sautéing; add ingredients to hot mixtures carefully. (Other answers are possible.)
4. Any three: measuring; chopping; slicing; shredding; melting; stirring; sprinkling; toasting; broiling; sautéing.
5. It would scorch and boil over.
6. Possible answers: another kind of soup, probably lower in calories; a salad; assorted breads and crackers; a beverage; dessert.

R-21: Coney Islands
1. a. 53%   b. 34%   c. 13%
2. Frankfurters; chili beef soup.
3. Frying; simmering.
4. Any three: handle sharp lids from opened cans carefully; stir mixture carefully when cooking to avoid spattering hot food; use medium heat to brown frankfurters to avoid grease spatter; check broiler frequently when toasting frankfurter buns to avoid burning. (Other answers are possible.)
5. Any two: microwavable container is used; soup is heated first; frankfurters are added to soup without browning.
6. Possible answers: salad or relishes, cooked vegetable, beverage.

R-22: Creole Spaghetti
1. a. 45%   b. 36%   c. 19%
2. Any three: measuring; mincing; grating; cooking spaghetti; melting, sautéing; blending; stirring; draining; pouring; browning.
3. Sautéing; simmering.
4. Possible answers: use moderate heat to prevent grease spatters and fire; drain off excess fat carefully to prevent spills and burns.
5. Handle glass cookware carefully to avoid chipping and breaking; colander and casserole will heat up from the food, so use a potholder when removing them from the oven. (See p. 250 of text for other possible answers.)
6. Answers will vary.

R-23: Sweet and Sour Pork
1. a. 31%   b. 44%   c. 25%
2. a. Carrots.
   b. Green peppers.
3. Pork
4. Any three: measuring; cubing; slicing; braising; draining; browning; simmering; stirring; sautéing; combining; tossing.
5. Sautéing; simmering.
6. Any three: handle sharp can lid carefully; use cutting board and sharp knife when cutting pork and vegetables; brown meat carefully to avoid spatters and burns; toss final mixture carefully to avoid hot spatters. (Other answers are possible.)

R-24: Surprise Burgers
1. a. 63%   b. 3%   c. 32%
2. Meat; cheese.
3. Possible answers: wash hands carefully before shaping patties; avoid cross-contamination by washing cutting board and tools before using them for raw foods such as tomatoes and cheese.
4. Possible answers: check broiler regularly to make certain fat is not burning; turn burgers carefully; have a clear area ready before removing broiler pan from oven.
5. Use microwavable roasting rack or bacon rack; racks will get hot from food so use potholders to handle them. (See p. 250 of text for other possible answers.)
6. Possible answers: taco sauce; chopped cooked vegetables.

R-25: Oriental Chicken
1. a. 31%   b. 38%   c. 31%
2. Chicken; rice.
3. Red or green pepper.
4. Any three: use cutting board and sharp knife to cut foods; do not overheat wok; add food carefully to prevent hot spatters; lift cover so steam flows away from you. (Other answers are possible.)
5. Any two: measuring; cutting; shredding; dicing; draining; skinning and deboning chicken; stir-frying; browning; simmering; stirring.
6. After chicken is cut, scrub cutting board and knife in hot sudsy water, then rinse and dry. After chicken is put in pan to cook, wash hands carefully to remove traces of raw chicken.
7. Fresh ginger root has a stronger flavor and adds more "bite." Ground ginger is commonly used in baked goods.

R-26: Crispy Catfish
1. a. 56%   b. 20%   c. 23%
2. Any two: measuring; breading; combining; thawing; washing; drying; frying; draining; turning.
3. Frying.
4. Any three: do not let fat overheat — it will smoke and burn; keep paper towels away from burners; place fish in hot fat carefully to avoid spatters and burns; wipe up any fat that may spatter on the floor. (Other answers are possible.)
5. Bacon fat adds more flavor to the fish.
6. Corn oil is unsaturated and has no cholesterol.
7. Fish requires little or no tenderizing. If fish is overcooked, the protein toughens and the fish becomes rubbery.
8. Rub them with a piece of lemon or rinse them in vinegar.

R-27: Italian Tuna Burgers
1. a. 46%   b. 26%   c. 27%
2. Any two: use sharp knife and cutting board to trim off bread crusts; set timer and check on broiling food; handle sharp can lids carefully. (Other answers are possible.)
3. Any three: measuring; slicing; draining; beating; crumbling; cutting; grating; shredding; flaking; stirring; mixing; broiling; sprinkling.
4. Use paper towel and plate instead of broiler pan; only 2 to 4 sandwiches are heated at a time; longer cooking time required; sandwiches must stand 1 minute before serving.
5. Answers will vary.

R-28: Tuna-Cheese Casserole
1. a. 39%   b. 32%   c. 30%
2. Any three: measuring; slicing; chopping; draining; flaking; shredding; combining; mixing; pouring; topping; baking; sprinkling; grating; cooking noodles; assembling casserole.
3. Simmering, baking.
4. Possible answers: be careful when carrying hot pan of boiling water and noodles; be careful of steam when draining hot noodles.
5. Add a little oil to the water.
6. Possible answers: dill pickles; celery fans; carrot curls; watercress; radish roses.
7. Possible answers: whole wheat noodles; flavored noodles such as spinach; macaroni in different shapes, such as shells.

R-29: Cheese Omelet
1. a. 76%   b. 2%   c. 23%
2. Reduce amount of cheese; substitute a low-fat filling, such as mushrooms, green pepper, or tomato sauce, for the cheese; use egg substitute; use spray pan coating instead of butter.
3. Any two: measuring; cooking, filling, and folding omelet; stirring; shredding.
4. Any three: handle hot skillet carefully; do not wear long sleeves that might catch fire; keep burnable items away from the range; do not use a high heat that might cause fat to spatter or burn. (Other answers are possible.)
5. Use care in handling glass plate; use potholder to handle glass plate during cooking procedures; lift plastic wrap so steam flows away from you. (See p. 250 of text for other possible answers.)
6. Answers will vary.

R-30: Egg Foo Yung
1. a. 71%   b. 16%   c. 18%
2. Butter or margarine; oil; eggs.
3. Any two: measuring; chopping; beating; draining; browning; blending; turning; stirring; sautéing.
4. Any three: handle sharp can lids carefully; pour egg mixture into skillet carefully; turn or stir mixture carefully to avoid spattering; keep pan handles turned toward range. (Other answers are possible.)
5. Frying or sautéing.
6. Possible answers: rice; cooked vegetable or salad; bread or rolls; beverage.

R-31: Huevos Rancheros
1. a. 62%   b. 29%   c. 12%
2. Any three: measuring; frying; sautéing; simmering; combining; chopping.
3. Frying; sautéing; simmering.
4. Any three: handle chili peppers with a fork, spoon, or tongs and not hands; do not overheat fat; add food carefully to hot fat to prevent spatters; handle sharp can lids carefully. (Other answers ae possible.)
5. Answers will vary.
6. Possible answers: juice; assorted fruits; hot muffins or rolls; cereal; bacon or sausage; beverage.

R-32: Pumpkin Custard
1. a. 25%   b. 56%   c. 19%
2. Pumpkin.
3. Any two: measuring; beating; mashing; boiling; mixing; baking; stirring; pouring.
4. Any two: stay clear of the steam as you pour hot water into the pan; be careful when removing pan from oven so you don't spill hot water on yourself; pull oven rack in and out to place pan in oven, test for doneness, and remove pan. (Other answers are possible.)
5. Possible answers: use muffin tin with paper liners; use oven-proof cups or mugs.
6. Mixture is pre-cooked in a glass mixing bowl, then stirred as it heats. Mixture is poured into custard cups to finish cooking.
7. Answers will vary.

R-33: Broccoli and Cheese Spaghetti
1. a. 34%   b. 45%   c. 20%
2. Boiling and sautéing.
3. Any three: watch spaghetti to make sure the water does not boil over; use moderate heat to keep fat from spattering and burning; drain spaghetti carefully to avoid steam burns; lift cover from saucepan so steam flows away from you. (Other answers are possible.)
4. Mushrooms are not cooked at the beginning with the other vegetables but are added later with the remaining ingredients; dish is allowed to stand after adding cheese.
5. Answers will vary.
6. Possible answers: cooked carrots; green peas; chopped spinach.

R-34: Pizza with Rice Crust
1. a. 38%   b. 42%   c. 21%
2. Any three: measuring; beating; grating; mincing; chopping; slicing; combining; sautéing; simmering; browning; draining; pressing out crust; spreading sauce; topping; baking.
3. Any two: baking; sautéing; simmering.
4. Any three: take care to avoid scraping fingers or knuckles when grating cheese; handle sharp can lids carefully; use a cutting board and sharp knife for chopping and slicing; do not overheat fat when sautéing and browning. (Other answers are possible.)
5. To simmer means to cook food in liquid at temperatures just below boiling. When a liquid simmers, the bubbles rise slowly but do not break the surface.
6. Possible answers: pepperoni; Italian sausage; vegetables, such as zucchini slices, green pepper rings, broccoli slices, cauliflower slices, cooked carrots, cooked peas.

R-35: Tabbouleh
1. a. 25%   b. 69%   c. 11%
2. Any two: pour boiling water carefully; use cutting board and sharp knife for dicing and chopping; take care to avoid fingers when snipping parsley with scissors. (Other answers are possible.)
3. Possible answers: wash hands in soap and warm water before squeezing out bulgur; clean work surface and tools carefully before mixing ingredients; serve immediately or chill.
4. Torn greens look more natural on the plate and their edges won't turn brown if you intend to refrigerate the salad before serving it.
5. A legume, such as beans, peas, lentils, or peanuts.
6. Answers will vary but should include a food from each of the food groups.

R-36: Oatmeal Muffins
1. a. 29%   b. 65%   c. 10%
2. Any two: measuring; sifting; greasing; mixing; beating; combining; baking; stirring; filling tins; sprinkling; testing for doneness.
3. The muffin method of mixing in which you stir only until the dry ingredients are moistened.
4. If you overmix, the muffins may be tough, and the batter may form peaks and tunnels while baking.
5. Baking.
6. Possible answers: handle glass measuring cups carefully to prevent breaking or chipping; pull oven racks in and out to place muffin pan in oven and remove it.
7. Any three: use paper baking cups and microwave-safe pan; fill cups only half full; baking time is much shorter; muffins do not brown.
8. You could use a wire whisk or fork.

R-37: Spoon Bread
1. a. 61%   b. 27%   c. 14%
2. Butter or margarine; eggs; milk.
3. Use skim milk instead of low-fat.
4. Any two: measuring; separating eggs; melting; greasing; combining; stirring; beating; folding; pouring; baking; simmering.
5. Beaten egg whites contain trapped air; they make the spoon bread lighter.
6. Yolks contain fat, prevent the whites from being beaten into a light, fluffy consistency.
7. Baking; simmering.
8. Any three: handle melted butter or margarine carefully; stir cornmeal mixture carefully; use potholder to remove casserole from oven; pull oven racks in and out to place casserole in oven and to remove it. (Other answers are possible.)
9. Answers will vary but should include a food from each of the other food groups.

R-38: Tortillas
1. a. 21%   b. 71%   c. 10%
2. Any four: measuring; combining; kneading; rolling and pressing dough; baking; turning.
3. Possible answers: to prevent spatters and burns, do not overheat fat; keep paper towels used for draining tortillas away from the burners; wipe up any fat that may spatter on the floor.
4. Possible answers: eggs; bacon or sausage; refried beans; assorted fruits or juices; beverage.
5. Answers will vary.

R-39: White Bread
1. a. 14%   b. 74%   c. 12%
2. Any four: measuring; mixing; combining; beating; stirring; kneading; greasing pans; shaping loaves; punching down dough; baking.
3. Possible answers: keep fingers away from beaters when mixer is on; pull oven racks in and out when placing pans in oven and removing them; use potholders when removing them; use potholders when removing baked bread from hot pans.
4. Use glass loaf pans; reduce rising time; lower baking temperature because glass pans retain heat.
5. Any two: bread would not be as nutritious; bread would not have as much flavor; you might need to add a little flour since milk contains solids.

R-40: Whole Wheat Bread
1. a. 16%   b. 74%   c. 13%
2. Any two: measuring; sifting; mixing; combining; beating; stirring; kneading; greasing pans; shaping loaves; punching down dough; baking.
3. Possible answers: keep fingers away from beaters when mixer is on; pull oven racks in and out when placing pans in oven and removing them; use potholders when removing baked bread from hot pans.
4. Any three: make sure work surface for kneading and shaping dough is clean; wash hands in soap and warm water before handling dough; use a clean towel to cover rising dough and rising loaves; use clean potholders to help remove bread from hot pan. (Other answers are possible.)
5. It leavens the bread and imparts the characteristic flavor and aroma of yeast breads.
6. Bubbles of gas form just under the surface of the dough. This indicates that carbon dioxide is being given off by the yeast and that the cell walls are stretching and gluten is forming.

R-41: Brownies
1. a. 62%   b. 41%   c. 5%
2. Bar cookie.
3. Any two: measuring; melting; sifting; chopping; greasing and flouring pan; creaming; beating; blending; stirring; pouring; baking; cooling; frosting; cutting.
4. Any two: handle hot pan carefully when melting chocolate; pull oven racks in and out when placing pan in oven and removing it; use potholders to handle hot pan; use sharp knife to cut brownies. (Other answers are possible.)
5. Handle glass cookware carefully to prevent chipping and breaking; use potholder when removing cookware from oven. (See p. 250 of text for other possible answers.)
6. Chocolate, butter, and sugar are melted together; amount of flour is increased; vanilla, eggs, flour, and nuts are added to chocolate; baking time is cut to one-fifth of the conventional time.
7. Answers will vary.

R-42: Double-Chocolate Frosting
1. a. 38%   b. 68%   c. 2%
2. Any three: measuring; melting; sifting; stirring; beating; combining.
3. Possible answers: use potholder to hold pan while stirring chocolate, but make sure it doesn't touch the burner; use low heat so chocolate mixture does not smoke or burn; be careful of hot pan when beating frosting.
4. Answers will vary.
5. Possible answers: dust the brownies with powdered sugar; leave them plain.

R-43: Carrot Cookies
1. a. 43%   b. 58%   c. 5%
2. Drop cookie.
3. Carrots.
4. The carrot cookies would be more nutritious than some other types. But like most cookies, they are high in fat and calories in relation to nutrients.
5. Any five: measuring; grating; combining; stirring; creaming; beating; blending; dropping dough onto cookie sheet; baking; removing cookies from cookie sheet; cooling.
6. Possible answers: Pull oven racks in and out when placing cookie sheets in oven, testing cookies, and removing pan; use hot pads to handle cookie sheets.
7. Add more flour.

R-44: Scandinavian Spice Cookies
1. a. 38%   b. 60%   c. 4%
2. Rolled cookie.
3. Possible answers: wash, rinse, and dry hands carefully before handling the dough; don't lick fingers or nibble on pieces of dough while working; make sure surface used for rolling the dough is clean and dry.
4. Any three: cookies are baked on waxed paper placed on microwavable sheet; a small number of cookies are baked at a time; baking time is cut in about half; cookies are cooled before removing from waxed paper.
5. Possible answers: nutmeg; mace; allspice; apple pie seasoning; pumpkin pie seasoning.
6. Use a pastry cloth.
7. Possible answers: sprinkle with colored sugar or nuts before baking; frost after baking.

R-45: Swedish Spritz
1. a. 54%   b. 40%   c. 4%
2. Pressed cookie.
3. Any five: measuring; separating egg; sifting; creaming; blending; mixing; using a cookie press; baking.
4. Possible answers: use electric mixer carefully; pull oven racks in and out when placing cookie sheets in oven, testing cookies, and removing pan; handle hot cookie sheet carefully when removing baked cookies.
5. Possible answers: orange color with pumpkin pie seasoning; green color with nutmeg, cinnamon, and cloves.
6. Answers will vary.

R-46: Twinkle Cookies
1. a. 59%   b. 34%   c. 8%
2. Molded cookie.
3. Any two: rolling dough into balls; beating egg whites; dipping balls of dough into egg whites; rolling balls of dough in chopped walnuts; placing on cookie sheets.
4. Possible answers: pull oven racks in and out when placing cookie sheets in oven, testing cookies, and removing them; do not touch hot dough with hand when pressing hot cookies with teaspoon; when pressing cookies with teaspoon, hold cookie sheet with potholder so it does not slide off cooling rack; handle hot cookie sheet carefully when removing baked cookies.
5. Answers will vary.
6. So they will bake evenly.

553

7. Possible answers: other flavored jams, preserves, and marmalade; other candied fruit, such as pineapple; frosting; walnut or pecan halves; chocolate "kisses."

R-47: Banana Bundt Cake
1. a. 41%   b. 56%   c. 5%
2. Any three: measuring; greasing and flouring pan; pouring; peeling and cutting; beating; baking; removing from pan; cooling; sprinkling.
3. Any four: insert beaters before plugging in mixer; do not plug in mixer until ready to use; keep fingers away from beaters when mixer is on; keep tools, such as spoons and spatulas, away from beaters when mixer is on; turn mixer off to scrape bowl and beaters; disconnect mixer before removing beaters.
4. Any two: reduce the amount of hot water; use a microwavable tube pan; prepare pan by oiling and then coating with sugar; reduce baking time by two-thirds.
5. The fluted edges and center tube help the heat get to the middle quickly, so the cake bakes evenly.
6. Possible answers: drizzle with icing; place chocolate candy on hot cake and let it melt.

R-48: Pineapple Upside Down Cake
1. a. 46%   b. 53%   c. 4%
2. Any four: measuring; draining; melting; stirring; arranging pineapple slices; preparing cake mix; pouring; baking; testing cake for doneness; cooling; inverting hot pan on serving plate.
3. Any four: be careful in arranging pineapple slices in hot butter mixture to avoid spatters and burns; handle sharp can lid carefully; keep fingers away from beaters when using electric mixer; pull oven racks in and out when placing pan in oven, testing cake, and removing pan; be careful when inverting hot pan on serving plate. (Other answers are possible.)
4. Any two: decrease the liquid; make cupcakes as well as cake from the batter; use a microwavable baking pan; cut baking time by more than two-thirds.
5. Answers will vary.
6. A 10-inch round cake pan.

R-49: Apple Pie
1. a. 44%   b. 54%   c. 4%
2. Shortening; butter or margarine.
3. Possible answers: omit bottom crust and bake filling in individual casseroles with just a crumb crust or pastry cut-outs; serve baked apples.
4. Possible answers: mixing pie crust; rolling out pie crust; preparing the filling; fitting lower pie crust into pan; filling the pie; fitting the top crust; sealing edges of crust; baking the pie.
5. Any four: use a paring knife when peeling apples; use a sharp knife and cutting board to slice apples; be careful when grating lemon to avoid scraping fingers; pull oven racks in and out when placing pan in oven and removing it; handle hot pie carefully. (Other answers are possible.)
6. Possible answers: crumb topping; pastry cut-outs.

R-50: Pea Soup with Ham
1. a. 56%   b. 21%   c. 24%
2. a. Green peas.
   b. Ham.

3. Any three: make sure clothes and apron are clean; if wearing long sleeves, roll them up; if hair is long, pin it back; clean work surface thoroughly; wash hands. (Other answers are possible.)
4. Any three: stir sauce carefully to avoid spattering; hold pan handle when stirring; keep pan handles turned toward range; handle hot pan carefully. (Other answers are possible.)
5. Any two: store leftover food; wash dishes, equipment, and cookware; put away dishes, equipment, and cookware; clean counters; clean rangetop.
6. Possible answers: bread; salad; dessert; beverage.

R-51: Hot Taco Dip
1. a. 75%   b. 25%   c. 13%
2. Use low-fat yogurt instead of sour cream; omit the cheese.
3. Possible answers: use implement to handle chilies; handle sharp can lids carefully; use grater carefully to avoid scraping fingers and knuckles; pour cooked mixture carefully into serving dish.
4. Possible answers: fresh vegetables; another dip lower in fat and calories; beverage.
5. Chilies contain an oil that is irritating to the skin and eyes.

R-52: Nectar Tempter
1. a. Apricot nectar.   b. Lime juice.
2. Possible answers: club soda; lemon-lime soda; carbonated lemon- or lime-flavored water.
3. You could heat a half-cup of water to boiling in the microwave and use a teabag, loose tea, or mint leaves to make tea.
4. Possible answers: snack crackers or pretzels and dip; popcorn; mixed nuts; cookies or bars.
5. Possible answers: maraschino cherries; fresh fruit, such as strawberries or orange slices; fresh mint leaves.
6. Possible answers: serve the beverage in glasses with different pastel shades; decorate the glasses with miniature paper umbrellas or colorful straws; use decorative coasters under the glasses.
7. Answers will vary but could include items from nature.

R-53: Peanut Banana Cooler
1. a. 45%   b. 45%   c. 16%
2. Any seven: handle sharp edges, such as beaters and blades, carefully; plug in appliance only when you are ready to use it; keep cord away from range burners and other heat sources; keep appliance away from sink and other sources of water; handle appliances with dry hands; don't let appliance cord hang over edge of counter, where it may get pulled off accidentally; be on alert for frayed cords and damaged plugs; if lights dim when the appliance is on, have an electrician check the appliance and the wiring system; avoid the electrical octopus — one outlet with a number of cords plugged into it. (See p. 201 of text for other possible answers.)
3. Mash the bananas, put the mixture in a deep bowl, and use an electric or hand beater.
4. Possible answers: whipped cream; grated chocolate; chocolate sprinkles.
5. Possible answers: snack crackers; plain cookies; a party mix.

R-54: Freezing Vegetables

1. Possible answers: wash and trim all vegetables carefully; to prevent cross-contamination, clean work surface and equipment; make sure hands and clothes are clean.
2. Possible answers: lower vegetables into boiling water carefully to avoid steam burns; remove blanched vegetables from boiling water carefully to avoid being scalded by hot water.
3. Answers will vary.
4. Blanching stops the enzyme action. Blanched vegetables retain their nutrients, color, flavor, and texture far longer than vegetables that have not been blanched before freezing.
5. Since vegetables are not frozen in one clump, you can use any amount needed rather than the entire contents of the container.
6. Pack vegetables in vapor- and moisture-proof containers.
7. This gives food room to expand as it freezes.
8. Answers will vary.

R-55: Creative Casseroles

1. Possible answers: water; milk; broth; liquid from canned or cooked vegetables.
2. Answers will vary.
3. Possible answers: almonds; cheese; Chinese noodles; tomatoes; French fried onion rings.
4. Answers will vary.

R-56: Master Baking Mix

1. Any two: measuring; combining; cutting shortening into dry ingredients.
2. Using the water displacement method, first fill a 250 mL (1 cup) measure with 125 mL (½ cup) of water. Then spoon shortening into the cup until the water reaches the 250-mL (1-cup) mark.
3. Mixing the shortening with the dry ingredients.
4. Any two: cookie or brownie mixes; sauce mixes; seasoning mixes; hot cocoa mixes. (Other answers are possible.)
5. Possible answers: it costs less; contains only the essential ingredients (no additives); allows you to custom mix amounts and ingredients.
6. Possible answer: in small plastic bags, each containing 250 mL (1 cup) (the amount called for in the biscuit recipe) of the baking mix.

R-57: Master Mix Biscuits

1. Any two: saves time; is more convenient; is a more efficient use of time; allows a child to prepare the biscuits. (Other answers are possible.)

2. Possible answers: you save money; if you're concerned about food additives, a home-made mix contains only the essential ingredients.
3. Possible answers: mix dough; knead dough slightly; roll out dough; cut out biscuits; place biscuits on baking sheet; bake biscuits.
4. Possible answers: make certain work surface is clean; if pastry cloth is used for rolling out biscuits, be sure it is clean; wash hands thoroughly before handling dough.
5. Possible answers: as a sandwich; as a topping for pot pies; as a base for creamed foods, such as Chicken a la King; as a base for desserts, such as strawberry shortcake.

R-58: Master Mix Carrot Bread

1. a. 42%   b. 52%   c. 9%
2. Carrots.
3. Any five: measuring; beating; grating; chopping; greasing pan; combining; mixing; stirring; blending; pouring; baking; testing for doneness; cooling; removing bread from pan.
4. Possible answers: grate carefully to avoid scraping fingers or knuckles; chop nuts with a sharp knife on a cutting board; pull oven racks in and out when placing pan in oven, testing loaf for doneness, and removing pan; handle hot bread pan carefully.
5. Any three: as a bread accompaniment for a meal; as a sandwich; as a snack; as a dessert. (Other answers are possible.)
6. Package it tightly, using aluminum foil or heavy-duty plastic wrap or bags; double wrap or tape any edges that do not seal tightly; label package with the name of the bread and the date.

R-59: Master Mix Banana Bread

1. a. 40%   b. 56%   c. 9%
2. Possible answers: make certain clothes and apron are clean; clean counter or work area carefully; wash hands thoroughly.
3. Answers will vary but should include foods from each of the food groups.
4. Answers will vary.
5. Any two: cottage cheese spread; cream cheese spread; a thin layer of butter, peanut butter, or jam. (Other answers are possible.)
6. Answers will vary. In general, a garnish should not overpower the sandwich. It can mirror the shape of the sandwich.

CHAPTER AND PART TEST ANSWERS

Chapter 1 Test

1. true	2. true	3. false	4. false
5. true	6. true	7. true	8. true
9. false	10. false	11. true	12. false
13. false			
14. C	15. B	16. D	17. A	18. D
19. culture		20. customs	
21. substitutes		22. starvation	
23. nutrients		24. management	
25. values		26. ethnic	
27. regional		28. lifestyle	
29. D	30. B	31. G	32. A	33. E

Chapter 2 Test

1. true	2. false	3. true	4. true
5. true	6. true	7. false	8. true
9. false	10. false	11. true	12. true
13. false	14. true	15. false	16. false
17. true	18. false	19. true	20. true
21. J	22. G	23. B	24. A	25. F
26. E	27. I			
28. fads		29. quacks	
30. organic		31. shelf	
32. contaminants		33. three	

Part 1 Test

1. J 2. E 3. C 4. H 5. B
6. G 7. L 8. K 9. A 10. D
11. false 12. true 13. true 14. false
15. true 16. false 17. false 18. false
19. true 20. false 21. true 22. true
23. evaluate 24. Nutrients
25. psychological 26. values
27. regional 28. Additives
29. restoration 30. natural
31. antibiotics 32. fortified
33. self-esteem

Chapter 3 Test

1. false 2. true 3. true 4. false
5. true 6. true 7. false 8. true
9. false 10. false 11. true 12. false
13. true 14. false 15. false 16. true
17. false 18. false 19. true 20. true
21. true
22. I 23. J 24. D 25. C 26. A
27. B 28. E
29. variety 30. nutrition
31. method 32. fifty
33. moderation

Chapter 4 Test

1. K 2. F 3. B 4. J 5. D
6. A 7. G 8. E
9. true 10. false 11. true 12. false
13. true 14. true 15. false 16. true
17. true 18. true 19. false 20. false
21. true
22. B 23. C 24. C 25. D 26. A
27. C 28. B 29. D
30. provitamin 31. legumes
32. complementarity 33. hydrogenation

Chapter 5 Test

1. K 2. A 3. B 4. H 5. J
6. I 7. F 8. C 9. L
10. true 11. true 12. false 13. false
14. true 15. false 16. false 17. true
18. true 19. false
20. C 21. D 22. B 23. C 24. A
25. D 26. B
27. stress 28. calories
29. smoking 30. small
31. aerobic 32. wellness
33. water

Chapter 6 Test

1. K 2. A 3. E 4. H 5. D
6. C 7. F
8. false 9. true 10. false 11. true
12. true 13. false 14. true 15. true
16. true 17. false 18. false 19. false
20. A 21. C 22. B 23. C 24. D
25. B 26. C
27. four 28. size
29. nutrients 30. small
31. grains 32. yogurt
33. salad bar

Chapter 7 Test

1. false 2. true 3. true 4. true
5. false 6. false 7. true 8. true
9. true 10. false 11. true 12. true
13. false 14. true 15. true
16. B 17. C 18. C 19. A 20. B
21. A 22. D 23. D 24. A
25. K 26. L 27. H 28. I 29. A
30. G 31. B 32. E 33. J

Chapter 8 Test

1. false 2. true 3. true 4. false
5. false 6. false 7. false 8. true
9. true 10. true 11. false 12. true
13. C 14. B 15. A 16. B 17. C
18. B
19. J 20. B 21. K 22. G 23. F
24. L 25. E 26. H 27. C 28. I
29. cravings 30. fetal
31. sterile 32. nursing
33. choke

Part 2 Test

1. O 2. W 3. T 4. E 5. K
6. U 7. C 8. Q 9. L 10. I
11. F 12. M 13. P 14. N 15. A
16. true 17. false 18. false 19. true
20. false 21. true 22. true 23. true
24. false 25. false 26. false 27. true
28. true 29. false 30. false 31. true
32. false
33. D 34. D 35. B 36. C 37. A
38. B 39. D 40. B 41. D 42. B
43. A 44. B 45. D 46. C 47. B
48. C 49. B 50. C

Chapter 9 Test

1. false 2. false 3. false 4. true
5. false 6. true 7. true 8. true
9. false 10. false 11. false 12. false
13. true 14. true
15. D 16. A 17. A 18. C 19. B
20. D 21. C 22. B 23. B
24. D 25. K 26. F 27. J 28. L
29. A 30. C 31. E 32. H 33. I

Chapter 10 Test

1. D 2. F 3. E 4. A 5. G
6. H
7. C 8. A 9. B 10. B 11. C
12. A 13. D 14. C 15. A 16. B
17. D
18. false 19. false 20. true 21. true
22. true 23. false 24. true 25. false
26. false 27. true 28. false 29. true
30. false 31. true 32. true 33. false

Chapter 11 Test

1. false 2. true 3. true 4. true
5. false 6. true 7. true 8. false
9. true 10. true 11. false 12. true
13. true 14. true 15. false
16. C 17. B 18. D 19. D 20. B
21. A 22. B 23. B

24. G 25. I 26. D 27. H 28. L
29. E 30. C 31. K 32. A 33. B

Chapter 12 Test
1. J 2. A 3. G 4. C 5. I
6. F 7. E
8. true 9. true 10. false 11. true
12. false 13. true 14. true 15. false
16. true 17. true 18. false 19. false
20. false 21. true 22. false 23. true
24. true 25. true 26. false
27. head space 28. inventory
29. microorganisms 30. toxins
31. molds 32. perishable
33. temperature

Part 3 Test
1. true 2. false 3. false 4. false
5. true 6. true 7. false 8. false
9. true 10. false 11. true 12. false
13. false 14. false 15. false 16. true
17. false 18. false 19. false 20. false
21. false 22. false 23. true 24. false
25. true 26. true 27. false 28. false
29. false
30. F 31. O 32. E 33. L 34. N
35. A 36. M 37. H 38. G 39. I
40. B
41. A 42. D 43. A 44. B 45. B
46. A 47. D 48. C 49. B 50. C

Chapter 13 Test
1. true 2. true 3. false 4. true
5. true 6. true 7. true 8. false
9. true 10. false 11. true 12. false
13. true 14. true 15. false 16. false
17. false
18. L 19. B 20. D 21. J 22. K
23. C
24. C 25. B 26. A 27. A 28. B
29. D
30. hygiene 31. flammable
32. breathing 33. floor

Chapter 14 Test
1. K 2. E 3. D 4. H 5. G
6. B 7. L 8. A 9. C
10. true 11. true 12. false 13. false
14. true 15. true 16. false 17. true
18. false 19. true
20. L 21. O 22. S 23. E 24. R
25. P 26. K 27. A 28. G 29. M
30. N 31. D 32. H 33. Q

Chapter 15 Test
1. true 2. false 3. false 4. true
5. false 6. false 7. true 8. true
9. poaching 10. broiling
11. stir-frying 12. braising
13. packed 14. metric
15. H 16. I 17. B 18. D 19. J
20. A 21. C
22. P 23. E 24. D 25. A 26. C
27. M 28. J 29. F 30. L 31. K
32. H 33. N

Chapter 16 Test
1. false 2. true 3. false 4. false
5. true 6. true 7. true 8. false
9. false 10. true 11. false 12. true
13. true 14. false 15. true
16. A 17. C 18. B 19. D 20. A
21. C 22. B 23. A
24. circle 25. exploding
26. standing time 27. Salt
28. slower
29. B 30. A 31. G 32. C 33. E

Chapter 17 Test
1. false 2. false 3. true 4. true
5. false 6. false 7. false 8. false
9. true 10. true 11. true 12. false
13. false 14. true 15. true 16. false
17. false 18. false 19. true 20. true
21. J 22. D 23. E 24. G 25. K
26. F 27. C
28. recycle 29. conservation
30. limited 31. computers
32. simplification 33. dovetailing

Chapter 18 Test
1. A 2. E 3. G 4. H 5. B
6. D 7. I
8. true 9. true 10. true 11. true
12. false 13. true 14. true 15. false
16. false 17. false
18. E 19. N 20. F 21. C 22. J
23. G 24. I 25. A 26. K
27. B 28. D 29. D 30. B 31. D
32. A 33. C

Part 4 Test
1. false 2. false 3. false 4. true
5. false 6. true 7. false 8. true
9. false 10. true 11. false 12. true
13. false 14. true 15. true 16. false
17. true 18. false 19. false 20. false
21. E 22. O 23. P 24. B 25. A
26. Q 27. C 28. W 29. I 30. L
31. T 32. H 33. M 34. R 35. F
36. D 37. C 38. A 39. B 40. D
41. C 42. B 43. B 44. C 45. A
46. D 47. D 48. C 49. C 50. B

Chapter 19 Test
1. true 2. true 3. true 4. false
5. false 6. false 7. true 8. true
9. true 10. false
11. produce 12. baked
13. presoaked 14. convenience
15. seasonal 16. fiber
17. unitized 18. regreening
19. orange 20. nutrients
21. dried 22. fritters
23. canned 24. potassium
25. large 26. sugar
27. J 28. F 29. A 30. H 31. D
32. B 33. E

Chapter 20 Test

1. G	2. B	3. E	4. D	5. A
6. F	7. D	8. H	9. G	10. A
11. B				
12. true	13. false	14. true	15. true	
16. true	17. false	18. false	19. true	
20. true	21. true	22. false	23. false	
24. true	25. false			
26. A	27. C	28. B	29. B	30. D
31. B	32. A	33. C		

Chapter 21 Test

1. true	2. true	3. false	4. true
5. false	6. true	7. true	8. false
9. false	10. true	11. false	12. false
13. true	14. true	15. false	
16. B	17. D	18. C	19. B	20. D
21. B	22. A	23. B	
24. J	25. G	26. K	27. F	28. H
29. L	30. C	31. A	32. E	33. M

Chapter 22 Test

1. true	2. true	3. false	4. true
5. false	6. false	7. false	8. true
9. false	10. false	11. true	
12. F	13. D	14. G	15. C	16. I
17. J	18. E	19. A	
20. L	21. B	22. J	23. F	24. C
25. I	26. A	27. K	28. E	29. D
30. C	31. A	32. B	33. A

Chapter 23 Test

1. true	2. false	3. false	4. true
5. false	6. true	7. false	8. true
9. true	10. false	11. true	12. false
13. true	14. true	15. false	16. true
17. false	18. true	19. false	
20. A	21. D	22. A	23. B	24. D
25. C	26. D	27. C	
28. H	29. G	30. A	31. D	32. E
33. J			

Chapter 24 Test

1. true	2. false	3. true	4. false
5. false	6. true	7. true	8. true
9. false	10. false	11. true	12. false
13. false	14. true	15. true	16. false
17. true	18. true	19. true	
20. class		21. self-basting	
22. giblets		23. braised	
24. truss		25. capon	
26. A	27. D	28. D	29. B	30. C
31. B	32. C	33. C	

Chapter 25 Test

1. false	2. false	3. true	4. true
5. true	6. true	7. true	8. true
9. false	10. false	11. true	12. true
13. false	14. true	15. true	16. true
17. C	18. B	19. C	20. B	21. D
22. A	23. D	24. A	
25. I	26. K	27. H	28. D	29. A
30. B	31. C	32. E	33. F

Chapter 26 Test

1. G	2. D	3. H	4. C	5. I
6. E	7. B	8. K	9. J	
10. false	11. true	12. false	13. true
14. true	15. false	16. true	17. true
18. false	19. true	20. false	21. false
22. true	23. false	24. false	
25. A	26. A	27. B	28. C	29. B
30. C	31. B	32. C	33. D

Chapter 27 Test

1. true	2. true	3. false	4. false
5. true	6. false	7. true	8. false
9. false	10. false		
11. L	12. H	13. I	14. B	15. K
16. D	17. E	18. F	
19. B	20. C	21. D	22. D	23. A
24. C	25. A		
26. bulgur		27. berries
28. precooked		29. grits
30. durum		31. fruits
32. long-grain		33. converted

Chapter 28 Test

1. D	2. J	3. I	4. H	5. E
6. A	7. F	8. K		
9. true	10. false	11. false	12. true
13. false	14. false	15. false	16. true
17. true	18. false	19. false	
20. C	21. B	22. A	23. A	24. B
25. A	26. C		
27. steam		28. stone-ground
29. sweeteners		30. eggs
31. Aspartame		32. olive
33. lard		

Chapter 29 Test

1. true	2. false	3. true	4. true
5. true	6. false	7. false	8. true
9. false	10. false	11. true	12. false
13. true	14. false	15. true	
16. C	17. B	18. D	19. A	20. A
21. D	22. C	23. B	
24. M	25. K	26. J	27. D	28. L
29. C	30. N	31. F	32. G	33. A

Chapter 30 Test

1. false	2. false	3. true	4. false
5. true	6. false	7. true	8. false
9. false	10. true	11. true	12. false
13. true	14. false	15. true	16. true
17. B	18. A	19. D	20. B	21. C
22. A	23. D	24. C	
25. H	26. D	27. K	28. J	29. G
30. C	31. I	32. B	33. A

Chapter 31 Test

1. false	2. false	3. true	4. false
5. false	6. true	7. false	8. false
9. true	10. true	11. true	12. false
13. true	14. true	15. false	16. false
17. false			
18. D	19. A	20. A	21. B	22. C
23. D	24. B		

25. E   26. I   27. B   28. L   29. F
30. C   31. J   32. A   33. D

Chapter 32 Test
1. false   2. true   3. true   4. false
5. false   6. false   7. true   8. true
9. true   10. false   11. true   12. true
13. true   14. false   15. true
16. cornstarch   17. marrow
18. White   19. Tapioca
20. C   21. B   22. D   23. A   24. D
25. D   26. C   27. E   28. K   29. B
30. G   31. I   32. A   33. F

Chapter 33 Test
1. true   2. false   3. true   4. true
5. true   6. false   7. true   8. true
9. false   10. false   11. false   12. false
13. true   14. true   15. false   16. false
17. true   18. true   19. true   20. false
21. G   22. C   23. F   24. D   25. I
26. H
27. C   28. D   29. A   30. B   31. D
32. B   33. C

Chapter 34 Test
1. false   2. true   3. true   4. true
5. false   6. false   7. true   8. false
9. false   10. true   11. true   12. false
13. false   14. false   15. false   16. true
17. true
18. A   19. B   20. C   21. D   22. A
23. B   24. C   25. A
26. D   27. A   28. H   29. B   30. G
31. I   32. J   33. K

Part 5 Test
1. true   2. true   3. false   4. true
5. false   6. false   7. true   8. false
9. true   10. true   11. true   12. false
13. false   14. false   15. false   16. true
17. false   18. true
19. mature   20. legumes
21. dressing   22. pasteurized
23. tenderizer   24. broiled
25. Dry-heat   26. scrambled
27. liquid   28. gluten
29. fast-rising   30. nutrients
31. rest   32. degrease
33. acidifiers   34. citrus
35. C   36. D   37. B   38. A   39. C
40. A   41. D   42. B   43. C   44. B
45. D   46. C   47. A   48. C   49. B
50. D

Chapter 35 Test
1. true   2. false   3. true   4. true
5. false   6. false   7. false   8. true
9. true   10. false
11. F   12. J   13. G   14. B   15. L
16. I   17. E   18. A   19. C
20. A   21. A   22. C   23. B   24. B
25. D   26. C   27. C
28. smorgasbord   29. fish
30. crepes   31. a la mode
32. tortilla   33. shish kebabs

Chapter 36 Test
1. J   2. I   3. G   4. N   5. L
6. C   7. K   8. B   9. D
10. true   11. false   12. false   13. true
14. true   15. true   16. false   17. false
18. B   19. D   20. D   21. C   22. C
23. C   24. A   25. C   26. D   27. A
28. South   29. Corn
30. Cajun   31. Spanish
32. fish   33. Amerindians

Chapter 37 Test
1. true   2. false   3. true   4. false
5. true   6. false   7. false   8. false
9. true   10. false   11. true   12. false
13. J   14. M   15. H   16. N   17. I
18. C   19. G   20. A
21. B   22. C   23. A   24. B   25. C
26. C   27. A   28. B   29. D   30. A
31. C   32. D   33. C

Part 6 Test
1. Q   2. G   3. Z   4. A   5. T
6. V   7. B   8. X   9. D   10. U
11. M   12. O   13. R   14. W   15. S
16. P   17. E   18. N   19. F   20. J
21. false   22. false   23. true   24. true
25. false   26. true   27. true   28. false
29. true   30. false   31. false   32. false
33. true   34. true   35. false
36. B   37. C   38. C   39. D   40. B
41. A   42. C   43. D   44. B   45. C
46. A   47. B   48. B   49. D   50. C

Chapter 38 Test
1. false   2. false   3. false   4. false
5. true   6. true   7. true   8. false
9. false   10. true
11. A   12. B   13. B   14. D   15. C
16. F   17. G   18. L   19. P   20. R
21. C   22. N   23. K   24. M   25. O
26. J   27. K   28. H   29. F   30. G
31. E   32. C   33. B

Chapter 39 Test

1. false	2. true	3. true	4. true	25. dress code	26. wages
5. false	6. false	7. false	8. true	27. FICA	28. application
9. true	10. false	11. false	12. false	29. references	30. health certificate
13. true	14. true	15. true	16. false	31. interview	32. counselor
17. B	18. A	19. D	20. C	21. A	33. résumé
22. D	23. B	24. B			

Part 7 Test

1. G	2. E	3. N	4. Q	5. C
6. A	7. R	8. L	9. D	10. J
11. O	12. H	13. S	14. M	15. B
16. K	17. U			

18. true	19. true	20. true	21. false
22. true	23. true	24. false	25. true
26. false	27. true		
28. D	29. C	30. C	31. C	32. D
33. B				

Student Workbook
Answer Key

Chapter 1: Your Food Choices
Charting Your Choices (p. 7)

1. emotional

```
E — M C T H S Q B
V O — T T Z E A S
F N I — O Y S D Y
C E C N — A L K H
R A C V Q E L B
W Q I O C M X S
```

2. starvation

```
M A E J R Z A L
U P U L A Q I V
E O I R — V — A T A
G S — T — A I V I I
N C T U O A O H
A M G X N B N H
```

3. concentrate

```
A O D C — O Z Y J
T M M X N H E T
K S U N C — E — N — T
A R R I T Y F R
S G V F L U P A
K Q T M U A E — T
```

4. secure

```
A T K V Q S U X
N G W I F S O E
B A S R T E A D
T K X E M C H L
M I I E — R — U K M
B V J Q O X M P
```

5. enjoyment

```
S E U R B B C Y
G S P H A I I N
R O Q E X L H D
S J — O — Y — M — E R V
U N P F Z N B A
L E W E R T G N
```

6. belonging

```
D C N — O — L E J A
M I G V E M D S
G — N — I V B T O H
O G C B O J D Q
M O H T N L E X
K S U L B G I S
```

7. decisions

```
O F E R K M P C
D D H W Y D I X
E C O S Y S I A
C S M X E R C Q
I U C S C E G S
S — I — O — N O P E R
```

8. resources

```
B D O J R S A L
U P U L A E I V
E O I U — R — C P A
G P K O I V W I
N R — E — S O A D H
S U S X N J O W
```

9. technology

```
H Z F V Q S U X
O G W I F C — E — T
B A S R T H A D
G C O — L — O — N H L
M I G G N L K M
B V Y Q O X M P
```

10. knowledge

```
D O F Y A V C C
X O — W — L — E K P O
C N H J D H B R
C K U M G R W M
E S L R E T E H
U M C Z D G S N
```

11. ethnic

```
F O I T Y L T O
O N S P S F O E
T B S R G W J N
H O D E C Y Q B
T M K N I — N — H — T
U D P Y R Z B E
```

12. regional

```
A O E N A W R G
S G D K L Q A M
L R — E — G D E L U
W J D I M B L E
L C L O — N — A D C
E V P N Y L X B
```

13. advertising

```
A — D — V F P G R E
M O E N W L S N
E Y R A P S E G
T D T — I — S — I O M
M T Q V J N X U
A I W Y F G N R
```

14. trends

```
D C F O O E J A
M I F V U M D S
S — D — N — E P T O H
O G C R O J D Q
F I N T N L E X
K S U L B G I S
```

15. lifestyle

```
C R P D I B F I
A D E — S — T P O R
H C F F Y R I B
M W I O L H V U
M J L K E N A T
F D N S R N A E
```

16. values

```
G U R A B B C Y
R S P H A I I N
C O Q E X L H D
S I L — U — E F R V
U B A E S N B A
L X V E R J G N
```

17. planning

```
O R C T H A — L — P
V M U T Z N O R
A K G — N — I — N D Y
C E C I C T Z H
K H A V Q E L P
W Q I V C M X S
```

18. evaluate

```
E N L — U — A — T U Z
E — V — A K T N O N
B Y K A E S E G
T D C R H R O M
M T Q V J A X U
A I W Y F D N R
```

Likes and Dislikes (p. 9)
Answers will vary.

Dealing with Decisions (p. 10)
Step 1: Set your goals.
Step 2: Consider your resources.
Step 3: Make a plan.
Step 4: Carry out and monitor your plan.
Step 5: Evaluate the results.
Examples will vary.

Chapter 2: Food Facts and Fallacies
Peddling Propaganda (p. 11)
Answers will vary.

What's Fact? (p. 12)
1. Myth — People of all ages need a good supply of calcium, and milk is the best source.
2. Fact (The color of the shell has nothing to do with the nutritive value. Certain kinds of hens lay brown eggs.)
3. Myth — It's impossible to tell the difference between organically grown and regular food.
4. Myth — Grapefruit is an excellent source of vitamin C. However, it cannot break down body fat. No food can.
5. Fact (Additives help preserve the quality of many foods. Without additives, our food supply would be seriously limited.)
6. Myth — Poor quality soil does not affect the nutrients in food, just the size of the crop.
7. Myth — The soil is enriched with organic fertilizers, such as animal manure and plant matter, instead of chemical fertilizers.
8. Myth — Although honey has a few additional nutrients, it doesn't have enough to recommend it over white sugar. Both are high in calories.
9. Fact (Additives on the GRAS list can be used by a manufacturer without getting permission from the FDA.)
10. Myth — According to scientific tests, fertilized and unfertilized eggs have the same nutrients.

Safe to Eat? (p. 13)
1. food fads
2. food quacks
3. poor quality soil
4. a food expert
5. organic foods
6. natural ingredients
7. additive
8. nutritional value
9. natural food
10. artificial ingredients
11. vitamin D
12. enriched or fortified
13. GRAS list
14. restoration
15. shelf life
16. contaminants
17. pesticides
18. tolerance level

Chapter 3: The Science of Nutrition
The Nutrition Story (p. 15)
1. nutrients
2. cells
3. processes
4. energy
5. teams
6. adequate
7. all
8. small
9. different
10. large
11. few
12. U.S. RDA
13. average
14. age
15. large-boned
16. athletes
17. poor
18. basic
19. malnutrition
20. deficiency
21. iron

A Picture of Good Health (p. 16)
Answers will vary.

Searching for Good Nutrition (p. 17)

```
V T A D E T H J K L W E R T I O P L K J H G F D S
A S W E R A G H N F G T R E D C V G H J K M B C V
S A R E W N C F U U I J K L I O U J Y T G T R A E
H Y U I K E W E T R G U I O P L I J A W E R T C B
S A Y D D M W I R L S W D F R G H J A M O U N T I
P O R T Y A A I R E I T H J I O L P E R V B I N
L A W E R A Q L E I P I R T F H J N F R T Y U V M
K D E R I M F O N A W O K A T Y E T Y E J P N E C
S H A N N O N E T U R V L O P R T Y I W R E O P M
W I L L Q R T O S I T E K E L L Y P O Y N A E R K
P L M N K I O J H B U R T R P R O T E I N S T U M
K L I R K F L U G D O D I B S C H E R I T Z P O L
E R G I E N E R G Y O O P T I L L A Y O O D L E S
G I D E E A P S C H N S L T I P O M A D D L E O R
M E D A L I O P S C I E N F O O M S T I P L E C U
A R T N I G K O P D A R P I D F N A M E N E G H J
E R T G F D S W F G E K L U J K J K P W A U P T O Y
L O P E R D Y W A T E F O F T I K L E A T O P R E
Q S D A E F G T H Y J I I A P O I U Y H R U N M C
W E R F I O P J N E R T Y C A R T Y U G I R E Y P
O A C T I F O R O U S L Y T I P S W O S T E W E P
Q U O E T O R I P R O C E S S E S S I O I B N O S
L A S S L O P W E L K I N G B O N N E R O B N I T
D A G F O L O P E R T U K L S I C C L Y N O S T R
M A C F L O S S M O R E T I L O P E Y E S T E R N
```

1. Nutrients
2. cells
3. processes
4. energy
5. proteins
6. teams
7. amount
8. mature
9. facts
10. overdose
11. RDA
12. active
13. nutrition
14. Malnutrition
15. deficiency
16. Anemia

Chapter 4: The Nutrients You Need
Nutrient Notes (p. 19)
1. Health experts recommend limiting the amount of cholesterol in the diet.
2. A person's diet should include more natural carbohydrates than processed carbohydrates.
3. Vitamins help speed chemical reactions in the body.
4. Calcium, phosphorus, and vitamin D work together to build and maintain strong bones and teeth.
5. Fruits, vegetables, grains, and beans are common natural sources of carbohydrates.
6. Fat-soluble vitamins are stored by the body, but water-soluble vitamins are not.
7. Trace elements are minerals needed by the body in very small amounts.
8. Scurvy is caused by a lack of vitamin C in the diet.
9. Complete proteins come from animal products and incomplete proteins come from plant products.
10. Fat is important as a source of fatty acids and energy and to carry fat-soluble vitamins.

Food Power (p. 20)
Part A

Across:
2. ascorbic acid
8. lactose
10. carbohydrates
12. thiamin
13. corn oil
14. rickets
18. magnesium
19. unsaturated
20. amino acids
21. citrus
23. grains
24. complex
25. niacin

Down:
1. zinc
3. saturated
4. nutrients
5. fish
6. trace elements
7. potassium
9. iodine
11. calcium
15. vitamins
16. minerals
17. carotene
22. fats

Part B

To prevent osteoporosis, you should eat a well-balanced diet, including plenty of calcium-rich foods; exercise regularly to strengthen bones; avoid smoking; and be cautious about getting too much phosphorus from food items such as soft drinks.

Testing for Fats (p. 22)

Butter: Water beads.
Potato: Water doesn't bead.
Apple: Water doesn't bead.
Peanut: Water beads.

Conclusions: Butter and peanuts contain fat. Potatoes and apples do not.

Chapter 5: Food and Your Well-Being

The "Wellness" Road to Health (p. 23)

Answers will vary but might include such statements as:
Eat nutritious snacks.
Talk over your problems with someone.
Eat a greater variety of foods.
Control your temper. Try counting to 100.
Exercise regularly — at least 3 times a week.

What's Your Health Score? (p. 24)

1. +	2. O	3. +	4. O	5. O
6. +	7. O	8. O	9. O	10. O
11. O	12. +	13. O	14. +	15. +
16. +	17. O	18. +	19. O	20. O
21. O	22. +	23. +	24. O	25. +

Your Digestive System (p. 25)

1. nutrients	2. digested	3. chewing
4. saliva	5. enzyme	6. sugar
7. esophagus	8. peristaltic waves	9. stomach
10. gastric	11. hydrochloric acid	12. pepsin
13. churned	14. gastric juices	15. chyme
16. pepsin	17. protein	18. four
19. small intestine	20. villi	21. nutrients
22. bile	23. fats	24. emulsion
25. proteins	26. starches	27. bloodstream
28. vitamins	29. liver	30. stored
31. ten	32. colon	33. kidneys
34. urine	35. solid	

Chapter 6: Plan Your Daily Food Choices

Using the Daily Food Guide (p. 27)

Answers may vary slightly.
Orange juice — 1 fruit-vegetable serving.
Cereal with milk — ½ or 1 milk-cheese serving; 1 bread-cereal serving.
Toast with butter — 1 bread-cereal serving; 1 fats-sweets serving.
Ham and cheese sandwich on wheat bread — 1 milk-cheese serving; 1 meat-fish-beans serving; 1 bread-cereal serving.
Glass of milk — 1 milk-cheese serving.
Brownie — 1 fats-sweets serving.
Spaghetti with meat sauce — 1 fruit-vegetable serving; 1 meat-fish-beans serving; 1 bread-cereal serving.
Garlic bread — 1 bread-cereal serving; 1 fats-sweets serving.
Green beans — 1 fruit-vegetable serving.
Soft drink — 1 bread-cereal serving; 1 fats-sweets serving.
Popcorn with butter — 1 bread-cereal serving; 1 fats-sweets serving.
Candy bar — 1 fats-sweets serving.

Total servings — 2½-3 milk-cheese; 3 fruits-vegetables; 2 meat-fish-beans; 6 bread-cereal; 6 fats-sweets.
Total servings required each day — 4 or more milk-cheese; 4 fruit-vegetables; 2 meat-fish-beans; 4 bread-cereal; 0 fats-sweets.

Observations
Sara was short on servings from the milk-cheese and fruit-vegetable groups. She had the correct number of servings from the meat-fish-poultry-beans group, but she had too many in the bread-cereal and fats-sweets groups. To be closer to the guidelines, Sara might have: replaced the soft drink with a glass of milk; eaten carrot sticks at lunch; skipped the garlic bread at dinner; and cut down on fats and sweets.

Checking Your Diet (p. 28)

Answers will vary.

Invest in Nutrient Density (p. 30)

```
P E A N U T   B U T T E R
    S U G A R
S O F T   D R I N K S
    B R O C C O L I   (or BROWNIES)
C O O K I E S
O A T M E A L
    O R A N G E S   (or SPINACH)
P O T A T O   C H I P S
S A L A D   D R E S S I N G
    C H E E S E
    T U N A
E G G S
    M I L K   (or RICE)
W H E A T   G E R M
C A N D Y
```

1. H	2. H	3. H	4. H	5. H
6. L	7. L	8. H	9. L	10. L
11. H	12. L	13. H	14. H	15. H
16. H	17. L	18. H	19. H	20. H
21. L	22. L	23. L	24. L	25. H
26. L	27. L	28. H	29. H	30. H

Chapter 7: Controlling Your Weight

Weight Woes (p. 31)

Answers will vary.

Diet Facts and Fantasies (p. 33)

1. True	2. True	3. True	4. False
5. False	6. False	7. False	8. True
9. False	10. False	11. True	12. False
13. True	14. False	15. False	16. True
17. True	18. True	19. True	20. False
21. True	22. True	23. True	24. False
25. False			

Be a Diet Detective (p. 34)

Answers will vary.

Chapter 8: Special Food Needs

Stages of Life (p. 35)

Answers will vary but should be consistent with pages 107-119 of the textbook.

Bonus: Girls should develop good eating habits and continue them into their adult life. That way, if they become pregnant, they can be sure of supplying all the nutrients needed during the first important weeks of pregnancy. A doctor's care is essential during pregnancy and will include diet recommendations.

Fit for Life? (p. 36)

1. F	2. A	3. G	4. I	5. J
6. K	7. D	8. C	9. L	10. B

Hotline to Health (p. 37)
1. good nutrition
2. life cycle
3. nutrition requirements
4. level of activity
5. poor nutrition
6. low birth weight
7. weight gain
8. growth spurts
9. strenuous activities
10. nutritious snacks
11. carbohydrates
12. exercise
13. sedentary
14. a sound diet program
15. Milk-Cheese Group
16. Fruit-Vegetable Group
17. Meat-Poultry-Fish-Beans Group

Chapter 9: Your Kitchen
Know Your Kitchen (p. 39)
Part A (Note: Answers 1, 2, and 3 can be given in any order.)

1. range	2. refrigerator-freezer
3. sink	4. triangle
5. work	6. triangle
7. flow	8. sink
9. range	10. mixing
11. storage	12. electrical outlets
13. planning	14. eating
15. laundry	

Part B

16. B	17. E	18. C	19. A	20. D
21. E	22. A	23. B	24. D	25. C

Plans

A. island	B. L-shape
C. U-shape	D. corridor
E. one-wall	

Electrical Safety (p. 41)

A. 3	B. 13	C. 7	D. 2	E. 10
F. 11	G. 6	H. 12	I. 5	

The clue number is __23__.

Bonus
A conductor is a substance or body capable of transmitting electricity. Water and metals, such as aluminum, copper, silver, and gold, are conductors. An insulator is a poor conductor of electricity. Glass and rubber are examples of insulators.

Space Strategies (p. 42)
Answers will vary.

Chapter 10: Kitchen Equipment and Appliances
Be a Careful Consumer (p. 43)
1. EnergyGuide labels are required on many major appliances, including refrigerators, freezers, and dishwashers. The labels give the description of the appliance and its estimated yearly energy cost based on an average rate. The higher the energy cost number, the more it costs to operate the appliance.

2. The Underwriters' Laboratories, Inc. (UL) certification seal is found on all electrical equipment, appliances, and materials UL has tested and approved as being safe to use.

3. The American Gas Association (AGA) certification seal is found on all gas appliances tested by the AGA laboratories. These products conform to safety and performance standards established by the American National Standards Institute.

Consumer Alert (p. 44)

Across:
- 2. microwave
- 10. UL
- 11. appliance
- 14. EnergyGuide
- 17. budget
- 18. lender
- 19. contract
- 21. frostfree
- 23. enamel
- 29. portable
- 30. tool
- 33. rebuilt
- 34. down payment
- 35. interest

Down:
- 1. computer
- 4. quality
- 5. toaster
- 7. warranty
- 9. label
- 13. cycle defrost
- 16. range
- 22. equipment
- 25. drip
- 27. safety
- 29. price
- 32. seals
- 3. refrigerator-freezer
- 6. blender
- 8. limited
- 12. installment
- 15. full
- 20. credit
- 24. guarantee
- 26. service
- 28. cookware
- 31. AGA

Handy Helpers (p. 46)
Answers will vary.

Chapter 11: Buying Food
The Food Shopping Scene (p. 47)
Answers will vary, but might include:
Smart food shopper — Plan your spending, comparison shop, avoid shopping when hungry, shop specials if they meet your needs, read labels, avoid impulse buying.
Pet peeves — People opening packages, different prices on the same product, purchases poorly bagged, unclean store, long wait for checkout, specials that are out of stock, rude employees.

What's a Bargain? (p. 48)
1. Answers will vary.
2. Answers will vary.
3. Products will vary. Advantages:
   Uncooked — Least expensive form.
   Quick cooking — Less expensive than ready-to-eat and quicker to prepare than uncooked.
   Ready-to-eat — Most convenient form.

Making Money Behave! (p. 49)

1a. $140.00	1b. $215.50	1c. $107.75	1d. $82.25
2a. $165.66	2b. $496.98	2c. $457.98	2d. $76.33
3a. $8.05	3b. $658.83	3c. $3952.98	3d. $1317.66
4a. $153.25	4b. $30.65	4c. $275.85	4d. $247.85
5a. $308.00	5b. $320.48	5c. $80.12	5d. $71.82
6a. $7.00	6b. $483.35	6c. $966.70	6d. $883.86
7a. $504.00	7b. $457.36	7c. $479.58	7d. $159.86
8a. $26.72	8b. $374.08	8c. $93.52	8d. $663.01

What's Your Consumer R & R? (p. 50)
Information — You should gather information before you buy so you can make an informed decision.

Selection — You should compare products and services by reading consumer magazines and by comparison shopping at various stores.

Performance — You should check the quality of a product you wish to purchase, as well as warranties offered by the manufacturer.

Safety — You should make sure that you use the product correctly by consulting the owner's manual or following directions provided.

Heard — You should shop as carefully as possible to avoid purchasing poor quality goods or services. You should know where to get help when needed.

Chapter 12: Storing Food
Storage Strategies (p. 51)

Dry storage
unopened peanut butter
granulated sugar
wheat flakes cereal
canned tuna
bread
dry macaroni
potatoes

Freezer
orange juice concentrate
ice cream
frozen peas
fresh chicken
    (long-term storage)
beef roast
    (long-term storage)

Refrigerator
cheese
apples
leftover casserole (short-term storage)
eggs
butter
opened package of raisins

Food Storage Stumpers (p. 52)

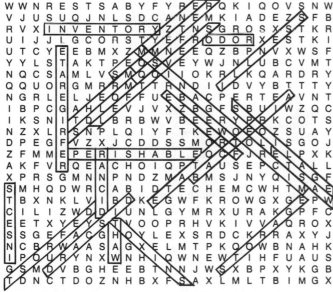

1. Bacteria
2. Discard (*or* Defrost)
3. Defrost (*or* Discard)
4. Enzymes
5. Freeze
6. Illness
7. Insects (*or* Illness)
8. Inventory
9. Leftovers
10. Molds
11. Microorganism
12. Odor
13. Perishable
14. Rancid (*or* Rotate)
15. Rotate (*or* Rancid)
16. Refrigerate
17. Storage
18. Spoilage
19. Thaw
20. Toxins
21. Thermometer
22. Waste

Chilling Facts (p. 54)

Refrigerator			Freezer		
1. Don't	2. Don't		1. Don't	2. Do	
3. Do	4. Don't		3. Don't	4. Don't	
5. Don't	6. Don't		5. Do	6. Do	
7. Don't	8. Do		7. Do	8. Do	
9. Do	10. Don't		9. Do	10. Don't	
11. Don't	12. Do		11. Do	12. Do	

Chapter 13: Safety and Sanitation
Emergency! (p. 55)

1. *Equipment* — baking soda
   Action — Turn off the burner or appliance. Cover the pan with a lid or pour baking soda over the fire.
2. *Equipment* — broom, dustpan, paper towels
   Action — Sweep up broken glass immediately. Use several thicknesses of damp paper towel to pick up small pieces safely.
3. *Equipment* — phone
   Action — Do not move the person. Inform the teacher and call for medical help.
4. *Equipment* — phone
   Action — If the person can cough, speak, or breathe, don't do anything. If not, use the airway passage first aid technique. Have someone call for medical help.
5. *Equipment* — wooden broom handle, rope, or dry cloth, phone
   Action — If the person is still in contact with electricity, pull plug or break contact with a wooden broom handle, rope, or dry cloth. Do not touch the person directly until contact is broken. Call for medical help immediately.
6. *Equipment* — fire extinguisher
   Action — Inform your teacher. Try to put out a small fire with a fire extinguisher. If you can't put out the fire quickly, get out and call the fire department. Your teacher will pull the fire alarm to alert the school.
7. *Equipment* — first aid kit
   Action — For a minor cut, wash the wound with soap and water. Blot dry and apply a dry, clean bandage. Stop severe bleeding by covering the wound with a thick cloth pad and pressing firmly. Notify your teacher.
8. *Equipment* — first aid kit
   Action — Cool the burn with cold water. Cover with a clean, dry bandage, if needed. If the burn is large or serious, get medical help.

The Kitchen Trap! (p. 57)
Answers will vary. Possible answers include:
1. Store matches in glass or metal containers.
2. Strike the match before you turn the burner on.
3. Keep pan handles turned toward the center.
4. Use a dry pot holder, not a towel, to remove a pan from the range.
5. Avoid loose garments and long sleeves.
6. Cover the pan with a lid or pour baking soda over the fire.
7. Never store poisons in the same cabinet with food.
8. Use a wet paper towel to pick up the pieces.
9. Wash knives separately and dry them immediately.
10. Know where fire extinguishers are located and how to use them.
11. Make sure cords don't hang down where small children can pull them.
12. After using an appliance, always unplug it.
13. Wipe spills off the floor immediately.
14. Keep curtains away from the top of the range.

15. Have sufficient light at all work areas.
16. Do not plug too many cords into one outlet.
17. Be sure pot holders are thick and dry.
18. Do not store these under a sink where children can get at them.
19. Cut off the lid completely and throw it away.
20. Keep pets out of the kitchen.

Sanitation Sense (p. 58)
1. To keep bacteria in the cut from contaminating the food.
2. So the food will cool quickly, minimizing bacterial growth.
3. Bacteria accumulate in cuts and scratches on wooden cutting boards.
4. Raw meat contains bacteria and your hands could transfer them to other foods.
5. Food left on surfaces provides a place for bacteria to grow.
6. Pets carry bacteria.
7. This helps keep it out of food.
8. Bacteria grow most rapidly at room temperature.
9. Food left on dishes provides a place for bacteria to multiply.
10. Bacteria from your hands could contaminate clean dishes.

Chapter 14: Food Preparation Tools
Tools of the Trade (p. 59)
1. Sharpening steel — sharpening knives
2. Flour sifter — sifting dry ingredients
3. Double boiler — heating foods which burn easily
4. Pastry blender — cutting fat into dry ingredients
5. Peeler — peeling fruits and vegetables
6. Liquid measuring cup — measuring liquid ingredients
7. Wooden spoon — mixing hot foods
8. Straight-edge spatula — spreading frosting; measuring dry ingredients
9. Pressure cooker — cooking foods quickly using steam under pressure
10. Laddle — serving liquids
11. Grater — grating, shredding, slicing
12. Baster — basting foods with liquid
13. Wire whisk — beating and blending
14. Rotary beater — beating together ingredients
15. Vegetable brush — cleaning fresh vegetables
16. Funnel — filling bottles
17. Tongs — lifting and turning hot foods
18. Rubber scraper — removing food from bowl or pan
19. Colander — draining liquid from food
20. Strainer — removing solids from liquids

The Cook's Helpers (p. 61)
1. tongs
2. slotted spoon
3. steamer
4. flour sifter
5. grater
6. colander
7. peeler
8. pastry blender
9. rolling pin
10. thermometer
11. kitchen shears
12. wooden spoon
13. strainer
14. timer
15. double boiler

Small Wonders (p. 62)
Part A
1. Bread knife — cutting bread or cake
2. Slicing knife — slicing and shredding
3. Utility knife — cutting and slicing
4. Boning knife — boning and/or cutting meat and poultry
5. Paring knife — cleaning, paring, and cutting
6. Butcher knife — dividing large fruits, vegetables, or cuts of meat
7. Chef's knife — slicing, dicing, chopping vegetables and fruits
8. Carving knife — carving and slicing meat and poultry

Experiment — When using a dull knife, it is difficult to cut, the food is not cut cleanly, and accidents are more common.

Part B
Answers will vary.

Chapter 15: Food Preparation Techniques
What's in a Recipe? (p. 63)
Answers will vary.

Preparation Passwords (p. 64)
Part A
1. dredge
2. stir
3. sear
4. chop
5. puree
6. cube
7. fold in
8. scald
9. knead
10. sift
11. baste
12. simmer
13. marinate
14. dilute
15. score
16. beat
17. whip
18. flake
19. cream
20. reduce
21. blend
22. mince
23. dice
24. mix

Part B
See pages 232-233 in the textbook.

Decoding Recipes (p. 65)
Part A
1. C
2. M
3. C
4. C
5. M
6. M
7. C
8. M
9. M
10. C

Part B
11. 16
12. 20
13. 6
14. 25
15. 4
16. 1000
17. 8
18. 16
19. 1½
20. 200
21. 6
22. 1½
23. 4
24. 210
25. 3
26. 12
27. 2½
28. 1
29. 1000
30. ½

Using Your Measuring Skills (p. 66)

Ingredient	6 cupcakes	24 cupcakes
Flour	½ cup	2 cups
Baking powder	¾ tsp.	1 Tbsp.
Cinnamon	¼ tsp.	1 tsp.
Salt	⅛ tsp.	½ tsp.
Butter/margarine	2 Tbsp. + 2 tsp.	⅔ cup
Sugar	⅓ cup	1⅓ cup
Egg	½ egg	2 eggs
Vanilla	¼ tsp.	1 tsp.
Milk	1 Tbsp.	¼ cup
Grated carrots	½ cup	2 cups
Chopped walnuts	2 Tbsp. (⅛ cup)	½ cup

Chapter 16: Microwave Cooking
Microwave Matchup (p. 67)
A. 22
B. 2
C. 3
D. 20
E. 13
F. 24
G. 9
H. 1
I. 12
J. 11
K. 16
L. 8
M. 0
N. 10
O. 19
P. 18
The Matchup Number is __47__.

Mastering the Microwave (p. 68)
1. On a microwave oven you control the cooking power, not the temperature.
2. Microwaves are not evenly distributed in the oven so food may cook unevenly.
3. Microwave cooking saves both time and energy.
4. Some types of containers can be used in both conventional and microwave ovens, but others cannot.
5. Standing time is the time cooking continues after the microwave power has been turned off.

6. If a recipe gives a range of microwave time, always check the food after the shortest amount of time.
7. The amount of liquid and seasoning must be reduced when converting a conventional recipe to microwave cooking.
8. Turning and stirring food during microwave cooking helps distribute the heat evenly.
9. Pieces of food that are small and thin cook more quickly than those that are large and thick.
10. Never turn on a microwave oven when it is empty.

Experimenting with Microwave Cooking (p. 69)

Part A
Conclusions: It will help to determine how to place, shield, and/or turn foods so that they cook evenly.

Part B
Answers will vary.

Chapter 17: Meal Management
Food Enough for All? (p. 71)

Answers may vary but might include the following ideas.
1. Inadequate food supplies can have the following effects on people:
   Growth and health — Inadequately fed people may be underweight or overweight. They often have skin problems, serious illnesses, and tooth decay. Many feel tired all the time.
   Emotional well-being — People often feel cranky or depressed.
   Social relationships — Tiredness and stress have a negative effect on relationships with others.
   Learning — It is difficult to concentrate or study. In young children, retardation may result.
2. Yes, it exists in this country. Government and private food programs have not eliminated the problem. Even those who can afford to buy adequate food are sometimes malnourished because they make poor food choices.
3. Americans waste food at school, at home, and in supermarkets. Students often throw away edible food. At home careless food handling and lack of meal planning often create waste. In supermarkets improper handling by employees and customers as well as rodents and poor sanitation all contribute to waste.
4. Reasons include politics, lack of transportation and food distribution systems in poor countries, and economic problems of farmers.
5. They can actively participate in hunger-related programs, become informed, contact legislators, and avoid food waste.

Putting Your Act Together (p. 72)
Sentences will vary.

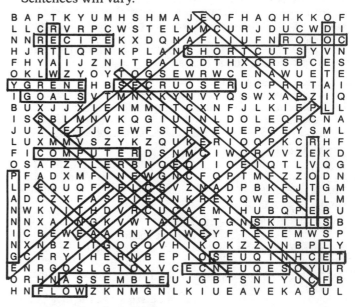

Rate Your Work Habits (p. 74)
Answers will vary.

Chapter 18: Serving and Eating Food
Set It Right (p. 75)

Part A

Part B
Note: Many variations are possible as long as traffic flows smoothly. Saucers need not be used for coffee if plates are large enough to hold beverage.

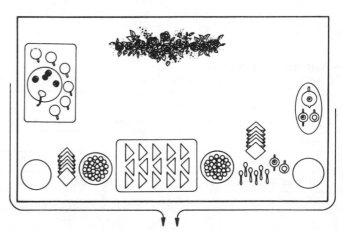

Serving with Style (p. 76)

1. Family Service
Description — Food is put in serving dishes in the kitchen and brought to the table. People help themselves, passing the serving dishes.
Adv. & Disadv. — Informal and simple; can control the amount you care to eat.

2. Plate Service
Description — The food is portioned on individual plates in the kitchen and brought to the table.
Adv. & Disadv. — Reduces the clean up because there are no serving dishes to wash; may be more food waste.

3. Modified English Service
Description — Food for main course is brought to the table in serving dishes. Host/hostess places the meat and vegetables on the plates which are passed to the right. Accompaniments are passed around.
Adv. & Disadv. — Host/hostess serves guests; more dishes to wash.

4. Formal Service
Description — Includes a number of courses, each served separately on clean plates. Flatware is needed for each course.
Adv. & Disadv. — Hired help needed to serve the meal; dignified style; extra tableware needed.

5. Compromise Service
Description — The appetizer is served in individual portions. The main course and accompaniments are served as in modified English style. Salad and dessert are served in individual portions from the kitchen.
Adv. & Disadv. — Good for groups up to 8 people; can be efficient and dignified; requires hired help.

Mind Your Manners! (p. 77)

1. Wait for the host/hostess or guest of honor to begin eating or until at least 8 people have been served.
2. Quietly ask for another napkin.
3. Wait for hot food to cool. Don't blow to cool it.
4. Ask your neighbor to pass it to you. Don't reach across the table.
5. Leave what you cannot eat on your plate. At the restaurant, it is permissible to ask the waiter/waitress to wrap it for you to take with you.
6. Remove fish bones from your mouth with your fingers. Put bones on one side of your plate, not on the table.
7. Turn your head away and use a handkerchief or disposable tissue. Do not use the napkin.
8. Mop it up quickly with your napkin or ask what you can do to help the situation. Offer to reimburse for any cleaning bill, etc.
9. Take a small serving and don't comment on not liking it.
10. Avoid talking with food in your mouth. Wait until you have swallowed the food.

(Continued top right)

11. Watch your host or hostess.
12. Excuse yourself and leave the table.
13. Tuck the napkin into your belt or waistline.
14. Use a knife and fork to cut off as much meat as you can. Do not pick the bones up to eat remaining meat.
15. Watch your host or hostess. Also, the general rule is to start from the outside and work in.

Food for Thought: Your table behavior is a reflection of your personality and "know-how." Using correct table manners will help you feel more confident and relaxed. It also shows respect for others.

Chapter 19: Fruits
Facts About Fruits (p. 79)

Part A

1. +	2. O	3. O	4. O	5. +
6. +	7. O	8. +	9. O	10. O
11. O	12. O	13. O	14. O	15. +

Part B

16. dried
17. sugar
18. produce
19. unitized
20. ripe
21. shipping
22. regreening
23. shape
24. heavy
25. perishable
26. light
27. softer
28. brown
29. digest
30. shape
31. presoaked
32. fried
33. citrus
34. fiber
35. fresh
36. extra heavy
37. drink
38. Fritters
39. skin
40. mature

Name That Fruit (p. 81)

1. Apple
2. Avocado (*or* Apricot)
3. Apricot (*or* Avocado)
4. Banana
5. Cantaloupe
6. Grape
7. Grapefruit
8. Kiwi
9. Lime
10. Lemon
11. Mango
12. Nectarine
13. Orange
14. Pear
15. Peach
16. Persimmon
17. Pomegranate
18. Strawberry
19. Tangelo
20. Ugli
21. Watermelon

Nutrition News (p. 82)

1. Most fresh fruits are ready to eat with little or no preparation.
2.

Food	Calories	Protein	Vit. A	Vit. C	Thiamin	Riboflavin	Niacin	Calcium	Iron
						Percentage of U.S. RDA			
Raw Apple	80	0	2	10	2	2	0	0	2
Unsweetened applesauce	100	0	2	4	4	2	0	0	6
Sweetened applesauce	230	0	2	4	4	2	0	2	8
Apple pie	400	6	0	2	10	8	8	2	6

3. raw apple
4. Some products contain other high-calorie ingredients such as sugar and fat.
5. cantaloupe, apricots
6. orange juice, lemon juice, strawberries, cantaloupe, grapefruit juice, papayas
7. rhubarb, dates, raisins (Answers may vary.)
8. dates, raisins
9. dates, raisins
10. Answers will vary.

Chapter 20: Vegetables
Mixed Vegetables (p. 83)
1. brussels sprouts
2. radishes
3. water-soluble
4. tomatoes
5. celeriac
6. kidney beans
7. vegetables
8. solanine
9. flavones
10. cauliflower
11. bell pepper
12. chayote
13. artichoke
14. kohlrabi
15. garbanzos
16. legumes
17. chlorophyll
18. carotene
19. red cabbage
20. asparagus
21. jicama

Vegetables Are Vital! (p. 84)
1. celeriac
2. ripeness
3. solanine
4. flavones
5. artichoke
6. steam
7. legumes
8. overripe
9. carotene
10. chlorophyll
11. stir-frying
12. leek

Circled letters — cactus leaves

What's Your Vegetable Taste? (p. 85)
Answers will vary.

Vegetable Values (p. 87)
1. Answers will vary.
2. Answers will vary.
3. Seasonal supplies of food affect the price. In winter months, fresh vegetables can only be grown in warm climates and must be shipped to the rest of the country. Prices are higher. In the summer, most areas can produce their own vegetables, so supplies are up and prices down.
4. Answers will vary.
5. Answers will vary. Examples include:
   Fresh vegetables must be used within a few days.
   Canned vegetables are always available and stable in price.
   Frozen vegetables are closest in nutrients, color, and flavor to fresh.
   Convenience may or may not be worth the extra cost.
6. Answers will vary.
7. Answers will vary.
8. Answers will vary.
9. Answers will vary. Examples include: Season, weather conditions, supply and demand, marketing costs, type of store.

The Vegetable Review (p. 88)
Part A
1-8. Answers will vary. Examples include:
   They are low in calories.
   They add color, shape, and texture to meals.
   They are among the best sources of vitamins and minerals.
   They are convenient and versatile.
   They are high in fiber.
Part B — see below

	How to Buy	How to Store	How to Cook
Fresh Vegetables	• Peak of ripeness. • Typical shape & color. • Medium size. • Crisp texture. • Good condition.	Refrigerate immediately in plastic bags, air-tight containers, or crisper compartment to maintain freshness and crispness.	• Cook in liquid. • Steam. • Bake. • Fry or stir-fry. • Cream or scallop. • Glaze.
Canned vegetables	• Don't buy damaged, leaking, rusty, or bulging cans. • Whole vegetables usually cost more than pieces.	Store in a dry, cool place. May be stored about one year.	• Already cooked. • Only need heating.
Frozen vegetables	• Check that package is solidly frozen. • Available whole or cut in pieces. • Bag with loose-frozen pieces can be a good buy.	Store in freezer 8-12 months.	• Cook the same as fresh, but slightly shorter time. • Follow directions on package.
Legumes and other dried forms	• Uniform, bright color and size. • No visible defects.	Store in cool, dark place. Once package is opened, store in glass or plastic container with tight-fitting lid.	• Soak peas and beans before cooking. • Lentils do not need soaking.

Chapter 21: Salads and Salad Dressings
Know Your Greens (p. 89)
Puzzle
1. curly endive
2. butterhead
3. iceberg
4. escarole
5. leaf
6. Chinese cabbage
7. spinach
8. romaine

Descriptions
1. 5
2. 7
3. 3
4. 6
5. 8
6. 4
7. 2
8. 1
9. 3
10. 8

Main Dish Salads (p. 90)
Answers will vary.

The Well-Dressed Salad (p. 91)
Part A

	Appearance	Texture	Flavor
Lettuce with dressing (prepared & refrigerated)	wilted	soggy	unpleasant
Lettuce with dressing (freshly prepared)	crisp	firm, retains shape	pleasant, distinct dressing taste

Conclusions: Add the dressing just before serving the salad. If dressing is added too early, it wilts the lettuce and the salad develops an unpleasant texture and flavor.

Part B
Answers will vary.

Part C
Answers will vary.

Chapter 22: Dairy Foods
Say Cheese! (p. 93)
Part A
Reading down, the answers are:
Swiss, ricotta, cream, Gouda, Romano, Monterey, Muenster, Neufchatel, mozzarella, Parmesan, cheddar, Limburger, and provolone.
Message: Cheese provides proteins, calcium, riboflavin, and vitamins A and D.

Part B
Answers may vary. Possible answers include:
Soft: Ricotta, cream, Neufchatel, and Limburger.
Semisoft: Muenster, Monterey, Gouda, and mozzarella.
Hard: Swiss, cheddar, and provolone.
Very hard: Romano and Parmesan.

Dairy Discoveries (p. 94)
Across:
1. sherbet
6. goat
9. raw
11. mozzarella
15. dry
19. scorch
21. evaporated
24. natural
26. scald

5. bombe
7. cottage cheese
10. protein
14. milk
16. Swiss
20. bacteria
22. lactose
25. lowfat

Down:
2. homogenized
3. butter
4. low power
5. buttermilk
7. curdle
8. custard
12. aged
13. unsaturated
14. mousse
17. yogurt
18. cheese
23. cow

Dairy Products in Your Diet (p. 96)
Part A
Answers will vary.

Part B
Answers will vary. Possible answers include:
1. margarine
2. nonfat dry milk; evaporated milk
3. yogurt; soured, blended cottage cheese
4. another hard cheese
5. nondairy whipped topping
(Continued top right)

6. fresh milk soured with vinegar or lemon juice
7. none (There is a homemade equivalent, but it is not in most charts.)
8. milk; light or coffee cream
9. Romano
10. another soft cheese

Chapter 23: Meat
Check Your Meat Knowledge (p. 97)
1. muscle, bone, fat, connective tissue
2. Both are connective tissues, but only collagen softens during cooking. Elastin does not.
3. The meat comes from young animals that do not vary much in eating quality.
4.

Type	Wholesale Cut	Retail Cut — Example
Veal	Round or Leg	Rump roast
Pork	Loin	Country-style ribs
Beef	Sirloin	Answer will vary.
Lamb	Rib	Crown roast
Beef	Flank	Flank steak

5. Standard name of cut, net weight, cost per pound, total cost
6. mechanical, acids, meat tenderizer
7. a. T b. LT c. T d. T e. LT f. T
8. Yes and no. Fatty meat and large pieces cooked longer than 10 minutes brown. Small pieces and nonfatty meats do not brown because there isn't carmelization of fat. However, these cuts do change color and look cooked.

Focus on Meat (p. 98)
Across:
1. soybeans
7. well done
10. tenderizer
13. kidney
16. panfry
20. prime
22. cured
25. juicy
30. fats
32. broil
35. corned beef
37. chop
43. rare
44. round steak

5. lamb
9. collagen
12. extender
14. veal
19. pot roast
21. protein
24. sausage
26. rib
31. medium
34. stirfry
36. pork
38. internal
temperature
45. lean

Down:
2. elastin
3. heart
4. pepperoni
6. marbling
8. marinate
10. trichinosis
11. sirloin
15. grinding
17. au jus
18. processed
23. back bone
27. braise
28. mutton
29. bologna
33. dry heat
36. pounding
39. rack
40. T bone
41. muscle
42. leg

Activity 3: Getting the Most for Your Money (p. 100)

Meat	Serv. Size	Calories	Protein	Vit. A	Vit. C	Thiamin	Riboflavin	Niacin	Calcium	Iron
Beef pot roast	3 oz.	250	50	0	0	2	10	20	2	15
Lean ground beef	3 oz.	270	50	0	0	4	10	25	2	15
Beef sirloin steak	3 oz.	330	45	0	0	4	10	20	0	15
Veal cutlet	3 oz.	180	50	0	0	4	15	25	0	15
Leg of lamb	3 oz.	240	50	0	0	8	15	25	0	8
Pork loin chop	2 oz.	150	40	0	0	40	10	20	0	10
Spareribs	3 oz.	370	40	0	0	25	10	15	0	10
Sliced ham	3 oz.	160	50	0	0	35	10	20	0	15
Calf's liver	3 oz.	220	60	560	50	15	210	70	2	70

1. Highest — beef sirloin steak
   Lowest — sliced ham or pork loin chop
2. protein
3. vitamin A, vitamin C, calcium
4. The liver processes and stores nutrients, so it contains more nutrients than meats made up of muscles and than other variety meats.
5. thiamin

Chapter 24: Poultry
Poultry Pointers (p. 101)
Part A

Part B
1. The tenderness of poultry depends on its age and weight rather than its grade.
2. To truss poultry means to tie the wings and legs close to the body of the bird.
3. The giblets are the edible internal organs of the bird.
4. Frozen poultry should never be left at room temperature to thaw.
5. Poultry is generally lower in calories and lower in price than meats.
6. A larger bird will give more servings per pound.
7. Poultry is an excellent source of high-quality protein, vitamins, and minerals.
8. Leftover poultry and stuffing must be refrigerated separately.
9. Poultry should be completely thawed before cooking in a microwave oven.
10. Fresh poultry should be wrapped loosely in waxed paper and refrigerated immediately.

Poultry Primer (p. 103)
1. The most common types are chicken, turkey, duck, and goose. Chicken can be packaged whole, cut-up, or as parts only, canned boneless, sandwich spreads, luncheon meats, or precooked. Turkeys come whole, prestuffed, or as parts. Turkey ham and luncheon meats are available.
2. Grade A is the highest grade. Grade B is seldom found in stores. Poultry is chosen by class based on age and weight.
3. Fresh poultry should be loosely wrapped in waxed paper or left in its original plastic wrapper and immediately refrigerated or stored in its original wrapper. Use within 1-2 days. Frozen in airtight wrapping it can be stored several months.
4. Thaw wrapped in the refrigerator or in cold water. May also be thawed in a microwave oven.
5. Very young chickens and turkeys can be broiled or roasted whole. Pieces can be panfried or oven-fried. Mature birds can be braised or stewed.

6. To panfry means to cook food over high heat in a small amount of fat. To oven-fry means to prepare poultry as for frying, but place it in a roasting pan and bake.
7. Allow bird to thaw. Remove giblets and wash bird thoroughly in cold, running water. Prepare stuffing (or season cavity.) Stuff bird, close cavity, and truss.
8. To truss means to bind the legs and wings to make the bird compact, easier to handle and cook, and more attractive to serve. Metal skewers are inserted across the body cavity opening and string is laced between the skewers. String is tied around the tail and legs. The neck flap is closed with a skewer.
9. Stuff immediately before cooking, never the day before.
10. The internal temperature in the thigh or breast reaches 85°C (185°F). The meat is easy to pierce with a fork and the drumstick twists easily in the joint.
11. The meat and stuffing must always be refrigerated separately. Use both within a day or two. For longer storage, freeze.
12. Thaw completely before cooking. Make the shape as even as possible. Pierce the skin with a fork or sharp knife. Don't salt the surface. Roast breast-side down, but turn for even cooking.

Chapter 25: Fish and Shellfish
Fishing for Facts (p. 105)
A. 2   B. 7   C. 18   D. 12   E. 8
F. 5   G. 11   H. 15   I. 13   J. 17
K. 6   L. 3   M. 16   N. 10   O. 4
P. 9
The Matchup Number is 39 .

Fish and Tips (p. 106)
1. fins	2. shell	3. calories
4. flavor	5. mollusks	6. crustaceans
7. shucked	8. connective	9. low
10. odors	11. refrigerator	12. one
13. flakes	14. moist	15. overcooked
16. protein	17. servings	18. grading
19. microwave	20. aquaculture (*or* mariculture)	

The Fish Market (p. 107)
1a. Dressed — cleaned and scaled; head, tail, and fins cut off
 b. Fillets — side sections cut from fish, usually boneless
 c. Whole — only scales and insides removed
 d. Steaks — crosswise cuts of fish
2.
Fresh Fish	Frozen Fish
Firm flesh	Frozen solid
Fresh, mild aroma	Little or no odor
Bright, clear, bulging eyes	Tightly wrapped
Red gills, no slime	Good color
Shiny, bright skin	Breading crisp and dry

3.-8. Answers will vary.

Chapter 26: Eggs
The ABCs of Eggs (p. 109)
Part A

Function	Description	Food Examples
1. Thickening	The protein thickens as eggs cook.	Custards, puddings, sauces
2. Leavening	Beaten eggs, especially egg whites, contain air & liquid (steam) to leaven.	Angel food, sponge, & chiffon cakes
3. Binding	During cooking the egg protein thickens and helps food hold its shape.	Meat loaf, fish or chicken dipped in eggs & crumbs
4. Emulsifying	Help keep ingredients from separating	Mayonnaise

Part B
5. O   6. +   7. O   8. O   9. O
10. +   11. +   12. +   13. +   14. O
15. +   16. +   17. +   18. O   19. O
20. +

Scrambled Eggs (p. 110)

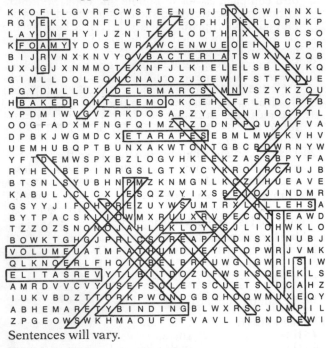

Sentences will vary.

What's Your Egg Score? (p. 112)
1. Wet the inside of the carton and the eggs will loosen.
2. Add salt or sugar to the yolks before freezing.
3. Prick the large end of the egg with a pin or thumbtack before cooking.
4. Add a small amount of vinegar to the cooking water.
5. Immediately after cooking, pour off the hot water and cover eggs with cold water.
6. Tap the shell all over. Roll the egg between your hands. Peel, beginning at the large end, under cold water.
7. Break one egg at a time into a small bowl. Slip the egg from the bowl into the skillet.
8. Break each cold egg so the white falls into a small bowl or cup. Then pour it into the mixing bowl.
9. Use a folding motion to blend.
10. When spreading the meringue over the filling, make sure it touches the crust all the way around. This prevents shrinking.

Chapter 27: Grain Products
The Selling of Cereal (p. 113)
Answers will vary.

Kernels of Knowledge (p. 114)
Across:
2. refined
5. wheat berries
10. pierogi
12. bulgur
15. wild rice
19. hominy
22. pasta
24. grits
27. kernel
30. strudel
33. flour
35. pastitsio
37. white rice
3. brown rice
8. macaroni
11. hollow
13. carbohydrates
17. corn
20. oats
23. cereal
26. legumes
28. germ
32. wheat
34. triticale
36. enriched

Down:
1. durum
2. ravioli
3. bran
4. spaghetti
5. wheat germ
6. barley
7. rice
9. noodles
14. tortilla
15. won tons
16. endosperm
17. converted
18. semolina
21. processed
25. fortified
27. kasha
29. manicotti
31. cornmeal

Pick Your Grains (p. 116)
1. grits
3. regular white rice
5. brown rice
7. breakfast cereals
9. precooked rice
11. triticale
13. wheat germ
15. kasha
2. pasta
4. bulgur
6. semolina flour
8. wheat berries
10. wild rice
12. cornmeal
14. barley

Diagram
a. bran   b. endosperm   c. germ

Chapter 28: The Basics of Baking
Meet the Ingredients (p. 117)
Part A
1. G   2. D   3. C   4. M   5. B
6. A   7. K   8. J   9. L   10. I

Part B
11. Flour — Store in cool, dry place. After opening, put in tightly covered container.
12. Baking soda — Store in cool, dry place.
13. Baking powder — Store in cool, dry place with lid on tightly. Discard after stamped date.
14. Butter — Store well-wrapped in refrigerator. Freeze for longer storage.
15. Compressed yeast — Refrigerate.
16. Active dry yeast — Store in a cool, dry place.
17. Cooking oil — Store in cool, dry place. Refrigerate if you will not use up within a month.
18. Shortening — Store in a cool, dry place unless labeled otherwise.
19. Honey — Store in tightly closed container in a cool, dry place. Refrigerate after opening.
20. Brown sugar — Store in tightly closed container in a cool, dry place.

What Am I? (p. 118)
1. flour
3. leavening agents
5. steam
7. baking powder
9. shortening
11. eggs
13. hot spot
15. sugar
2. gluten
4. yeast
6. baking soda
8. fats and oils
10. lard
12. milk
14. corn syrup

Thinking It Through (p. 119)
1. The more highly developed the gluten, the coarser the texture of the finished product.
2.

Type	Special Requirements
Yeast	Warm water, flour or sugar
Baking soda	Acidic ingredient
Air	Mixing, creaming, or beating ingredients
Steam	Water, high baking temperature
Baking powder	Liquid

3. a. Add tenderness by coating the gluten
   b. Add richness
   c. Add flavor
   d. Help brown the crust
4. No. Sweeteners are not usually interchangeable in baked goods because of their different consistencies (liquid vs. dry), amounts of sweetness, and other characteristics. (Examples will vary.)
5. Remove the lid and place the jar in warm water.
6. a. Cake would probably overflow the pans.
   b. It will be difficult or impossible to remove the layers from the pans.
   c. The cake may fall or be underdone.
   d. The layers will overbrown where the pans touch.
   e. The cake will not brown, but will have greater volume. May have to adjust recipe. Do not flour pans.
   f. The crust may overbrown and stick.
   g. The cake will have a different flavor.
   h. The cake will not rise properly.

Chapter 29: Quick and Yeast Breads
Quick Breads Quiz (p. 121)
Part A

Across:
3. drop
5. quick breads
8. muffin
9. batter
10. pancakes

Down:
1. pour
2. dough
4. biscuit
6. knead
7. tunnels

Part B

1. A	2. B	3. A	4. B	5. A
6. B	7. A	8. B	9. B	10. A
11. A	12. A	13. B	14. A	15. A

Biscuit Basics (p. 123)
Part A

1. 5	2. 2	3. 8	4. 7	5. Blank
6. 4	7. Blank	8. 11	9. 6	10. 9
11. 10	12. 13	13. 12	14. 3	15. 1

Part B
Answers will vary.

Yeast Bread Brain Teasers (p. 124)
Part A
Answers will vary. Possible answers include:

Yeast Bread Product	Advantages	Disadvantages
Ready-to-eat loaves and rolls	Quick, easy to use	Variety somewhat limited, quality may not be best, stales quickly
Frozen bread dough	Faster than homemade, but baked fresh, inexpensive	Variety limited, quality may vary, takes time
Refrigerated brown-and-serve rolls	Baked fresh at time of use, quick, easy	Not as good as homemade, some prep. time, little variety
Dry yeast bread mix	Easy to store and prepare, faster than homemade	Limited variety, time-consuming, fairly expensive
Made-from-scratch yeast breads	Often best quality, unlimited variety, inexpensive	Time-consuming, stales quickly, requires skill

Part B
1. Answers will vary. (One example — sourdough)
2. a. Many people would not have the time to bake without such convenience products.
   b. Emphasis on health and fitness is a current trend. People are paying more attention to the types of foods they eat and making changes in their diet. Bread is easily enriched to increase nutrient and fiber content.

Chapter 30: Cookies, Cakes, and Frostings
Cake Closeup (p. 125)
Part A
1. Shortened
2. Foam
3. sponge
4. Chiffon
5. steam
6. butter
7. tube
8. angel food
9. clinging
10. conventional

Part B
11. Removes lumps, mixes ingredients, improves accuracy of measuring.
12. Foam cakes rise by clinging to the sides of the pan. If the pan is greased, the batter cannot cling and the cake will not rise well.
13. Recipes are developed to fit a certain size pan. Changing the pan will change the baking time and may cause the cake to overflow or be undersized.
14. The cool air that rushes in can affect the way the cake rises.
15. Beating would allow the air in the beaten eggs to escape. The cake depends on this trapped air for leavening.

Cookies, Cakes, and Cultures (p. 126)
Examples will vary.

Chapter 31: Pies and Pastries
Pastry Pointers (p. 127)
1. Pastry
2. tart
3. pastry blender
4. water
5. quiche
6. little
7. flaky
8. less
9. shell
10. steam
11. 1 or 2
12. cream
13. chiffon
14. 1-crust
15. blistered
16. fruit
17. custard
18. lattice crust
19. Microwaved
20. all-purpose

Test Your Pastry Skills (p. 128)

1. 10	2. 15	3. 19	4. 23	5. 3
6. 12	7. 9	8. 21	9. 17	10. 1
11. 11	12. 22	13. 6	14. 2	15. 20
16. 8	17. 4	18. 13	19. 5	20. 14
21. 7	22. 18	23. 16		

Chapter 32: Stocks, Soups, and Sauces
Hidden Terms (p. 129)

1. beurre manie
2. bouillon
3. chowder
4. consomme
5. curdle
6. degrease
7. pureed
8. roux
9. stew
10. thickeners
11. bisque
12. broth
13. clarify
14. cream
15. custard
16. strain
17. reduce
18. sauce
19. stock

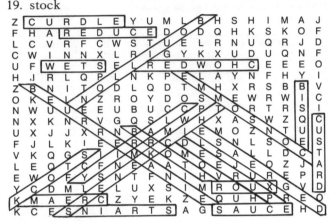

What's Your Stock, Soup, and Sauce Score? (p. 130)

Part A
1. +
2. O
3. O
4. +
5. O
6. O
7. O
8. +
9. +
10. O
11. O

Part B
12. vegetable
13. marrow
14. Custards
15. six
16. milk
17. overcooked
18. cloudy
19. roux
20. cornstarch
21. Beurre manie

Flour as a Thickener (p. 131)
Part A

Type of White Sauce	Milk	Fat	Flour	Salt (optional)	Suggested Uses
Thin sauce	1 cup	1 Tbsp.	1 Tbsp.	½ tsp.	Cream soups
Medium sauce	1 cup	2 Tbsp.	2 Tbsp.	½ tsp.	Gravies, creamed and scalloped foods
Thick sauce	1 cup	3 Tbsp.	3 Tbsp.	½ tsp.	Baked or fried mixtures

1. Blend melted fat with flour in saucepan.
2. Cook and stir over low heat until mixture bubbles.
3. Add the milk.
4. Cook and stir until thickened.

Part B
5. Brown the butter and flour mixture.
6. Increase the amount of flour.

Part C
7. Combine the flour and cold liquid until smooth.
8. Slowly add the flour mixture to the liquid to be thickened while stirring.
9. Cook and stir until the mixture thickens.

Problem Solvers (p. 132)
1. This allows the liquid to evaporate slowly, concentrating the flavors.
2. Beat vigorously. Adding one or two ice cubes to lower the temperature may prevent further curdling.
3. Cured meats are too highly salted.
4. They will cook into lumps.

5. High heat speeds up evaporation and may make the mixture too thick.
6. Reduce the stock — boil it so that more of the liquid evaporates, concentrating the flavor.
7. Use fresh milk in making the white sauce and avoid oversalting.
8. Beat it briskly with a wire whisk or a spoon, or work it through a sieve.
9. They become thick and sticky if stirred too much.
10. Mixtures thickened with flour may separate when thawed.
11. They make a cloudy stock that will sour rapidly if stored.
12. Use a meat baster to draw off the layer of liquid fat after it rises to the top or remove the fat that rises to the top and solidifies as the stock cools.

Chapter 33: Beverages
What's Your Choice? (p. 133)
Answers will vary.

What's Brewing? (p. 134)
1. Cocoa does not contain as much cocoa butter as chocolate.
2. Chocolate is usually more expensive than cocoa because it contains more cocoa butter.
3. Because it has less fat, cocoa blends more easily with hot liquid and is less likely to separate.
4. This is cocoa butter that has come to the surface. It does not affect flavor or use.
5. Both scorch easily.
6. Coffee loses its flavor easily.
7. Coffee makers vary. Check step-by-step directions.
8. Oils in coffee stick to the inside of the coffee maker. They become rancid quickly and give coffee an off-flavor.
9. Boiling, overcooking, and reheating make coffee bitter.
10. The differences are determined not by the plant, but by how the leaves were processed.
11. Pigments in tea react with metal and give the tea a bitter flavor. They also create a light film over the surface of the tea that clings to the inside of the cup as you drink.
12. Some varieties have a light color and a very strong flavor while others brew to a very dark color with a light flavor.
13. Boiling makes tea bitter.
14. This allows for dilution by the ice cubes.
15. If not stirred, the smooth surface of a beverage could keep steam from escaping, causing the beverage to spurt out of the container.

Chapter 34: Preserving Food At Home
The Language of Preservation (p. 135)

Across:
1. fruits
4. vegetables
7. gel
8. vinegar
11. jam
12. boiling water bath
14. microorganisms
16. lids
18. jelly
19. drying
20. relish
24. pressure
25. process
26. smoking
28. sliminess
29. spores
30. blanched
31. botulism

Down:
1. freezing
2. toxin
3. oven canning
5. bubbling
6. yeast
9. marmalade
10. high acid foods
13. pickles
15. open kettle
17. cured
21. sterile
22. preserve
23. brine
25. pack
27. spoil

"Why Must I . . .?" (p. 137)
1. Jars from commercial products can never be used for home canning because they cannot be properly processed and sealed.
2. Blanching stops enzyme action. Blanched vegetables retain their nutrients, color, flavor, and texture far longer than vegetables that have not been blanched.
3. Foods that dry out in freezing are said to have freezer burn — they have a dry, discolored surface and usually have an off-flavor. Your dried out beef was not packaged correctly or may not have been sealed tightly.
4. Drying food in the sun is not a reliable method in most parts of the country. Often the humidity outdoors prolongs the drying process and the food spoils.
5. Vegetables are low-acid foods and must be processed by the pressure canning method.
6. Do not use a microwave oven for canning. Since a lid cannot be put on the jars in the oven, dust and germs can contaminate the food. In addition, microwave temperatures are too uneven to kill the harmful micro-organisms.
7. High-acid foods are processed in a boiling water bath. Low-acid foods need higher temperatures to kill microorganisms, so they are processed by the pressure canning method.
8. First, sugar, sugar syrup, or ascorbic acid is used to stop the enzyme action. Fruits can be frozen one layer deep on a tray for about 24 hours and then packed in containers.
9. Jelly is made by cooking fruit, extracting the juice, and combining it with sugar. Preserves are whole fruits or large pieces cooked with sugar. The fruit keeps its shape and is clear, shiny, and tender.
10. Signs of spoilage include mold, bubbling, spurting, off odor, unusual softness, and cloudiness. Home-canned vegetables and other low-acid foods must be boiled 15-20 minutes before tasting. Destroy if there is any sign of spoilage.

Chapter 35: Foods of the World
Global Connections (p. 139)
1. Schnitzel — Germany — meat cutlet
2. Crepes — France — thin pancakes rolled around a filling
3. Shish kebabs — Near and Middle East — skewered roasted meat
4. Pasta — Italy — spaghetti, macaroni, noodles, etc.
5. Yams — West Africa — starchy root vegetable
6. Dal — India — lentil
7. Tofu — Far East — bean curd
8. Couscous — North Africa — steamed, ground wheat
9. Sukiyaki — Japan — meat and vegetable combination
10. Masa — Mexico — ground, dried corn
11. Sofrito — Caribbean Islands — seasonings
12. Cassava — Brazil/West Africa — starchy root

Where in the World? (p. 140)
1. England — beet soup
2. Caribbean Islands — pfeffernusse
3. France — antipasto
4. Soviet Union — phyllo
5. Spain — smorgasbord
6. Japan — shish kebabs
7. Italy — goulash
8. Mexico — ceviche
9. Scandinavia — saffron
10. South America — sauerbraten
11. India — cassava
12. China — peanut butter
13. Africa — masala
14. Near and Middle East — plantain
15. Germany — Lucia buns

Chapter 36: American Regional Foods
A Tour of States and Tastes (p. 141)
Map

AL — 19	AK — 50	AZ — 49
AR — 22	CA — 46	CO — 40
CT — 5	DE — 8	DC — 10
FL — 18	GA — 17	HI — 51
ID — 43	IL — 28	IN — 27
IA — 31	KS — 36	KY — 24
LA — 21	ME — 1	MD — 9
MA — 3	MI — 26	MN — 30
MS — 20	MO — 32	MT — 42
NE — 35	NV — 47	NH — 2
NJ — 7	NM — 39	NY — 11
NC — 15	ND — 33	OH — 25
OK — 37	OR — 45	PA — 12
RI — 4	SC — 16	SD — 34
TN — 23	TX — 38	UT — 48
VT — 6	VA — 14	WA — 44
WV — 13	WI — 29	WY — 41

Foods
1. oranges
2. chowder
3. pinto beans
4. gumbo
5. hush puppies
6. succotash
7. turnips
8. Hopping John
9. sweetbreads
10. kimchi

Our Cooking Heritage (p. 142)
Answers will vary.

Chapter 37: Creative Cooking
Is There a Difference? (p. 143)
Answers will vary.

Using Your Creativity (p. 144)
Answers will vary.

Herbs and Spices (p. 145)
Examples will vary but many include:
1. S — baked ham
2. S — poultry stuffing, rye bread
3. H — potato salad
4. H — seafood
5. H — sour cream
6. S — cookies
7. S — apple cake
8. S — cookies
9. H — marinades
10. H — corned beef
11. H — eggplant
12. S — apple pie
13. H — fish
14. H — stewed fruit
15. H — lamb

Garnish with Glamour (p. 146)
Examples will vary.

Chapter 38: Careers In Food and Nutrition
What's Right for You? (p. 147)
Answers will vary.

Checking Food Careers (p. 148)
Part A
Examples will vary. Possible answers include:

Working with Things
Food production worker
Food photographer or stylist
Caterer
Hospital dietitian
Meat cutter

Working with Ideas
Food technologist
Research dietitian
Test kitchen home economist
Ad writer for food products
Pastry chef

Working with People
Restaurant manager
Foods and nutrition teacher
Waiter or waitress
Consumer affairs representative for a food business
Food or equipment demonstrator

Part B
Answers will vary.

Chapter 39: How to Get and Keep a Job
If You Were the Boss . . . (p. 149)
Answers will vary.

"Help Wanted" Ads (p. 151)
Part A

1. morning	2. noon to midnight
3. appointment	4. building
5. business	6. opportunity
7. excellent	8. advancement
9. necessary	10. company
11. good	12. hour
13. salary	14. manufacturing
15. references	16. preference or preferred
17. trainee	18. telephone
19. paid	20. background
21. agency	22. temporary
23. experienced	24. qualify or quality
25. extension	26. information
27. miscellaneous	28. required or request
29. location	30. commission
31. route	32. large
33. benefits	34. overtime
35. personnel	36. reliable

From reading the "help wanted" ads, you can learn:
Job opportunities in your community
Skills that are in demand
Range of salaries
Educational requirements
Job trends
(Other answers are possible.)

Part B
Letters will vary. See text page 573 for sample letter.

Job Interviews: Know the Questions! (p. 153)
Answers will vary. In the examples given below, A is an appropriate answer. B is an inappropriate answer.
1. A. Name a specific position.
   B. *"Whatever pays most."*
2. A. "No, but I have experience as a volunteer."
   B. *"No."*
3. A. Be specific, giving information that could be related to employment.
   B. *"What do you want to know?"*
4. A. "I know that I am qualified and will do my best to be a good employee."
   B. *"I need a job."*
5. A. "Your company has an excellent reputation."
   B. *"I need money."*
6. A. "I spend time with my friends and on extracurricular activities."
   B. *"I watch TV and call my friends."*
7. A. "I like the challenge. I enjoy my classes, athletics, and the clubs I belong to."
   B. *"I hate school."*
8. A. "They are above average."
   B. *"I'm not really interested in grades."*
9. A. "Gain experience and begin a satisfying career."
   B. *"Make a lot of money."*
10. A. "Thank you for your time and consideration."
    B. *"I hope you'll pick me."*

Would You Hire Yourself? (p. 154)
Answers will vary. Possible answers include:
1. a. Try to relax and be yourself.
   b. Answer questions briefly and pleasantly.
   c. Be prepared to answer common questions.
   d. Use Standard English — no slang.
   e. Smile and show enthusiasm and confidence.
2. a. Do not fidget.
   b. Do not talk too long about your interests or personal problems.
   c. Do not talk negatively about other jobs or people.
   d. Be assertive, but not aggressive.
   e. Do not sit down until you are asked to do so.
3. They are afraid they will not know what to say and will not make a good impression.
4. You would want to know what would be expected of you on the job, whether it would further your career goals, and what salary you could expect.
5. You gain self-confidence and experience in presenting yourself as a desirable prospective employee.
6. a. Being late for a job interview.
   b. Poor appearance.
   c. Talking too much about yourself.
   d. Arriving late for the job or leaving early.
   e. Inappropriate dress on the job.
   f. Complaining to fellow employees.
   g. Rudeness to customers.
   h. Breaking work rules.
   i. Too many absences.
   j. Can't accept constructive criticism.